Sir Hans Sloane

T.Murray pinx.   I.Faber fecit 1728.

D.^{nus} *Hans Sloane* Baronettus

Collegij Regij Medicorum Londinensiũ, & Regiæ Societatis Præses, &c

Sold by Philip Overton at ij Golden Buck near St Dunstans Church Fleet Stree..

Frontispiece Portrait of Sir Hans Sloane, engraved by John Faber jun. after a painting by Thomas Murray, 1728. BM, PD, C.S. 329, I.
Reproduced by courtesy of the Trustees of the British Museum.

SIR HANS SLOANE

Collector, Scientist, Antiquary
Founding Father of the British Museum

Edited by Arthur MacGregor

Published for the Trustees of the British Museum
by
British Museum Press
in association with
Alistair McAlpine

© 1994 Alistair McAlpine

Published by
British Museum Press
A division of British Museum Publications Ltd
46 Bloomsbury Street
London WC1B 3QQ

British Library Cataloguing in Publication Data
Sir Hans Sloane, collector, scientist, antiquary,
founding father of the British Museum
1. Collecting. Great Britain, science, history
I. MacGregor, Arthur, 1941–

ISBN 0 7141 2085 5

Designed by Gordon House
Printed in Great Britain by BAS Printers Limited,
Over Wallop, Hampshire

Contents

Acknowledgements

Professor William R. Mead generously agreed to the reproduction here of that part of his unpublished translation of Per Kalm's account of his visit to England which relates to Sloane's museum (pp. 31–4). Dr Peter Murray Jones kindly allowed his list of the Sloane catalogues (pp. 291–4) to form the basis of the referencing system used here: thanks are due to Dr Jones and to the editor of the *British Library Journal* in which the list was first published. Mr J.P.B. Brooke-Little, cvo, Norroy and Ulster King of Arms, kindly arranged for production of the facsimile of Sir Hans Sloane's arms which appears in Fig. 4.

Abbreviations and Conventions

BL The British Library, London
      OIOC Oriental and India Office Collections

BM The British Museum, London
      CM Department of Coins and Medals
      EA Department of Egyptian Antiquities
      Ethno Department of Ethnography
      GR Department of Greek and Roman Antiquities
      JA Department of Japanese Antiquities
      MLA Department of Medieval and Later Antiquities
      OA Department of Oriental Antiquities
      PD Department of Prints and Drawings
      PRB Department of Prehistoric and Romano-British Antiquities

Catalogus plantarum Hans Sloane, *Catalogus plantarum quæ in insula Jamaica sponte proveniunt, vel vulgò coluntur, cum earundem Synonymis & locis natalibus; adjectis aliis quibusdam quæ in insulis Maderæ, Barbados, Nieves, & Sancti Christophori nascuntur. Seu prodromi Historiæ Naturalis Jamaicæ pars prima* (London, 1696).

DNB Dictionary of National Biography

Museum Britannicum J. and A. Van Rymsdyk, *Museum Britannicum, being an exhibition of a great variety of natural curiosities, belonging to that noble and magnificent cabinet, the British Museum* (London, 1778)

Natural History Hans Sloane, *A Voyage to the Islands Madera, Barbados, Nieves, S. Christophers and Jamaica, with the natural history of the herbs and trees, four-footed beasts, fishes, birds, insects, reptiles, &c. of the last of those islands; to which is prefix'd an Introduction wherein is an account of the inhabitants, air, waters, diseases, trade &c of that place, with some relations concerning the neighbouring continent and islands of America.* 2 vols. (London, 1707–25)

NHM The Natural History Museum, London

Notes and Records Notes and Records of the Royal Society of London

Philosophical Transactions Philosophical Transactions of the Royal Society of London

PRO   Public Record Office, London

VCH The Victoria History of the Counties of England

All dates cited in the text are given according to the Georgian ('New Style') calendar, in which the new year begins on 1 January.

List of Illustrations

Preface

The year 1660 was a momentous one for Great Britain, both constitutionally and intellectually. It saw the Restoration of the Monarchy and the foundation of the Royal Society. It was also the year when, in a modest house in the Irish village of Killyleagh, Hans Sloane was born.

Sloane was to become one of the most significant cultural figures of his age. He was a renowned scientist, physician and antiquarian and for many years he served as President of the Royal Society. But it is for his collecting that he is best remembered. When in 1748 he was visited at his home by the Prince and Princess of Wales, the royal couple was shown 'drawers fitted with all sorts of precious stones . . . *jewels*, polish'd and set after the modern fashion . . . tables spread with *gold* and *silver ores* . . . brilliant *butterflies* . . . large animals preserved in the skin . . . curious and venerable antiquities of *Egypt, Greece, Hetruria, Rome, Britain* and even *America*'. This collection was to become the basis of the British Museum in 1753, the year of Sloane's death.

This volume is the first comprehensive assessment of Sloane's widespread collecting activities, an appropriate task as the British Museum approaches its 250th anniversary. It is gratifying that essays have been offered by authors drawn from all three institutions which have arisen from the original foundation: the British Museum itself, the Natural History Museum and the British Library. The exercise which the contributors undertook originated in an initiative by Lord McAlpine of West Green, himself a well-known collector with catholic tastes. The costs of preparing the text were borne by Lord McAlpine up to publication stage, at which point the responsibility fell to British Museum Press. All those involved are owed the thanks of the British Museum but most especially the editor, Arthur MacGregor of the Ashmolean Museum, who has guided this book through every stage, from inception to its final production.

R. G. W. Anderson
Director
The British Museum

1 The Life, Character and Career of Sir Hans Sloane

Arthur MacGregor

The salient features in the life of Sir Hans Sloane have been mapped out in a number of biographical studies.[1] Since our principal concern in this volume will be with Sloane the collector, a brief survey will suffice here to provide a background against which the following essays may be set.

Almost all we know of Sloane's antecedents can be gleaned from a brief pedigree certified by Hans together with his brother William in 1726,[2] and from a memoir[3] thought to be based on information culled from personal interviews with Sloane by Thomas Birch,[4] conducted for a projected series of biographical studies of contemporary notables. We learn that Hans 'was descended of a Family originally of Scotland, but settled in the North of Ireland upon the new Plantation of that part of the Kingdom in the Reign of King James I'.[5] He was born at Killyleagh, Co. Down, on 16 April 1660, the seventh son of Alexander Sloane, by faith a Protestant and by profession the agent for James Hamilton, 2nd Viscount Clandeboye and later Earl of Clanbrassill.[6] Hans's mother, Sarah Hicks, came to Ireland in the company of Anne Carey, daughter of the Earl of Monmouth, who was to marry James Hamilton.[7]

Alexander Sloane died six years after Hans was born and Sarah remarried by the time he reached eleven, moving away from the village with her new husband. Hans appears to have remained in Killyleagh and to have attended school there. A 'strong Inclination to the study of the Works of Nature'[8] developed in the young Sloane, as he recalled in later life:

I had from my Youth been very much pleas'd with the Study of Plants, and other Parts of Nature, and had seen most of those Kinds of Curiosities, which were to be found either in the Fields, or in the Gardens or Cabinets of the Curious in these Parts.[9]

At the age of sixteen he was struck by a bout of spitting blood, a pulmonary affliction that took three years to subdue and from which, despite a prudent regime, he was to suffer periodic relapses for the remainder of his life.[10] None the less, at the age of nineteen he was judged sufficiently recovered to leave Ireland in order to further his education in London.

There the young Sloane was lodged in a house in Water Lane, adjacent to the Apothecaries' Hall where he was to study chemistry. His lodgings were shared by Nicholas Staphorst, the Apothecaries' 'chemical operator', with whom Sloane acquired 'a perfect Knowledge of the Preparations and Uses of most chemical Medicines'.[11] Lectures in anatomy and physic complemented this training, while his botanical studies were carried out at the Physic Garden in Chelsea, established by the Apothecaries in 1673 and directed by John Watts.[12]

Perhaps as important in Sloane's development as this formal training was the influence of two acquaintances first encountered during this period, who were to remain his firm friends for the rest of their lives. The first was John Ray (1627–1705): over thirty years older than Sloane, Ray was a former fellow of Trinity College, Cambridge and had been elected FRS in 1667; the first of several important publications by his hand, the *Methodus Plantarum Nova* which established the basis of a new method of classifying plants, appeared in 1682 while Sloane was in London. The particular bond of friendship established between them is illustrated by the extracts from their lifelong correspondence, marked by mutal respect as well as affection, which appear below.[13] The second of Sloane's mentors at this time was 'that great & good Man', Robert Boyle (1627–91), an exact contemporary of Ray, who occupies a position in the history of chemistry and physics as exalted as that of Ray in the natural sciences.[14] Birch reports candidly that Sloane cultivated Boyle's friendship 'by communicating to him whatever occur'd to himself, which seem'd curious & important, & which Mr Boyle always receiv'd with his usual Candour & return'd with every Mark of Civility and Esteem'.[15] There seems little doubt that the acquaintance of these two scholarly figures produced a powerful formative influence on the development of Sloane's interests.

After four years of formal education in medicine, 'having made use of all the Advantages, which London afforded him for the Study of Physic', Sloane thought it desirable for his further development to travel abroad.[16] He sought new fields in France in the company of two fellow physicians in the making, Tancred Robinson[17] and a companion named Wakely, of whom nothing further is recorded. In the spring of 1683 the trio arrived in Paris, where for some three months, Sloane followed an intensive regime 'which afforded him full Employment for the Day', sharing his time between the Jardin Royal des Plantes and the Hôpital de la Charité:

He enter'd at six in the morning the Royal Garden of Plants with Monsr Tournefort, who demonstrated the Plants after the Order of Caspar Bauhin in his *Pinax* till eight, when Monsr Duforty explain'd their Virtues till ten; & at two in the afternoon Monsr du Verney read upon Anatomy till four, & was succeeded by Monsr Sanlyon, the Chemical Professor, who discours'd in French on the Operations to be perform'd that day by Mon^r Faveur.[18]

Birch records that Sloane was 'assidious in his Attendance upon all these Professors, by whom he was treated with great Respect, as likewise by those of the Royal College & others eminent for their Skill in Physic, Natural History, or Philosophy'.[19] Of his tutors, Joseph Pitton de Tournefort

(1656–1708) was perhaps to have the most lasting influence. As well as being an ardent botanist, Tournefort was, like Sloane, a physician by training and a collector by inclination; not surprisingly, the two became life-long friends.[20]

When the time came for Sloane to take his doctorate, his Protestant faith dictated that the only university in France where he could be admitted was that of Orange, a principality of the Netherlandish House of Orange whose head at the time was Prince William, the future King William III of Great Britain. At this time the University of Orange enjoyed no very high reputation for academic rigour, and the formalities did not take long: on 27 July 1683 the oral examination was begun and on the following morning was completed, Sloane maintaining a thesis 'with great applause'.[21] The examiners awarded him the highest honours, 'tamquam optime meritus de Rigore examinis nemine prorsus Discrepante'[22] and forthwith the University conferred on him the degree of Doctor of Physic.[23]

Still anxious to extend this learning, Sloane now attended the University of Montpellier (where his friends Ray, Boyle and Tournefort had all preceded him). He went there with a recommendation from Tournefort to Pierre Chirac, 'the chief Professor, to whose lectures & those of the other Professors there, he was admitted without any Fee or Reward, & became particularly acquainted with Monsʳ Magnol the Botanist, whom he accompanied in his herborisations round that City'.[24] There he further studied anatomy, medicine and botany. Both Tournefort and Pierre Magnol (1638–1715) were avid searchers for new species and both were to devise new classificatory schemes; their close acquaintance undoubtedly had a lasting effect on Sloane's own development. When his two English companions went on to Italy, Sloane extended his stay in Montpellier as 'more useful', lodging with Monsieur Carquets, an apothecary, in whose home he was to mix with numerous physicians. Eventually, on 23 May 1684 he set out again for London, 'with a Resolution to fix himself there for the Exercise of his Profession'.[25]

On returning to London he settled in Fleet Street, reviving his earlier acquaintanceships and forming others anew. In a letter to Ray written shortly after his return, Sloane encourages him in his intentions to produce a history of plants, mentioning his new-found friend Tournefort's enthusiasm for the project and adding:

... if you will be pleased but to let me know anything you may have occasion for that can be procured at Paris or Montpellier, I will do all in my power to help you to it. I have several plants that I brought from both places; amongst which are several nondescripts; all which shall be at your service, with what remarks I made about them, either as to their growth or virtues.[26]

Botany and the natural sciences in general clearly were of absorbing interest to the young Sloane at this time. After his return from France he continued collecting in the field, as testified in a letter to Ray mentioning a 'simpling journey'

to the Isle of Sheppey and a number of natural curiosities gathered on that occasion.[27]

On 21 January 1685, Sloane was elected FRS. His association with the Royal Society, which was to endure for the rest of his life, was of enormous importance to Sloane and is considered in some detail below.

Following his avowed aim to settle in his profession of medicine, Sloane arranged to call on Dr Thomas Sydenham, the foremost physician of his day in London, known as 'the English Hippocrates'. Sydenham was dismissive of the skills in anatomy and botany alluded to in Sloane's letter of introduction, maintaining that it was only at the bedside that he could 'learn disease', but the two got on well. Sloane soon entered into 'the greatest Intimacy of Friendship' with Sydenham and was 'desir'd by him to settle in his Neighbourhood, that he might introduce him into practice ... recommending him in the strongest terms to his Patients, when he was disabled by the Gout from attending them himself, & carrying him to them, when he was able'.[28] Sydenham's particular strength lay in his capacity for precise observation and his systematic approach to diagnosis, skills which he communicated to the receptive Sloane, who was quickly established to the point where, on 12 April 1687, he was admitted a Fellow of the Royal College of Physicians.

At just this time Sloane was considering a tempting proposition, that he should join the household of Christopher Monck, 2nd Duke of Albemarle, recently appointed governor of Jamaica, as the Duke's personal physician.[29] The prospects opened up by this appointment were communicated in a letter to Ray,[30] one of several friends whose advice Sloane sought before committing himself: 'next to the serving of his grace and family in my profession, my business is to see what I can meet withall that is extraordinary in nature in those places'. He also acknowledged that the voyage 'seem'd likewise to promise to be useful to me, as a Physician; many of the Antient and best Physicians having travell'd to the Places whence their Drugs were brought, to inform themselves concerning them.'[31] Ray's reply must have gone a long way to confirming him in his resolve to go:

Were it not for the danger and hazard of so long a voyage, I could heartily wish such a person as yourself might travel to Jamaica, and search out and examine thoroughly the natural varieties of that island. Much light might be given to the history of the American plants, by one so well prepared for such an undertaking, by a comprehensive knowledge of the European. Nay (which is more), that history, we might justly expect, would not only be illustrated but much improved and advanced.[32]

The same author wrote that 'We expect great things from you, no less than the resolving of all our doubts about the names we meet with of plants in that part of America ... You may also please to observe whether there be any species of plants common to America and Europe'.[33]

Martin Lister was equally encouraging, setting out a

number of questions which Sloane might answer on the spot and further desiring him to 'collect & transmitte hither' specimens of all kinds of shells. Pausing further only to negotiate himself an additional contract to act as physician to the Fleet,[34] Sloane was committed. The following autumn, on 12 September 1687 he boarded the *Assistance*, a frigate of forty-four guns, at Spithead. That afternoon the small fleet, comprising also the Duke's yacht and two large merchantmen, set sail, but by next morning contrary winds and rain forced them back to land, where they lay for a week before setting out for Plymouth; another fortnight passed there until finally, on 5 October, they put out to sea.

From Sloane's own observations made on the voyage,[35] it seems that he adopted immediately and quite expertly the mode of recorder not only of the daily routines of the ship but of all the natural phenomena encountered along the way. His notes and speculations begin with the nature of and cures for the sea-sickness that struck the passengers as soon as they went on board, and continue with detailed descriptions of the appearance and behaviour of birds, fishes and even insects encountered *en route* (discussed further in the following chapters), as well as natural marvels such as sea phosphorus. The voyage proceeded via Madeira and the Canaries, and by 25 November the fleet made land at Bridgetown, Barbados. Immediately Sloane's delight with the exotic flora encountered there is made evident, for he launches straight into an account of the bearded fig. Resting in Barbados for ten days, the company progressed over the following two weeks by way of Nevis, Santa Cruz, Puerto Rico and Hispaniola to Jamaica, the Duke having a commission to 'muster all the Forces of the English-Caribe-Islands' along the way. Eventually they reached their destination on 19 December 1687.

During fifteen months there, Sloane reports that he 'took what pains I could at leisure-Hours from the Business of my Profession, to search the several Places I could think afforded Natural Productions, and immediately described them in a Journal'. He made notes on the weather, the topography, natural phenomena such as earthquakes, but above all on the flora, penetrating to the north of the island collecting, noting and recording. He describes his routine thus:

After I had gather'd and describ'd the Plants, I dried as fair Samples of them as I could, to bring over with me. When I met with Fruits that could not be dried or kept, I employ'd the Reverend Mr. [Garret] Moore, one of the best Designers I could meet with there, to take the Figures of them, as also of the Fishes, Birds, Insects, &c in Crayons, and carried him with me into several places of the Country that he might take them on the place.[36]

Elsewhere, Sloane gives a flavour of the less favourable aspects of life in Jamaica:

In that distant Climate the Heats and Rains are excessive ... The Parts not inhabited ... are often full of Serpents and other venomous Creatures ... The same Places remote from Settlements

are very often full of run away Negros, who lye in Ambush to kill the Whites who come within their reach ...[37]

Even those specimens safely collected were at further risk from rodents, pests, and humidity. He records, for example:

I attempted to preserve the Skins and Feathers of Humming Birds, and was oblig'd, to keep them from [the] Ants, by hanging them at the End of a String from a Pully fasten'd in the Cieling and yet they would find the Way by the Cieling to come at and destroy them.[38]

Within a year of Sloane's arrival in Jamaica, what must have been an agreeable mixture of professional and leisure-time activity was interrupted by the death on 6 October 1688 of the Duke of Albemarle.[39] Sloane's last duty to his patron was to embalm his body for shipment to England – a very necessary expedient, since the upheavals then surrounding the English throne delayed the departure of the dead Duke and his household for a further five months. Eventually, on 16 March 1689, they set sail for home. Sloane's baggage was swelled by many specimens, including initially a number of live animals, none of which survived to see England (see Chapter 4). His plant collection alone amounted to 800 specimens, 'most whereof were New'.[40]

Returning to London on 29 May 1689 to find King William on the throne, Sloane continued for nearly four years in the service of the Duchess of Albemarle (a sojourn which no doubt contributed to his success as a society physician)[41] before setting up in practice in Bloomsbury. There on 11 May 1695 he married Elizabeth, daughter and co-heir of John Langley, a London alderman, and widow of Fulk Rose, formerly of Jamaica.[42] The marriage was an advantageous one for Sloane, since his wife inherited not only her father's estate but also one third of the income from her former husband's properties in Jamaica.[43] The newly-married couple set up house in what is now 3 Bloomsbury Place, then at the centre of a fashionable residential area (Fig. 1).[44] There Sloane (Plate 1) established his immensely successful practice, his patients including many of the most prestigious figures of the day. At the same time he maintained close relations with the most active members in the community of scientists, several of whose names, along with that of Sloane himself, have been associated with a naturalists' 'club' that met at regular intervals, sometimes, at least, in the Temple Coffee House and sometimes making forays into the countryside.[45]

In the years that followed, Sloane began to publish his observations from the West Indies. At first they were submitted to the *Philosophical Transactions*, where papers appeared on species such as coffee and the Jamaican pepper tree, and on the earthquakes that devastated Lima and struck Jamaica in 1687–8 and were felt in Jamaica again in 1692. In the latter papers Sloane reveals the importance he attached to exact observation:

... considering that they give Account of different Earthquakes,

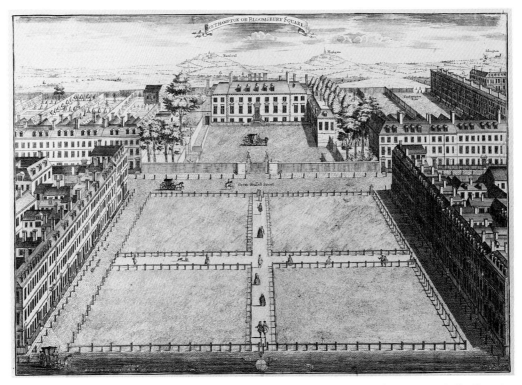

Fig. 1 View of Bloomsbury Square in the early eighteenth century, from an engraving by Sutton Nicholls. Sloane's house stands in what is now Bloomsbury Place (leading to the right from the back of the square) in the facing block; it survives today, much altered internally. BM, PD, 1880—11—13—4405. Reproduced by courtesy of the Trustees of the British Museum.

or that they contain differing Observations of the same Earthquake; and that we cannot have too many of the *Phænomena*, or Matters of Fact accompanying them recorded, I think it will be best they be all preserved for future use, and I have sent the Papers themselves as most satisfactory.[46]

Sloane's talent for accurate notation (an essential trait in a practitioner of scientific field work) is all too often overlooked by those who belittle his scholarly importance, but they were well enough appreciated by those who knew him. Ray, for example, wrote to him in the following terms on 28 February 1693:

I cannot again but admire your industry in collecting so great a number of species in so short a time, and not only collecting, but so exactly observing and describing them.[47]

Six years after his return, in 1696, his *Catalogus plantarum* came to fruition, an octavo volume of 232 pages with a forty-three page index. Written in Latin, it lists all the plants Sloane found growing in Jamaica; it is dedicated jointly to the Royal Society and the College of Physicians.[48] Its appearance had been long delayed while Sloane sought opinions and criticism among his friends, notably John Ray, and consulted numerous printed authorities, the most recent being Charles Plumier's lavish *Description des plantes de l'Amerique*, which appeared in 1693.[49] Sloane placed great emphasis on these cross-references:

I thought it necessary to look into the Books in several Languages, which treated of those Subjects either designedly or accidentally. Some men seem to have a great desire to be the first Authors of discovering such or such Plants, and to have them carry their Names in the first Place, but I endeavour'd rather to find if any thing I had observ'd was taken Notice of by other Persons. I therefore looked into most Books of this Nature, and the greatest part of what I found is publish'd [in the *Catalogus plantarum*], which I think for Synonymous Names of the Plants therein mentioned, is somewhat more Copious and exact than any other before it.

The process of collation and rationalization alluded to here represents one of Sloane's most valuable contributions to the advancement of science. His readiness to subordinate his own independent discoveries to the prior claims of others was characteristic of him in a way that was unmatched among his contemporaries, but he did not fail to castigate those who contributed unnecessarily to the proliferation of terminology.[50] While acknowledging the valuable original contributions that he had made to the progress of botanical research, Ray paid particular tribute to Sloane's success in 'clearing up many obscurities in authors, and contracting and reducing to one many plants distracted into many species by the unskilfulness of some, and misapprehension of others ... who have not seen the plants themselves'. It was a theme he returned to on more than one occasion in his letters to Sloane and others:

I cannot but admire your industry and patience in reading and comparing such a multitude of relations and accounts of voyages, and referring to its proper place what you found therein relating to your subject, and that with so much circumspection and judgment. You have done botanists great sevice in distributing or reducing the confused heap of names, and contracting the number of species. But who is able to do the like? No man but who is alike qualified, and hath seen the things growing in their natural places.[51]

The new volume rendered obsolete many of the clumsy synonyms that littered earlier literature and brought about an improvement in nomenclature that was to be superseded only by the system of Linnaeus. But its value was greater than this: in a letter to Edward Lhwyd (1660–1709), Ray described Sloane's work as '. . . a great treasure, he having very exactly described every species.'[52]

On 2 November 1694, meanwhile, Sloane had been appointed physician in charge of Christ's Hospital, a post he was to hold until 1730. With a generosity that was also characteristic of him, he returned his salary of £30 a year to the Hospital on a regular basis, for the relief of the more needy incumbents. He was a supporter of the College of Physicians' dispensary, where medicines could be obtained by the needy at cost price. He was always generous with his own money and free with medical advice to his friends[53] and to those who were unable to pay, running a free surgery for the poor every morning.[54] He was later to become a governor of most of London's hospitals and financial donor to many of them, giving £100 to each of those with which he was associated.[55]

In 1701 Sloane was awarded the degree of Doctor of Medicine by the University of Oxford and in 1705 was elected to the College of Physicians of Edinburgh.[56] Later, in 1719, at the age of fifty-nine, he was elected President of the College of Physicians in London,[57] which office he was to hold for sixteen years.

Further recognition of his medical prowess came in 1712 with an appointment as Physician Extraordinary to Queen Anne, and in 1714 he attended her in her final illness. Under George I he continued to serve as a Physician Extraordinary and on 3 April 1716, shortly after the King's accession, was created a baronet – one of the first physicians to be so honoured.[58] A court appointment followed in the succeeding reign when, in 1727, Sloane became Physician in Ordinary to George II, 'having been before constantly employ'd about the whole Royal Family, & always honour'd with the Esteem & favour of the Queen Consort'.[59]

In 1722, meanwhile, he had been appointed Physician General to the Army, a part-time office of a largely administrative and advisory nature during Sloane's period of tenure.[60] His principal concerns here would have been with the commissioning of regimental and garrison surgeons and with exercising control over the military apothecaries. The appointment carried with it considerable prestige, however, the incumbent being selected by the sovereign from amongst his personal physicians. Sloane was to hold

the post for five years until his appointment as Physician in Ordinary.

Estimates of Sloane's contributions to medicine are generally in line with those of his standing in the broader world of science. He was not a great innovator,[61] but he was cautiously progressive and contributed to the establishment of scientific diagnosis and prescription, based on accurate observation rather than hypothesis. He favoured minimal medical intervention and was moderate by the standards of his day in the prescriptions which he issued.[62] Certainly he was against the administration of remedies in anticipation of illness.[63] On the other hand, he was a keen promoter (against entrenched medical opinion) of the introduction and practice of innoculation in England, not fearing to apply it to his own family nor to advocate its administration to the royal children of the Princess of Wales.[64]

He evidently had a good understanding of the properties of the simples which he dispensed,[65] although, on the other hand, he occasionally gave credit to remedies that now seem bizarre, such as 'Millipedes alive, to one hundred in a morning', to be taken in a glass of water, or 'crabs eyes in large quantities',[66] although in both instances he is careful to record the observed benefits which these treatments were said to have wrought. He was never a slavish follower of established practices, and declared himself 'always very attentive to Matters of Fact' concerning the efficacy of cures.[67] His first hand experience of those elements of the materia medica emanating from the West Indies no doubt also helped; these were described in his Natural History (see below). Sloane's name is also linked with the popularization of quinine, distilled from 'Peruvian bark': on returning from Jamaica he is said to have invested 'the greatest part of the Fortune he acquired there' in the bark, so acquiring a valuable stock of medicine which he actively promoted by prescription (for a range of complaints beyond those hitherto treated in this way) and by writing about it in Philosophical Transactions.[68] As might be expected, his enthusiasm for the bark was well-founded on the basis of observed success in the treatment of fevers, and it was maintained in the face of reactionary opposition on theoretical grounds. Further, he made a considerable amount of money from the promotion of milk chocolate, recommended as a drink 'For its Lightness on the Stomach & its great Use in all Consumptive Cases' (Fig. 2).[69]

In parallel with these highly successful efforts to establish his medical practice, Sloane worked towards the completion of the first volume of his major work, the Voyage to the Islands Madera, Barbados, Nieves, S. Christophers and Jamaica . . . with the natural history of the . . . last of those islands . . . (hereafter Natural History). Yet he evidently feared it might arouse a degree of controversy and equivocated over its publication, for on 8 November 1705 Thomas Hearne recorded a rumour that Sloane '. . . would never print it, because he was well assur'd there were 2 or 3 ill natur'd men who would write ag^t it, & endeavour to expose it. W^{ch} tho' amongst men of Sense 'twould be no disgrace,

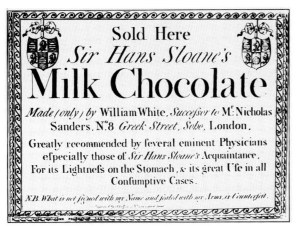

Fig. 2 Trade card for 'Sir Hans Sloane's Milk Chocolate'.
Reproduced by courtesy of Cadbury Ltd.

yet he is too modest to publish w[t] he finds must undergoe ye Publick Censure of ill natur'd men.'[70] However, the first volume (dedicated to Queen Anne) was in due course brought out in 1707, though the scholarly world had to wait until 1725 for the appearance of the second volume (dedicated to George I).[71] Posterity has judged the work a worthy effort. It is extensively illustrated and noteworthy like the earlier *Catalogus* for the pains that Sloane took to acknowledge the opinions of earlier scholars than himself. Furthermore, it is, as Birch acknowledges, 'written with an unaffected plainness & simplicity of Style most suited to the capacity of common Readers, & therefore likely to engage their Attention, & gratify their Curiosity'.[72] Critical acclaim was duly forthcoming, and not only in England: the *Journal des Sçavans* reviewed it warmly on 21 May 1708, despite the fact that Britain and France were then engaged in war. The first volume alone, concerned principally with plants, established Sloane's status unequivocally in the academic world. Many illustrations were engraved for it (adding to the delay in appearance)[73] at Sloane's own expense by Michael van der Gucht and John Savage, working from drawings by Everhardus Kickius[74] and Garrett Moore. Once again, Sloane was content to acknowledge the precedence of others in this area: Plumier's engravings of plants from the West Indies, for example, were judged by Sloane to be so good that it was unnecessary for the same species to be illustrated in his own work (where the scientific value of the illustrations is, admittedly, less than satisfactory).[75]

The second volume includes much more than plants — beasts, birds, fish, insects, reptiles, climate, disease and trade are all considered. It also contains observations on the fact that in the waters around Jamaica were to be found many 'Vegetables and Animals, Real Sea-Shells and Substances . . . found in as great plenty in the Inland Parts of England imbedded in the Earth, Clay, Sand, Chalk or Stone, as if

it had once been the natural Place of their Production and Increase'.[76] These inklings are complemented by observations of similarities in plants on both sides of the Atlantic (fulfilling Ray's earlier admonitions). Similarly, Sloane was able to use his own collection to draw comparisons with species of plants common to Jamaica and England, Spain, Portugal, Barbary, Guinea and the East Indies.

Sloane's workman-like approach to scholarship marked him out from his more intellectually-minded contemporaries,[77] not all of whom were sympathetic in response.[78] There seems little enough offence in his everyday Baconian empiricism, however, and it was an approach that also found adherents among more exalted scholars. John Locke, for example, paid tribute to it:

I conclude that there is noe thing constantly observable in nature, which will not always bring some light with it, and lead us farther into the knowledge of her ways of workeing.[79]

Sloane himself had expressed the basis of his personal philosophy in the preface to his *Natural History*: '. . . the Knowledge of *Natural-History*, being Observations of Matters of Fact, is more certain than most Others, and in my slender Opinion, less subjected to Mistakes than *Reasonings, Hypotheses,* and *Deductions* are'. He had a clear perception too that his researches in part proceeded from and had practical applications for society at large: one of the uses he foresaw for his *Natural History* of Jamaica, for example, was 'to teach the Inhabitants of the Parts where these Plants grow, their several Uses, which I have endeavour'd to do, by the best Informations I can get from Books, and the Inhabitants, either *Europeans, Indians* or *Blacks*'.

Although the *Catalogus* had been published in Latin (as indeed its nature demanded), Sloane was evidently glad to revert to English for the *Natural History*. His attitude to the use of Latin was typically anti-elitist,[80] even if it gave trouble occasionally to his friends.[81]

In addition to his skills in medicine and in botany, Sloane developed a considerable range of knowledge in other areas of natural history which are too easily overlooked. On 16 August 1704, for example, Ray wrote to tell Sloane of his progress with writing:

. . . an history of insects, for which you would have been a far fitter person . . . I desire you to afford me your help in carrying on this history, and enrich it with some of your observations, especially about flies, wherein we are most deficient.[82]

Indeed his interests seem at times to have been almost too miscellaneous for his own good, attracting the derision of contemporary satirists,[83] but here again he had the encouragement of figures such as Locke, who wrote to him on 2 December 1699 concerning the feats of strength then being performed in London by one William Joy; these, Locke suggested:

. . . would be beyond belief were there not soe many witnesses of it. I think they deserve to be communicated to the present age and recorded to posterity. And therefor I think you cannot omit

THE NORTH FRONT of the MANOR HOUSE at CHELSEA built by KING HENRY VIII.

Fig. 3 Sir Hans Sloane's manor house at Chelsea, partly originating in a palace of Henry VIII. Reproduced from Thomas Faulkner, *An Historical and Topographical Description of Chelsea* (1829).

to give him a place in your transactions . . . his strength . . . may be a subject of speculation and enquiry to the philosophical world.[84]

Sloane's extensive pharmaceutical knowledge is alluded to in an account of a debate at the House of Lords of the Physicians' Bill on 14 April 1720, which Sloane attended with other members of the College of Physicians: when the Apothecaries, who were also represented, attempted to insinuate that the Physicians 'did not understand drugs', Sloane 'offerd to contend with them, & sayd he would bring 500 drugs that all the Apothecarys in town should not know one of'.[85]

Since acquiring the manor of Chelsea (Fig. 3) some years earlier,[86] Sloane had become landlord of the Apothecaries' physic garden there and in 1722 he entered into an agreement with the Society by which, for an annual payment of £5 he conveyed the garden and all its appurtenances to them.[87] In gratitude the Society commissioned a statue of Sloane, to be executed by the sculptor of his choosing. Sloane's choice fell on Michael Rysbrack, who had recently completed the monument to Newton in Westminster Abbey. The bust prepared by Rysbrack as a model for this figure (Plate 2) presents the most powerful image that survives of our subject. The finished sculpture (Plate 3) stood in the garden from 1737 until erosion from the elements forced its removal in 1985 to the British Museum.[88]

In 1724 Sloane's wife Elizabeth died. Together they had had four children, a son, Hans, who had died in infancy,

Fig. 4 Facsimile of enrolment of the arms of Sir Hans Sloane. From College of Arms, MS Grants 7, p. 440, with canton of a baronet's hand added. Reproduced by kind permission of the Chapter of the College of Arms.

and three daughters of whom one, Mary, had also died an infant. Of the surviving daughters, Sarah married George Stanley of Paultons in Hampshire, while Elizabeth married Colonel Charles [later 2nd Baron] Cadogan.[89]

In 1726 Hans and his brother William applied for registration of their arms, which were confirmed as follows:

Gules, a Sword in Pale the Point Downwards Argent, Hilt and Pommell Or, between two Boars Heads couped at the neck of the third, on a Cheif Ermin a Lyon Passant Gules between two Mascles Sable; and for the Crest on a Wreath of the Collours, a Lyons Head Eras'd Or, collar'd with Mascles interlaced, Sable.[90]

Hans's own arms (Fig. 4) were differenced in the dexter canton with the red hand of Ulster, in acknowledgement of his baronetcy.

In 1739, at the age of seventy-nine, Sloane was smitten by a paralytic disorder from which he never fully recovered. Three years later, in 1742, he retired to Chelsea after a further serious illness.[91] His retirement from London, however, 'did not prevent him from being constantly visited as before by all persons of Distinction, & Foreigners who came to England ... or from continuing to give Advice to great Numbers who consulted him'.[92] The impression of reluctant resignation to the march of time is confirmed by Birch, who records that 'His custom was to rise very early in the morning, & from his first getting up was constantly dresst fit to have gone abroad, though for some of his last years he stirr'd not out of his House, & lay down on the Bed several times in a Day.' A visitor in 1748 noted alongside the other curiosities 'Sir Hans Sloane's three-wheeled chair, with two wheels in front and a little one behind, in which he was drawn around his garden' (see Appendix 3); in 1752 Birch found him 'cheerfull and healthfull but ... almost incapable of conversation from his Defects of hearing and speech'.[93]

At the end of his days Sloane was carried off after only a short, three-day illness. One of the last to see him was George Edwards, keeper of the library of the College of Physicians, who had at Sloane's request called on him on a weekly basis throughout the fourteen years of his retirement at Chelsea '... in order to divert him, for an hour or two, with the common news of the town, and with any thing particular that should happen amongst his acquaintance of the Royal Society and other ingenious Gentlemen.'[94] He died on the afternoon of 11 January 1753 and was buried on 18 January next his wife, in the south-east corner of the churchyard at Chelsea Old Church. The pallbearers at the funeral included Sir John Evelyn, Sir John Heathcote, the Right Hon. Edward Southwell, Lieutenant-General Oglethorpe, James West and James Theobald; according to a contemporary account:

The Corpse ... was carried with a grand procession, from his late Dwelling-House at Chelsea ... Several Gentlemen of Fortune attended the Funeral, and the Principal Tradesmen of Chelsea went in Procession on Horseback before the Corpse.[95]

The sermon was preached, as Sloane had desired, by his friend Dr Zachary Pearce, Bishop of Bangor, reading from the twelfth verse of the ninetieth Psalm: 'So teach us to number our days, that we may apply our Hearts unto Wisdom'.[96] A Palladian aedicula in Portland stone was erected ten years later, in 1763, to mark the tomb.[97]

Sloane was well loved by his friends such as Ray,[98] Locke[99] and Pepys[100] and certainly never went out of his way to make enemies, for he had none of the contentiousness characteristic of many of his contemporaries. Following one bitter confrontation at the Royal Society (see below), he had written that 'There is nothing I love so much as quiet; and, having a great deal of business in my profession, as well as my family and museum, I would be pleased with nothing so much as quietus ...'[101] Self-effacement seems to have been a prominent character trait: in the opening pages of his *Natural History* he had stated: 'I am sensible there are herein a great many faults, not only in Hypotheses or Opinions, which I propose only as Conjectures, and shall easily part with ... [knowing] too well how unduly qualified I am for such an Undertaking ...'[102] These twin virtues of industry and modesty were further alluded to by William Stukeley, in an assessment of Sloane that is otherwise critical enough to be clearly unbiased:

Sr Hans Sloan is an instance of the great power of industry which can advance a man to a considerable height in the worlds esteem with moderate parts & learning ... He has no faculty of speaking, either fluently or eloquently, especially before any number of people, & he do's it with great timidity. His most commendabl quality is his love for natural learning, & the pains he takes to promote it.[103]

While some have been only too willing to endorse and to amplify Sloane's modest opinion of himself, the degree to which friends and contemporaries sought and valued his advice is striking and must give the lie to his detractors.[104] Sloane's scholarship was, in any case, only one of several gifts for which contemporary society and posterity have had reason to be grateful.

Sloane and the Royal Society

The Royal Society was founded in 1660, the year of Sloane's birth, with a declared interest in 'the promotion of Physico-Mathematicall Experimental Learning'. Although not, therefore, a member of the first generation of Fellows, Sloane was elected to the Society as a young man of twenty-four on 21 January 1685;[105] he remained an active participant in the Society's affairs for sixty-eight years. His sponsor was fellow-physician and antiquary, Martin Lister, and his election brought him within the circle of the most distinguished scientists of the day.

Sloane seems to have been encouraged and positively moved by his admission to the Royal Society, as also by his election two years later to the College of Physicians — 'unmerited Favours', as he called them, which 'incited me to do what I could to be no useless Member, but to cast in my Mite towards the Advancement of Natural Knowlege ... and by that means endeavour to deserve a Place amongst so many Great and Worthy Persons'.[106] Almost immediately (July 1685), as though to give effect to this sentiment, he stood as a candidate for the office of Clerk but failed to become elected.

With better fortune, in 1693 he was elected second Secretary of the Society,[107] the first Secretary at the time being Richard Waller. By the following year Waller was writing to Sloane declaring himself unable to cope with the burden of office and the year after that Sloane was made first Secretary. The appointment carried with it, in addition to a considerable burden of administrative duties, responsibility for publication of the *Philosophical Transactions*, which were administered as the personal property of the secretaries.[108] Publication of the *Transactions* had lapsed for a number of years before Sloane became involved and the Society as a whole was at the time in a state of decline; he played a key role in revitalizing both, although a start had been made in setting the *Transactions* in train once again before he took over.[109] There can be little doubt that the shouldering of these considerable responsibilities inhibited Sloane's own opportunities for further scientific work.

An additional responsibility of the Secretary lay in the provision of papers for communication to the Society. Here Sloane called for support on his wide circle of friends and acquaintances, and issued the following circular to stimulate interest among the Fellows:

The Royal Society are resolved to prosecute vigorously the whole design of their institution, and accordingly they desire you will be pleased to give them an account of what you meet with, or hear of, that is curious in nature, or in any way tending to the advancement of natural knowledge, or useful arts. They in turn will always be glad to serve you in anything in their power.[110]

The appointment placed Sloane at the hub of the learned world. It is hard to conceive that a more appropriate person could have been found to occupy this position, for Sloane's wide circle of acquaintances, his assiduousness as a correspondent[111] and his easy relations with foreign scholars, combined with the status loaned by his office, placed the Royal Society in a key strategic position within the European scholarly community. The fact that so many of the communications printed in the *Philosophical Transactions* at this time were in the nature of extended letters to the editor underlines the important role played by the editor as correspondent.

Sloane's correspondence was indeed prodigious. Many intimations of gratitude survive from those favoured with his letters. His importance within the academic communications network is acknowledged in a letter from Tournefort, dated 1701/2: writing from Mykonos, Tournefort laments that he has no other company but Greek monks and pirates and begs Sloane for news from 'the republic of letters'.[112] John Locke later alluded in similar vein to Sloane's key position in the 'commonwealth of letters'.[113] At a period when

Europe was repeatedly riven by warfare, the unity of intellectual purpose within the academic community remained remarkably untrammelled by national frontiers; Sloane's real contribution in maintaining the concept of citizenship of this international republic deserves recognition. He enjoyed easy relations with foreigners in general (von Uffenbach found him particularly amiable towards Germans: see Appendix 1), and his early experience in France rendered him doubly suited to the task. His extensive correspondence with the Abbé Bignon, master of the King's Library in Paris and the editor of the *Journal des Sçavans*, may be singled out as a particularly fruitful conduit through which the latest scientific ideas (and gossip) were transmitted across the Channel. Bignon has been described as 'not a creative scholar but a skilled communicator of the ideas of other men',[114] a judgement that might with justification be applied to Sloane himself.

Papers in the *Transactions* dealing with medicine and natural history increased in number, coming mostly from Sloane's friends; there has also been detected an increasing element of miscellaneity amongst the papers published at this time. It was not a development that found universal approval. John Woodward, professor of Physic at Gresham College and a man whose abrasive character brought him into conflict with so many of his generation, was the most vociferous of Sloane's critics. Woodward bore an undoubted emnity for Sloane, fuelled by more than a hint of jealousy, but his antipathy also had a genuine scholarly dimension to it. With some justification, Woodward felt that the experimental and philosophical objectives of the Royal Society (as reflected in the papers published in the *Transactions*) were neglected or even undermined during Sloane's secretaryship; not only did Sloane lack the intellectual capacity to forward these pursuits but, in Woodward's opinion, he subverted the course of progress by forwarding the theories of his cronies at the expense of others (notably Woodward himself).[115] Failing to get satisfaction from a formal complaint lodged with the Council of the Society,[116] Woodward launched a campaign to unseat Sloane from the Secretary's office: he succeeded in having his friend Dr John Harris elected as second Secretary, but overplayed his hand by openly ridiculing Sloane during the presentation of a paper by the latter and was himself ejected from the Council for his behaviour.[117]

Others took exception to the very language in which some of these papers (including those of Sloane himself) was couched. The 'close, naked natural way of speaking' espoused by the earliest fellows of the Royal Society, in which 'all the amplifications, digressions, and swellings of style' were to be eschewed, gave way all too often in the papers published under Sloane's editorship to a flaccid and convoluted prose style that mirrored a general lack of direction in the contents. The most devastating attack came in the form of a parody on Sloane and the journal he edited, published anonymously in 1700 by William King, under the title of *The Transactioneer*.[118] Although an official inquiry into its authorship was mounted by the Council, King remained undiscovered.

Sloane's willingness to admit papers of the most diverse subject matter may be seen more positively as a reflection of his own universal interests. Certainly he was commendably open-minded about his own contributions, declaring that 'such Hypotheses as are, or shall be found in any Papers of mine, I have so little regard for them, that . . . I must conclude, that future Accidents, and Observations will make them go off, and be hereafter succeeded by others more plausible.'[119] The principles espoused by the Royal Society (and in particular the prominence given to close observation) corresponded with – and no doubt reinforced – those of Sloane, who insisted upon a clear distinction between 'Matter of Fact, Experiment, or Observation, and what is *Hypothesis*', a theme to which he returned in the preface to his *Natural History* (see above).

This brand of scholarship was in any case only one of the gifts that Sloane had to offer. Of as much importance from the Society's point of view was his business-like outlook, which resulted in a striking improvement in its finances.

He also encouraged donations to the 'Repository',[120] whose history is of some interest in our assessment of Sloane's own collecting activities. Within five years of its foundation the Society had set up 'a *repository* to keep their Instruments, Books, Rarities, Papers, and whatever else belongs to them'.[121] Formally it was placed in the care of the Society's Curator of Experiments (the first incumbent being Robert Hooke, appointed in 1662), and its establishment as a sizable museum dated from 1666 when the Council purchased for £100 the entire collection of natural rarities belonging to Robert Hubert. An enhanced degree of direction and purpose was brought to the Repository when responsibility passed in 1677 to Nehemiah Grew, a taxonomist who applied his skills to the registering of the collections and to the publication of a systematic catalogue under the title *Musaeum Regalis Societatis* (1681). Grew was formally named Curator in the following year, and during Sloane's period as Secretary the Society appointed a full-time servant, Henry Hunt, to look after its premises including the library and the Repository.[122] A plan emerged to 'complete' the collection and for a time a systematic acquisition policy was adopted; this resulted in the employment of Thomas Willisel as botanical collector to perambulate the British Isles in search of 'such natural things, as may be had in England, and were yet wanting in the Society's repository', but the results were unsatisfactory and short-lived.

By the early years of the eighteenth century severe shortcomings in the administration of the Repository were already becoming apparent, and by 1710 it presented a picture of abject neglect:

[The Museum] consists of what appear to be two long narrow chambers, where lie the finest instruments and other articles . . .

not only in no sort of order or tidiness but covered with dust, filth and coal-smoke, and many of them broken and utterly ruined. If one inquires after anything, the operator [Hunt] who shows strangers round . . . will usually say: 'A rogue had stolen it away,' or he will show you pieces of it, saying: 'It is corrupted or broken'; and such is the care they take of things! Hardly a thing to be recognized, so wretched do they all look.[123]

Hunt remained in charge during the transfer of the Society's premises to Crane Court in 1711, but died shortly afterwards, to be replaced by Alban Thomas, who also held the position of Clerk to the Society. During the ten years in which he occupied the post, Thomas's acknowledged effectiveness in the administration of the Library was not matched in the Repository: after his departure a Committee appointed to inspect both these premises reported that 'we have been in the Repository, but as the Curiosities there are not numbered, and we find no Catalogue, we are not able to give any particular account of them'.[124]

During the period of his secretaryship, which came to an end in 1713,[125] Sloane seems to have brought no detectable influence to bear on the administration of the Repository. Shortly after his election as President, however, the Committee for the Repository was reconvened and its reports to the Council confirm the picture of neglect, with everything in 'confusion and disorder', and 'the greater part of what was expected to be there being lost or imbezzled, and most of what remained in such bad condition either thro' want or care or injury of time'.[126] Some order was re-established as a result of the Committee's reports, particularly after the appointment of Cromwell Mortimer, Secretary of the Society from 1730 to 1752, to the task of preparing a detailed catalogue of its contents: Mortimer's years of experience as amanuensis in Sloane's museum (see below) must have been of major importance here, and indeed on one occasion the Committee adjourned to Sloane's house 'in order to view yᵉ manner of the preserving & ranging the severall sorts of Curiosities in his Collection yᵗ they might yᵉ better judge what may be proper to be order'd in the Repository'. By 1736 the Society was able to congratulate itself on 'the Good State and Condition wherein the Repository is at length brought, by the great care and Application of the Gentlemen of the Committee', but the effectiveness of these measures seems to have been short-lived.[127]

Sloane himself contributed enormously to the Society's collections of plant specimens by including in the agreement with the Apothecaries (see above) a proviso that the Chelsea Physic Garden should annually supply the Royal Society with fifty specimens of plants of different species, by which means over 2,000 specimens were received. These were to be supplied dried, mounted and named; no two were to be alike.[128] To judge from a letter of *c.*1720 to Sloane from Richard Richardson, his importance in promoting this aspect of the Society's work seems to have been paramount:

If any thing in Natural History occurs that is worthy of your notice, I will not fail to communicate it to you, being the only Patron of that curious part of learning. The rest of the [Royal] Society are so much taken up with their mathematical schemes, that often things as useful are thereby neglected.[129]

He also presented the Society with his own portrait and with a bust of Charles II.

The President of the Society from 1703 was Sir Isaac Newton. Although lacking the academic stature of Newton, much of the responsibility for running the Society fell on Sloane during the period of his secretaryship and when Newton died in 1727 Sloane seems to have been widely perceived as Newton's natural successor in the office. On 29 March of that year the Council unanimously voted him President.

The membership at large was split in its loyalties (both personal and political), however, and at the annual general meeting on 30 November there was a lengthy debate before Sloane was confirmed in office by a three-to-one majority. He was to remain in office for fourteen years until, at the age of eighty-one, indifferent health caused him to stand down. An impression of the high esteem in which he was held can be gained from the reluctance of the membership to let him go: a deputation was sent to see if he could be persuaded to alter his decision but he remained inflexible and wrote to the Society insisting on his decision.[130] Thereon the Society passed a vote of thanks to him, hoping that they would continue to enjoy the benefit of 'the advices he daily receives in his extensive and learned correspondence'. A medal struck in 1744 (Fig. 5) commemorates his distinguished presidency. He proved an effective officer, introducing reforms to improve the running of the Society within months of his election: these freed foreign members from the burden of annual subscriptions while enforcing payment from the many Fellows who were in arrears at that time; controls over the election of candidates were also tightened at this time. Commenting on the President's chair to which Sloane had been 'so great an ornament', Roger Gale expressed the opinion that 'no man that ever satt in it had the prosperity of the Society more at heart, was a greater benefactor to it, or putt its affairs into better order'.[131]

Attention has been drawn to an engraving (Fig. 6) showing Newton and Sloane with the inscription 'Ecce Gloriae Mathematicarum et Physicarum'.[132] The comparison may seem over-generous and difficult to sustain in the light of denigratory attacks which Sloane has suffered from his own time until the present day,[133] but there seems no reason to doubt that at that moment the comparison seemed entirely apposite.[134]

In the course of his term of office, honours had come from other bodies. The French Académie Royale des Sciences appointed him Correspondent in 1699 and Foreign Associate in 1709.[135] He was elected to the foreign membership of the Royal Prussian Academy of Sciences in its

Fig. 5 Jacques-Antoine Dassier, bronze medal with bust of Sir Hans Sloane. BM, CM, Hawkins Collection, M8490. Reproduced by courtesy of the Trustees of the British Museum.

founding year of 1712, to the Academies of Sciences in St. Petersburg[136] in 1734 and Madrid in 1735, and to membership of the Academy of Sciences in Göttingen in 1752, at the age of ninety-two.

In 1748 he was visited on behalf of the Russian Academy of Sciences by Johann Caspar Taubert (1717–71), whose mission included the discovery of how Sloane intended to dispose of his collections, what they contained and what their current value might be. The Academy's interest evidently had some influence on Sloane's will, for after Taubert's visit he added a codicil in which the Russian Academy was moved from the sixth position in a list of institutions which were to be offered them if Parliament refused to the point where it was to have first refusal (see Chapter 2).[137] Given the Academy's intense interest, there seems little chance that it would have passed up the opportunity of acquiring the collections, had it been given the chance.

Sloane the Collector

The first elements of Sloane's collection were doubtless formed in the course of his youthful botanizing expeditions,

Fig. 6 Sir Isaac Newton and Sir Hans Sloane, from an engraving by Jacob Smith. BM, PD, P.8/225. Reproduced by courtesy of the Trustees of the British Museum.

possibly during his years as a student in London,[138] certainly by the time of his studies in Paris and Montpellier: a number of specimens survive in a *hortus siccus* annotated 'Plants rare gathered by me H.S. in the fields and gardens about Montpeliers, Paris, and in several parts of France, about the year 1683'.[139] Understandably, the Jamaican voyage resulted in a very substantial increase both in the size of the collection and in perceptions of its value.

As early as 1691, John Evelyn gives a description of the collection that reveals its already considerable size as well as its diversity:

I went to see Dr. Sloans Curiosities, being an universal Collection of the natural productions of Jamaica consisting of Plants, [fruits,] Corralls, Minerals, [stones,] Earth, shells, animals, Insects &c: collected by him with great Judgement, several folios of Dried plants & one which had about 80: severall sorts of Fernes, & another of Grasses: &c: The Jamaica pepper in branch, leaves, flowers, fruits &c: [which] with his Journal, & other Philosophical & naturall discourses & observations is indeede very extraordinary and Copious, sufficient to furnish an excellent History of that Iland, to which I encouraged him, & exceedingly approved his Industry.[140]

Clearly there were limits to the extent to which Sloane's own efforts could expand the collection and indeed its subsequent development depended largely on other ready-made museums which Sloane was able to incorporate into

his own. Of these the first and most important was that of William Courten (1642–1702), otherwise known as Charleton, which he acquired on the latter's death in 1702. Courten and Sloane had been friends since they had first met in their youth, probably in Montpellier where Courten studied natural sciences. His grandfather had been a successful London merchant but his father had died insolvent in France. In 1684 Courten established himself and his collection in a suite of rooms at the Temple. There he received several visits from John Evelyn, the first in December 1686:

. . . Mr. Charleton . . . shewed us such a Collection of Miniatures, Drawings, Shells, Insects, Medailes, & natural things, Animals whereoff divers were kept in glasses of Sp[irits] of wine, I think an hundred, besids, Minerals, precious stones, vessels & curiosities in Amber, Achat, chrystal &c: as I had never in all my Travells abroad seene any either of private Gent: or Princes exceede it; all being very perfect & rare in their kind, espec[i]ally his booke of Birds, Fish: flowers, shells &c, drawn & miniatured to the life.[141]

When Courten died, on 26 March 1702, an epitaph was composed for this tomb by Sloane, to whom Courten had bequeathed his entire collection,[142] then valued at some £50,000, on condition that he fulfilled several legacies amounting in value to a mere £2,500. In his own will, Sloane was later to acknowledge the fundamental importance to his own collecting activities of 'my ever honoured, late friend William Courten, Esq; who spent the greatest part of his life and estate in collecting such things, in and from most parts of the earth, which he left me at his death, subject to several debts and legacies ... and his collections [being] kept intire'.[143] When Richard Richardson visited Sloane in May of that year, he found that 'Mr. Charlton's collection, which Dr Sloane now has, lies all in confusion as yet, and will require some time to put them in order'.[144] Although best known for his medals and antiquities (see Chapters 9 and 12), Courten had an interest in botanical specimens too, for he was a subscriber to a scheme to send James Reed on a plant-collecting expedition to Barbados.[145]

Considering the plaudits the Courten collection had already received from contemporary connoisseurs we may begin to form an impression of the scale and quality of the collection that Sloane was to amass.

Less costly than Courten's but of more importance from a scientific point of view was the collection of 8,000 specimens from the herbarium of Leonard Plukenet (1642–1706), which had earlier been acquired by Dr John Moore, Bishop of Norwich, and which later came into Sloane's possession.[146] Plukenet had also practised medicine, though whether as a physician or an apothecary is unknown. In 1690 he was appointed superintendent of the Hampton Court gardens with the title 'Queen's botanist'. From 1691 he began to publish the specimens in his own collection with full illustrations – the largest body of material hitherto illustrated in that way – which publication was much admired and used by Linnaeus. The book also included an extensive and useful synonymy.[147] His plant collection contained Chinese, Indian and Virginian material. Writing of Plukenent in a letter to Sloane in 1696, Ray calls him 'a man reserved, jealous of his reputation, and none of the best-natured, not to give him a worse character, being my friend ...' The difficulties which Sloane experienced with Plukenet are mentioned below.

A third major acquisition was the collection of James Petiver (c.1663–1718), which Sloane acquired in 1718. Petiver's professional career had begun when he became apprenticed to Charles Feltham, the apothecary of St. Bartholomew's hospital, and around 1692 he set himself up in practice in Aldersgate. Later, with support from Sloane and others of his acquaintance, he was appointed apothecary to the Charterhouse. Although Petiver bemoaned his 'not being allowed ... academical learning' beyond his youth, he expanded his knowledge of botany to the point where Ray considered him 'the best skilled in oriental and indeed in all exotic plants of any man I know'.[148] He is credited with the discovery a number of new species, and gained formal recognition for his work with his election to the Royal Society in 1695. Petiver initiated an ambitious project to publish the contents of his collections in a series of fascicules or 'centuries', each listing 100 specimens. The first of these appeared in 1695 with the title *Musei Petiveriani Centuria Prima*, listing animals and plants in the collection. The foreward includes an acknowledgement to those who had already contributed to the collection (including Sloane) and an appeal to others, notably 'all practitioners in Physick, Sea-Surgeons or other curious persons, who travel into foreign countries', to follow their example by sending all manner of plants, shells, insects, etc. His magnum opus, the *Gazophylacium Naturae et Artis*, was begun in 1702.

In 1711 Sloane asked Petiver to go to the Netherlands to buy for him Paul Hermann's collection of South African plants, which he accomplished with some success, reporting to Sloane that 'I ... have bought you the greatest share of the choisest of them'. This was Petiver's only recorded foreign excursion. Before leaving, he wrote to Sloane that 'In case I should dy before my return from Holland, I make you sole possessor of all my collections of naturall things whatsoever', with the condition that Sloane should pay certain modest bequests. At Petiver's death in 1718, however, the collection and associated manuscripts went to his sister, from whom Sloane bought them for £4,000 – a huge sum.[149] Sloane himself described Petiver as:

... a Person sufficiently well known by his Understanding in Natural History all over the learned World ... He had taken great Pains to gather together the Productions of Nature in *England*, and by his Correspondents, and Acquaintance all over the World procured, I believe, a greater Quantity than any Man before him. He did not take equal Care to keep them, but put them into heaps, with sometimes small labels of Paper, where they were many of them injured by Dust, Insects, Rain &c.[150]

Certainly when it came into Sloane's possession the collection lay in considerable confusion and the need to rearrange it was cited as one of the causes for the delay in appearance of the second volume of his *Natural History*.[151]

In addition to these major acquisitions which, added to the material already collected by Sloane himself, would themselves have established the museum as the greatest in the land, a number of smaller but historically important groups were added over the years. In the field of botany, for example, he bought Nehemiah Grew's collection of seeds and fruits.[152] He also acquired the collection of plants built up by Christopher Merrett (1614–95), physician and writer, who had for a time acted as curator of the College of Physicians' 'museum' and had published a printed catalogue of its holdings (in fact composed largely of books). Other collections of plants that came into Sloane's possession had been compiled by Jakob Breyne (1637–97) of Danzig, by James Cunningham (or Cunninghame) in China, and by Georg Joseph Kamel in the Philippines.

Smaller numbers of specimens (including shells as well as plants) were contributed directly or indirectly by an array of famous personalities such as William Dampier (1652–1715). The material from Dampier was brought back from his second circumnavigation of the world, but how it came into Sloane's possession is unrecorded.[153]

Plants, shells and other specimens again came to Sloane from the collection of Dr Engelbert Kaempfer (1651–1716), sometime physician of the Dutch East India Company, who spent two years in that capacity in Japan between 1690 and 1692. On receiving news of Kaempfer's death at Lemgo, some forty miles south-west of Hanover, Sloane asked Dr Johan Georg Steigerthal, Physician in Ordinary to George I, to make enquiries in the course of a journey to the Hanoverian court concerning the fate of the Kaempfer collections. The result was that Sloane (at no small cost) acquired not only the specimens but also many of Kaempfer's papers. The latter included the unpublished manuscript text for Kaempfer's *History of Japan*, whose translation and subsequent publication were undertaken at Sloane's expense.[154]

In addition to these already-established collections, newly collected plants continued to flow into the collection. These included specimens brought from the West Indies in 1692 by James Harlow, at the behest of Sir Arthur Rawdon: some years later, at Sloane's request, Rawdon's grandson was to send him Harlow's dried specimens, which remain today in the Sloane herbarium.[155] Sloane himself was a subscriber to certain plant-hunting expeditions: on 27 January 1722, for instance, William Sherard wrote somewhat plaintively to Richardson:

Mr. Catesby goes next week for Carolina . . . I have got him sufficient subscriptions . . . I will put you and our friend the Doctor down for a small sum. Sir Hans is ready to promote such designs, wallowing in money; but will not procure a subscription among his friends, as he easily might. I cannot think he has been unsuccessful, having had a large share of all that has come into England, and I never yet had a single Plant.[156]

In 1723 Catesby himself wrote to Sloane from Carolina: 'I hope you have received the remains of a Cargo of Plants, Birds, Shells, etc. which unfortunately fell into the hands of pirat[e]s. I shall be glad to hear the damage less than I expect.'[157] Eight years later, the first volume of his *Natural History of Carolina* was published with an acknowledgement to his 'curious Friends' to whom he had sent seeds, plants, corals, etc, '. . . more particularly (as I had the greatest Obligations) to that great Naturallist and promoter of Science Sir *Hans Sloane*, Bar^t to whose goodness I attribute much of the Success I had in this Undertaking.'[158]

Other facets of the collection were bolstered by acquisitions from elsewhere. The antiquarian elements from Courten's museum, for example, were boosted by a number of items which had formerly been in the collection of John Conyers (c.1633–94). An apothecary by profession, Conyers was never elected to the Royal Society, although he was a frequent guest at its meetings and an intimate of many fellows, including Robert Hooke and Sloane himself. As a result of careful observation of diggings for the foundations of buildings and the extraction of gravel, Conyers built up 'a world of antique curiosities found during excavations in the Ruines of London'.[159] Seeing some possibility of profit from his resource, he organized (or 'methodized') his collections in 1691 with a view to opening

them 'to such as shall be curious to see them', but nothing came of it.[160]

The antiquities mentioned in Sloane's catalogues arrived by an indirect route from Conyers' collection. In the first instance they seem to have been acquired by John Woodward, one of the most important figures on the contemporary collecting scene. His most valuable contributions to scholarship were in the field of geology, in which his activities as a systematic collector, cataloguer and interpreter of specimens have been judged to merit him consideration as a pioneer of modern science;[161] he was the author of *An Essay towards a natural history of the Earth* (1695) and Professor of Physic at Gresham College, being elected FRS in 1693 and FRCP in 1702. Although he could display charm on occasion,[162] his strongly opinionated personality led to his being embroiled repeatedly in scientific disputes.[163] According to the 1695 edition of Camden's *Britannia*, much of Conyers' collection was already in Woodward's hands by that time.

Later, some of Conyers' material passed to John Kemp (1665–1717), who, in Petiver's words, 'At great Charge and Indefatigable Pains . . . collected a Treasury of Antiquities, the like in its kind not to be seen amongst us', which by his 'generous Temper' was made accessible to 'any that are to his purpose'.[164] In addition to Egyptian antiquities (see Chapter 11), the collection embraced numerous Greek and Roman pieces, including 'Several Marble Statues of the *Roman* Gods; others in Brass, and 34 Marble Inscriptions, Originals; rare Marble Urns curiously carv'd, variety of others in Glass and Brass, enamell'd and in several sorts of Earth, and divers Shapes and Fashions'.[165] The presence of some of this material in Sloane's museum is a testament to the degree of continuity that already ensured the survival of artefacts from one collection to another: in addition to specimens from Conyers, Kemp's collection had contained material originally gathered by Jean Gaillhard, governor to George, 1st Lord Carteret, to whom it was sold before passing to Kemp; other specimens had been owned by the influential French antiquary Jacob Spon. Kemp's will, drawn up on 21 June 1714, made very specific provision for the disposal of his antiquities; in the event the collections went to auction four years after his death, and it was here, presumably, that Sloane acquired the specimens in question.[166]

In the course of these acquisitions, elements of Sloane's collection developed into valuable systematic collections in their own right. On the insects in the collection, for example, Ray wrote on 27 July 1703:

It is now a good while since that I acquainted you that some friends advised me, in order to the compiling of a History of Insects, to describe such exotic species as were to be found in the cabinets of the curious in and about London and elsewhere . . . whereupon you very freely and generously offered me the use of your collection, which far transcends all the rest, and wherein there are not many species wanting that are in other men's hands, especially of such as are for their rarity or beauty most valuable . . .[167]

Although coins and medals were not a major preoccupation for Sloane, he acquired an outstanding collection as part of Courten's bequest to which he added on occasion: he is said, for example, to have possessed coins and gems formerly belonging to the painter John Michael Wright.[168] At New Year 1697/8 John Evelyn recorded in his diary: 'I presented my Booke of Medals &c [i.e. his *Numismata*] to divers noblemen, before I suffered it to be exposed to sale'; it is perhaps a measure of the reputation of Sloane's collection that he was among the favoured recipients.[169]

The emergence of ethnology as a distinct discipline began to take place only a century or so after Sloane's death, but in common with other early collections his museum housed a number of 'artificial curiosities' which, by virtue of the early date at which they were collected, have an historical importance in addition to their intrinsic value. As might be expected, there is little obvious pattern to the acquisitions which Sloane made in this field: the bulk of his material came from the Americas, where his personal contacts were particularly numerous, while other material came from Persia and Turkey to the Far East, with a few items from Africa (see Chapter 15). Some of these items undoubtedly arrived as incidental parts of established collections acquired by Sloane.

Sloane also acquired a number of lesser collections as they became available. One of these had been gathered by William Stonestreet (died 1716), rector of St. Stephen's Walbrook: visiting 'the very courteous Parson Stonestreet' in 1701, Ralph Thoresby found there 'a good collection of Roman coins, and a most surprising one of shells, a thousand of several sorts from all parts of the world, curious for their form, size, colour &c.'[170] Another belonged to Austin Oldsworth, whose collection was described by Thoresby as including '. . . several animals, and some antiquities, but for variety of shells, is reputed the best in town, save Mr Stonestreet's'.[171]

Needless to say, Sloane's friends and acquaintances contributed smaller amounts of material. Thoresby (from Leeds) and Richard Richardson (a physician from North Bierley in Yorkshire) both sent geological specimens from the coalpits in their county. In 1729, while rearranging his museum, Sloane wrote to Richardson of his wish that 'some time or other you will give yourself leisure to look over deliberately what I have, where you will find a great number communicated by yourself both to me and to Mr. Petiver'.[172]

The Revd John Morton, from whom Sloane had many specimens, attributed his own passion for natural history and antiquities to an early acquaintance with John Ray and to the influence of the published works of Martin Lister. His researches resulted in the publication in 1712 of *The Natural History of Northampton-shire*. In a letter of 1704 to Richardson he mentions that he had left specimens with Sloane in London 'upon obligations he had generously laid upon me'; several such specimens, formerly published by Morton, are indentifiable in the Sloane catalogues (see Chapter 12).[173]

Another benefactor, Peter Collinson (1694–1768), is said to have befriended Sloane at an early age. He was an early member of the Society of Antiquaries and an accomplished naturalist; in 1728 he was elected FRS for his services to science, which included promoting publication of the researches of John Clayton in Virginia and of Catesby in Carolina. His family had professional (mercery) dealings with the Americas, and Collinson encouraged the cultivation there of flax, hemp, and even silk. He was a correspondent and friend of Benjamin Franklin. Collinson was a contributor to the natural history collections of the British Museum and his appointment as curator of the botanical division was mooted but never implemented.[174]

Sir Charles Wager (1666–1743), First Lord of the Admiralty, collected 'a variety of curiosities' on his voyages (seemingly at the instigation of Collinson), some of which went to swell the Sloane collection. 'With the same kind and liberal view', it is said, he encouraged the commanders under him, who were stationed in different parts of the globe, to procure whatever was rare and valuable in the several branches of Natural History'.[175] Some of Wager's prizes, at least, were sent originally to Philip Miller at the Apothecaries' garden in Chelsea, finding their way later into Sloane's museum.[176]

Sloane was not entirely immune from the lure of curiosities in general: writing from Jamaica to his friend Rawdon he mentions the recovery of a great deal of treasure from the wreck of a Spanish galleon from which he salvaged a fragment of the ship's timbers encrusted with coral and with an iron bolt through it and some pieces-of-eight.[177] On a later occasion, around 1710, John Fuller of Brightling in Sussex, sent him a pair of recently-farrowed 'monstrous piggs', one of which had been born dead and the other succumbed shortly afterwards. He was generally free of the gullibility that characterized other omniverous but less discerning collectors and recognized false curiosities when he saw them.[178]

One of the few contemporary figures who might have been expected to feature among the benefactors (at least with the occasional mutually-advantageous exchange), but whose name does not so appear in the records, is Dr Richard Mead (1673–1754), one of the most illustrious figures in contemporary medicine and himself a hugely successful collector. A nonconformist, Mead had acquired a knowledge of classical literature and antiquities at the university of Utrecht and studied botany and medicine at Leiden before graduating MD at Padua in 1695. In England he set up practice in Stepney, his birthplace, before becoming physician to St. Thomas's Hospital. His fortunes prospered to the point where he was consulted on a regular basis by the royal family. He was elected FRS in 1703, joining the council two years later and becoming a vice-president in 1717. Among his friends were numbered Sir Isaac Newton and

John Radcliffe, whose house in Bloomsbury Square Mead bought and there set himself up in practice, moving later to Great Ormonde Street. He was to become the most fashionable and prosperous physician of his day – he was reputed to make £5,000 to £6,000 a year from his practice – surpassing Sloane in this respect with his sophisticated bedside manner. Like Sloane he became a medical adviser to Queen Anne and to George I, and was involved in the experiments that resulted in innoculation of the royal family.

Mead's collection of books, manuscripts, drawings and antiquities formed something of a rival for Sloane's; although it was numerically less extensive, it was of particularly high quality. His library of 10,000 volumes was sold after his death for £5,518. 10s. 11d.[179] The pictures, coins, gems, statuary and other antiquities realized £10,550. 18s.[180]

As Sloane's collection grew in size it became too diverse to retain an overall homogeneity. It also presented problems of accommodation, which Sloane solved by acquiring 4 Bloomsbury Place, the property adjacent to his own house to accommodate the ever-expanding museum. In 1700 the collection escaped an attempt to set fire to the house in order that robbery could be committed in the ensuing confusion.[181]

The ever-increasing numbers of specimens led in later life to the need for Sloane to employ a series of curatorial assistants (several of whom also contributed to the collections), although the degree of control which he delegated to them seems always to have been limited.

It had been suggested in a letter of 4 January 1725 that Johann Caspar [or Gaspar], son of Johann Jakob Scheuchzer, professor of mathematics and physic at Zürich, might help Sloane in making a catalogue of his collections. Sloane replied that this had already been done, but instead he employed Scheuchzer to make indexes of his books and to put them in order.[182] Scheuchzer meanwhile studied for his medical degree and was awarded his doctorate from Cambridge in 1728, but he died in the following year. He was considered a good medallist, antiquary and natural historian; it was he who undertook, at Sloane's behest, the translation of Kaempfer's *History of Japan* (see Chapter 18).

Scheuchzer was succeeded as Sloane's amanuensis by Cromwell Mortimer (1698–1752). Sloane had been a kindly ally in the forwarding of Mortimer's career in medicine, recommending him to Herman Boerhaave in Leiden where Mortimer was to obtain his doctorate in medicine; his thesis, presented in 1724, was dedicated to Sloane.[183] In a letter dated 23 July 1729, Mortimer explained that he moved to Bloomsbury 'to be near Sir Hans Sloane, for on Dr. Scheuchzer's death, who lived in the house with him, he desired my coming into his neighbourhood, and so I have the pleasure of being at Sir Hans' at all leisure hours in the day, continually entertained with new curiosities in his prodigious collection, and having the opportunity of

the use of his library, as well as his ingenious and learned conversation.'[184] In the following year he was elected secretary of the Royal Society, which office he held until 1752. It was he who presided over Linnaeus's introduction to Sloane in 1736[185] and who conducted the Prince and Princess of Wales around Sloane's museum in Chelsea in 1748 (see Appendix 4).

During the earlier part of Mortimer's employment with Sloane, Johann Amman (1707–41) shared some of the curatorial responsibilities. A native of Schaffhausen, Amman had studied medicine at Leiden and was like Sloane a botanist by inclination. In 1730 he was taken on by Sloane as a curator of the natural history collections and in 1731 was elected FRS. Perhaps as a result of some jealousy between Amman and Mortimer, Amman left Sloane's service in 1733 when he signed a four-year contract to work for the Academy in St. Petersburg. Thereafter Sloane and Amman kept up an amicable correspondence in which they exchanged scientific information until Amman's premature death at the age of thirty-four in 1741.[186] Sloane also sent seeds for the garden which Amman established in Russia, while the latter sent in return botanical and other specimens for Sloane's garden and for his museum.[187]

His other curators included James Empson (died 1765), who played an important role in tending the collections after Sloane's death. Empson was nominated in Sloane's will as a trustee and was given charge of the collection, with a salary of £100 a year, until such time as its fate had been decided. In the chancery proceedings of 1753 (in which Empson acted as secretary of the Trustees), he mentioned that he had had the care of the collections for twelve years before that date (see Chapter 2). He was later appointed first keeper of the Department of Natural Productions at the British Museum.

A particular virtue of Sloane's (without which this volume could hardly have been attempted) was his punctiliousness in compiling catalogues of every aspect of his collection and library. He has indeed been described as '. . . a pioneer cataloguer who perceived the need to document his collections in a systematic way'. Many were produced by his own hand, over a period stretching from (at latest) the mid 1680s to the late 1740s;[188] contributions by his various assistants (including Dr Thomas Stack, his librarian), are comparatively minor in importance and concentrated mostly in the catalogues of books. Some thirty-one volumes of an original forty-six of the manuscript catalogues have survived (see below, pp. 291–4).[189] It is true that some of the lists show signs of the haste in which they evidently were compiled, with various items entered more than once, others omitted, and a number appearing in inappropriate sections of the catalogues. Many of the specimens, meanwhile, retain their original catalogue numbers, some written in ink on paper labels, others inscribed directly on to the specimen itself.

It is clear that he spent enormous effort both in arranging

the collections and in recording them. In the preface to the second volume of his *Natural History*, Sloane explains the long delay in its appearance as being occasioned partly by the demands of his profession[190] and partly by the fact that his leisure has been largely employed in putting his collections in order. In a striking self-analysis, Sloane wrote to the Abbé Bignon that '. . . the collection and accurate arrangement of these curiosities constituted my major contribution to the advancement of science'.[191]

Sloane was notably free with access to his specimens and was '. . . always ready on proper Notice to admit the Curious to the sight of his Musæum'.[192] Neither was he reluctant, on the whole, to share the benefits of collections with the academic community. He records, for example, on his return from Jamaica: 'I gave my very particular and intimate Friend Mr. Courten whatever I brought with me, and he wanted in his extraordinary Museum'.

The twin virtues of orderliness and accessibility made Sloane's museum one of the most desirable resting places for other collections which came on the market. Hearing that Ralph Thoresby's collections were in danger of dispersal, Hearne wrote to Richardson on 1 January 1726: 'I wish they may fall into good hands. Methinks they might be proper to be joy'nd with Sir Hans Sloane's',[193] and seven years later wished a similar fate on Edward Lhwyd's letters, for 'it is well that any thing of that kind falls into his hands'.[194]

Sloane does indeed seem to have been motivated by a strong sense of public utility in forming and expanding his collection. Birch, whose notes are thought to have been compiled from direct conversations with Sloane, expressed it as follows:

It was not . . . a trifling or vain Inclination of merely getting together a great Number of uncommon things, that induc'd him to spend 50,000£ in purchasing the Rarities which every country produced. His constant Endeavour was to employ them to the best purposes, by making himself acquainted, as far as possible, with the Properties, Qualities, & Uses, either in Food, Medicine, or Manufacture of every Plant, Mineral, or Animal, that came into his possession. By which means he became both the greatest Naturalist, & one of the ablest Physicians of his Age and Country; & in this last Character he was so distinguish'd that for many years he had a Flow of Business which inabled him not only to lay out such vast Sums on his Collection, & to portion out his two Daughters, but to leave besides a Fortune behind him of [£]100,000.[195]

An element of piety may also be detected in the way that Sloane, like some at least of his contemporaries, viewed the purpose of collecting. Sloane himself wrote of his friend Courten that he 'gave himself up to the contemplation of the works of GOD, whose infinite power, wisdom, and providence he saw and admired, in the creation and preservation of all things'.[196] Similar sentiments were expressed in Sloane's own will (see Chapter 2), and although a degree of hindsight (not to say self-interest) may have infiltrated

the old man's perception of his achievement, he may be allowed his due of reverence.

Inevitably, there were difficulties and misunderstandings from time to time. Sloane gives his own account of how these developed:

When I first return'd from *Jamaica*, I brought with me a Collection of dried Samples of some very strange Plants, which excited the Curiosity of People who loved Things of that Nature to see them, and who were welcome, 'till I observ'd some so very curious, as to desire to carry part of them home with them privately, and injure what they left. This made me upon my guard with them . . .[197]

William Sherard was one of those with whom Sloane suffered a falling out over the collection. Their relationship had started amicably enough, but later, while compiling an edition of Bauhin's *Pinax*, Sherard asked Sloane for the loan of certain specimens to help his researches: these included not only specimens collected by Sloane himself but others he had acquired from the collections of Buddle, Plukenet, Petiver and others. Sloane prevaricated, claiming with evident justification that Petiver's collection in particular still lay in disarray. Later, Sloane offered to let Sherard have the specimens in batches but the latter demurred. Richardson, a mutual friend, spent a great deal of effort in trying to reconcile the two.[198]

Meanwhile, the museum became one of the sights of London for visiting connoisseurs. In 1710 it received a visit from the acerbic von Uffenbach, whose record of his visit is reproduced in Appendix 1. Having comprehensively criticized the Ashmolean, the Royal Society's repository and Dr Woodward's collection, he found by contrast a great deal to recommend both Sloane and his 'large and wonderful collection'. Later, in 1729, a further account was compiled by Sauveur Morand, which is reproduced here in Appendix 2. From these sources, some impression can be formed of the appearance and character of the museum at 3–4 Bloomsbury Place.

Morand mentions that the collection, including the library, occupied eleven large rooms. Von Uffenbach describes one such room (characterized as of moderate size and quite full), in which cabinets for various specimens lined the lower areas of the walls, with three or four tiers of bookshelves above, so that the two elements evidently overlapped to some degree. Items in the individual cabinets were segregated according to their nature: some were filled with mineral specimens, butterflies, shells, or birds' eggs; one contained '7,000 different fruits'. To judge from the flow of the descriptions, however, the sequence in which these cabinets followed each other was less rigorous: in von Uffenbach's account, shells and butterflies are followed by costumes and weapons, and then by agates, coins, zoological specimens and birds' nests; Morand has anatomical specimens followed by medals, Egyptian antiquities sandwiched on either side by zoological exhibits, while shoes, clothing and antiquities alternate with fossils, pearls and crystals. However, since no indication is given of where one room ends and the next begins (not to mention linking halls and passageways), it is impossible to assess the significance of these observations.[199] Wet specimens were stored in jars of spirits of wine, while larger horns, antlers and stuffed animals would no doubt have been accommodated on top of the cabinets or on the walls. No sculptures or pictures are mentioned in either of these descriptions, apart from 'The originals of the insects of Surinam' by Sybilla Merian, the portfolio of engravings of plants prepared by Nicolas Robert and others, and further pictures 'which Mr Sloane has had sent to him from all countries' – all of them clearly complementary to the natural specimens. The skeleton of a whale occupied a courtyard.

Other visitors at this period included Linnaeus, who came in August 1736 bearing a letter of introduction from Herman Boerhaave.[200] There seems to have been little meeting of minds between the two of them, communication being hindered by difficulties of language and a great difference in age (Linnaeus was twenty-nine at the time while Sloane was seventy-six, tending to deafness and partly paralysed). The old man failed to respond to the innovative theories of the young Swede, published the previous year in his *Systema Naturae*, while Linnaeus was evidently disappointed with Sloane's renowned collection of *naturalia*, finding it (by the standards of his own system) 'in complete disorder'.[201]

An even more discordant note was sounded, so the story goes, during a visit in 1740 by George Frederic Handel. Sloane entertained him to tea, in the course of which the composer is said to have placed his muffin carelessly on a precious manuscript, indelibly staining it with butter and causing understandable outrage to its owner.[202]

Needless to say, there were many other wits and satirists who lampooned the great collector, mostly with ponderous and unmemorable humour;[203] in general they seem to have been incapable of distinguishing between the seriousness of Sloane's intentions and the gimcrackery of less purposeful collectors.

Sloane was by now in poor health and his medical practice much curtailed. In 1740 wrote to Richardson:

Since my condition hath rendered me unable to follow the practice of my profession, I have employed myself in putting into some sort of order my collections of all sorts, which are very numerous, and in some particulars made so by yourself. I have taken such care as reasonably can be expected of me; but I cannot answer for what may happen to them . . .[204]

In 1742 with Sloane's retirement from practice, the time had come for him to transfer his household and of course his collections to the manor house at Chelsea. The move is recorded in hair-raising detail in the journal of Edmund Howard, a phlegmatic Quaker employed as caretaker at Chelsea by Sloane:

This house being very large and capable to contain his library and all his collection of gimcracks, he left his house in Little Russell

Street, near Bloomsbury Square, declined his practice of physic, and retired to the said house with all his vast collection, all which, except a few which he used to bring himself in his chariot, passed through my hands. Those he brought himself were chiefly gold and silver medals, diamond, jewels, and other precious stones; and among these I doubt not but he had had many gods of gold and gods of silver, for I one day unpacked a large case full of gods of the ancient Egyptians, Greeks and Romans, &c. But to give in detail only the sorts or kinds of things would far exceed my intention. Suffice it, then, to say, he had forty volumes in folio – catalogues of his collection – and forty-two thousand other books in his library, among which was one room full of specimens of dried plants, all which passed through my hands. He used to appoint the rooms in which the books were to be stored up, and I to receive them; they were sent loose in carts and tossed from the cart to a man on a ladder, who tossed them in at a window, up one pair of stairs, to a man who caught them there as men do bricks, and I was employed, as before mentioned, doing nearly all things for him belonging to his estate at Chelsea except collecting the rent.[205]

In a letter addressed to Claude-Joseph Geoffroy on 1 August of that year, Sloane recounts that he is amusing himself in rearranging the collection; he mentions too that he plans to dispose of his duplicates in a manner that will benefit the public and says that he would count it an honour if his duplicate plants could be placed with those of his old friend Tournefort.[206] Stukeley paid Sloane a visit on 13 April 1743 and found that 'His great house at Chelsea is full throughout; every closet & chimney with books, raritys, &c.'[207]

An estimation of the size of the collection at this time can be gained from the list transmitted to his executors after his death in 1753.[208] By comparing this with an earlier list, published in the introduction to volume II of his *Natural History* of 1725, in which Sloane mentions that he has entered the objects in his collection into books, and numbered them, an impression can be gained of the growth of the collection in the intervening quarter of a century:

	1725	1753
Earths and Salts	536	1035
Bitumens, Sulphurs, Ambers, Ambergreese	249	399
Metals and Minerals	1394	2725
Talcs, Micae &c.	169	388
Chrystals and Sparrs, or Fluores Crystallini	1025	1864
Flints, Stones and other remarkable Fossils that are anomalous	730	1275
Precious Stones, Agats, Jaspers, and fine Marbles	1394	2256
Corals, or such as are a kin to them, as Sponges and other Submarine Plants	804	1421
Vegetables, and Vegetable Substances, as Roots, Woods, Fruits, Seeds, Gums, Resines and inspissated Juices	8226	12506
Besides 200 large Volumes of dried		

Samples of Plants, amongst which are such Specimens as were collected by myself in *Europe*, the *Madera* Island, and *America*, as also those gathered by Dr. *Merret*, Dr. *Plukenet*, Mr. *Petiver* and other curious Persons all over the known World	[200]	334
Insects	3824	5439
Testacea, or Shells, and their Parts, both natural, found at Sea and Land, and Fossil	3753	5843
Echini, or Sea Urchins, and Parts of them, both natural and fossil, found at Sea and Land	486	659
Stellæ Marinæ &c		173
Crustacea, or Crabs, Lobsters, &c.	263	363
Fishes, and their Parts	1007	1555
Asteriae, Trochi, Entrochi &c.	183	241
Birds, and their Parts	568 ⎫	1172
Eggs	185 ⎭	
Quadrupeds, and their Parts	1194	1886
Vipers, Serpents &c.	345	521
Humana, *viz.* Stones of the Kidneys and Bladder, Anatomical Preparations, and the like	507	756
Miscellaneous Things not comprehended with the foregoing, both Natural and Artificial	1169	2098
Things relating to the Customs of ancient Times, or Antiquities, Urns, Instruments, &c.	302	1125
Large Seals	81	268
Pictures, many relating to natural History	319	310
Mathematical instruments	54	55
Large Vessels, Handles, and other Things made of Agats, Jaspers, Cornelians, Christals, besides many Camei and Seals, excisa, and incisa	441	542 700
Medals, antient, as Samaritan, Phænician, Greek, Consular, Roman, &c. and Modern, and Coins in all Metals	20228	[23000][209]
Books in Miniature or Colours, with fine Drawings of Plants, Insects, Birds, Fishes, Quadrupeds, and all sorts of natural and artificial Curiosities	136	These three heads with his printed books estimated at 50000
Books of Prints &c.	580	
Volumes of Manuscripts, the greatest Part of them relating to Physick, and Natural History, Travels, &c.	2666	

An account of the museum in its new setting was left by Linnaeus's pupil Per Kalm, who called on Sloane on his way to America in 1748 (reproduced as Appendix 3),[210] and in the same year the museum received the accolade of a visit from Prince and Princess of Wales, duly recorded in the press (see Appendix 4). These two accounts once again lend some character to the bald lists of exhibits.

The greater part of the collections there occupied a long gallery 110 feet in length, where once again the specimen cabinets were set against the walls while 'about a fathom from the floor above the Natural Curiosities the walls were all covered with books'. The 'great saloon' was lined on every side with jars and bottles containing specimens preserved in spirits, while the walls of various halls were hung with horns and antlers (including the impressive fossil antlers of Irish giant deer) and with weapons from several countries. In eight other rooms books covered the walls from floor to ceiling, and in one stood a great rotary book-rack that allowed Sloane to consult a number of large volumes simultaneously and with ease. Kalm was particularly impressed by the boxes in which insects were preserved, with glass sheets above and below so that the specimens could be conveniently examined; by the stuffed birds, mounted 'as naturally as if they still lived'; and by the house-shaped gem boxes comprising many drawers or trays, each forming in turn a lid for the other. While the record of the royal visit provides a good impression of the sumptuousness of the collection, its method of presentation on that occasion, in the form of a banquet of successive courses spread on the tables, tells us less of its habitual appearance.

By now Sloane was a venerable eighty-eight years of age, in declining health and contemplating his own fate and that of his collections.[211] 'This curious old Gentleman', Madame du Bocage reported two years later, 'intends, as it is said, to bequeath these fruits of his enquiries to the Royal Society of London'.[212] Such a course might have had a number of advantages in Sloane's eyes, notably in ensuring the continuing public accessibility of the collections. There would have been disadvantages, however: notable among these was the fact that the declared aims of the Royal Society would have rendered only the natural collections appropriate for its Repository and Sloane was anxious to maintain the integrity of the whole collection. Another contender would have been the Ashmolean at Oxford, but from promising beginnings eighty years earlier the curatorship of the Ashmolean had since the appointment in 1730 of George Huddesford, president of Trinity College, been reduced to a mere synecure, cynically exploited by its incumbent. Sloane was far too prudent to commit his treasures here[213] and after a great deal of thought arrived at the solutions discussed in the following chapter. Time has proved that he made a judicious choice.

Prudence and application, combined with sober temperament, a philanthropic nature and a sense of Christian virtue, marked every aspect of Sloane's career from beginning to end. There was to be no sequel in maturity corresponding to the youthful promise of his scientific fieldwork in Jamaica, but he earned in his own day almost universal respect for his able administration of the nation's foremost scientific and medical institutions. The richness of the collections he bequeathed to the nation has also been acknowledged since that time, but in the following analyses of their contents, based on Sloane's own inventory records, a picture emerges for the first time of the true value of these collections and of the acuteness of the man who founded them, shaped them, and ordered them. For the moment, we may leave the last word on Sloane to William Stukeley:

. . . Industry may be said to have raisd S^r. Hans, as Art did Radcliff, fortune Mead. S^r. Hans has had this piece of luck too, that being a vertuoso has made his fortune, which generally ruins others . . . The same industry has made him perfect master of the knowledg of his immense collection, begun by Mr. Charltons gift, carryd on by his own riches & pains & interest, & may be said to be the greatest that ever was a private mans possession.[214]

Appendix 1
Sloane's Museum at Bloomsbury, as described by Zacharias Conrad von Uffenbach, 1710[215]

In the afternoon Herr Campe took us to call on Dr Hans Sloane, who received us with vast politeness; in a very different manner from the coxcomb, Dr Woodward. He immediately addressed us in French, which was most amazing for an Englishman; for they would rather appear dumb than converse with a foreigner in any other language than their own, even if they should be quite capable of doing so. He took us into a room of moderate size, which was quite full. Above are three or four rows of books, while all the lower part is furnished with cabinets and natural curiosities. Not only is a large quantity here, but they are for the most part extraordinarily curious and valuable things. He has here the whole Charleton collection and many objects which Dr Sloane brought from India himself, while he is daily increasing them in England for vast sums of money. He assured us that the Venetian Ambassador had offered him fifteen thousand pounds sterling for this collection, but that he had refused. A great quantity of all manner of animals are to be seen here, some in spiritu vini and others preserved by drying. A prodigious variety of strange fishes, a large collection of ores, lapidibus figuratis, and an especially remarkable collection of lapidibus pretiosis, among them being several of uncommon size and value. He also had a handsome collection of all kinds of insects, which are kept in the same fashion as those we saw at Herr Dandridge's house, except that here, instead of glass, moonstone or Muscovy glass is used, which is much more delicate and light but more costly. Dr Sloane also showed us a cabinet of shells, which, though not at all numerous, consisted entirely of choice specimens. A Cochlea terristris was especially remarkable; not so much for its elegance as for its curious breeding from an egg such as we had seen in no other collections. Dr Sloane showed us both a whole egg and various shells that were not yet full grown and so were still partly surrounded by the crusta testacea. The shell entirely resembles an egg shell, and, on holding the egg against the light, one could see the concham lying concealed within it. The eggs are not large, being rather smaller than doves' eggs. Another cabinet was full of marinis, among which the collection of corals was especially charming, for they were not only of unusual size but also quality. Not only all kinds of red, black and white corals are to be found here, but also those half white, half red, red inside and white outside, etc. Next we saw a cabinet full of all manner of butterflies; not so handsome as those of Vincent in Amsterdam. Then we saw all kinds of Indian and other strange costumes, weapons, etc. Also a sort of cloth that is said to grow on a tree. Moreover some antlers well-nigh as large as those we saw at Windsor. Dr Sloane showed us further a small cabinet with about four hundred varieties of most handsome agates, of which most were figured. He considered them all to be natural, but this is extremely doubtful. Next a cabinet of all manner of vessels and objets d'art of agate and other costly stones and materials. We also saw a cabinet containing great quantities of Numismatibus ex omni metallo and a tolerable number of cut antique stones, but time was lacking to observe them all with care. Next a remarkable cabinet of all kinds of stuffed animals, especially birds, and also several nests of vastly curious structure. Among other things he pointed out to us the nests that are eaten as a delicacy. It is said that the material is formed in the sea like the succino and used by the birds to build their nests. But judging from its taste, appearance and feeling, I took it for a gum resin, though many persons, indeed, consider succinum to be this. After we had seen everything in all the rooms round about, as far as time permitted, Dr Sloane invited us into another room, where we sat down at a table and drank coffee while he showed us all manner of curious books. Namely, various large volumes containing nothing but paintings from life of all sorts of exotic beasts, birds, plants, flowers, shells, etc. A notable one with all kinds of national costumes. These paintings were done by the best artists and collected sheet by sheet from all parts of the world at a phenomenal cost, often by Dr Sloane himself on the long journeys he has taken. The book with excellent illuminations by Mad. Merian of insects and plants was among them, but it was by no means equal to the other. Finally he showed us some manuscripts, but they were for the most part modern and on medical subjects. The best was a description of the West Indian coasts in the Portuguese tongue, accompanied by elegant paintings. It was a pity that we had so few hours to look through his large collection and these handsome articles, since the gentleman had no time on account of his extensive practice. They say that he could earn a guinea an hour. We thought, indeed, that he did us a very great honour by sparing us the time between half past two and seven o'clock. Being a much-travelled man he is vastly amiable, in especial to Germans and such persons as have some knowledge of his treasures. I presented him with a Lohenstein hystero lythibus, such as he had never seen before, and it was especially welcome; on this account he showed us more courtesy than to other persons.

Appendix 2
Sloane's Museum at Bloomsbury, as described by Sauveur Morand, 1729[216]

Mr Sloane's cabinet comprises eleven large rooms, including his library, which is the most complete in Europe for books on medicine; he has 3,000 manuscripts on this subject. In this cabinet are to be seen

1 Extremely rare anatomical pieces, amongst others many preparations by Ruysch; the foetus which Ciprien removed by caesarian operation in 1694 without causing the death of the mother; various injections of the principal vessels of a body of which the tunics are full of knots caused by a tophaceous matter, produced by the gout; various skeletons, including that of a syphillitic, full of growths; several pieces exhibiting maladies of the bones; stones removed from different parts of the body – there are 400 of them; from the bladder, and several from the intestines.

2 A collection of medals; there are as many ancient as modern; 23,000.

3 Skeletons of leaves of various trees, produced by insects.

4 Various birds, amongst others humming birds and 'oiseaux du mogol'.

5 Skins of all sorts of animals.

6 Teeth of all sorts of animals, amongst others elephants' teeth, swollen and distended, having been penetrated by foreign bodies which remain inside; in one is an iron ball. M. Ruysch makes mention of a similar observation in his Decades.

7 A great number of Egyptian antiquities.

8 4,000 different insects; the Surinam toad.

9 A complete history of butterflies all in glazed boxes. Also there are curious leaves resembling flying insects, which are called *folia ambulantia.*

10 A collection of beetles.

11 A collection of all the species of spiders.

12 A cupboard where there are 7,000 different fruits.

13 Another full of petrifications and a great many dendrites.

14 One full of eggs and nests of all kinds of birds; the eggs of a crocodile.

15 Feathers of all sorts of birds, amongst others the condor.

16 Beaks of all sorts of birds.

17 A large collection of snakes in spirits.

18 A large quantity of fish in spirits.

The wings of several sorts of flying fish; he has in his courtyard the skeleton of a large whale

19 A series of madrepores, corals, and lithophytes of all sorts.

20 A large series of crabs, crayfish, lobsters, and shell fish, amongst others the soldier.

21 All sorts of mines, with the method of working them in relief.

22 A large cabinet of shells.

23 A collection of sponges, and their formation.

24 A collection of all sorts of fossils.

25 A series of all sorts of shoes of different nations.

26 Indian clothes.

27 Pearls with their formation and growth.

28 A collection of instruments of the ancients, urns, lacrymatories, etc.

29 A history of crystals.

30 A little vessel made of cloves.

31 Various wasps' nests, and their sections.

32 A collection of horns of all sorts of animals.

33 A little cabinet in which are all the uncut precious stones, in their matrices.

34 A large series of jaspers, agates, amber, cornelian, precious cups and costly vessels, of which one is made of three sorts of stones.

35 A large series of eye agates and other forms.

36 A large collection of Florentine stones, figured, and engraved rings.

37 A large quantity of bezoars, amongst others a western one weighing 22 ounces.

A herbarium comprising 230 volumes in folio; the pages of these volumes are carefully mounted with natural dried plants, amongst others tea, coffee, cocoa, camphor, cloves, cinnamon, cedar of Lebanon.

The plant called lagetto [lace bark] of which the stem, the leaves and the bark provide four different kinds of fibre, one of which makes very beautiful lace, two others winter and summer materials, and the fourth a kind of yellow cloth from which one can make shirts.

39 The originals of the insects of Surinam, painted by Sybilla Marie Merian.

40 The famous compilation of engravings [of the King's collection] by Robert,[217] considerably augmented by the pictures which Mr Sloane has had sent to him from all countries.

Appendix 3
Sloane's Museum at Chelsea, as described by Per Kalm, 1748
Translated by Professor William R. Mead[218]

Today [26 May], I accompanied several gentlemen to Sir Hans Sloane, to see his Natural History Collection and especially to look at the snake *Cobra de Capello*, which has markings on its neck like spectacles, to have an account of the *Scuta abdominalia* and *Squames caudales*, as requested in a letter from Herr Archiater Linnaeus. I have already given some account of the things that I saw here. I will now add to it, and in the order in which they were shown to us. We had the privilege of Sir Hans Sloane's presence for a couple of hours, during which we saw his great collection of all kinds of precious stones. Among the things that we saw, the following were especially noteworthy:

8 great drawers filled with all sorts of rare and precious stones, partly in their matrix as found in nature, partly polished or artistically treated in one way or another. There was a case full of all kinds of stones produced in animals, the same as stones generated in the gall bladder of mankind, of which some were as big as fist. There were also all sorts of bezoar stones.

A polished agate which displayed in a most naturalistic manner an eclipse of the sun.

A polished agate, the natural lining of which represented fortification.

Another, representing a tree and a wood.

Jasper with cinnabar ore in it.

A polished agate with protuberances on it resembling frog spawn.

A snuffbox, entirely of pure jasper.

Jasper polished in which a picture of two women who stood and gossiped; n.b. imagination was needed to make this out.

Pudding-stone is the name of a stone of which we saw quantities around Little Gaddesden and other places in Hertfordshire. It is nothing other than a conglomerate of various flintstones. In Hertfordshire, it was used mostly as marking and boundary stones. A great deal of it was seen there. Here, in Sir Hans Sloane's collection we saw some of it polished, and it greatly resembled pudding of various kinds, from which it has derived its name. In the section devoted to the work of craftsmen, snuffboxes were to be seen made from it and they looked very attractive.

The man who showed us them told how a certain Englishman had bought several bits of polished puddingstone, taken them to China and sold them, thereby making a profit of 1200 pro cent. Very good business.

Flintstone resembling a foot.

A polished stone which resembled a human being.

Various tea cups and saucers made of agate, carbuncle and sardonyx, all of which had a matchless appearance.

A single example of them had cost Sir Hans Sloane 50 guineas.

Several different boxes had also been made from these stones, and they were beautifully worked.

A little rectangular box with a lock made entirely of transparent jasper.

A goblet of jasper, speckled as if flies had settled on it.

Various kinds of spoons made of transparent jasper, beautifully coloured.

A largish number of cups, beakers, flasks, small boxes or chests with locks on all of jasper.

Pieces of jasper rounded like globes with the poles indicated on them. Stones with water inside, which squelched when shaken.

Egyptian pebbles, shaped like a man's face.

A large goblet made of three different kinds of natural stone, the bottom part of so-called bloodstone, the central part of jasper, and the top part of agate. Then the most expensive stones were shown to us, which were kept in a box made in a special way. The box was four cornered, a little more than a *quarter* long, and rather less than a *quarter* broad, and about a *quarter* in depth. From the top it sloped on all sides, resembling a monument over a grave or a house with an Italian roof. It consisted of a large number of drawers which did not pull out in the usual manner, but were so arranged that the upper drawer always locked the one beneath it, and the bottommost drawer locked all of the others. The precious stones were small and lay in little round holes hollowed out in the drawers.

It was said that there were 1,300 different kinds of precious stones in this cabinet.

The heads of various men, emperors, kings, gods etc. worked in and ornamented with various kinds of precious stones.

Stones like sore eyes: item, like an eye with a cataract.

An opal with green and other colours in it.

Alexander, Mars, a goddess from Ceylon, modelled in onyx.

Many rings with divers precious stones set in them.

Mocca stone set in a ring, in which a tree had been painted by nature. Sir Hans Sloane had paid 100 pounds for this.

A stone on which a fly had been carved and set in a ring.

A beryl, which the Great Mogul was said to have worn in his cap. A stone made in the shape of a *torndyfvel* with the letters of the Egyptian alphabet on it.

The shoes of a grown up Chinese woman which were no bigger than those of a child of 2 or 3 years in Sweden.

A device made of elephant bone with which the women of the East Indies scratch their backs.

Another of onyx.

Various kinds of combs used by people in the East Indies, some made of wooden pins bound together.

Many different kinds of pearls.

An Indian god to be carried in the pocket.

Rattling and jingling things, which the East Indians put on their hands and feet when they dance.

A bird's nest which is eaten in the West Indies,

which was white and almost looked as though it was made of white wax.

Afterwards we went into a room in which a number of paintings hung on the wall. Among them we noticed Sir Hans Sloane's name on one picture which consisted entirely of naked women who twisted themselves into various postures. Thus, one of them inscribed the letter S by inclining forwards and bending her knees, and there was a naked child on the soles of both feet lying on the ground behind her.

In another room we saw a number of representations of kings, learned men and others. Among them was a portrait of Mr. John Ray which must be the only one of him to be found in England. It very much resembles that which is found on the title page of his *Wisdom of God in the Creation.*

Then we went into the little narrow room where most of Sir Hans Sloane's treasures are. It is about two *famnar* broad, about 7 *alnar* high, and 110 English feet long. Along the sides the bottom-most cabinets contain all sorts of natural curiosities with other exhibits lying on them or hanging from the wall; but about six feet up from the floor and above the exhibits, the walls are covered with books. Among an endless number of other items were noticed

A cupboard filled with all sorts of goblets made from *Cochleis.*

An immense quantity of all sorts of corals.

A magnet capable of attracting a piece of iron as big as a large axe.

Bottles which had lain for a long time at the bottom of the sea which were covered with a growth of various kinds of coral.

A great collection of crystals.

All kinds of bird eggs.

The headdress of a West Indian King made out of red feathers.

Feathers from various kinds of birds.

Various kinds of birds' nests.

A large number of various kinds of insects which filled many cabinets. They were all mounted in large drawers. Each species or individual was laid in a rectangular box the bottom of which was wooden. But among them, some had both the cover and the bottom of the box made of a crystal-clear glass, while some had only a transparent glass lid. At the joints where the glass ran up to the sides of the box it was sealed tight with paper in such a way that no air let alone any moth or other insect could get inside to damage the contents. Where the box had a glass bottom, the insects were firmly fixed to it.

A West Indian axe, similar to those that were used in former times before they discovered iron. It was used to chop down trees, to build boats and so on. The shaft was of wood while the axe itself consisted

of a sharp wedge-shaped stone which was bound fast with a coarse thread or string to the shaft.

The stuffed skin of a rattlesnake.

Many *Testudines* and *Lazertae* stuffed or dried.

Many stuffed birds which perched as if they were alive.

A large number of stuffed fish.

The horn of the fish that is called unicorn.

The saw of a sawfish.

Various *Canceres echinati.*

Indian musical instruments of many different kinds.

A cupboard filled with various *Testaceis*, both bigger and some smaller.

Some very valuable, *Omnium generum et specierum.*

A Lapp drum.

A piece of petrified wood from Ireland, about 5 *quarters* long.

A number of strange tobacco pipes.

A fairly large collection of different kinds of petrified objects.

Phytolithi plantarum (Waller. Min p. 337) among the sheets of pressed plants.

Ichthyoty polithi (Waller. Min. 368) among the sheets of pressed plants

Berries of the candleberry bush and some of its green transparent leaves.

Bark of a tree from Jamaica, said to be called Ligoto, which resembled a piece of white chamois skin. Some pieces of it were like linen or paper: others like a thin net of cambric, so that it was said to be usable for ruffles.

A cupboard with little drawers full of all kinds of seed, some of which were in their fruits, others of which were removed from them. The seeds lay in the kind of glass drawers described above when dealing with insects, save that these drawers had wooden bottoms.

Bottles of *pumpoyn.*

A cupboard full of *materia medica.*

In another room we then saw

336 volumes of dried and bound plants in royal folio, with as many plants mounted on each page as there was room for.

A coral called *Barba Neptuni*, very beautiful.

An apparatus to lay books on when reading, or when there is need to use a number of books at the same time. I mention it because it reminded me of a wheel that is found at Norrbro in Stockholm, but in the place of the blades or boards of the wheel that was driven by water, there was here a long rectangular shelf, mounted upon an axle and balanced on the underside with a weight. As the wheel was turned round all of the shelves rotated simultaneously. The book was laid on the upper side of the shelf and consequently remained in the same position however the wheel was rotated. The length of this wheel was about 10 *quarters*: the diameter about six. I do not recall how many shelves there were, but it was possible to have a considerable number of books lying on it at the same time.

24 volumes of rare books, all in costly bindings, sent to Sir Hans Sloane by the king of France.

5300 volumes of manuscripts on medicine and natural history, bound in fine bindings.

A book of Chinese paper with a number of splendid paintings in it.

In addition to the aforementioned long and narrow room there were 8 other rooms all the walls of which were filled from floor to ceiling with books. These rooms were generally 7 *alnar* high. Their length and breadth was about two and a half to three *famnar*; sometimes more, sometimes less.

Small round plates made from the cartilage of the vertebrae of *Balaena*, which were porous like pumicestone.

A cabinet full of *echinis marinis* and other marine animals in glass-covered drawers the same as described above.

The skeletons of various kinds of small animals.

Hystrices and other animals, stuffed.

A porcupine from Hudson Bay.

The skeleton of an armadillo.

The shoes of different kinds of people, though the bark shoes of the Finns and the bast shoes of the Russians were missing.

A loving cup made entirely out of the shell of different kinds of tortoise.

Various kinds of plants and flowers, resembling tulips, roses and others fashioned in the same way out of tortoise shell in a variety of colours.

Many drawers and cupboards full of *testaceis omnium generum et speciorum*, of which some were exceedingly beautiful.

Large pieces of crystal, transparent as the clearest ice.

Cups, jugs, ewers, plates, models of animals etc. made from natural crystal, which was very *täcka*.

A *Cochlea* which laid eggs of the shape and size of swallows' eggs and white in colour, in which were found little *Cochleae*, which then grew into big ones.

Another *Cochlea* of a remarkable size which had a special kind of intestine. It formed a long strip with many divisions. In these divisions were found little *Cochleae* which eventually grew up to their mother's size.

The nests of bees, wasps and other insects.

A cupboard filled with various kinds of coral. Notice that a large number of all of these cabinets had glass doors, so that you could see what was inside.

In another room were kept books which contained coloured drawings of different kinds of natural objects, such as the costly works of Mariana [? Merian], Catesby, Seba, Blackwell etc.

In another room we were shown an Egyptian mummy, all sorts of anatomical objects, human skeletons etc.

Another contained all sorts of Roman and other antiquities. They have been partly dug up in the ground. Some of them, such as the clay pitchers and bowls had been partly obtained from other sources.

There was one large room filled with a collection of fishes, birds, insects, *lacertae*, snakes, different kinds of small animals, various examples of human beings and of animals all kept in spirit. I had wished that I would not need to go through all this, but Herr Archiater Linnaeus requested that I should provide him with a description of the snake *Cobra de capello*, as to how large was the number of its *scutis abdominalbus* [abdominal plates] and *squamo caudalibus* [scales]. So while the others went around and looked at everything, I had to spend my time trying to count them up, which was very difficult, since the snake was in a flask which was sealed at the top so that the alcohol should not become contaminated. We also found here

The snake *Cobra de capello* which has as if it were a pair of spectacles painted on its neck and which had 183 *scutas abdominales*, and 60–61 *squamas caudales*, counted up several times and accurately. If the little *squamae* [scales], which are found under the chin parallel with the *scuta abdominalia*, are also counted, there are two more of the *scut. abdom.* than recorded above.

Another room, with the clothes of native people in various kinds of leather and other material. In this room were also

A stuffed camel.

A striped donkey from the Cape of Good Hope: *Equus lineis transversis versiculor*. Linn.

West Indian boats made of bark.

In the garden we saw Sir Hans Sloane's three-wheeled chair, with two wheels in front and a little one behind, in which he was drawn around his garden.

In an outbuilding, we saw the head of a whale, the whale was said to have been 90 feet long. The length of the bones in the whale's head was 3 *famnar*.

Appendix 4
An account of Sloane's museum at Chelsea, on the occasion of a visit by the Prince and Princess of Wales, 1748[219]

Dr. *Mortimer*, secretary to the Royal society, conducted their Royal Highnesses into the room where Sir *Hans* was sitting, being antient and infirm. The Prince took a chair and sat down by the good old gentleman some time, when he expressed the great esteem and value he had for him personally, and how much the learned world was obliged to him for his having collected such a vast library of curious books, and such immense treasures of the valuable and instructive productions of nature and art. Sir *Hans*'s house forms a square of above 100 feet each side, inclosing a court; and three front-rooms had tables set along the middle, which were spread over with drawers fitted with all sorts of precious stones in their natural beds, or state as they are found in the earth, except the first, that contained stones formed in animals, which are so many diseases of the creature that bears them; as the most beautiful pearls, which are but warts in the shell fish, the *bezoars*, concretions in the stomach; and stones generated in the kidneys and bladder, of which man woefully knows the effects; but the earth in her bosom generates the verdant *emerald*, the purple *amethist*, the golden *topaz*, the azure *saphire*, the crimson *garnet*, the scarlet *ruby*, the brilliant *diamond*, the glowing *opal*, and all the painted varieties that *Flora* herself might wish to be deck'd with; here the most magnificent vessels of cornelian, onyx, sardonyx and jasper, delighted the eye, and raised the mind to praise the great creator of all things.

When their Royal Highnesses had view'd one room, and went into another, the scene was shifted, for, when they returned, the same tables were covered for a second course with all sorts of *jewels*, polish'd and set after the modern fashion; or with *gems* carv'd or engraved; the stately and instructive remains of antiquity; for the third course the tables were spread with *gold* and *silver ores*, with the most precious and remarkable ornaments used in the *habits* of men, from *Siberia* to the Cape of *Good Hope*, from *Japan* to *Peru*; and with both ancient and modern *coins* and *medals* in gold and silver, the lasting monuments of historical facts; and those of a *Prusias*, King of Bithynia, who betray'd his allies; of an *Alexander*, who, mad with ambition, over-run and invaded his neighbours; of a *Caesar*, who inslaved his country to satisfy his own pride; of a *Titus*, the delight of mankind; of a Pope *Gregory* XIII, recording on a silver medal his blind zeal for *religion*, in perpetuating thereon the *massacre* of the *protestants* in *France*; as did *Charles* IX, the then reigning king in that country; here may be seen the coins of a *king* of *England*, crown'd at *Paris*, a medal representing *France* and *Spain*, striving which should first pay their obeissance to *Britannia*; others shewing the effect of popular rage, when overmuch oppressed by their superiors, as in the case of the *De Witts* in *Holland*; the happy deliverance of *Britain*, by the arrival of King *William*; the glorious exploits of a Duke of *Marlborough*, and the happy arrival of the present illustrious *royal family* amongst us.

The gallery, 110 feet in length, presented a most surprising prospect; the most beautiful *corals, crystals*, and figured stones, the most brilliant *butterflies* and other insects, *shells* painted with as great variety as the precious stones; and feathers of *birds* vying with gems; here the remains of the *Antediluvian* world excited the awful idea of that catastrophe, so many evident testimonies of the truth of *Moses*'s history; the variety of animals shews us ye great beauty of all parts of the creation.

Then a noble vista presented itself thro' several rooms filled with books, among these many hundred volumes of dry'd plants; a room full of choice and valuable manuscripts; the noble present sent by the present *French* king to Sir *Hans*, [prints] of his collections of paintings, medals, statues, palaces, &c. in 25 large atlas volumes;[220] besides other things too many to mention here.

Below-stairs some rooms are filled with curious and venerable antiquities of *Egypt, Greece, Hetruria, Rome, Britain*, and even *America*; others with large animals preserved in the skin; the great *saloon* lined on every side with bottles filled with spirits, containing various animals. The halls are adorned with the horns of divers creatures, as the double-horn'd *Rhinoceros* of *Africa*, the fossil deer's horns from *Ireland* nine feet wide; and with weapons of different countries, among which it appears that the Mayalese, and not our most *Christian* neighbours the *French*, had the honour of inventing that butcherly weapon the *bayonet*. Fifty volumes in folio would scarcely suffice to contain a detail of this immense museum, consisting of above 200,000 articles.

Their *royal highnesses* were not wanting in expressing their satisfaction and pleasure at seeing a collection, which surpass'd all the notions or ideas they had formed from even the most favourable accounts of it. The Prince on this occasion shew'd his great reading and most happy memory; for in such a multiplicity, such a variety of the productions of nature and art; upon any thing being shewn him he had not seen before, he was ready in recollecting where he had read of it; and upon viewing the ancient and modern *medals*, he made so many judicious remarks, that he appear'd to be a perfect master of *history* and *chronology*; he express'd the great pleasure it gave him to see so magnificent a collection in *England*, esteeming it an ornament to the nation; and expressed his sentiments how much it must conduce to the benefit of learning, and how great an honour will redound to *Britain*, to have it established for publick use to the latest posterity.

Acknowledgements

References to sources in the Royal Society archives are quoted by permission of the President and Council of the Royal Society. I am also grateful for access granted to the library of the Wellcome Institute for the History of Medicine.

Notes and References

1. See principally, E. Edwards, *The Lives of the Founders of the British Museum* (London, 1870), vol. I, pp. 247–312; G.R. de Beer, *Sir Hans Sloane and the British Museum* (London, 1953), and E. St. J. Brooks, *Sir Hans Sloane. The Great Collector and his Circle* (London, 1954).

2. College of Arms, MS 3 D. 14, pp. 85–6. The pedigree, in the form of an annotated family tree, was compiled when the Sloanes applied for registration of their arms: see below, note 90.

3. [Thomas Birch], 'Memoirs relating to the Life of Sʳ Hans Sloane Barᵗ formerly President of the Royal Society', BL, Additional MS 4241.

4. Birch was secretary of the Royal Society from 1752 to 1765 and author of *The History of the Royal Society of London* (London, 1756–7); his biographical notes on Sloane, however, were never brought to press.

5. Birch, op. cit. (note 3), p. 1.

6. Alexander Sloane's antecedents remain somewhat obscure but evidently originated in the south-west of Scotland; for the most recently-published biographical information, adding to evidence for an origin in Galloway, see W.R. Sloan, 'Sir Hans Sloane, F.R.S., legend and lineage', *Notes and Records of the Royal Society* 35 no. 2 (1980), pp. 125–9, expanded by the same author in *Sir Hans Sloane, Founder of the British Museum. Legend and Lineage* (published privately, 1981). In the Sloane pedigree (op. cit. (note 2) Alexander Sloane is described more grandly as 'Receiver Generˡˡ of the Taxes' for County Down; following the Restoration of Charles II, he was appointed a Commissioner of Array for the local militia.

7. According to Birch (op. cit. (note 3), p. 1), Sarah's father had been the Revd Dr Hicks, 'an eminent Divine, Prebendary of the Cathedral Church of Winchester, and Chaplain to Dr. Laud, Archbishop of Canterbury'. Although the same information was supplied by Hans and William Sloane in the pedigree submitted to the College of Arms (op. cit., note 2), no such cleric has been traced.

8. Birch, op. cit. (note 3), p. 2.

9. Sloane, *Natural History*, vol. I, preface. On another occasion a poignant image from what may have been a rather solitary youth recurred to the old man: 'I have been on many small uninhabited Islands on the coast of Ireland, where the ordinary Sea-mews &c. have laid their eggs often on the ground, without any or with at least very small nests, so thick, that it was difficult to pass along without treading on them; while the Birds made a terrible noise over our heads . . .' (letter from Sloane to Richard Richardson, 20 November 1725, quoted in J. Nichols, *Illustrations of the Literary History of the Eighteenth Century* (London, 1817), vol. I, p. 283).

10. In Birch's words: '. . . by Temperance & abstaining from Wine & other fermented Liquors, & the prudent Management of himself in all other Respects, he avoided the Consequences of a Disorder, which must otherwise have prov'd fatal to him, and extended a Life of various & incessant Labours much beyond the ordinary period'. Throughout his life, however, he was 'frequently attacked with great Vomitings of Blood' (Birch, op. cit. (note 3), pp. 2, 25 [suppl.]). The degree to which he became reconciled to his condition is revealed in a letter dated 18 September 1705, addressed by Sloane to 'Mr Dummer at Swathling', near Southampton': 'I . . . am sorry you have been frighted with spitting blood. I have spitt blood this 25 years & Dʳ. Barwick who is lately dead of another disease spitt blood for yᵉ last 50 years of the 89 that he lived . . . fear no ill consequences of bleeding for you are in no danger by loosing a little blood . . .' (Wellcome Institute for the History of Medicine, London, Autograph letter 348402). It has been suggested that Sloane's haemoptysis may have been due to tuberculosis of the lungs: see Burton Chance, 'Sketches of the life and interests of Sir Hans Sloane: naturalist, physician, collector and benefactor', *Annals of Medical History* new ser. 10 (1938), p. 390.

11. Birch, op. cit. (note 3), p. 3.

12. The garden was established on ground leased in 1673 from Charles Cheyne, later Lord Cheyne.

13. Ray's scholarship was complemented by his young friend's energy and natural application. In later life he was the beneficiary of much medical advice from Sloane, as well as books, small presents of sugar etc. and botanical specimens. Ray had lost his Cambridge fellowship by refusing to assent to the Act of Uniformity. Later he lived in some poverty in his native Essex as rector of Black Notley and never had financial means to match his scholarly status. Sloane consulted him frequently, describing him as 'the greatest judge I could advise with' (*Natural History*, vol. I, preface). For Ray see C.E. Raven, *John Ray, Naturalist* (Cambridge, 1942).

14. It has been noted that Boyle (brother of the Earl of Cork) had links with the family of the Earl of Clanbrassill, patron of Sloane's father (de Beer, op. cit. (note 1), p. 16).

15. Birch, op. cit. (note 3), pp. 3–4.

16. Ibid., p. 4.

17. Later Sir Tancred Robinson, Physician in Ordinary to George I. It was Robinson who had first introduced Sloane to John Ray.

18. Birch, op. cit. (note 3), pp. 4–5.

19. Ibid., p. 5.

20. His collection is said to have included 'figured stones, rare marcasites, extraordinary petrifications and crystallizations, metals, habiliments, arms and instruments of war of foreign nations': Andrew Kippis, *Biographia Britannica, or the Lives of the most Eminent Persons who have flourished in Great Britain and Ireland*, vol. VI (London, 1763), p. 3699. At Tournefort's death it was bequeathed to the King of France.

21. Birch, op. cit. (note 3), p. 5.

22. '. . . highly deserving because of the rigorous examination, with absolutely no one dissenting'. From Sloane's conferment of degree, preserved in the Archives de Vaucluse; photographic copy in the Library of The Natural History Museum (96.A.o.SLO).

23. Sloane's diploma includes the earliest-known description of him: '. . . of medium height, hair very short, light chestnut, face rather long and grave, marked with the small-pox, aged 21 years' (ibid.).

24. Birch, op. cit. (note 3), pp. 5–6. Towards the end of his life, Sloane was to look back with fondness to these expeditions, when 'M. Magnol m'apprit que l'herborisation a sec avoit ses utilités: je l'ai bien senti depuis . . .' (Sloane to Claude-Joseph Geoffroy, 1 August 1742, reproduced in Jean Jacquot, 'Sir Hans Sloane and French men of science', *Notes and Records of the Royal Society* 10 (1953), pp. 97–8.

25. Birch, op. cit. (note 3), p. 6.

26. John Ray, *The Correspondence of John Ray*, ed. Edwin Lankester (London, 1848), pp. 156–7; letter dated 11 November 1684. Sloane was to act as a mollifying influence in the differences of opinion that were later to emerge between Ray and Tournefort: see Jacquot, op. cit. (note 24), pp. 88–9.

27. Sloane to Ray, 10 August 1686: 'In our simpling journey to Sheppey we found a perennial Kali . . . as also that Fucus I formerly told you of, to look like a honeycomb, which I found cast upon the shore on Sheppey, as well as at Nesson . . . On Sheppey, searching for the copperasstones, or *Pyrites*, I found that the most part of those taken up in that island are after northeasterly storms, that they are beat up by the waves, and taken up at a low water . . .' (Ray, op. cit. (note 26), p. 186). Ray later wrote to Sloane on 24 August 1686, providing information on the plant specimens he describes (and of which, evidently, he had sent specimens) (ibid., pp. 190–1).

28. Birch, op. cit. (note 3), p. 7; see also J.F. Payne, *Thomas Sydenham* (London, 1900), pp. 190–1.

29. Albemarle had asked his personal physician, Dr Peter Barwick, to recommend a suitably-qualified person for the post; Barwick in turn had asked Sloane's advice, and after lengthy consideration Sloane put his own name forward (*Natural History*, vol. I, preface).

30. Ray, op. cit. (note 26), pp. 189–90. A letter from Sloane to Ray (11 November 1684) congratulates him on his proposed natural history (*Historia generalis plantarum*) and offers him plant specimens brought back from France and undertakes to enlist help of Tournefort (ibid., pp. 156–7).

31. Sloane reiterated these practical concerns in the same essay, declaring himself 'better appris'd' of plants to be found growing in English gardens when he had seen them in their wild habitat overseas (Sloane, *Natural History*, vol. I, preface).

32. Ray, op. cit. (note 26), p. 192.

33. Ibid., pp. 194–5.

34. See BL, Sloane MS 4069, fols. 200–1, 'Proposalls made by Dr Sloane if it be thought fitt that he goe Physitian to ye W. India fleet'. Here Sloane undertakes to 'take all care possible of the sick of the Fleet, or troopes, in their voyage to Barbados, provided the Surgeons of the respective ships where such sick shall be, be ordered to observe his directions.' Thereafter, he will provide care for the troops '. . . either at their Lodgings or Hospitall, provided that an Apothecary & Surgeon be likewise ordered to attend . . . with med'cines & instruments, to putt his advice in execution', such services to be provided only 'at the principall port of the Island'. If the fleet were called home, he was to have leave to stay on if he pleased. His fee was to be £600 per annum.

35. Sloane, *Natural History*, vol. I, preface.

36. Ibid.

37. The description is given in the course of an 'Apology for what Imperfections remain' in his *Natural History*, vol. II, p. xviii.

38. Ibid., vol. II, p. 222.

39. The Duke, who was notably intemperate in his habits, had been ill since before his departure from England. He was thirty-four at the time of his death, six years older than Sloane himself. After its return to England, the Duke's body was buried in Westminster Abbey: see Estelle Frances Ward, *Christopher Monck, Duke of Albemarle* (London, 1915), pp. 322, 334.
It has been suggested that another noteworthy patient of Sloane's during this time (and one who proved every bit as difficult as Albemarle) was Sir Henry Morgan, the former buccaneer who became Lieutenant Governor of Jamaica: see Richard B. Sheridan, 'The doctor and the buccaneer: Sir Hans Sloane's case history of Sir Henry Morgan, Jamaica, 1688', *Journal of the History of Medicine and Allied Sciences* 41 no. 1 (1986), pp. 76–87. However, the true identity of this patient, identified by Sloane only as 'Sir H.M.', is still the subject of dispute: see G.M. Longfield-Jones, 'The case history of "Sir H.M."', *Medical History* 32 (1988), pp. 449–60.

40. Sloane, *Natural History*, vol. I, preface; a number of these specimens survive today in the Sloane herbarium (see Chapter 8). Brooks, op.

cit. (note 1), p. 57, notes the possibility that Sloane may have intended to return to Jamaica, quoting a letter from Garrett Moore, one of Sloane's illustrators, in which he mentions his intention to draw whatever he can 'against yr coming heare' (BL, Sloane MS 4036, fol. 49).

41. The Duchess was to contract a second favourable marriage with the Earl [later Duke] of Montagu. As the heir to New Hall in Essex, the Duchess provided Sloane with the opportunity to visit his friend Ray, living nearby in the village of Black Notley; following Sloane's return from Jamaica, Ray wrote to him reminding him that New Hall 'is not above eight miles from us' and entreating him to 'make a further step hither' (Ray, op. cit. (note 26), p. 211).

42. Sloane pedigree, op. cit. (note 2). Fulk Rose, 'a surgeon bred, and a very discreet and virtuous man', acted as a consultant during the final illness of the Duke of Albemarle. Descended from a Gloucestershire family, he was one of the original Jamaica settlers; he owned 3,000 acres there which were said to bring him £4,000 a year in addition to the £600 rendered by his practice. He was elected to the Assembly and in 1693 was appointed to the Council; returning to England in the course of the following year he died in London in March 1694. See 'Rose of Jamaica', *Caribbeana* 5 pt. iv (1917), pp. 130–9; David Crossley and Richard Saville (eds.), *The Fuller Letters 1728–1755* (Sussex Record Society 76) (Lewes, 1991), p. xxiv.

43. Birch, op. cit. (note 3), p. 9. Elizabeth Rose brought Sloane four step-daughters, one of whom, Philippa, was later to marry the Revd Hoby Stanley of Paultons in Hampshire. The Sloanes had four children of their own, of whom a son, Hans, and a daughter, Mary, died in infancy; another daughter, Sarah, married George Stanley of Paultons, while Elizabeth married Colonel Charles Cadogan, later the 2nd Lord Cadogan. The latter marriage led to the formation of the estate in south-west London in which the Sloane family affiliations are preserved in the present-day street names – Hans Crescent, Sloane Street, Cadogan Square, Paultons Square.

44. De Beer (op. cit. (note 1), pp. 52–3) notes that Sloane's near neighbours included several peers of the realm, Drs John Radcliffe and Richard Mead, Sir Godfrey Kneller and Sir Christopher Wren.

45. For what is known (and not known) of this club see L. Jessop, 'The club at the Temple Coffee House – facts and supposition', *Archives of Natural History* 16 (1989), pp. 263–74.

46. Hans Sloane, 'A description of the pimienta or Jamaica pepper-tree, and of the tree that bears the Cortex Winteranus', *Philosophical Transactions* 16 no. 192 (1691), pp. 462–8; idem, 'An account of the true Cortex Winteranus, and the tree that bears it', ibid., 17 no. 204 (1693), pp. 922–4; idem, 'A letter from Hans Sloane, M.D. and S.R.S. with several accounts of the earthquakes in Peru, October the 20th, 1687, and at Jamaica, February 19th, 1687/8 and June the 7th, 1692', ibid., 18 no. 209 (1694), pp. 78–80.

47. Ray, op. cit. (note 26), p. 261.

48. Hans Sloane, *Catalogus plantarum* (London, 1696).

49. Plumier's expedition had been inspired by the success of Sloane's own researches in the West Indies, and had received the backing of the French king.

50. In the later *Natural History* (vol. I, pp. xvii–xviii), he wrote as follows: 'As to the Names and Method, notwithstanding they are every day changed without (I humbly conceive) sufficient Reasons by every Person who almost treats of them … It doth seem to me to be a great Obstruction of the Knowledge of Natural Things, that every several Writer should assume to himself the liberty of treating very ill, and sometimes scurrilously very great Men, such as Monsieur *Tournefort* and others, for not taking notice of some slender *minutiae* … [they bring] into Natural History such divers Names, that it would require sometimes a days labour to find out what Plant described by other Writers they mean to give an Account of.'

51. Ray to Sloane, 23 June 1696: see Ray, op. cit. (note 26), pp. 295–6; see also same to same, 12 February 1695 (ibid., pp. 286–7) and 21 February 1695 (ibid., pp. 287–9) and Ray's review of the *Catalogus* in *Philosophical Transactions* 19 no. 221 (1696), pp. 293–6, where he writes: 'no man can be well qualified, but he that hath a Comprehensive Knowledge of such Plants as grow wild, or are commonly Cultivated in Gardens here in *Europe*, and hath seen the *non-descript Americans* … and hath read, considered, and compared what hath been written of them … All which qualities occur in our Author'.

52. Ray acknowledged that Sloane's discoveries would make up 'a third part' of the *Supplement* to his *Historia plantarum*: Ray to Edward Lhwyd, 15 May 1697, in R.W.T. Gunther (ed.), *Further Correspondence of John Ray* (Ray Society 114) (London, 1928), p. 271.

53. For acknowledgements of gratitude for treatment from Ray and from Pepys, see de Beer, op. cit. (note 1), p. 65.

54. This concern for the underprivileged had manifested itself early in Sloane's career. After setting out in fairly precise terms the conditions for his West Indian contract with the military (see note 34), he volunteered the following: 'That he will be ready in all the plantations to give his advice for nothing to all the poor who shall come to ask it, & recomends it as the best piece of charity to lett such who are in reall want, have medicines & the help of the surgeon likewise at certain houres of the day at the said hospitall …' (BL, Sloane MS 4069, fol. 201). In later years, soon after his election to the presidency of the College of Physicians in 1719, he proposed that the membership should give some of their time 'for the relief of their poor sick neighbours', a resolution that met with general approval: see Sir George Clark, *A History of the Royal College of Physicians of London* (Oxford, 1964–72), vol. II, p. 482.

55. Birch, op. cit. (note 3), pp. 22–3. He also enrolled as a supporter of Captain Coram's Foundling Hospital in 1739.

56. Later, in 1743, he was awarded the degree of Doctor of Medicine by University College, Dublin.

57. Sloane had previously held office as Censor (with responsibility for licensing medical practice and publication) and as an Elect of the College: see William Munk, *The Roll of the Royal College of Physicians of London* vol. I *1580–1700* (London, 1878), p. 463. The Royal College today holds a portrait of Sloane by Thomas Murray, dating from *c.*1725 (see G. Wolstenholme (ed.), *The Royal College of Physicians of London Portraits* (London, 1964), pp. 392–3); it was reproduced (presumably in Sloane's own day) as a print on glass, a copy of which is owned by the New Jersey Historical Society; see Helen M. Wright, *A Painted Glass Portrait of Sir Hans Sloane* (Jersey City, 1934).

58. A surviving petition from Sloane to the King asks for discharge of the sum of £1,095, payable on the conferment of his baronetcy; this was a compound fee which many recipients of this honour elected to pay in lieu of providing men for service in the plantation and defence of Ulster: see *Proceedings of the Society of Antiquaries of London* 2nd ser. 2 (1861–4), pp. 62, 73–4).

59. Birch, op. cit (note 3), p. 14. See also S.D. Clippingdale, 'Medical Court-Roll. Physicians and surgeons who have attended the sovereigns of England from William I to George V, with a medical note on Harold' (Royal College of Surgeons, MS 163/n.1–2), vol. I, fols. 156, 169; I am grateful to the Librarian of the Royal College for access to this unpublished manuscript. For Sloane's appointment as Physician Extraordinary to Queen Anne see PRO, LC5/166, 282, and for appointment as Physician in Ordinary to George II see PRO, LC3/30, 109. There seems to be no formal record of his appointment being continued under George I, but it is alluded to in other contemporary sources. I am grateful to Lady de Bellaigue, Registrar of the Royal Archives at Windsor Castle, for guidance in these matters.

One mark of this 'favour of esteem' is noted by William Stukeley on 14 June 1720 when, he records, 'The young Princesses din'd with Sr Hans Sloan' (*The Family Memoirs of the Rev. William Stukeley, M.D.*, vols. I–III (Publications of the Surtees Society 73, 76, 80) (London, 1880–5), vol. I, p. 67).

60. See Lt. Gen. Sir Neil Cantlie, *A History of the Army Medical Department*, vol. I (Edinburgh and London, 1974), pp. 59–60.

61. It has been observed that he issued only one medical publication (see below, note 67), but he contributed a number of papers on related subjects to the *Philosophical Transactions*, while the *Natural History* also contains numerous medical observations and case histories.

62. For an account of Sloane's cabinet of *materia medica* see F.C.J. Spurrell, 'On remedies in the Sloane collections, and on alchemical symbols',

Archaeological Journal 51 (1894), pp. 81–98. See also Chapter 3.

63. In his opinion, medical intervention on a healthy patient could only bring harm: under the rubric 'Preventive Physick consider'd', Sloane declared that '… it seems as reasonable to me that a Soldier should before a Fight come to a Chirurgeon to ask a remedy to prevent his being Shot, as when one is altogether Well, to a Physician for a Remedy against Sickness' (*Natural History*, vol. I, p. 1). Elsewhere (p. 25) he carries his positivist approach rather far, following a misconceived discourse on the heat rash suffered by his hapless fellow passengers with the statement that '… instead of prescribing a Remedy for its Cure, I told those who importun'd me, that I thought this Distemper was the greatest advantage they could have …'

64. Sloane had asked William Sherard, when resident at Smyrna, for details of the practice as it was already used in Turkey; Sherard arranged for Dr Giovanni Pylarini, a physician in Smyrna, to supply Sloane with an account, which was later published in the *Philosophical Transactions* 29 (1716), pp. 393–9. In 1736 Sloane drew up an historical account of the introduction of the practice into England, later published in *Philosophical Transactions* 49 (1756), pp. 516–20. (The process required a strong nerve, the outcome being much less predictable than that of vaccination with cow-pox serum).

65. According to a dedication addressed to Sloane by John Hill, translator of Pierre Pomet's *History of Drugs* (1712), he was 'the only Person of the Faculty in these Kingdoms, who of late Years hath made the *Materia Medica* [his] Study' (quoted from the fourth edition of 1748, p. iii). The author of this eulogy raises our scepticism, however, when he continues: '… it is hard to say, whether your Discoveries in the Theory of Medicine, or your judicious Improvements of those Discoveries in the Practice, have exceeded'.

66. *Natural History*, vol. I, p. civ; see also pp. cx, cxxi–cxxii, 13. Crabs' eyes are included among the *materia medica* surviving in the Sloane collection at The Natural History Museum: see J.M. Sweet, 'Sir Hans Sloane: life and mineral collection', *Natural History Magazine* 5 (1935), p. 145. We should be unreasonable to expect Sloane to have been entirely immune to the more questionable practices of his day: for a review of such prescriptions see William Brockbank, 'Sovereign remedies: a critical depreciation of the 17th-century London Pharmacopoeia', *Medical History* 8 (1964), pp. 1–14.

67. This statement was made in the support of a linament for the eyes composed of tutty (zinc oxide), *lapis haematites*, aloes and prepared pearl, all mixed with viper's grease; the context may seem a curious one in which to find such an assertion, yet Sloane claimed to have found the concoction 'so surprisingly beneficial, that by the right Use of it not one in five Hundred missed of a cure': Hans Sloane, *An Account of a most Efficacious Medicine for Soreness, Weakness, and several other Distempers of the Eyes* (London, 1745); translated into German (Danzig, 1745) and French (Paris, 1746). Chance, op. cit. (note

10), p. 397, concludes that the remedy 'cannot today be considered other than harmful'. For a defence of Sloane's practices in prescription see Julius A. Oshlag, 'The ethical practices of Sir Hans Sloane', *Bulletin of the History of Medicine* 21 (1947), pp. 918–21.

68. Birch, op. cit. (note 3), p. 25 [suppl.]; *Natural History*, vol. I, pp. cxxxiv–cxxxv; the properties of the root of ipecacuanha were discussed in *Philosophical Transactions* 20 no. 238 (1698), pp. 69–79. Not all recipients shared such a high opinion of the remedy: reporting in 1705 on the progress of a patient being treated under Sloane's guidance, James Keill wrote that 'The very sight or name of the bark does put him in an agony . . .': see F.M. Valadez and C.D. O'Malley, 'James Keill of Northampton, physician, anatomist and physiologist', *Medical History* 15 (1971), p. 323.

69. He had first encountered drinking chocolate in Jamaica (*Natural History*, vol. I, p. xx). A trade card for 'Sir Hans Sloane's Milk Chocolate' (Fig. 2) indicates that it was made up for Sloane first by Nicholas Sanders and later by William White of Greek Street, Soho; the chocolate was sold in bar form, in squares.

70. *Remarks and Collections of Thomas Hearne* (Oxford Historical Society) (Oxford, 1885–1921), vol. I, p. 67.

71. Amongst the reasons for the long delay, Sloane cites 'a multiplicity of Business in the Practice of Physick', the 'putting into some kind of Order my Curiosities, numbring them, and entring their Names, and Accounts receiv'd with them, in Books, which was necessary in order to their Preservation and Uses', and the need to take immediate steps to preserve and order Petiver's collection when it came into his possession. Concerning the latter, he writes: 'I have taken as much Care as I can to bring his Collections and Papers out of the Confusion I found them in', declaring his intention to see that they '. . . shall not be lost, but preserved and published for the good of the Publick, doing right to his Memory and my own Reputation' (*Natural History*, vol. II, pp. i–v.

72. Birch, op. cit. (note 3), p. 12.

73. Impatient at the inevitable delay to the publication of the *Natural History*, Ray had written to Sloane concerning the illustrations: 'I am sensible that the charge of figures may deter you, therefore I think it were adviseable to imitate Dr. Plukenet, to draw them *in piccolo*, using a small scale, and thrust many species into a plate. I would not have the ingenious deferred the fruition of such a treasure, the sight of so grateful objects, nor you the credit of your inventions' (Ray to Sloane, 8 June 1691: Ray, op. cit. (note 26), p. 130). Sloane, however, 'caused near 400 folio Copper Plates to be engraven at a prodigious Expence' (Birch, op. cit. (note 3), p. 13).

74. The same Kickius (or 'Kychious') later spent two years from July 1703 to July 1705 producing two volumes of drawings of plants 'from the Life growing' for the Duchess of Beaufort at Badminton: see J.E. Dandy (ed.), *The Sloane Herbarium* (London, 1958), pp. 204, 209.

75. Ibid., p. 204.

76. *Natural History*, vol. I, preface and pp. 54–5.

77. One senses almost a relish in Sloane's recounting of the way in which an Indian cured the wife of the Governor of Peru with the treatment of Peruvian bark in 1638, stating that he 'overthrew with one simple Medicine, without any preparation, all the Hypotheses, and Theories of Agues, which were supported by some Scores not to say Hundreds of Volumes, and 'tis plain did mischief by hindering the advantage Men might have received sooner from so innocent and beneficial a remedy, *Philosophical Transactions* 21 (1669), preface.

78. To a degree, Sloane has suffered from the same prejudice ever since: it has been rightly observed that 'This anti-theoretical attitude has not endeared Sloane to modern historians of science', although it was 'a common-sense empiricism that agreed with Sloane's clinical training' under Sydenham, Maarten Ultee, 'Sir Hans Sloane, scientist', *British Library Journal* 14 (1988), p. 8.

79. *The Correspondence of John Locke*, ed. E.S. de Beer (Oxford, 1976–89), vol. v, p. 128.

80. In the preface to volume II of the *Natural History* (p. xiv), for example, he writes: 'I have never observ'd, that those Physitians who regarded the Latin Turns and Words of their Prescriptions, more than the other material Things to be consider'd, were more fortunate in their Cures of Diseases than others, who took a sort of Lingua Franca, the common Language known in Apothecaries Shops, and which all other Professions use in their Affairs, as well as Physitians . . .'

81. Writing of the *Natural History*, for example, Ray observed that Sloane had '. . . described all in English, so that I am at pains of turning it into Latine': Ray to Lhwyd, 15 May 1697, reproduced in Ray, op. cit. (note 52), p. 271.

82. Ray to Sloane, 16 August 1704: Ray, op. cit. (note 26), p. 452.

83. The most notable example was published anonymously by William King with the title *The Transactioneer* (London, 1700), the central character of which is first secretary of the Royal Society and editor of the *Philosophical Transactions*. It is prefaced as follows: 'By the following Dialogues it is Apparent, that by Industry alone a Man may get so much Reputation almost in any Profession as shall be sufficient to amuse the World, tho' he has neither Parts nor Learning to support it. The Person who makes the Chief Figure in them, has certainly nothing but a bustling temper to recommend him . . .' King later returned to the attack with *Useful Transactions, to be continued monthly as they sell* (London 1708–9) of which the first number was entitled 'The Present State of Physick in the Island of Cajamai', while the third and final volume, 'A Voyage to the Island of Cajamai . . . by Jasper von Slonenbergh', was an attack on Sloane's *Natural History*.
Joseph Addison mounted a more general criticism of the Royal Society and its preoccupations

in the mocking 'Will of a virtuoso', Sir Nicholas Gimcrack: 'I would not discourage any searches that are made into the most minute and trivial parts of the creation. However, since the world abounds in the noblest fields of speculation, it is methinks, the mark of a little genius to be wholly conversant among insects, reptiles, animalcules, and those trifling rarities that furnish out the apartment of a virtuoso . . . Observations of this kind are apt to alienate us too much from the knowledge of the world, and to make us serious upon trifles; by which means they expose philosophy to the ridicule of the witty, and contempt of the ignorant.'

84. Locke, op. cit. (note 79), vol. VI, p. 746.

85. Stukeley, op. cit. (note 59), vol. I, p. 74. Sloane also contributed a catalogue of simples to the fourth *London Pharmacopoeia* published in 1724.

86. Sloane had bought the manor house of Chelsea in 1712 from William Cheyne, 2nd Viscount Newhaven. While continuing to live in Bloomsbury, he and his family regularly spent weekends there until Elizabeth Sloane's death in 1724.

87. In the event of the Apothecaries ceasing to cultivate it, the Garden was to revert jointly to the Royal Society and the College of Physicians.

88. See the essays by Hannah Lane and Timothy Wilson in *British Museum Society Bulletin* no. 49 (1985), pp. 16–19.

89. Hearne (op. cit. (note 70), vol. VI, p. 75) records that Jenny [i.e. ELizabeth] Sloane, to whom he ascribes 'a vast fortune', is married to 'Collonel Cadogan, Brother of General Cadogan, a loose person, & of no great Income'.

90. College of Arms, MS Grants 7, pp. 439–42. The grant of arms was made in favour of William Sloane, Hans's eldest surviving brother, and to the descendants of Alexander Sloane, his father. Application was made at this late date since, 'by reason of their late settlement in this Kingdom, the Coat of Arms born by his Father and Family . . . are not hitherto enter'd in the College of Arms'.

91. His poor health is referred to in a letter from John Fuller to Dr Rose Fuller, dated 1 January 1742: 'Sir Hans Sloane keeps his Bed, and can live but a very little while' (Crossley and Saville, op. cit. (note 42), p. 156.

92. Birch, op. cit. (note 3), p. 18.

93. A.E. Gunther, *The Life of the Rev. Thomas Birch DD, FRS, 1705–1766* (published privately, 1984), p. 72.

94. G. Edwards, *Gleanings of Natural History* (London, 1760), vol. II, p. iii.

95. For descriptions of the funeral see Birch, op. cit. (note 3), pp. 10–11, 20; Thomas Faulkner, *An Historical and Topographical Description of Chelsea and its Environs* (Chelsea, 1829), pp. 349, 362–3, which includes an extract from the sermon; *London Magazine* (January 1753), p. 44;

London Daily Advertiser (19 January 1753). There is some confusion as to the pall-bearers: de Beer (op. cit. (note 1), p. 140) lists a William Wynne (not noted elsewhere) and the *London Daily Advertiser* adds James Theobald. With the exception of Wynne, all were Trustees of Sloane's will. I am grateful to Marjorie Caygill for information on this matter.

96. Sloane's will, published as *The Will of Sir Hans Sloane, Bart. Deceased* (London, 1753), had decreed as follows: '. . . my body shall be buried in a decent manner, in the church-yard at Chelsea, about noon, or at a convenient time of the day: And I will, that there be invited to my funeral all such persons as I shall leave in a list by me signed, or if no such list be left, then such persons as my executors shall know to have been my most intimate friends and acquaintance; and that they shall have rings of twenty shillings value, given to each of them'.

97. The monument, an early work of Joseph Wilton (1722–1803), is inscribed as follows: 'To the memory of/Sir Hans Sloane, Bart./President of the Royal Society/and of the College of Physicians;/who, in the year of our Lord 1753/ the 92d year of his age,/Without the least pain of body,/and with a conscious serenity of mind,/ ended a virtuous life,/This monument was erected/by his two daughters/Eliz. Cadogan and Sarah Stanley.' The monument was repaired in 1977, the British Museum contributing.

98. On the day before he died, on 7 January 1704, Ray had addressed a farewell letter to Sloane in the following terms: 'Dear Sir, the Best of Friends, These are to take a final leave of you as to this world. I look upon myself as a dying man. God requite your kindness expressed anyways towards me an hundredfold, bless you with a confluence of all good things in this world, and eternal life and happiness hereafter, and grant us a happy meeting in Heaven. I am, Sir, Eternally yours, John Ray' (Ray, op. cit. (note 26), p. 459).

99. Locke wrote to Sloane on 21 February 1704 of 'the particular esteem I have for you and the obligations I have to you' (Locke, op. cit. (note 79), vol. VIII, p. 207).

100. Pepys almost wished himself an invalid 'that I might have a pretence to invite you for an hour or two by yourselfe' (*The Life, Journals, and Correspondence of Samuel Pepys*, ed. J. Smith (London, 1841), vol. II, p. 274).

101. Sloane to Thoresby 3 June 1710. Sloane had evidently had to be persuaded to defend his position for, he continued, 'most of the Society that have been witnesses of what hath passed, were very earnest with me not to lay down' (*Letters of Eminent Men addressed to Ralph Thoresby, FRS* (London, 1832), vol. II, pp. 251–2.

102. Sloane, *Natural History*, vol. I, preface.

103. Bodleian Library, Oxford, MS Eng. Misc. e 260, fol. 101ᵛ.

104. See, for example, Ray to Sloane, 25 May 1692: 'Those instances you would have added to my discourse concerning the wisdom of God

I know are so considerable, that I am sorry my book wants them, which might have recommended it to the reader . . . I am this morning sending away my discourses concerning the Primitive Chaos and Creation of the World, the General Deluge, and Future Conflagration, with additions for a second edition. If you please to revise and correct it before it be printed, I will order Mr. Smith to deliver the copy to you for that purpose' (Ray, op. cit. (note 26), p. 250).

In the same vein, on 10 August 1698, Ray sent Sloane a supplement to his *Dendrology*, with the message: 'I entreat your pains in correcting what is erroneous or mistaken in supplying what is wanting, in altering and amending what is obscurely delivered, or not well expressed, and whatever other faults of any kind you shall find therein' (ibid., p. 342).

105. It may be noted that election to a Fellowship of the Royal Society was at this time not so much a distinction as an expression on the part of an individual of his interest in the sciences: see E.S. de Beer, 'The earliest Fellows of the Royal Society', *Bulletin of the Institute of Historical Research* 15 (1937–8), p. 80.

106. Sloane, *Natural History*, vol. I, preface.

107. Sloane's friend Tancred Robinson had held this office in 1685.

108. For the burden of duties falling on the secretaries see H.W. Robinson, 'The administrative staff of the Royal Society', *Notes and Records of the Royal Society* 4 (1946), p. 195. Brooks (op. cit. (note 1), p. 102) notices that an inserted note in one of Sloane's contributions to the *Philosophical Transactions* shows that he did not actually edit all the texts himself.

109. Cf. Raven, op. cit. (note 13), p. 244: 'There was no money in the Society's hand, no readiness to take office, no opportunity for scientific work.' According to Birch (op. cit. (note 3), p. 9), Sloane's part as editor extended from vol. 19 for the year 1695 to the end of vol. 38 for 1713.

110. Quoted in de Beer, op. cit. (note 1), p. 84.

111. Although a prolific letter writer, the many revised drafts of his letters that survive suggest that in this as in other fields Sloane's effectiveness was based on industriousness rather than natural flair: see Jack A. Clarke, 'Sir Hans Sloane and Abbé Bignon: notes on collection building in the eighteenth century', *Library Quarterly* 50 (1980), p. 479.

112. 'Comme nous ne fréquentons ici que des moines grecs et des corsaires nous sommes très affames de nouvelles de la republique des lettres ainsi vous ne sauriez me faire de plus grand plaisir que de m'en donner': Tournefort to Sloane, 14 January 1701/2, reproduced in Jacquot, op. cit. (note 24), pp. 89–90. For a recent account of this movement see Maarten Ultee, 'The Republic of Letters: learned correspondence, 1680–1720', *The Seventeenth Century* 17 no. 2 (1987), pp. 95–112.

113. 'It is very kindly and charitably done of you to send me some news from the commonwealth of letters into a place where I seldom

meet with any thing beyond the observation of a scabby sheep or a lame horse': Locke to Sloane, 14 September 1694 (Locke, op. cit. (note 79), vol. V, p. 127). This and the other mutual correspondence is also reproduced in Kenneth Dewhurst, 'The correspondence between John Locke and Sir Hans Sloane', *Irish Journal of Medical Science* 6th ser. no. 143 (1960), pp. 201–12.

114. See Clark, op. cit. (note 111), p. 477.

115. Woodward was not alone in this opinion, and the veracity of his complaints seems to be borne out in a letter addressed to Sloane himself by one well-disposed towards him, John Chamberlyne: 'were it true, I say, that you Take too much upon you, that you Govern us, & even that you bestow Places upon your Creatures . . . yet I think we ought even to connive at all this, rather than lose an old Able and Experienced officer who is the very Life and Soul of the Society, & who has thus long kept up the Honor and Dignity of it by his Personal Merit both abroad & at Home' (Chamberlayne to Sloane, 19 October 1713; BL, Sloane MS 4043, fol. 195). For a full account of the dispute between Woodward and Sloane, see Joseph M. Levine, *Dr Woodward's Shield. History, Science and Satire in Augustan England* (Berkeley, Los Angeles and London, 1977), pp. 88–91.

116. The council ruled that the *Transactions* were entirely in the hands of the Secretary and that authors rather than Council were responsible for the content of papers.

117. The incident, recounted in Brooks (op. cit. (note 1), pp. 108–9), is described at length in an anonymous letter to Newton, dated 28 March 1710, reproduced in *The Correspondence of Isaac Newton* vol. V: *1709–1713*, ed. A.R. Hall and L. Tilling (Cambridge, 1975), pp. 17–24; see also p. 45 note 3. Sloane mentions it in a letter to Thoresby of 3 June 1710, in which he goes on to say: 'There is nothing I love so much as quiet; and, having a great deal of business in my profession, as well as my family and museum, I would be pleased with nothing so much as quietus, but most of the Society that have been witnesses of what hath passed, were very earnest with me not to lay down' (Thoresby, op. cit. (note 101), vol. II, pp. 251–2). Concerning Woodward's low opinion of Sloane, it is worth remembering that he was equally scathing of Newton, commenting that 'this age has little regard to learning. 'Tis quite sunk and lost in England, since Dr. Sloane and Sir Isaac Newton have quite confounded and sunk the Royal Society' (Woodward to J.J. Scheuchzer, 5 October 1714, Zentral Bibliothek, Zürich, MS H 294, pp. 253–5; quoted in Ultee, op. cit. (note 78), p. 1).

118. A very able analysis of this work is to be found in Roger D. Lund, '"More strange than true". Sir Hans Sloane, King's Transactioneer, and the deformation of English prose', *Studies in Eighteenth-Century Culture* 14 (1985), pp. 213–30.

119. *Philosophical Transactions* 21 (1699), preface.

120. For example, in vols. 20–1, nos. 246–50 (1698–9) of *Philosophical Transactions*, Sloane reported on a 'China cabinet' filled with medical

instruments and medicines used by native surgeons in India and forwarded to the Society by a Mr Buckley, chief surgeon at Fort St. George (Madras): 'It were to be wished other travellers into foreign parts would make such enquiries (as Mr Buckly, who sent these to the Royal Society, has done) into the instruments and materials made use of in the places where they come, that are any manner of way for the benefit or innocent delight of mankind, that we may content ourselves with our own inventions, where we go beyond them, and imitate theirs where they go beyond ours.' See also the correspondence between Sloane and Hooke concerning 'monstrous nailes' or horny substances destined for the Repository (Locke, op. cit. (note 79), vol. VI, pp. 55, 59). Sloane himself donated a series of minerals to the Repository: a list of fifty specimens presented by him is given in Royal Society, MS MM.15.35.

121. Thomas Sprat, The History of the Royal Society of London for the Improving of Natural Knowledge (London, 1667), p. 93. Sprat described it as one of the principal intentions of the Society. The considerable Philosophical and Usefull purposes' of the Repository were stressed in an announcement which appeared in the Philosophical Transactions 1 no. 18 (1666), p. 136. For more recent accounts of the Repository see A.D.C. Simpson, 'Newton's telescope and the cataloguing of the Royal Society's Repository', Notes and Records of the Royal Society of London 38 (1984), pp. 187–214; Michael Hunter, 'The cabinet institutionalized: the Royal Society's "Repository" and its background', in Oliver Impey and Arthur MacGregor (eds.), The Origins of Museums (Oxford, 1985), pp. 159–68.

122. Hunt had first entered the employment of the Society on 9 January 1673 as a boy, assisting Robert Hooke with his experiments. He was appointed the Society's 'operator' and subsequently keeper of the Library and the Repository, remaining in service until his death in 1713: see Robinson, op. cit. (note 108), pp. 196–7.

123. Z.C. von Uffenbach, Merkwürdige Reisen durch Niedersachsen, Holland und Engelland (Ulm, 1753–4), vol. II, p. 546; translated in W.H. Quarrell and M. Mare, London in 1710 from the Travels of Zacharias Conrad von Uffenbach (London, 1934), p. 98.

124. Simpson, op. cit. (note 121), p. 194.

125. Edmond Halley, who had beaten him to the Clerk's post earlier, succeeded him in the office. Sloane and Halley seem to have maintained amicable relations: a few letters of a general kind addressed to Sloane, including intimations of support in his dispute with Woodward, are included in Correspondence and Papers of Edmond Halley, ed. Eugene F. MacPike (Oxford, 1932), passim.

126. Simpson, op. cit. (note 121), p. 195. The notes of the Committee are preserved in the 'Report of the Committee for inspecting the State of the Repository and Libraries', annexed to the Royal Society Council Minutes of 6 November 1729.

127. Royal Society, MS 490 CMB 63, minutes of 8 May 1733. Simpson (op. cit. (note 121), p. 199) notes that by 1752 William Stukeley, writing of the Repository, refers to the 'ruinous forlorn condition it was now in, and prayed it might be amended'. Eventually, in 1781, the remnants of the Repository were transferred to the British Museum.

128. The agreeement was adhered to: the Philosophical Transactions record each year those specimens received during previous session.

129. Letter from Sloane to Richard Richardson, [?] 1720, quoted in Nichols, op. cit. (note 9), vol. I, p. 289.

130. Sloane wrote that he was 'very sensible' of the benefits he had received from his association with the Society; regretting that his health would no longer permit him to attend, he none the less hoped that he might communicate from time to time 'any curious notices which he shall receive, either at home or from abroad, concerning natural knowledge, during the small remainder of his life'.

131. Stukeley, op. cit. (note 59), vol. I, p. 327.

132. Ultee, op. cit. (note 78), p. 1. Ultee comments that 'while Newton has remained a household word for scientific genius, Sloane is remembered (if at all) as a collector of curiosities . . . but not as a scientist of note'.

133. See, for example, Levine, op. cit. (note 115), p. 88, where Sloane is characterized as 'essentially a dilettante collector' who was 'certainly no philosopher'; J.L. Heilbron, Physics at the Royal Society during Newton's Presidency (Los Angeles, 1983), p. 10, where he is described as 'a compulsive collector, who began by stuffing the Transactions with the trifles he enjoyed'; also Lund, op. cit. (note 118), p. 214, where it is said that 'Sloane symbolized all that was most excessive, self-aggrandizing and ridiculous in the activities of the modern virtuoso', and where his collections are dismissed as 'a prodigious aggregation of stuff'. Although none of these statements finds support in the present volume, all have contributed to an unwarranted debasement of Sloane's reputation.

134. A similar comparison was made with another of the great figures in the history of natural science, whose reputation has stood the test of time better than Sloane's: Boerhaave introduced Linnaeus to Sloane by letter in 1736 with the words 'He who sees you together will look upon a pair of men whose like can hardly be found in the world' (BL, Sloane MS 4045, fol. 278); the comparison, which may have seemed almost impertinent in view of Linnaeus's youthfulness at the time, has been more than justified by time. See Daydon Jackson, 'The visit of Carl Linnaeus to England in 1736', Svenska Linné-Sällskapets Årsskrift 9 (1926), pp. 6, 8. Birch (op. cit. (note 3), p. 25) wrote in similar vein: 'He may simply be stil'd the Father of Philosophy in these Kingdoms & perhaps in Europe; for at the time, when he began to search after & collect the productions of Nature, the Knowledge of & even Relish for such matter were confin'd to very few. But the Encouragement which he gave

to Mariners, Travellers & others to bring hither the curiosities of every Country . . . induc'd them to furnish him with whatsoever they could meet with of that kind, & his Example & the Sight of his Musaeum excited many ingenious persons to send yᵉ Natural History, & collect the Materials of it; whereby a Desire of the Knowledge being propagated from one to another, many useful Collections have been made both in Great Britain & other Kingdoms.'

135. Since England and France were locked in war at this time, Sloane had to obtain permission from the Queen to accept this honour from an enemy power. For the intellectual intercourse that continued between the two countries at this time, see G.R. de Beer, 'The relations between Fellows of the Royal Society and the French men of science when France and Britain were at war', Notes and Records of the Royal Society 9 (1952), pp. 244–99; see also I.B. Cohen, 'Isaac Newton, Hans Sloane and the Académie Royale des Sciences', in Alexandre Koyré, L'aventure de la science vol. I (Histoire de la pensée vol. XII) (Paris, 1964), pp. 81–102.

136. Sloane had been visited in 1721 by Johann Daniel Schumacher (1690–1761) who was at the time (among other things) curator of Peter the Great's Kunstkammer in St. Petersburg; he later enjoyed a long career at the Academy of Sciences and maintained a correspondence with Sloane. He was followed in 1730 by Gerhard Friedrich Müller (1705–83) who had a specific commission to identify potential foreign members of the Academy. In respect of Sloane he reported that 'This most outstanding man . . . showed me so much kindness that everything I saw, heard and learned when with him left me with an indelible memory of him': see Christine G. Thomas, 'Sir Hans Sloane and the Russian Academy of Sciences', British Library Journal 14 (1988), pp. 21–4.

137. Ibid., p. 33.

138. A surviving hortus siccus is annotated in Sloane's hand, 'Plants gathered in the fields and gardens about London about the year 1682 for my own and Mr Courten's collections' (Dandy, op. cit. (note 74), p. 27).

139. Ibid. p. 27. It has been suggested that the surviving remnants of the cabinet of materia medica (in which a specimen of bismuth bears a label dated 6 September 1682) formed the earliest element of the collection (see Spurrell, op. cit. (note 62), pp. 81–98, and Sweet, op. cit. (note 66), p. 162). The degree to which the materia medica formed part of the museum rather than Sloane's stock-in-trade as a physician is unclear: some of the specimens in the cabinet are undoubtedly ancient (sixteenth-century) and they seem to form a complement to the historical tracts on medicine and alchemy in Sloane's library.

140. The Diary of John Evelyn, ed. E.S. de Beer (Oxford, 1955), vol. V, p. 48.

141. Ibid., vol. IV, pp. 531–2. Four years later, on 11 March 1690. Evelyn returned: 'I went againe to see Mr. Charltons Curiosities both of Art & nature; as also his full & rare collection

of Medals: which taken altogether in all kinds, is doubtlesse one of the most perfect assemblys of rarities that can any where be seene' (ibid., vol. v, p. 13). Ralph Thoresby was equally impressed: he judged it '... perhaps the most noble collection of natural and artificial curiosities, of ancient and modern coins and medals, that any private person in the world enjoys; it is said to have cost him £7,000 or £8,000 sterling; there is, I think, the greatest variety of insects and animals, corals, shells, petrifactions &c. that ever I beheld. But I spent the greatest part of my time amongst the coins .. He has also a costly collection of medals, of eminent persons in church and state, domestic and foreign reformers' (*The Diary of Ralph Thoresby*, FRS, ed. Joseph Hunter (London, 1830), vol. I, p. 299).

142. Following his initial visit to Sloane on 11 May 1702, Richard Richardson reported to Thoresby that he had found that 'Mr Charleton's collection, which Dr. Sloane now has, lies all in confusion as yet, and will require some time to put them into order' (Thoresby, op. cit. (note 101), vol. I, p. 409).

143. Sloane's will, op. cit. (note 96), p. 3; see also Chapter 2.

144. Thoresby, op. cit. (note 101), vol. I, p. 409.

145. Sloane may have been responsible for organizing this expedition: Brooks, op. cit. (note 1), p. 132.

146. Moore had earlier bought the collection from Plukenet's executors. Sloane himself records that he in turn bought the collection 'from Dr Moor' (see below, p. 291, no. 7), an event which Dandy (op. cit. (note 74), p. 183) places in the year 1710; elsewhere it is dated to 1716 and the vendor is given as Moore's wife (meaning, presumably, his widow, since he died in 1714): see P.M. Hammond, 'Seventeenth-century British coleoptera from the collection of Leonard Plukenet (1642–1706)', *Entomologist's Gazette* 26 (1975), p. 261.

147. Phyllis I. Edwards, 'Sir Hans Sloane and his curious friends', in *History in the Service of Systematics* (London, 1981), pp. 31–2.

148. Petiver is said to have served for a time as Demonstrator of plants at the Apothecaries' physic garden in Chelsea: see F. Dawtrey Drewitt, 'The romance of the Apothecaries' garden at Chelsea Physic Garden', *Herbal Review* (Winter, 1983), p. 9.

149. See Raymond P. Stearns, 'James Petiver, promoter of natural science, c.1663–1718', *Proceedings of the American Antiquarian Society* 62 (1952), pp. 244, 282. Hearne also mentions this sum (op. cit. (note 70), vol. VI, p. 255), confirming that Petiver's collections 'were in no Method'. Amongst the contacts Petiver made in the Netherlands was Dr Frederic Ruysch, whose collection of injected human specimens was renowned; several attempts were made through Petiver to persuade Sloane to exchange specimens with Ruysch or to buy his entire collection (see F.N. Egerton, 'Richard Bradley's relationship with Sir Hans Sloane', *Notes and Records of the Royal Society* 25 (1970), pp. 60–1. In time a number of Ruysch's specimens did reach Sloane's collection (see above, and Chapter 3).

150. *Natural History*, vol. II, preface. Petiver's collection consisted overwhelmingly of natural specimens: posterity learns of the character of his museum from the acerbic Zacharias Conrad von Uffenbach, who observed that it 'was kept in true English fashion in prodigious confusion in one wrteched cabinet and in boxes' (von Uffenbach, op. cit. (note 123), vol. II, p. 583; Quarrell and Mare, op. cit. (note 123), pp. 126–7).

151. On Linnaeus's opinion of the chaotic state of Sloane's own collections, however, see p. 147.

152. One of the Sloane catalogues (see p. 291, no. 7) includes a note explaining interpolations in the text as follows 'G + GR Dr Grews Mus. S. Reg. + collection of seeds fruit & which I bought'. See also Dandy, op. cit. (note 74), p. 132.

153. Guy L. Wilkins, 'The shell collections of Sir Hans Sloane (1660–1753)', *Journal of Conchology* 23 (1952), pp. 247–59.

154. Engelbert Kaempfer, *The History of Japan* (London, 1727). The translator, Sloane's amanuensis J.C. Scheuchzer, pays tribute to his master in the introduction: 'It was upon his intimation, which deservedly hath with me the weight of a command, that I undertook to translate it ... And I went about it with more chearfulness, as out of his known communicative disposition, and unwearied efforts to promote all useful, and in particular natural knowledge, he was pleased not only to grant me use of his Library, which I may venture to call the completest of its kind in Europe, but likewise to give me leave to copy out of his invaluable treasures of curiosities in nature and art, what would serve to illustrate it ...' Several letters written from Germany by Steigerthal to Sloane in the course of negotiations to acquire the collections are in BL, Sloane MS 4047, *passim*. See further, Chapter 18.

155. Rawdon sent Harlow to Jamaica to collect living plants for his garden at Moira, near Lisburn, Co. Down – the first garden of exotics in Ireland: see Jean O'Neill, 'Father of Irish gardening. Sir Arthur Rawdon and his plant introductions', *Country Life* 172 (1982), pp. 1406–7. In Sloane's own words Harlow 'not only brought over with him a Ship almost laden with Cases of Trees, and Herbs, planted and growing in Earth, but also a great number of Samples of them very well preserv'd in Paper' (*Natural History*, vol. I, preface).

156. Letter from Sherard to Richard Richardson, 27 January 1722, quoted in Nichols, op. cit. (note 9), vol. I, p. 378.

157. Letter from Catesby to Sloane, 15 November 1723: BL, Sloane MS 4047, fol. 90.

158. Earlier Catesby had acknowledged 'that great Naturallist and promoter of Science Sir Hans Sloane, Bar'. to whose goodness I attribute much of the Success I had in this undertaking' (Mark Catesby, *The Natural History of Carolina, Florida, and the Bahama Islands* (London, 1731–43), p. x). Later Sloane's involvement as a subscriber to the Georgia colony brought further returns in the form of specimens.

159. Bodleian Library, Oxford, MS Top. Gen. c24, fol. 244^v.

160. Reporting on Conyers' museum and on his intention to throw it open, the *Athenian Mercury* of 21 November 1691 affirmed that '... it may be in many ways useful to the Publick: For the worthy Collector and Keeper of it, hath both with great Industry and Charge, for above 30 years together, made it his Business, upon all occasion to procure such Subjects, either of nature or Art, that had any thing of Rarity in them ...' Among the artificial curiosities, it went on, '... you will find Antiquities and valuable both Egyptian, Jewish, Grecian, Roman, British, Saxon, Danish, etc. viz. their Deities or Idols, Icunculae, Amulets, Tallismans, ancient vessels used in sacrifices, Sepulchral Urns, Lachrymatories, Lamps, Gemms, Meddals, Coyns, Seals, Tessarae, Rings, Armour, Shields, Weapons ...'

161. See David Price, 'John Woodward and a surviving British geological collection from the early eighteenth century', *Journal of the History of Collections* 1 no. 1 (1989), p. 79. Also, most extensively, Levine, op. cit. (note 115), *passim* (with further bibliography). Woodward's *Brief Instructions for making Observations in all parts of the World, as also for collecting, preserving and sending over Natural Things ...* (London, 1696) provided practical advice and aspired to being 'an Attempt to settle an universal correspondence for the advancement of knowledge both natural and Civil'.

162. Richard Richardson reported to Thoresby that Woodward had received him very civilly, 'and showed me the noblest collection of fossils of all sorts that I ever saw', but he also acknowledged his tricky personality by adding: 'It is pity so ingenious a person should not have more friends' (Thoresby, op. cit. (note 101), vol. I, p. 409).

163. In antiquarian matters, his most famous imbroglio concerned an elaborate shield which he considered to have 'the most indubitable Marks of it being truly ancient', but in which opinion he was deceived: see Levine, op. cit. (note 115), chapter ix. The shield is now BM, MLA, OA4710.

164. 'A description of the Musæum of Mr. J. Kemp near the Hay-Market', *The Monthly Miscellany, or Memoirs for the Curious* 2 (1707–8), pp. 259.

165. Ibid.

166. PRO, PCC 171 Whitfield (PROB 11/559). Kemp directed that: 'the Right Honorable the Earle of Oxford and his son the Lord Harley or one of them [shall have] my whole Collection of Antiquities with my Books relating to such Antiquities' upon their paying Kemp's executor £2,000 within three months of his decease but if they failed to do so then the collection was to be sold to the best purchaser within eighteen months. For an account of the collection see Robert Ainsworth, *Monumenta Vetustatis Kempiana* (London, 1720).

167. Ray, op. cit. (note 26), pp. 430–1.

168. George Vertue, *Note-Books* vol. I (Walpole Society 18), p. 136.

169. Evelyn, op. cit. (note 140), vol. V, p. 283.

170. Thoresby, op. cit. (note 141), vol. I, p. 343. Woodward visited him and admired his 'sagacity in searching into natural things and success in methodizing them'. Nicolson also found him 'Nicely skill'd in Antiquities of all kinds and especially in Medals and Coins of which he has a good stock' (Nicolson to Lhwyd, 25 February 1702: Bodleian Library, Oxford, MS Ashmole 1816, fol. 523, quoted in Levine op. cit. (note 115), p. 323, note 18.

171. Thoresby, op. cit. (note 141), vol. II, p. 143. On another visit Thoresby bought some 'Indian curiosities' at Oldsworth's museum (ibid., p. 162).

172. Sloane and Richardson had been introduced to each other by Thoresby in 1702. Sloane wrote a letter of thanks for the introduction to Thoresby on 26 May 1702 (Thoresby, op. cit. (note 101), vol. I, p. 414. Richardson did likewise on 11 May: he had found Sloane '. . . the very epitome of courtesy; and though he had several persons of worth to wait upon, yet he deferred his visits till he had shown me his Jamaica collection, which is very fine and well prepared' (ibid., p. 409).

173. See *Extracts from the Literary and Scientific Correspondence of Richard Richardson, MD, FRS* (Yarmouth, 1835), p. 118.

174. The writer of Collinson's entry in Andrew Kippis's *Biographia Britannica: or the Lives of the most Eminent Persons who have flourished in Great Britain and Ireland* 2nd edn., vol. IV, (London, 1789), pp. 34–42, writes as follows: 'Why Mr. Collinson was not elected a Curator of the British Museum, may continue a matter of surprize, so long as the Museum itself exists. He was one of the founder's most intimate and ancient friends, was well acquainted with every subject it contained, and had done perhaps more to promote the knowledge of Natural History, than any individual in that trust.' See also his *Life* by John Fothergill 1771, reprinted in Fothergill's *Works* (London, 1781); and Norman Brett-James, *The Life of Peter Collinson, FRS, FSA* (London, [1925]).

175. Kippis, op. cit. (note 174), vol. IV, p. 35.

176. See Dandy, op. cit. (note 74), p. 228.

177. According to Sloane's *Natural History* (vol. I, p. lxxx) Albemarle made £50,000 from his investment of £800 towards recovering the ship's cargo.

178. For example, he mentions that '. . . the Fore-fin of a Whale, stripp'd of its Web and Skin was not long ago publickly shewn for the Bones of a Giant's Hand; and I have in my own Posession . . . the Vertebra of the Loin of a large Whale which was brought me from *Oxfordshire* . . . and afterwards made Use of for a Stool to sit on' (Hans Sloane, 'Of fossile teeth and bones of elephants', *Philosophical Transactions* 35 no. 404 (1728), p. 497).

179. John Nichols, *Literary Anecdotes of the Eighteenth Century* (London, 1812–15), vol. VI, p. 219.

180. *Notes and Queries*, 2nd ser. 11 (1861), p. 443.

181. 'The original information of Robert Johnson [King's Evidence] of an attempt to burn and rob the house of Dr. Sloane' (BL, Additional MS 38855, fol. 171), dated 27 April 1700: '. . . about three weeks since, hee [Johnson] together with one – Wake and John Davis went with an intent to committ a Burglary in the dwelling house of doctor Sloane . . . they endeavoured to break in at the back doore, but it being made very strong & fast they were not able to get into the said house; upon which they . . . lighted a candle, and cut some splinters & shaveings, and placed them betweene the shutter of the celler window (wᶜʰ they had splitt) & then sett them to fire; with an intent . . . that whilst the people therein should runn out of the said house in a fright, that [they] would goe therein and rob the said house'. See also a printed sheet dated 1700, *An Account of the Apprehending and Taking of John Davis and Phillip Wake for setting Dr Sloan's House on Fire, to Robb the Same*: BL, 515.1.2 (183).

182. See G.R. de Beer, 'Johann Gaspar Scheuchzer, FRS, 1702–1729', *Notes and Records of the Royal Society* 6 (1948), pp. 56–66; M.E. Jahn, 'John Woodward, Hans Sloane, and Johann Gaspar Scheuchzer: a re-examination', *Journal of the Society for the Bibliography of Natural History* 7 (1974), pp. 19–27; W.J. Tjaden, 'John Woodward, Hans Sloane, and Johann Gaspar Scheuchzer: some further information', *Journal of the Society for the Bibliograpy of Natural History* 8 (1976), pp. 74–7.
Little has been said so far of Sloane's library of printed books and over 4,000 manuscripts: see Chapter 17. Despite the many valuable volumes which it contained, it was none the less primarily a working library and not one of prestige. A large proportion of the volumes dealt with medical subjects, and many were concerned with botany.

183. Later Mortimer attempted unsuccessfully to introduce a medical insurance scheme: for this and for other details of his life, see F.W. Gibbs, 'Cromwell Mortimer, FRCS, Secretary, Royal Society, 1730–1752', *Notes and Records of the Royal Society* 7 no. 2 (1950), pp. 259–63. According to A.E. Gunther (op. cit. (note 93), p. 7), Mortimer and Sloane were related to each other.

184. Mortimer to Dr Waller, quoted in Stukeley, op. cit. (note 59), vol. II, p. 11.

185. See p. 28.

186. Thomas, op. cit. (note 136), pp. 25–32.

187. In 1736, for example, Amman forwarded to Sloane '. . . some dryed specimens of rare & curious plants . . . a map showing the warlike expeditions of the Russian army near Asoph & in the Crim; an Alphabet in the Callmuck language; another of the Tangutan; some very curious copper oares; two kinds of Sibirian Talck; a little piece of sulphur nativum from Casan; a very fine medalion of her Imperial Majesty . . .' These were followed in 1739 by

'A curious Lead oar from China . . . The powder of ye Alcanna from which ye Turks & Persians colour their hairs & nails . . . A sort of very curious reddish sand from ye Lake Baikal . . . A Fucus with which ye Chinese Weemen paint themselves . . . a very small lock made at Casan by a peasant . . . A Callmuch cheese . . .' (ibid., p. 32).

188. Wilkins, op. cit. (note 153), p. 250, notes that the third from last entry in the shell catalogue is dated 17 September 1747.

189. Peter Murray Jones, 'A preliminary checklist of Sir Hans Sloane's catalogues', *British Library Journal* 14 (1988), pp. 38–40.

190. To his credit, Sloane never allowed collecting to get in the way of his medical duties. 'I never, unless very extraordinary business carries me out of town, neglect any matter that is relating to sick persons, whatever I may do as to curiosities' (letter from Sloane to Richard Richardson, 24 December 1702, quoted in Nichols, op. cit. (note 9), vol. I, p. 270). Much the same sentiment was expressed in a letter to the Abbé Bignon: '. . . je m'estimerois coupable d'homicide, si je faisois la moindre chose, tant par omission que par commission, qui fut contraire à ce que je jugeois raisonable, apres avoir meurement pesé toutes les circonstances des maladies que je traitois' (reproduced in Jacquot, op. cit. (note 24), p. 96).

191. Bibliothèque Nationale, Paris, fonds français, MS 22.236; quoted in Clarke, op. cit. (note 111), p. 478.

192. Birch, op. cit. (note 3), p. 21.

193. Hearne to Richardson, 1 January 1726; see Richardson, op. cit. (note 173), p. 227. Hearne goes on: 'He [Thoresby] had some manuscripts that I should have been glad to have seen . . . now I never expect to see any of them, unless they fall into some such hands as Sir Hans Sloane's.' It was unfortunate for the fate of Thoresby's collections that they were not merged with those of Sloane, for most of them, 'having lain in a garret like a Heap of Rubbish from 1726 to 1743, the rain, snow, etc. beating in on all sides, and during that time several persons rummaging them underfoot, so they became like a Dunghill', were eventually thrown out or sold off as scrap: see P.C.D. Brears, 'Ralph Thoresby, a museum visitor in Stuart England', *Journal of the History of Collections* 1 no. 2 (1989), pp. 215–16.

194. Hearne to Richardson, 16 May 1733 (Richardson, op. cit. (note 173), p. 335).

195. Birch, op. cit. (note 3), pp. 24–5.

196. Kippis, op. cit. (note 174), vol. IV, p. 335.

197. Sloane, *Natural History*, vol. II, pp. xvi–xvii.

198. Sherard further complained to Richardson that Sloane had had the collections of Jakob Breyne of Danzig and had not shown them to him, whereas Sherard in the past had allowed Sloane to take home with him other specimens from the collections of Merrett, Plukenet and

Buddle which he had (see Richardson, op. cit. (note 173), pp. 151, 162–4). Dandy (op. cit. (note 74), p. 97), on the other hand, records that Breyne's son, Johann Philipp, sent his father's herbarium to Sherard for comparison and that he returned it without Sloane seeing it.

199. Although we may doubt that such disparate material could have been juxtaposed as a matter of deliberate policy, instances can be found on the Continent of natural and man-made specimens being arranged in just this way in a system of 'alternating symmetry' (see, for example, Laura Laurencich-Minelli, 'Museography and ethnographical collections in Bologna during the sixteenth and seventeenth centuries', in O. Impey and A. MacGregor (eds.), *The Origins of Museums. The Cabinet of Curiosities in Sixteenth- and Seventeenth-Century Europe* (Oxford, 1985), pp. 19–21).

200. BL, MS Sloane 4045, fol. 278. See also note 134.

201. Letter of 1736 from Linnaeus to Olaus Celsius, quoted in Dandy, op. cit. (note 74), p. 11.

202. The earliest source for this tale seems to be J.C. Jeaffreson, *A Book about Doctors* (London, 1860), vol. I, p. 197.

203. See de Beer, op. cit. (note 1), pp. 124–7.

204. This is no doubt a reference to his will, originally drawn up in 1739.

205. 'A narrative of some of the occurrences in the life of Edmund Howard, of the parish of Chelsea, wrote by himself in the year 1785', *Friends Quarterly Examiner* 40 (1906), pp. 58–9. An indigent exchange had taken place between Sloane and Howard over the rate of commission which might be paid to the latter for collecting the rents, a dispute which they were never able to resolve (ibid., pp. 59–60, 66). Howard's opinion of Sloane's intellect was equally uncompromising: while acknowledging his master to have been 'the philosopher's king', he maintained that he had been acquainted 'with many men superior to him both in natural talents and acquired accomplishments' (*Friends Quarterly Examiner* 39 (1905), p. 474).

206. Jacquot, op. cit. (note 24), p. 98.

207. Stukeley, op. cit. (note 59), vol. I, p. 358.

208. See *Authentic Copies of the Codicils belonging to the Last Will and Testament of Sir Hans Sloane* (London, 1753), pp. 34–5.

209. The *Authentic Copies of the Codicils*, op. cit. (note 208), gives the figure for coins as 32,000, but this is thought to be an error: see further, Chapter 9.

210. For an earlier published translation see *Kalm's account of his visit to England on his way to America in 1748*, trans. Joseph Lucas (London, 1892), pp. 97–106.

211. Birch (op. cit. (note 3), pp. 25–6) puts it thus: 'As the Study of Nature & the Improvement of Knowledge were the Employment & pleasure of his Life, the Desire next his Heart was, that his Collection might be kept together for the Instruction & Benefit of others engag'd in the same pursuits ... the whole ... intended for *the Glory of God & the Good of Man.*'

212. Mme du Bocage, *Letters concerning England, Holland and Italy* (London, 1770), vol. I, pp. 35–6. In its early days the Royal Society's Repository had been recommended to fellows as a place where gifts would be 'probably much better and safer than in their own private cabinets' (*Philosophical Transactions* 1 no. 18 (1666), p. 136), but experience had proved this to be a vain hope.

213. Sloane had earlier made some modest donations to the Ashmolean's collections and evidently a more substantial gesture was expected before he turned against the Museum on account of the neglect which it suffered under Huddesford: Bodleian Library, Oxford, MS Rawl. C989, fol. 188; see also A.G. MacGregor and A.J. Turner, 'The Ashmolean Museum', in *The History of the University of Oxford* vol. V: *The Eighteenth Century* ed. L.S. Sutherland and L.G. Mitchell (Oxford, 1986), p. 651.

214. Stukeley, op. cit. (note 59), vol. I, pp. 125–6.

215. Von Uffenbach, op. cit. (note 123), vol. III, pp. 247–51; translated in Quarrell and Mare, op. cit. (note 123), pp. 185–8.

216. Translated from the transcription in French in Jacquot, op. cit. (note 24), pp. 91–3. The original manuscript is in the Institut de France, Paris, MS 1797.

217. Amongst the surviving drawings in the Department of Prints and Drawings, British Museum, are two volumes (Sloane nos. 5277–8; inv. A16, now c198 and c203) comprising over 140 drawings by Nicolas Robert of plants, birds, shells, etc. From Morand's description of the 'fameux receuil de Robert et [*recte* du?] Roy en tailles douces', however, it would seem that he was referring to the folio series engraved by Robert and others at the behest of the Académie Royale des Sciences; of the projected publication for which they were intended, only one volume was to appear: *Mémoires pour servir à l'histoire des plantes*, compiled by M. Dodart of the Académie and published in 1676.

218. The text reproduced here is taken (with slight modifications approved by the translator) from 'Pehr Kalm, Journey in England on his Way to North America', translated from Dr Martti Kerkkonen's transcript of the original manuscript by Professor Mead. A copy of the complete transcript is held in the library of the Linnean Society, London, with the passage quoted here on pp. 336–42.

219. The account, written by Cromwell Mortimer, was first published in the *Gentleman's Magazine* 18 (1748), pp. 301–2.

220. Sloane was favoured with two gifts from Louis XV: the first, in 1730, was a set of the newly printed catalogues of the Royal Library, bound in calf and blazoned with the royal arms; the second, alluded to here, was a lavish collection of specially commissioned prints: see Clarke, op. cit. (note 111), p. 480.

2 Sloane's Will and the Establishment of the British Museum

Marjorie Caygill

Paradoxically, while Sir Hans Sloane is acknowledged by many as the founder of two great museums and the national library, there are others who aver that he can hardly be credited with founding his own collection. Edward Edwards, an early historian of the British Museum states bluntly:

Sir Hans Sloane cannot claim to be regarded individually or very specially, as the Founder of the British Museum. His last Will, indeed, gave an opportunity for the foundation. Strictly speaking he was not even the Founder of his own collection, as it stood in his lifetime.[1]

Mordaunt Crook goes further:

The real founder of the British Museum was the House of Commons.[2]

Similarly, while some commentators discern a great design in the establishment of the first national, secular and public museum in the world, others adhere to a more haphazard view of history. Sir George Hill (Director and Principal Librarian 1931–6),[3] for example, describes the Museum's foundation as 'more or less of an accident', comparing its establishment with the 'succession of fits of absence of mind' which led to the British Empire:

Those who began it [the British Museum] had no idea of the dimensions which the building, of which they laid the foundation, was to attain. And although those who have watched over its fortunes have been uniformly eager to do the best for it, it cannot be said that there has been any settled policy governing the lines on which the development was to be conducted.[4]

The British Museum was a product of its times but it was shaped by individuals. The catalyst for its foundation was provided by the will[5] of Sir Hans Sloane, adroitly worded by an old and worldly man who knew from experience how to manipulate the power structures of the eighteenth century to his advantage. The terms were sufficiently flexible so as to permit Parliament to take advantage of this windfall to establish an institution quite different from the old Sloane 'musaeum' and of whose eventual dimensions neither they nor Sloane could have guessed. If Sloane's will was flexible, so was the British Museum Act of 1753. Today, quite rightly, the weathered statue of Sloane by Rysbrack (Plate 2) greets the visitor on entry to the British Museum in Bloomsbury, a copy of Rysbrack's terracotta bust (see Plate 3) will have pride of place in the new British Library building at St. Pancras and his portrait graces the Boardroom of The Natural History Museum.

Sloane's Will

The first part of Sloane's will, an autograph document consisting of 'five sheets of paper fastened together with a black ribbond and black wax'[6] had been signed and witnessed on 9 October 1739 when he was in ill health. The severe winter of 1739 nearly proved fatal to him and he retired to Chelsea at the beginning of 1742. There were further codicils[7] on 18 October 1747 and 5 July 1749. The main provisions relating to his collections were laid down on 10 July 1749 with more codicils being added on 21 July 1750, 18 September 1750, 14 April 1751, 22 September 1751, 26 December 1751 (when a number of codicils were reaffirmed) and 17 June 1752 (an unwitnessed note).

He had initially named Charles, Lord Cadogan (his son-in-law), William Sloane (nephew), and Dr Sloane Elsmere (nephew, and Rector of Chelsea), as his executors. James Empson, curator of his collections was added on 14 April 1751. His original executors were charged to arrange the sale of his collection for £20,000. Lord Cadogan together with the Duke of Richmond, Sir Robert Walpole, Sir Paul Methuen, Mr Edgcombe and others with influence and access should 'promote so public a good'[8] by approaching King George II to offer him first refusal. Should the King not accept the collection within six months after the first overture then his executors should offer it in turn to the Royal Society of London, the University of Oxford, the College of Physicians at Edinburgh, the Royal Academies of Sciences at Paris, St. Petersburg, Berlin and Madrid,[9] each in turn being given one month in which to accept or refuse the offer. If all refused the collection should be sold or otherwise disposed of, piecemeal if necessary. Sloane directed, however, that this should be done with some care, the executors taking 'advice of such persons as are skilled in natural knowledge, medals, etc. allowing him or them what my executors and they think reasonable for their care and trouble in perusing and correcting my catalogues, which have been taken generally in great haste.'[10]

Sloane changed his mind in a codicil of 10 July 1749 [pp. 16–35] when earlier arrangements were revoked and more detailed provisions were made for his museum. On this occasion Sloane inserted a long list of some forty-eight Trustees (plus, *ex officio*, the President, Treasurer and two Secretaries of the Royal Society if not individually listed). Also listed was a new, grander, supervisory category of Visitors – twenty named individuals and some seventeen *ex officio* are set down.[11] The Trustees were directed to request the King or Parliament to provide £20,000 to be handed to the executors for Sloane's heirs. (Sloane [p. 22] estimated this sum as not even a quarter of the collection's value). The Trustees then had possession of the collection, the Chelsea manor house and its grounds, plus the advowson of Chelsea Church:

... for preserving and continuing my said collection or museum in such manner as they shall think most likely to answer the public benefit by me intended.[12]

The Trustees were to be supervised by the Visitors, who had the final say in resolving any disputes.

In this version, should the money and an Act of Parliament not be forthcoming within a year after Sloane's death the nation would have no second chance. The collection was then to be offered in turn to the Royal Academies of Science at St. Petersburg, Paris, Berlin and Madrid, each being given twelve months in which to reach a decision. Should all refuse then it should be sold 'speedily and advantageously'.

On 21 July 1750, perhaps as a result of family pressure, the manor and its lands were withdrawn from the bequest and allocated to the family. The advowson of Chelsea was also withdrawn on 18 September 1750 and reverted to the family. Further Trustees and Visitors were added on that date and on 17 June 1752 Sloane named his last Trustees among them members of the Moravian Church, the Unitas Fratrum.[13] The inclusion of the latter may have been something of an old man's fancy: Sloane had sold and leased land to members of the sect in 1750 and may have been impressed with the piety of a group that had originally fled persecution in Moravia and was now engaged in missionary work in North America and other distant British possessions.

Sloane's 'Musaeum'

What sort of an institution did Sloane envisage? Mordaunt Crook asserts '... he planned to make it [his museum] the nucleus of a major national collection',[14] Grigson that 'It was exactly congruent that he [Sloane] should have looked forward to a great public museum founded upon his own collections'.[15]

Nucleus it became, and national it certainly was but we should beware of teleological explanations which credit Sloane with a wider vision than he may have possessed and which link consequences with intentions. It was indeed an innovation for Sloane to hand over such an assemblage to the nation (although the nation had had the Cottonian library since 1702 and had not yet decided what to do with it). The Cottonian library[16] provided a format, if not a particularly happy one, for a national collection vested in trustees and intended to be available to scholars. There were, however, for Sloane, warning signs in the Cottonian library's neglect and near destruction by fire in 1731.

As an alternative to the nation Sloane could have left his collection to one of his great interests – the Royal Society, whose growing collection of rarities had first been put in order in 1666, preceding the British Museum by a century, and to which he had given specimens. Its history

of neglect, however, hardly imbued a prospective donor with confidence.

It is doubtful whether Sloane even in his wildest dreams envisaged the institution formed by the British Museum Act – a vast collection of books, manuscripts, natural history and antiquities. After all, there was no institution like the British Museum to provide a model as it would for future generations. This was a period when the great collections abroad were 'primarily expressions of private affluence and public power'[17] and when there was no long English tradition as, for instance in Italy, of rulers as great collectors. Any English tradition which had developed was private – collections little removed from cabinets of curiosities like those of Sloane himself, Mead, Courten, the Tradescants and Ashmole. The Ashmolean Museum, established in 1683, perhaps provided a prototype to follow – the first specifically designed modern museum, open to the public and didactic, although, true to its origins, it could more accurately be described as 'a Cabinet of Curiosities par excellence'.[18] Sloane was thus embarking on largely unchartered waters.

Sloane's choice of Trustees perhaps gives some indication of the direction he wished his museum to take, but even here their ultimate duty was to sell the lot and dissolve themselves if they failed to obtain Parliamentary backing. Their range of interests was wide – natural history, astronomy, antiquarianism, sciences – they had, like Sloane, profited from the interchange of ideas through the Royal Society and the Society of Antiquaries and many had used his library and collections. Sloane, with his sixty-eight years as a Fellow of the Royal Society, was in a unique position to appreciate the unfolding of scientific enquiry and the great strides which had been taken in his lifetime and how it was dependent on the interchange of ideas and the availability, for people of modest origins like himself, of private libraries and cabinets. Birch comments:

the Desire next his Heart was that his collection might be kept together for the instruction and Benefit of others engaged in the same pursuits. And tho the intrinsic value of it was too much to be given away entirely from his own Children, he left it to the public on such easy terms, as he thought would readily be complied with...[19]

A will does not necessarily reflect a testator's real motives or intentions and there are many who cannot resist a last opportunity to strike a pose and, frequently, totally confuse their executors. Sloane took two opportunities to make his views clear. On 9 October 1739, in his first will, he sets out his intentions thus:

Whereas from my youth I have been a great observer and admirer of the wonderful power, wisdom and contrivance of the Almighty God, appearing in the works of his Creation; and have gathered together many things in my own travels or voyages, or had them from others... Now desiring very much that these things tending many ways to the manifestation of the glory of God, the confutation of atheism and its consequences, the use and improvement of physic, and other arts and sciences, and benefit of mankind, may remain together and not be separated, and that chiefly in and about the city of London, where I have acquired most of my estates, and where they may by the great confluence of people be of most use. . .[20]

In the 10 July 1749 codicil he states in similar terms:

Having had from my youth a strong inclination to the study of plants, and all other productions of nature; and having through the course of many years with great labour and expence, gathered together whatever could be procured either in our own or foreign countries that was rare and curious; and being fully convinced that nothing tends more to raise our ideas of the power, wisdom, goodness, providence, and other perfections of the Deity, or more to the comfort and well being of his creatures than the enlargement of our knowledge in the works of nature, I do Will and desire that for the promoting of these noble ends, the glory of God, and the good of man, my collection in all its branches may be, if possible kept and preserved together whole and intire in my manor house, in the parish of Chelsea, situate near the physic garden, given by me to the company of apothecaries for the same purpose . . .[21]

The proposal for accessibility was not new – Sloane had always been generous with access to his 'musaeum', although access had been confined mostly to scholars and people of some distinction. The *Gentleman's Magazine* shortly after his death remarked that it was already a near-public collection 'the most magnificent private, if not publick collection upon earth. A collection the use or inspection of which he never refused to any one . . .'[22] This is echoed by the *London Magazine* which noted:

. . . we may venture to proclaim it the most valuable private collection (perhaps publick one) that ever yet has appeared upon earth. Those treasures, tho' collected at his private expence, have not been appropriated to his own pleasure alone. Mankind has enjoyed the benefits of them, and his noble mind never suffered him to refuse their use to whoever at home or abroad was desirous of satisfaction or improvement from them.[23]

The 10 July 1749 codicil contines:

. . . that the same may be, from time to time, visited and seen by all persons desirous of seeing and viewing the same, under such statutes, directions, rules, and orders, as shall be made, from time to time, by the said trustees . . . that the same may be rendered as useful as possible, as well towards satisfying the desire of the curious, as for the improvement, knowledge and information of all persons . . .[24]

His main themes were thus public access, utility and, following his contemporary and predecessor as President of the Royal Society, Sir Isaac Newton, the affirmation of the role of God in the workings of the universe. Sloane was perhaps a little mindful of the criticisms that had over the years plagued the Royal Society – that it was composed of dilettanti, that it was subversive of religion and that it concentrated too much on scientific pursuits. The Society's 1912 history points out that:

The general community was not yet prepared to welcome so novel an experiment as the association of a company of leisured men for the purpose not of political intrigue or of literary or anti-quarian co-operation, but devoting themselves to the earnest investigation of Nature. The Society had hardly taken definite shape before it was assailed with vituperation, and for about a century and a half it continued to be a mark for the shafts of ridicule launched by some of the foremost men of letters in each successive generation.[25]

It has been suggested that comments made by 'Poor Fred', the Prince of Wales, during a visit in 1748 to Sloane's manor house in Chelsea (possibly prompted by others) may have set Sloane musing on immortality and the nation:

He [Frederick] express'd the great pleasure it gave him to see so magnificent a collection in *England*, esteeming it an ornament to the nation; and expressed his sentiments, how much it must conduce to the benefit of learning, and how great an honour will redound to *Britain*, to have it established for publick use to the latest posterity.[26]

The 'old gentleman' kept his own counsel. The Prince's comments may have strengthened his resolve when he wrote his codicil the following year but some form of public provision had already been made.

Sloane was possessed by the daemon which sets apart the great collector from the rest of mankind, and someone who could fill two houses and then a manor house with a collection eventually numbering almost 80,000 objects plus an herbarium and library well merits the title of 'great collector'. Augustus Wollaston Franks, a nineteenth-century collector and Keeper at the British Museum, whose influence on the Museum equals if not surpasses Sloane's, summed up neatly in his 'Apology' the drive which distinguishes such individuals: 'Collecting is an hereditary disease, and I fear incurable . . .'[27]

For the really great collector the nightmare is that his life's work will be dispersed by bored or impecunious heirs. Sloane had no surviving sons and his grandchildren seem not to have inherited his interests to any great extent.

Sloane's curator, James Empson (who admittedly had a vested interest in the continuation of the Sloane collection as a separate entity), later put forward a more personal, less altruistic and rather convincing reason:

. . . having been with the Deceased to his last Moments; [I] can positively assert, that one of his greatest Inducements for disposing of his so extensive and large collection in the Manner he has done, has been that his Name, as the Collector of it, should be preserved to Posterity.[28]

Sloane did not insist that the museum should take his name but, having entrusted his collection to the nation, its chances of long-term survival were immeasurably increased.

Sloane's Trustees[29]

This, then, was the charge laid upon the Trustees of Sloane's will and on his four executors (three of whom – William Sloane, Sloane Elsmere and James Empson – were also Trustees). Some sixty-three Trustees were eventually listed, including *ex officio*, the President, Treasurer, and two Secretaries of the Royal Society. Some five of them predeceased Sloane. There were five members of his family – by blood or by marriage: The Hon. Charles Sloane Cadogan, the Revd Sloane Elsmere, James Fuller of Sussex, William Sloane, Hans Stanley.

For the rest Sloane had leaned heavily on the institution to which he had devoted much of his time – the Royal Society. Of those who can be identified, some forty were Fellows of the Royal Society; half of them also Fellows of the Society of Antiquaries.

Sloane chose his Trustees cannily. There was a group of seventeen or more Members of Parliament (many very active in Parliamentary affairs) and six ex-Members, of varied adherences, over half of them also Fellows of the Royal Society. As so often with influential men, there is a complex web of interlocking connections between individuals. They were involved in a range of Sloane's interests – Ireland, the West Indies, the Foundling Hospital, the Georgia Company, the Royal College of Physicians. Some were neighbours at Chelsea. Some shared his interest in natural history, others were more of an antiquarian or literary bent. Some were powerful or well connected men of letters, others were merely protégés of the great political families. Some had little money but much learning, others the reverse. Not surprisingly in the eighteenth century, the Church was well represented with eight professional churchmen, including three bishops. Sloane had a certain sympathy for dissenters: the Revd Henry Miles was a Dissenting Minister, two (Barnard and Collinson) were of Quaker origins, but he also included the Bishop of Exeter, an opponent of Methodism. To these should be added the five Moravian brethren (of whom little more is subsequently heard in this connection). A large group (eleven) had sufficient fortune and/or sinecures to devote themselves whole-heartedly to antiquarianism or scientific pursuits, with perhaps for some an occasional appearance in Parliament. About a dozen were active in politics and government. Around eight were successful businessmen; there were a couple of diplomats and three from the army. Surprisingly, only four practised medicine. There were three actively practising law and one architect. James Bradley, as Astronomer Royal, was a full-time scientist. Many had inherited large fortunes (Sir James Lowther was one of the richest commoners in England), others, like Sloane himself, had made their way in the world by talent and application.

Sloane had selected a combination which continues today among the Trustees of the British Museum – men of letters, antiquaries, businessmen, politicians, professionals – a variety of talents and influence. As a later Director of the British Museum remarked:

As the range of Sloane's collections influenced, if it did not dictate, the scope of the British Museum ... the wishes he expressed in his will for its government were in part responsible for the form of its constitution for over two hundred years.[30]

For an account of the Trustees' deliberations we have to rely largely on a rather odd source. There is in the collections of the British Library,[31] a printed copy of Sloane's will and its codicils, bound in brown leather. Inserted before and after the printed text are sections of blank paper. At the front there is a brief manuscript biography of Sloane which continues with a neat account, in a so far unidentified hand, of the meetings of the Trustees as they struggled to interest the King in Sloane's collection and to keep it from the Academies of St. Petersburg, Paris, Berlin and Madrid. An annotation to the volume by the then Principal Librarian, Sir Henry Ellis, records that on 25 August 1836 it was 'Bought at a Curiosity Shop at Sevenoaks'. This account, supplemented by the rather terse notes in the *Journals of the House of Commons* agrees largely with the reports in the *Gentleman's Magazine*[32] and *London Magazine* but provides notes of additional meetings.

On a more flippant note, Horace Walpole in a letter to Sir Horace Mann reveals something of the flavour of the Trustees' discussions:

You will scarce guess how I employ my time; chiefly at present in the guardianship of embryos and cockle-shells. Sir Hans Sloane is dead and has made me one of the trustees to his museum, which is to be offered for twenty thousand pounds to the King, the Parliament, the Royal Academy of Petersburgh, Berlin, Paris and Madrid. He valued it at fourscore thousand; and so would anybody who loves hippopotamuses, sharks with one ear, and spiders as big as geese! It is a rent-charge to keep the foetuses in spirit! You may believe that those who think money the most valuable of all curiosities, will not be purchasers. The King has excused himself, saying he did not believe that there are twenty thousand pounds in the Treasury. We are a charming wise set, all philosophers, botanists, antiquarians, and mathematicians; and adjourned our first meeting, because Lord Macclesfield, our chairman, was engaged to a party for finding out the longitude. One of our number is a Moravian, who signs himself Henry xxviii, Count de Reus.[33] The Moravian has settled a colony at Chelsea, in Sir Hans's neighbourhood, and I believe he intended to beg Count Henry xxviiith's skeleton for his museum.'[34]

Thirty-four Trustees attended the first meeting at the Manor House at Chelsea at ten o'clock on the morning of Saturday, 27 January 1753 to which they were bidden at the request of the executors (Lord Cadogan, William Sloane, Sloane Elsmere and James Empson) by letters dispatched by their attorney, Mr George Stubbs. Four family members were there, as were the President, Treasurer and two Secretaries of the Royal Society plus a rather colourful collection of eighteenth-century worthies.

The senior executor, Lord Cadogan, produced the will.

The Earl of Macclesfield (President of the Royal Society) then took the Chair and the section relating to the trust was read. Lieutenant General Oglethorpe 'gave an account of the intention of Sir Hans, of the nature and the value of the museum, and produced an abstract of the articles it contained'. Oglethorpe invited Empson to read the abstract and explain the articles. The Trustees confirmed that Empson should continue in charge of the museum and act as Secretary. At the suggestion of Sir George Lyttelton, seconded by James West, it was agreed that a committee should be appointed to draw up a memorial and to meet at Lord Cadogan's house on Tuesday 30 January at 7 p.m. The next full Trustees' meeting was held in the King's Arms Tavern, Palace Yard, Westminster on Thursday, 1 February. The committee's memorial was then signed and the Earl of Macclesfield was asked to present it to the King.

At the Trustees' next meeting on Saturday, 10 February the Earl of Macclesfield conveyed the depressing news that the King, while not formally replying to their memorial, had commented that he doubted if there was sufficient money in the Exchequer. Since the King was indifferent the Trustees decided to try a flanking manoeuvre through Parliament. A further committee, consisting of Trustees who were also members of the Lords or Commons was appointed to meet on Monday, 12 February at 7 p.m. at Lord Cadogan's house. On 28 February at a meeting at the King's Arms Tavern this committee's representation was signed and Edward Southwell,[35] Member for Bristol, was appointed to present it to Parliament. On 6 March a somewhat embarassed Parliament received the petition, Mr Southwell speaking in favour and the King having indicated that the House should do as they thought fit. Henry Pelham,[36] then First Lord of the Treasury, told the House that the King had consented to this course but would not become a purchaser and warned that something had to be done about the 'encumbrance of Trustees'. A proposal that the petition should lie on the table was felt to 'look like thro-ing cold water on the generous gift' so it was agreed to refer the matter to a Committee of the whole House on 13 March.

Much was going on behind the scenes. On Monday, 12 March the Trustees met again and noted William Sloane's view that were the Crown able to take control of the Museum all difficulties would be at an end. They agreed to await Parliament's comments. On 13 March Parliament again considered the matter and more pressure was put on Sloane's Trustees to relinquish their control. Both Henry Pelham and Fox advocated delaying a full debate until more was heard from the Trustees. The Trustees met again on 15 March and agreed in principle that, as the sticking point appeared to be the continuation of Trustees nominated by Sloane, they would agree to the appointment of fresh Trustees by the Crown. They did however dig their heels in with a resounding set of principles from which they could not 'in honour or conscience' depart:

1st That the collection be preserved intire without the least diminution or separation.

2dy That the same be kept for the use and benefit of the publick, who may have free Access to view and peruse the same, at all stated and convenient seasons agreeably to the Will and intentions of the Testator, and under such restrictions as the Parliament shall think fit.

3dly That in case it should hereafter be judged the most beneficial and advantageous for the publick use, to remove the collection from the manor house at Chelsea, where the same is now deposited, that it be placed properly in the Cities of London or Westminster or the suburbs thereof.[37]

The House on 16 March agreed that the full debate should take place on Monday, 19 March. During this vital three-hour debate a copy of a brief petition was before the House. Much of the credit for the debate's successful resolution should go to Speaker Arthur Onslow,[38] who vacated the Speaker's chair to Philip Yorke and spoke strongly in support of acquiring the collection. The will was read and Charles Gray (one of Sloane's Trustees) spoke first in favour. James Empson was summoned to the Bar of the House to convince MPs that they were getting a bargain in that the collection was worth more than £20,000 (Empson estimated £80,000, if not £100,000). Parliament wanted an assurance that it would not cost much to run. Empson obliged with an estimate: £100 for the curator, half that for a librarian and also a clerk; a porter at £30 and another man £30, two maids at £40, coals and candles £60, land tax £20 and spirits of wine £20. The Members were convinced and, no doubt to the relief of the Trustees present, declared that the collection was worth more than £20,000 and 'that it will be for the Honor and Advantage of this Country to accept of Sir Hans Sloane's Legacy'.

Pelham brought up the subject of the Cottonian library. This great collection, particularly noted for its manuscripts, had been amassed by the Cotton family and given to a less than grateful nation in 1700. Neglected since then it had narrowly escaped destruction in a fire at Ashburnham House in 1731. Speaker Onslow, as one of the Cottonian trustees, no doubt had this library on his conscience and concurred with the desirability of uniting this with the Sloane collection. Pelham also suggested the purchase of the Harleian manuscripts.[39] This collection, put together by the 1st and 2nd Earls of Oxford, consisted now only of manuscripts, the rest of the library having been dispersed by auction.

The Cottonian library would come with a dowry — £7,000 would be available on the reversion of a life interest from a bequest by Arthur Edwards,[40] which accompanied his library of antiquarian books. This money had been bequeathed to erect a repository for the combined collection or to extend it in the unlikely event that the government had bestirred itself after four decades to find a home for the Cottonian library. Pelham was not, however, prepared to commit Parliament until he received an assurance that the collection would no longer be vested in private

Trustees but in the public. Gray read the Trustees' resolution of 15 March and said they would resign if these conditions were observed. Speaker Onslow then launched into a long history of the Cottonian library.

Parliament then, as now, was permanently embarrassed for cash – had the King not said that he doubted that there was £20,000 in the Treasury? Speaker Onslow therefore had the inspired idea of raising the rest of the money from a state lottery. This was a frequent eighteenth-century device, grown somewhat dubious by the fact that even official lotteries, established to negate the ills of the even more shady private ones, had a habit of getting out of hand and leaving ruined citizenry in their wake. (The monopoly of state lotteries was introduced less from a sense of morality than from a desire to take over this profitable operation for the government). Provided, however, that at least some of the money reached its correct destination, lotteries could be used to raise vast sums – for example to defray the cost of building the new Westminster Bridge.

From this time we begin to lose sight of Sir Hans Sloane's 'musaeum', although the name lingered on for a few years. At some point in the debate, unrecorded, the decision was taken to call the new institution 'The British Museum'. Sloane's collection had contained 50,000 volumes of books and manuscripts, many on medical subjects. Although his natural history collection was beyond compare, his library was overshadowed by the vast and important collections of manuscripts of Cotton and Harley and the antiquities were relatively unremarkable when viewed on their own. The Sloane bias did, however, continue in the subsequent appointment of medical men to oversee the collections.

The House recorded its decisions on 6 April: that the collection was of greater value than £20,000; that it should be 'kept intire, and maintained for the use and Benefit of the Publick'; that a proper Repository for this and the Cottonian collection should be provided, the Edwards bequest accompanying the latter and the Harleian collection being a suitable addition at £10,000; and that the money should be raised by a lottery.

Parliament breathed a collective sigh of relief, national honour was satisfied and the Exchequer left alone. As one of the first historians of the British Museum wrote:

... a British Parliament could not summon up enough of public spirit to tax its own members, in common with their tax-paying fellow subjects throughout the realm ... in order to meet an obvious public want, to redeem an actual parliamentary pledge, and to secure a conspicuous national honour for all time to come ... The Museum had been founded grudgingly. It was kept up parsimoniously.[41]

The British Museum Act[42]
On Thursday, 7 June 1753[43] 'His Majesty, attended in the state coach by the Marquis of Hartington, and the Earl of Lincoln went to the house of peers'. The traditional ceremonial took place as the Hanoverian king gave his assent to the Act which established the British Museum. :

His Majesty being seated on the Throne, adorned with His Crown and Regal Ornaments, and attended by His Officers of State; the Duke of *Cumberland*, in his Robes sitting in his Place on His Majesty's Left Hand; the Lords being also in their Robes . . . the Clerk of the Crown read the Titles of the Bills to be passed.

Sandwiched between an Act 'to explain and prevent the spreading of the distemper amongst the horned cattle' and another 'for providing a reward for persons discovering the longitude at sea' was that for purchasing Sir Hans Sloane's museum, and the Harleian manuscripts. The title of the Act is the first known appearance of a name which is today recognized throughout the world – 'The British Museum'.

The Act established a new Board of Trustees.[44] There was a somewhat complicated arrangement of seventeen *ex officio* Trustees plus all the Principal Secretaries of State who were empowered to elect fifteen others. The *ex officio* trustees included three principal Trustees – The Archbishop of Canterbury, the Lord Chancellor and the Speaker – at least one of whom must attend General meetings and at least two of whom must approve all staff appointments. Provision was made for the Sloane, Cotton, and Harley families to nominate two Trustees each.

The Act echoed some of the provisions of Sloane's will. The collections were to be available, useful and perpetual:

[I, p. 333] Therefore, to the end that the said Museum or Collection may be preserved and maintained, not only for the Inspection and Entertainment of the learned and the curious, but for the general Use and Benefit of the Public.[45]
[IX, p. 339] . . . shall remain and be preserved therein for public Use to all Posterity.[46]
[IX, p. 341] . . . the said Museum or Collection of Sir Hans Sloane . . . and also the said Cottonian Library . . . and the said Harleian Collection of Manuscripts . . . and the said general Repository . . . shall be vested in the said Trustees by this Act appointed, and their Successors for ever, upon this Trust and Confidence nevertheless, that a free Access to the said general Repository, and to the Collections therein contained, shall be given to all studious and curious Persons, at such Times and in such Manner, and under such Regulations for inspecting and consulting the said Collections, as by the said Trustees or the major Part of them in any general Meeting assembled shall be limited for that Purpose.[47]

The first section of the Act had proclaimed the interrelatedness of knowledge, drawing on the universalist views of the Encyclopaedists:

[I, p. 333] Whereas all Arts and Sciences have a Connexion with each other, and Discoveries in Natural Philosophy and other Branches of speculative Knowledge, for the Advancement and Improvement whereof the said Museum or Collection was intended, do and may in many Instances give Help and success to the most useful Experiments and Inventions.[48]

The British Museum was not at birth fettered as an 'art' museum or a closed collection. There was scope for a truly universal museum to develop, illustrating the sum of human knowledge, collecting both the natural and artificial products of the whole world.

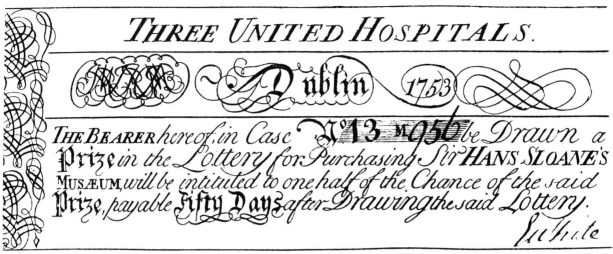

Fig. 7 Ticket issued in the Dublin Hospitals Lottery on the results of the main (State) lottery to purchase the Sloane and Harley collections and to erect a suitable repository for the British Museum. Wellcome Institute for the History of Medicine.

The Lottery[49]

Of the twenty-six pages of the British Museum Act 1753, over twelve are taken up with directions respecting the lottery. Yet again, in a triumph of enthusiasm over experience, money was to be raised for a good cause by appealing to the easily aroused gambling instincts of the populace. Alongside the summary of the Parliamentary debates on its outcome is quoted a censorious extract from the *London Magazine*:

Amongst the other vices in which the people of England were plunged at this time, an universal spirit of gaming, which had seized all ranks and degrees of people, was not the least. Mr Pelham had often declared himself on that account, to be an avowed enemy of lotteries, but in cases of absolute necessity. In the act for the lottery for purchasing Sir Hans Sloane's curiosities, the legislators had been at unusual pains to guard against the pernicious consequences of one person engrossing a great number of tickets, by which he was able to put what price he pleased upon them, to the great detriment of the public, through their insatiable passion for gaming.[50]

The Act laid down that the subscription was £300,000 in tickets of £3 each (payable in £1 and £2 instalments); £200,000 was to be distributed in prizes to the holders of 4,159 'fortunate tickets' varying from one prize of £10,000 by stages to 3,000 of £10 (see Fig. 7).

No one individual or group might hold more than twenty £3 tickets. No opening date was given but the first instalment was payable by 25 July, the second by 26 October to allow time for foreigners to participate. The draw would begin at the Guildhall on 26 November 1753 and the prizes were to be paid by 31 December 1754. Forging tickets merited the death sentence.

Parliament did its best to organize an honest lottery. It would appear from subsequent accounts that they failed to take full account of human greed and ingenuity and that they need hardly have bothered with their regulations.

While not quite the last public lottery — there were others throughout the second half of the eighteenth century and they were not abolished until 1826 — that on which the British Museum was founded did little to restore public confidence.

While the Parliamentary debate on the disposition of the Sloane collection was not regarded as important enough to be included in the few Parliamentary summaries of the period, the debate on the conduct of the lottery occupies many fascinating pages.[51] The accounts of the lottery were presented to Parliament on 12 December 1753. Since, even by eighteenth-century standards, it was already a full-blown public scandal, Parliament concluded that a Committee of Inquiry should be set up to try to disentangle the mess. Its findings,[52] published the following year, provide a splendid account of eighteenth-century chicanery.

Virtually all the blame for the entire affair was directed against one Peter Leheup[53] and this has since been echoed by historians of the British Museum. Edwards while reserving his greatest venom for the miserliness of Parliament, without which there would have been no lottery, comments:

One Peter Leheup was made Commissioner of the Lottery. This man had held some employment or other at Hanover, from which he had been recalled with circumstances of disgrace . . . [He] set on foot as thriving and as flagitious a traffic in Sloane lottery tickets, as was ever set on foot in railway shares by a clever promoter of our own day.[54]

Miller refers to 'a certain Peter Leheup, an "odious character", who was already notorious for his questionable practices in both England and Hanover.'[55]

The greatest profits from eighteenth-century lotteries came not from the prizes (except perhaps for a minute number of lucky punters who won top prize) but from manipulating the sale of tickets or controlling the betting on the outcome. One of the best schemes was to acquire large quantities and sell them at a premium, sometimes in fractions as low as sixty-fourths. A certain amount of skill was required to persuade the gullible to sell their tickets cheaply in the first instance and then to arouse the gambling fever so that people would buy high. Even better was to corner the market at the outset.

Large quantities of the tickets for the British Museum lottery had been sold before the lottery opened (receipts were issued even as the Act was being debated) and thousands were at an early stage being resold in Change Alley. Leheup placed an advertisement in the *Gazette* on Saturday, 9 June announcing that tickets would be sold on the following Thursday – thereby effectively excluding foreigners or anyone living more than thirty or forty miles outside London. Although Leheup asserted that he had initially been afraid that because of lack of interest it would be a flop (not an unknown event), no doubt with an eye to future complaints he took the precaution of dating his receipts 14 June for money taken in advance. There are vivid descriptions by Leheup of what happened when the subscription opened after most of the 100,000 tickets had been sold (in itself no mean feat of organization):

At about One of the Clock that Day, no Gentleman would have wished himself in my Place for 150 £ which was my Parliamentary Allowance: People broke in, upon me, above me, behind me, and before me, and in at the Windows, with Ladders, the Partitions of my Desk were broke down, while I lay exposed to be plundered of all my Money . . . Then Proclamation was made out of the Windows, That no more would be served that Day.[56]

In fact tickets continued to change hands. There were three managers/receivers of the lottery in addition to Leheup: the aptly named James Moneypenny, Thomas Mulso and James Postlethwaite, all of whom, if perhaps not entirely honest, obviously lacked Leheup's flair for real villainy since Leheup took about one half of the contributions.

As Parliament discovered, the books were a mess – tickets had been issued without final payment, forfeited tickets had disappeared, large numbers had been issued against lists of fictitious names. Where those trying to obtain large quantities of tickets lacked the intiative to turn up with lists of imaginary people, Leheup took them on one side and obliged with this suggestion.

The winning ticket, number 46885, was drawn at Guildhall in December 1753 and carried a prize of £10,000. The draw continued until the end of the month.[57]

A reading of the Committee's Report does leave the impression of a skilled and determined cover-up. While Leheup was, to put it mildly, a crook, he had plenty of company. Presumably sufficiently well protected to have been given the opportunity to transgress, he was judged to be expendable when awkward questions were asked. As the anti-establishment MP Nicholas Fazakerley[58] put it in the Parliamentary debate:

. . . for both from history and experience we may learn that parlia-

mentary enquiries into the conduct of any officers employed under the Crown, high or low, have always been opposed by ministers and their favourites; and if at any time they found themselves forced to submit, they have too often found means to defeat, in a great measure, the effect of the enquiry.[59]

Leheup's defenders argued (not necessarily from conviction) that the affair was not worthy of Parliamentary interest and was in any case not particularly heinous, the eighteenth century not being particularly noted for public honesty. Henry Fox[60] asserted:

. . . no gentleman, surely, can suppose that it would be consistent with the dignity of a British House of Commons to appear at the bar of the other House as the prosecutors of a little underclerk in one of our public offices.[61]

Horace Walpole wrote to Richard Bentley 19 December 1753:

Our House of Commons – mere poachers – are piddling with the torture of Leheup, who extracted so much money out of the lottery.[62]

Parliament found against Leheup who was prosecuted by the Attorney General in the Court of the King's Bench, dismissed and fined £1,000 (an enormous amount at that time) which, revealingly, he paid on the spot. In 1765 he was still writing pleading letters to his erstwhile patrons, the Duke of Newcastle and Lord Hardwicke asking for reinstatement, his early declarations of complete innocence and veiled threats to tell all, tailing off into pained declarations that he had suffered enough.[63] His pleas seem to have been ignored. Not surprisingly, Leheup, who was reported to have made £40,000 by his rascality, left a comfortable estate on his death in 1774.[64]

A particularly dubious character, the financier Sampson Gideon,[65] was conveniently in Paris when the scandal broke; he got his hands on between 4,000 and 6,000 tickets to sell at a premium and seems hardly to have noticed the affair. Someone who could bail out the British Government, as Gideon had done, was untouchable.

And as for the Museum, it received £95,194. 8s. 2d. after payment of expenses. £20,000 was paid to Sloane's two daughters, Mrs Stanley and Lady Cadogan, the Harleian manuscripts were purchased for £10,000, a repository for £10,000 and the balance laid out in the purchase of some £30,000 Government stock for the maintenance of the Museum.

Montagu House

The new Trustees met first on Tuesday, 11 December 1753 in the Great Room at the Duke of Newcastle's office, in the Cockpit, Whitehall,[66] the Lord Chancellor having previously directed that 'a good fire be made early in the room for . . . The Archbishop . . . will be unwilling to wait and fearful of catching cold in this weather'.[67] Present[68] were the Archbishop of Canterbury, the Lord High Chancellor, the Duke of Portland, the Earl of Holderness, the Earl of

Oxford, the Earl of Macclesfield, Lord Cadogan, the Speaker of the House of Commons, the Master of the Rolls, the Lord Chief Justice of the Common Pleas, the Attorney General, the Solicitor General, the President of the College of Physicians and Thomas Hart, Esq. They elected fifteen others:[69] statesmen who were men of letters (Dukes of Argyll and Northumberland), Lord Lyttelton, Philip Yorke 2nd Earl of Hardwick; an additional member of the Sloane family (William Sloane); several leading members of the Royal Society and the Society of Antiquaries (Birch, West and – perhaps not surprisingly given the change in emphasis – only one scientist, William Watson). Of the fifteen elected Trustees, ten had been Trustees of Sloane's will. Also with continuing responsibility for the collection were Lord Cadogan and Hans Stanley (Sloane family Trustees) and Lord Macclesfield (as President of the Royal Society).

The Harleian collection at Dover House was inspected on 19 January.[70] The Sloane collection remaining at the Manor House in Chelsea (the coins, medals and other small high-value items had been transferred to the Bank of England for safe keeping) was visited on 22 January 1754[71] and the Cottonian library in the Old Dormitory at Westminster was looked at on 2 February.[72]

The Sloane collection was considered to be well housed for the time being and James Empson was asked to indicate how long it would take to check it against the catalogues. The Harleian collection was not particularly safe; the presses were standing at ground level in a room:

. . . in which there is but one Small fireplace . . . too much exposed to Injury from the Damp attending such a Situation which renders it unsafe for any person to continue long enough in the said Room to make any Considerable Use or even a particular Inspection of the said Collection.[73]

The Cottonian library, nothing if not a survivor, was in reasonable condition, sharing the Old Dormitory with the Royal and Edwards libraries. The same could not be said for the Keeper, David Casley, 'disabled by age and infirmity'.

The Act[74] had directed the Trustees to find 'a more convenient Repository, more durable and more safe from Fire and nearer to the chief places of Public Resort'. They considered Buckingham House (the core of what is now Buckingham Palace) – too remote and at £30,000 too expensive. There was some inconclusive talk of housing the Museum in a new complex at Westminster. A committee of twenty Trustees with their surveyors went to view Montagu House,[75] a fine but decaying seventeenth-century French-style house in Bloomsbury (Plate 4), quite coincidentally a few hundred yards from the first home of Sloane's collection at Nos. 3 and 4 Bloomsbury Place and at one time the residence of the eccentric widow of his patron the Duke of Albemarle. The surveyor's report was favourable. Although £7,000 would be required for repairs and £1,600 for alterations, at £10,000 it was much the cheapest option.

Negotations for its purchase began in 1754 and were successfully concluded the following year.

The British Museum[76]

It has been said with justification that the British Museum was the product of two traditions, one historical, the other scientific: the antiquarianism of sixteenth- and seventeenth-century England, and the scientific curiosity of eighteenth-century Europe. The Sloane collections epitomized the latter, with a nod towards the former. The Cottonian and Harleian collections provided another dimension. Their universality was in tune with the spirit of the times, the availability of three great collections a fortunate occurrence.

Thomas Birch, a trustee of Sloane's will, who had known Sloane and who was also one of the first Trustees of the British Museum elected under the British Museum Act of 1753, sets out a view of the new museum:

The Treasure, which he bequeath'd to his country, and which is now purchas'd for it by the Parliament may be attended with numberless Advantages to the Public. Here the young Physician, Chemist and Apothecary may become well acquainted with every substance, Animal, Vegetable, or mineral, that is ever employ'd in medicine. The curious in Ores and Metals by viewing specimens of every sort, will be instructed in what Beds of Stone or other matter they usually are found, and by what means will be inabled to judge what Metals or Metallic Bodies the Rocks or Mountains which they examine may probably contain, whereby rich mines with which Great Britain unquestionably abounds, may more easily be discover'd. Even the Clays, Okers, Sands, Stones, Marbles, Earths, etc may lead to the finding better materials for the Potter, the painter, the Glass-maker, the Lapidary, and many other artists to improve their manufactures. In short, the Naturalist will find in this Musaeum almost every thing which he can wish, and will be greatly assisted in his Inquiries and observations by the catalogue of it in 38 volumes in fol and 8 in quarto containing short accounts of every particular, with References to the Authors, who have treated of them.[77]

Birch himself was busy in antiquarian pursuits, copying manuscripts in the new museum the moment these became available. By 1759 Thomas Gray could describe his scholarly companions in the new reading room as:

a man that writes for Lord Royston; a man that writes for Dr Barton of York; a third that writes for the Emperor of Germany or Dr Peacock, for he speaks the worst English I ever heard; Dr Stukeley who writes for himself, the very worst person he could write for; and I, who only read to know if there were anything worth writing, and that not without some difficulty.[78]

One of the first acts of the Board of Trustees was to design a seal, still in use today (Fig. 8).[79] This was entrusted to a Committee, although Dr John Ward, a Trustee, seems to have done most of the work. The Trustees' deliberations on the content of the design give one of the earliest indications of their perception of the British Museum, and, indeed, their Minutes declare:

. . . it was presumed, that any Foreigner abroad, who was at all

Fig. 8 The seal of the Trustees of the British Museum, designed by a committee of Trustees and engraved by Richard Yeo (d.1779). The seal, handed over on 7 April 1755, is still in use today. It depicts the Museum's patron deities: Tellus, Minerva and Apollo in front of a 'museum', a building dedicated to the service of the Muses. Reproduced by courtesy of the Trustees of the British Museum.

conversant with such things, might be sufficiently informed both of the History of this Museum, and the General parts of which it consists by inspecting only this Device of the Seal . . .

Although the combination of library, natural history and antiquities was to a certain extent fortuitous, the Trustees enthusiastically linked library with museum and harked back to ancient Egypt and Classical Greece. Ward's explanation of the seal declared:

. . . the word Museum properly Signifies a Building dedicated to the Service of the Muses, there were Several of these Antiently in Greece and other Countries particularly at Alexandria, which is described by Strabo, as assigned for the residence of Learned and Studious men, with a walk and Gallery furnished with Seats, belonging to it. It is said to have been founded by Ptolemy Philadelphus, whose Celebrated Library was Deposited there, tho in after Ages it received large Indowments from Several of the Roman Emperors.[80]

Ward noted, however, that the original concept had widened:

But of later times the Name Museum has been commonly applied to Signify any Repository of Natural and Artificial Curiosities, and that either with or without a Library. As the British Museum therefore contains both these, it was thought not improper to represent it upon the Seal by the Front of a Building, together with the Images of those deities, and their Different Attributes, which Agreeable to the Antient Mythology might emblematically denote the Several parts, of which this Museum Consists.

The Trustees eventually agreed that the patron deities of the British Museum should be Tellus (the natural productions of the Earth), Minerva (tutelary Deity of the Arts and Sciences), and the Sun as the symbol of Apollo (who presided over the Muses and was also the Inventor of the Art of Medicine, the principal subject of the Sloanian Library). (It had been hoped to include Britannia but as the design was already crowded she was dropped in favour of Apollo.)

In selecting from various alternative legends put forward to encircle the edge of the seal, a nineteenth-century Principal Librarian surmized that the Trustees rather bitterly dropped the words 'publica munificentia' from the proposed 'Sigillum Curatorum Musei Britannici publica munificentia conditi AD MDCCLIII' and substituted 'senatus consulto' since, 'no doubt it occurred to the Trustees that the purchase of lottery tickets could hardly be called public munificence'.[81]

The Trustees met[82] to appoint staff on 17 January 1756 wrangling until 1 o'clock in the morning over the size and composition of the establishment. There were two nominees, both medical men, for the post of Principal Librarian – an appointment made by the Sovereign: Dr John Mitchell[83] and Dr Gowin Knight.[84] On 3 June it was reported that the King had chosen the latter. Dr Charles Morton,[85] Dr Matthew Maty[86] and James Empson were appointed Under Librarians.

The initial division was (1) Sloane's Library, (2) Sloane's Natural and Artificial Curiosities, (3) the Cottonian and Harleian collections and Major Edwards's Library. The Act[87] had directed that the Sloane collection be preserved 'whole and entire, and with proper marks of distinction' and that the Harleian manuscripts be regarded as an addition to the Cottonian library.

In March 1758 following a report by the Principal Librarian a new arrangement was confirmed by the Trustees' decision to set up three departments: (1) Printed Books, (2) Manuscripts, (3) everything else lumped together under the heading of 'Natural & Artificial Productions'. The Museum's chief officer had the title of Principal Librarian. The scientific bias was maintained, at least until the end of the century by the appointment of medically-trained men as the first three Principal Librarians, but of these three and succeeding principal librarians only Matthew Maty was appointed from the natural history department. Printed Books and Manuscripts provided the holders of this post until the appointment of the numismatist George Hill in 1931.

A significant decision was to follow Sloane's practice and to allow the collections to expand by gift, a principle accepted with enthusiasm by the public who sent in some very strange things indeed, among them a hornet's nest found in Yorkshire (1757), a web of a silkworm wrought by the animal in the form of a ribband (1759), part of the trunk of a tree gnawed asunder by a beaver (1760), a piece of lace made of the hair of Queen Elizabeth (1762) – all worthy of any cabinet of curiosities and, where the donor was of the nobility, difficult to refuse.

But the Museum was moving inexorably in a more scientific and scholarly direction. The Trustees and staff busied themselves with preparing the Museum for the public whom the Act obliged them to admit. It was not the books which visitors were expected to flock to see (as later guidebooks pointed out 'the sight of the outside of books cannot convey either instruction or amusement') but rather the natural and artificial curiosities. James Empson produced a scheme for their exhibition which had the beginnings of an ordered public display. Empson first advised against repeating Sloane's arrangement at Chelsea in the new public museum:

How much soever a private Person may be at Liberty arbitrarily to dispose and place his Curiosities; we are sensible that the British Museum being a public Institution subject to the Visits of the Judicious and Intelligent, as well as Curious, Notice will be taken, whether or no the Collection has been arranged in a methodical Manner . . . [88]

This was echoed by the scientific Trustee, Sir William Watson, who wrote of the natural history display:

. . . the Department of Natural History . . . which though we sometimes hear the contrary at our general meetings, I cannot but consider as the basis of the British Museum upon the exact and scientific arrangement of which at our outset, the reputation of the Trustees in this particular, the utility of this part of the museum to the public, will very considerably depend. [89]

It was collegiate, the staff living on the premises. It was not yet the scholarly research institution which it was to become in the nineteenth and twentieth centuries but serious researchers (and others) had begun to use the Reading Room. Catalogues of the Harleian manuscripts were published from 1759, a catalogue of printed books in 1787, manuscripts in 1782 and 1802 and the first antiquities catalogue, of ancient terracottas, in 1810. Some of the earliest fieldwork was carried out by Daniel Solander, an Assistant in the Natural History Department who accompanied Captain James Cook on his first round-the-world voyage in 1768–71.

And so on 15 January 1759 – a date inscribed on the Trustees' silver-headed mace which still lies on the table at Board meetings – the British Museum opened its doors to the general public. Not at first the lower orders (or at least not without difficulties): visitors had to order tickets, return to collect them, were admitted only in escorted parties and were not permitted to linger. It is interesting that, again in keeping with Sloane's practice, the British Museum was never (at least officially) seen as the preserve only of the scholarly elite, 'the studious', but equally as a place of entertainment and wonder for 'the curious'.

Wider admission was allowed in 1805 when tickets were abolished, although visitors still for many years had to sign a visitors' book. After 1810 persons of decent appearance could even wander unescorted on certain days. The Museum did not open on a public holiday until 1837.

The Trustees at an early stage had accepted the principle of expansion, but it was not until 1772 that the first government grant for a purchase (£8,410 for the Hamilton collection of Classical antiquities, £840 for a repository) was grudgingly voted by Parliament. Some money for running costs was granted from 1762, and such grants became more frequent, but regular funding based on estimated annual expenditure had to wait until 1827. Special application had to be made for major purchases. Thus, throughout its history, the Museum has been very dependent on donations and, indeed, continues to be so. Edwards declares: [90]

The real founders of our British Museum have been neither our British monarchs nor our British legislators, as such. They have been, commonly, individual and private British subjects.

To which, one might add, particularly in this century, generous benefactors from overseas.

Sloane's Legacy

As indicated, from its beginnings the British Museum constituted something more than the Sloane collection: it recognizes three founding collections, Sloane, Cotton and Harley, to which is sometimes added a fourth, the Royal Library, donated in 1757.

However, Sloane provided the catalyst. He chose his Trustees well with a shrewd appreciation of how to get things done. Sir John Cotton had donated his family's library in 1700; it languished unloved and virtually forgotten for half a century. Sloane concentrated the politicians' minds by insisting on £20,000 cash and holding out the prospect of his collection's disappearance to the Continent. He was fortunate in finding a window of opportunity when Parliament could be galvanized by the national interest and the pressure to promote scientific enquiry. Today Sloane is still acknowledged as the founder of two great museums and a library: the British Museum, Bloomsbury, the Natural History Museum, South Kensington and the British Library, shortly to move from Bloomsbury to St. Pancras.

In 1809 medical and anatomical specimens, regarded as 'unfit to be preserved in the Museum' were transferred to a more suitable home – the Hunterian Museum at the Royal College of Surgeons in London. In the 1880s Sloane's wish that his collections should remain together foundered when the natural history collections moved to South Kensington to the new British Museum (Natural History). But by that time the remaining Sloanian objects formed only a tiny fraction of the accumulated collections.

The British Museum (Natural History) although located outside Bloomsbury remained the responsibility of the British Museum Trustees until 1963 when a new Act of Parliament was passed, completely changing the composition of the British Museum's Board and giving the Natural History departments their independence. The latter took their present institutional name, The Natural History Museum in 1989 (although Parliamentary approval is required if the original title is to be abandoned).

In 1973, under the terms of the British Library Act passed the previous year, the library Departments of the British Museum − Printed Books (including Maps, Music, Philatelic), Manuscripts and Oriental Manuscripts and Printed Books − became part of a new body, The British Library − which also took under its aegis the National Reference Library of Science and Invention, the National Library of Recorded Sound, and later the India Office Library. At the time plans to demolish the buildings to the south of the British Museum site and replace them with a new library building were well advanced, and the two institutions would have remained in close proximity. In 1974, acting on pressure from the Local Authority to preserve the Bloomsbury buildings, the Labour Government halted this expansion which had been planned since the 1950s. With pressure on space becoming acute in 1975 the British Library accepted, with the acquiescence of the Museum, the offer of a new site next to St. Pancras railway station.

And so there remains on the site of old Montagu House in Bloomsbury, the British Museum, the national collection of antiquities, prints and drawings, coins, medals and paper money, and ethnography. Likened to the 'cuckoo in the nest', from Sloane's bequest of some 2,500 items and 23,000 coins and medals within the scope of the present Museum, these collections have expanded in size to some seven or eight million objects. At St. Pancras will be the greater part of The British Library's collection of over sixty-seven million items and at South Kensington the sixty-five million specimens belonging to The Natural History Museum.

By the end of the century it is intended that The British Library will complete its move to St. Pancras; no longer will the public at Bloomsbury be excluded from areas where 'the mere outside of books provides little amusement'. The vacated library areas will be redeveloped and it is hoped that by the British Museum's 250th anniversary in 2003 a museum worthy of its founder will continue to be of benefit to the 'studious and curious' who have made their way to Bloomsbury since 1759.

Appendix 1
Trustees of the Will of Sir Hans Sloane
Listed in the Codicil of 10 July 1749 unless otherwise indicated.

Sources include: *Dictionary of National Biography* (DNB); Sir Lewis Namier and John Brooke, *The History of Parliament: The House of Commons 1754–1790* (HMSO, 1964) (N&B); Romney Sedgwick, *The History of Parliament: The House of Commons 1715–1754* (HMSO, 1970) (RS); British Library General Catalogue of Printed Books; Bulloch's Roll (chronological list of Fellows), MS, Royal Society (BR); Mark Noble, *Lives of the Fellows of the Society of Antiquaries* (1818)

manuscript now in the Getty Center for the History of Art, Santa Monica, copy in the Library of the Society of Antiquaries (MN); *Gentleman's Magazine* (GM).

Note: Although in most instances the identity of some individual trustees is evident, e.g. where a title is given, for others the name shown in Sloane's will provides no more than a clue. It is possible that some of the more obscure are among those listed in Bulloch's Roll. Dates are, where possible, New Style as introduced in 1752. In some sources it is not always apparent which system is being used and, inevitably, dates do not always agree.

*Present at the meeting of Sloane's Trustees held at the Manor House, Chelsea, Saturday 27 January 1753.

*AMES, Joseph (1689–1759)   [*Mr Joseph Ames*]
FRS (1743); FSA (1737), Secretary Society of Antiquaries 1741–d.
Bibliographer and antiquary, historian of printing. Apprenticed to a plane maker, he later became a ship's chandler, iron maker or pattern maker and maintained a lucrative business until his death. Acquainted with several antiquaries among them the Revd John Lewis of Margate who had made extensive collections for the history of printing, on which Ames drew for his publications: *A Catalogue of English Printers from the year 1471 to 1600* (London, 1745); *A Catalogue of English Heads* (London, 1748), the first attempt at a general history of English engraved portraits; *Typographical Antiquities* (London, 1749). Collected portraits, especially of printers, coins, natural curiosities, incriptions and antiquities which were sold after his death. 'No pretence to literary merit, but he was an excellent antiquary according to the lights of his day'.
(DNB) (BR) (MN)

*ANDREWS, Joseph (d. 22 April 1753)   [*Joseph Andrews, Esq*]
FRS (1727)
Deputy paymaster to the Forces in Scotland 1715, a sinecure office not necessarily involving residence outside London. GM, 23 (1753) reports the death on 22 April of 'Townshend Andrews, Esq., deputy paymaster of the Forces'.
(BR) (GM)

ARUNDELL, Hon. Richard (c.1696–1758)   [*the Hon Richard Arundell, Esq*]
FRS (1740)
MP (Knaresborough 16 April 1720–20 January 1758)
Of Allerton Mauleverer, son of John, 2nd Baron Arundell. Page to the Queen 1707 − November 1714; Surveyor General of Works 1727–37 and of the King's private roads 1731; Master of the Mint 1737–44; Lord of the Treasury 1744–6; Treasurer of the Chamber 1746–55; Clerk of the Pipe 1748–d. Close friend of Henry Pelham and intimate of Henry Fox and the Cavendish family, and a favourite of George II. A lifelong friend of the 3rd Earl of Burlington,

whose architectural tastes he shared. His mother was the daughter of Sir Thomas Slingsby MP, 2nd Bt. (see Slingsby Bethell, below). '[A] gentleman of great merit, knowledge and curiosity'.

(N&B) (RS) (BR)

*BAKER, Henry (1698–1774)   [Mr Henry Baker]
FRS (1741); FSA (1741)
Naturalist and poet. Son of a clerk in Chancery, he was apprenticed to a bookseller, became interested in speech defects, devised a method for the education of deaf mutes and thereby made a fortune. Author of The Microscope made Easy (London, 1742). Credited with the introduction into England of the Alpine strawberry and the rhubarb plant. Actively involved in the establishment of the Society of Arts in 1754. Son-in-law of Daniel Defoe. Awarded the Royal Society's Copley medal for his microscopical discoveries on the crystallization and configuration of saline particles. One of the early workers on the medical use of electricity. Maintained a considerable correspondence with scientists abroad. His extensive natural history and antiquarian collection was sold by auction in 1775.

(DNB) (BR) (MN)

*BARNARD, Sir John (c.1685–1764)   [Sir John Bernard]
Codicil 18 September 1750.
MP (London 1722–61)
Alderman, London 1728–58; Sheriff 1735–6; Lord Mayor 1737–8; President Christ's Hospital 1740–58. Of Quaker parentage, joined the Church of England as a young man. Entered his father's business (wine merchant) and became a prominent marine insurer at Lloyd's. Stood for the City in the popular Whig interest – an active independent. Knighted 1732. Tried to ameliorate the condition of poor debtors, to improve the police and reduce begging. In 1737 put forward a scheme (rejected) for reducing interest on the national debt. Restored confidence in the Bank of England during the 1745 panic. Consulted 1749 over a scheme for the national debt which was carried out. In 1756–7 his scheme to raise £3½ million by means of a lottery was adopted but raised little. 'Lord Chatham . . . frequently called him the great commoner'.

(DNB) (N&B) (RS)

BELL, George (?d. 1758)   [Mr George Bell]
FRS (1750)
Possibly 'George Bell of London, Surgeon' (Journal Book of the Royal Society) who died 4 June 1758 (GM 28 (1758) p. 292 quoted by BR records the death on 4 June of 'John Bell, Esq, surgeon and FRS'). There are two references to transactions between Hans Sloane and a George Bell in Faulkner's History of Chelsea (pp. 55, 56) and letters from George Bell MD to Sloane in BL, MSS.

(BR)

*BETHELL, Slingsby (1695–1758)   [Slingsby Bethell, Esq]
Codicil 18 September 1750.
MP (London 1747–1 November 1758)

Alderman of London 1749; Member of the Fishmongers' Company 1749–d. Sheriff 1751–2; Lord Mayor 1755–6; President of British white herring fishery 1750–d. As a young man went to Antigua and purchased a large plantation. Chief agent and manager of all the Antigua plantations of his brother-in-law, Sir William Codrington c.1720. Set up as a London merchant c.1730. Involved in the Africa trade. An Opposition Whig.

(N&B) (RS)

BRADLEY, Revd James (1693–1762)   [the Rev. James Bradley, Doctor in Divinity, Astron. Reg.]
FRS (1718)
Astronomer and mathematician. Collaborated with his uncle, Revd James Pound (1669–1724) one of the best astronomers in England. Ordained 1719. 1721 elected Savilian Professor of Astronomy, Oxford and resigned his ecclesiastical preferments. 1729 announced his discovery of the aberration of light. 1742 succeeded Halley as Regius Professor of Astronomy at Greenwich. 1748 published his discovery of the nutation of the earth's axis. 'He ranks as the founder of modern observational astronomy . . . his discoveries of aberration and nutation first rendered possible the exact knowledge of the places of the fixed stars'.

(DNB) (BR)

BURNET, Sir Thomas (1694 – 8 January 1753)   [Sir Thomas Burnet, Knt]
FRS (1784)
One of the Judges of the Common Pleas. Youngest son of Dr Gilbert Burnet, Bishop of Salisbury. Member of the Middle Temple, called to the Bar 1715. Was several years consul at Lisbon. Serjeant at Law 1736. November 1741 appointed one of the judges of the Common Pleas. Knighted 1745. 'By his death the publick has lost an able and upright judge, his friends a sincere, sensible and agreeable companion and the poor a great benefactor' (London Magazine (1753), p. 43).

(DNB) (BR)

*CADOGAN, Hon. Charles Sloane (1728–1807)   [the Right Hon. Charles Sloane Cadogan, Esq]
Sloane Family Trustee of the British Museum 1779–d. (in succession to his father)
MP (Cambridge 31 January 1749–54, 13 January 1755 – 24 September 1776)
Grandson of Sir Hans Sloane. Treasurer to Prince Edward (subsequently Duke of York) 1756–67; Surveyor of the King's Gardens 1764–9; Clerk of the Venison Warrant 1769–78; Master of the Mint 1769–84. Charles Sloane Cadogan was created Viscount Chelsea and Earl Cadogan 27 December 1800. Inherited Hans Stanley's half of the Sloane estate at Chelsea, 1780. (He should be distinguished from his father General Charles Cadogan (1685–1776), FRS, 1718, who succeeded his brother as 2nd Baron Cadogan in 1726. General Cadogan married Sloane's younger daughter Elizabeth). Lord Cadogan, one of Sloane's

executors, was appointed a Sloane family Trustee of the British Museum in 1753 and is among those listed as 'Visitors' by Sir Hans Sloane in his will.
(N&B) (RS) (BR)

*CALVERT, Sir William (?1703–61) [Sir William Calvert]
Codicil 18 September 1750
MP (London 13 July 1742–54; Old Sarum 18 March 1755–61)
Alderman of London 1741; Sheriff 1743–4; Lord Mayor 1748–9. Trained for the church but gave this up on marrying a widow who owned a London brewery. With his brother headed one of the largest breweries in London. From 1747 an Administration supporter. 'Zealous and generous, has a good trade, but is not over-rich' (Pelham).
(N&B) (RS)

CLARKE, Samuel [Samuel Clarke, Esq.]
FRS
Possibly one of the two FRS of this name listed in the period, the first elected 2 May 1728, died (according to BR) 1767 and the second elected 17 April 1735, of Staffordshire, died (according to BR) 1778. GM, however, lists the deaths of other Clark(e)s on these dates but no 'Samuel'. No other details are given.
(BR)

*CODRINGTON, Sir William (1719–92) [Sir William Codrington, Bart]
MP (Beverley 1747–61; Tewkesbury 1761 – 11 March 1792)
Nephew of Slingsby Bethell (q.v.). Owner of plantations in Barbados and Antigua.
(N&B) (RS)

*COLLINSON, Peter (1693/4–1768) [Mr Peter Collinson]
FRS (1728); FSA (1737)
Naturalist and antiquary. Of Quaker origins but later withdrew from the Society of Friends. Manufacturer of hosiery. Maintained a large business with the American colonies and through this many scientific contacts. Through his interest in natural history (particularly the metamorphoses of insects) came to Sloane's notice at an early age. Promoted the cultivation in America of non-native species such as flax, hemp, silk, wine. Friend of Benjamin Franklin. A considerable portion of his collections was eventually deposited in Sloane's museum (see Chapter 1). Active in the formation of the Society of Antiquaries. Introduced American plants into Britain.
(DNB) (BR) (MN)

COSSART, Henry [Cossart de St. Aubin d'Espiez]
(17 June 1752)
Member of the Moravian Church. Benham (see note 13, p. 206) refers to his approaches to influential people in England in 1749 in an attempt to obtain legal status for the Brethren in the British Empire. Cossart is described as the 'Agent' of the Unitas Fratrum, a description repeated in the

London Magazine (February 1753), p. 89. His agency continued from November 1746 to 1755.

*ELSMERE, The Revd Sloane (d.1766) [the Rev. Sloane Elsmere, Doctor in Divinity and the Rector of Chelsea for the time being]
Rector of Chelsea 1732–66. Son of Sir Hans Sloane's half-sister Alice Bailie (d. July 1752), who had married John Elsmere of Belfast. Matriculated Trinity College, Dublin, of which he was a scholar 1722. Presented to the Rectory of Chelsea by Sir Hans Sloane 1732. Founded the Girls' Charity School, Lordship Place, Chelsea. His Sermons on several important subjects were published in 1767. Died 23 June 1766 (GM 36 (1766)).

*EMPSON, James (d. 1765) [Mr James Empson]
Empson's mother worked for Sloane for some twenty-nine years (Sarah Stanley to Lord Hardwicke, 30 January 1756, BL, Additional MS 36,269, fol. 99). Empson himself worked for Sloane for some fifteen years (ibid, Empson to Hardwick fol. 97 received 24 January 1756). Curator of Sloane's collection. One of the three original Under-Librarians of the British Museum; initially in charge of the Sloanian library then of the natural history and miscellaneous antiquities. Died 25 April 1765 (GM 35 (1765), p. 299).

*EVELYN, Sir John (1684–1763) [Sir John Evelyn, Bart.]
FRS (1723); FSA (1725). Elected British Museum Trustee 1753
MP (Helston)
Commissioner of the Customs. Grandson of the diarist whom he succeeded 1706. Joint Postmaster-General 1708–15. Built a library at Wotton. Created 1st Baronet 1713.
(BR) (MN)

FOLKES, Martin (1690–1754) [Martin Folkes, Esq.]
FRS (1714) PRS (1741–53) (in succession to Sloane, with whom he had competed for the Presidency on Sir Isaac Newton's death); FSA (1720), VPSA 1737–50, PSA 1750–d.
Numismatist. Son of a Bencher of Gray's Inn. 1733–5 lived in Italy where he laid the foundations of his work on ancient and modern coins. Publications include A Table of English Gold Coins (London, 1736); A Table of English Silver Coins (London, 1745). Communications to Royal Society on astronomy and meteorology. Greatly extended the Royal Society's literary and antiquarian interests. First chief Master of the Academy at Woolwich. The sale of his library, prints, drawings, gems, pictures, coins, etc. lasted fifty-six days.
(DNB) (BR) (MN)

FULLER, John [John Fuller of Sussex, Esq.]
Probably one of the two John Fullers of Brightling, Sussex. The first (FRS 1704) married Sloane's step-daughter Elizabeth. She was the daughter of Fulke Rose of Jamaica and Sloane's wife Elizabeth (nee Langley) by her first marriage. John and Elizabeth Fuller's son (also John) (FRS 1727) (1706–55), and also of Brightling, Sussex, was MP for Boroughbridge 20 December 1754 – 1 February 1755 hav-

ing been elected in absentia 'in an infirm state of health'. The Fullers of Brightling Park were ironmasters.

(BR) (RS)

GERSDORF[F], Abraham von   [*Abraham Baron Gersdorff, Lord of Princeneck, Privy Councellor of War of the King of Poland, Elector of Saxony, and Chancellor of the Unitas Fratrum*] (17 June 1752)

Member of the Moravian Church. Benham (see note 13, p. 257) mentions his involvement in the acquisition of Lindsey House and other property at Chelsea, some of it from Sloane. He is referred to as 'Chancellor of the Advocate'.

GERSDORF[F], Sigismund von [*Sigismund Baron Gersdorff, Steward general of the Unitas Fratrum*] (17 June 1752)

Architect for the Moravian Church. In 1751 he was in London to inspect Lindsey House, Chelsea with a view to its conversion for use by the group. The LCC *Survey of London*, vol. IV, ii, *The Parish of Chelsea* (1913), p. 46, notes that an architect named Sigismund Gersdorff was employed by the Moravian Church to build the Chapel and Minister's House in the Burial Ground on the site of Beaufort House. The work was completed in 1753.

GOUGH, Henry (1681–1751)   [*Henry Gough, Esq*] MP (Bramber 1734–13 July 1751)

Director, East India Company 1730–3, 1736–51, Chairman on five occasions, Deputy Chairman five times. Travelled to China at the age of eleven with his uncle. From 1707–15 in command of a merchantman. Father of Richard Gough (1735–1809), the antiquary.

(RS)

*GRAY, Charles (1696–1782)   [*Charles Gray, Esq*] FRS (1754). Elected British Museum Trustee 1753. MP (Colchester 26 February 1742 – 13 March 1755, 1761–80)

Alderman Colchester 1734; bencher Gray's Inn 1737, treasurer 1755; recorder, Ipswich 1761–76. Disinherited by his father, a glazier and Alderman of Colchester, he acquired a fortune through his first wife Sarah Webster. Had a large practice as a barrister, steward of many local manors. A Tory with reforming and humanitarian interests, a Hebrew and classical scholar, numismatist and archaeologist.

(N&B) (BR) (RS)

HALES, The Revd Stephen (1677–1761)   [*the Rev Stephen Hales, Doctor in Divinity*] FRS (1718); Vice President, Society of Arts 1755 (active in its foundation).

Physiologist and inventor. Befriended William Stukeley at University (Corpus Christi College, Cambridge). 1709 appointed perpetual curate at Teddington and lived there most of his life, occasionally residing at Farrington, Hampshire. Carried out a large number of experiments in physiology, physics, chemistry and botany. Published *Vegetable Staticks* (London, 1727) and *Statical Essays* (London,

1731), also other scientific works and tracts against drinking. An active parish priest. Invented artificial ventilators and many other contrivances. Clerk of the Closet to the Princess Dowager of Wales 1751 and Chaplain to her son. A Trustee for the Colony of Georgia. 'A poor, good, primitive creature' (Walpole).

(DNB) (BR)

HALLET, William   [*Mr William Hallet, sen*] (17 June 1752)

Like some others named in the 1752 note, Mr Hallet appears not to have left an obvious mark for posterity.

*HAMPDEN, John (c.1695–1754)   [*John Hampden, Esq*] (17 June 1752)

MP (Wendover 1734 – 4 February 1754)

Page of honour of the royal stables before 1713–c.1715; Captain, Colonel Sir Robert Rich's regiment of Dragoons c.1715–18; Commissary General for Gibraltar 1735–47. '[A] very sensible and observing man [who] would have made a figure in the world if his unfortunate brother . . . had not ruined the estate'.

(RS)

HEATHCOTE, Sir John (c.1689–1759)   [*Sir John Heathcote, Bart*] MP (Grantham 1715–22; Bodmin 9 February 1733–41)

Director East India Company 1716–24 and 1728–31; Director Bank of England 1725–35 (with statutory intervals); President Foundling Hospital. Whig. After 1741 spent seven months of each year living the life of a country gentleman. Succeeded father as 2nd Baronet January 1733, cousin of Sir William Heathcote (q.v.).

(RS)

HEATHCOTE, Sir William (1693–1751)   [*Sir William Heathcote, Bart*] MP (Buckingham 22 October 1722–27; Southampton 29 May 1729–41)

Secretary and Registrar of Bankrupts 1723–d. Began as a merchant but retired on inheriting a fortune. On the common council of the Georgia Society until 1739 when he resigned. 1st Baronet 1733. Cousin of Sir John Heathcote (q.v.).

(RS)

JACOBSEN, Theodore (d. 1772)   [*Theodore Jacobson, Esq*] FRS (1727); FSA (1738)

Merchant and architect. Designed the Foundling Hospital, the plan for which was approved 1742. Became Governor of the Foundling Hospital and designed the Haslar Royal Hospital, Gosport. A Theodore Jacobsen, presumably the same, was called in to advise the British Museum Trustees on their proposed alterations to Montagu House.

(DNB) (BR) (MN)

LAVINGTON, Rt. Revd George (1684–1762)   [*the Right Rev George, Lord Bishop of Exeter*]

Chaplain to George I. 1719 appointed to Worcester

Cathedral. 1747 Bishop of Exeter. A strenuous opponent of Methodism. Among his publications was *The Moravians Compared and Detected* (1755). '[Even among his enemies] esteem'd a person of admirable natural parts, good manners, sound judgment, and of very remarkable sweetness of temper in all conversation' (Aycliffe).

(*DNB*)

LETHIEULLIER, Smart (1701–60) [*Smart Lethieullier, Esq*]
FRS (1724); FSA (1724).
Member of a family of distinguished City merchants, originally from Brabant. Antiquary and man of letters. Devoted himself to antiquities and formed collections and made drawings while travelling in France, Italy, Germany and all parts of England. Acquired manuscripts, books, medals, drawings, ancient marbles and fossils. 'An excellent scholar and a polite gentleman'. (His cousin Col. William Lethieullier FSA had travelled extensively in Egypt and it was his collection, added to by Smart and by William's son Pitt Lethieullier, which was presented to the Museum in 1756).
(*DNB*) (BR) (MN)

LOWTHER, Sir James (?1673–1755) [*Sir James Lowther, Bart*]
FRS (1736)
MP (Carlisle 26 November 1694–1702, Cumberland 1708–22, Appleby 2 May 1723–7, Cumberland 1727 – 2 January 1755).
Succeeded his brother as 4th Baronet 1731. Principal Storekeeper of the Ordnance 1696–1712; Director South Sea Company 1733–6; Vice Admiral of Cumberland and Westmorland; Alderman Carlisle 1739–d.; Vice President Foundling Hospital 1753. An independent Whig. Colliery owner (Whitehaven). Scientific interests included the performance of an experiment with mine damp before the Royal Society. One of the richest commoners in the kingdom, he left a fortune estimated at over £1 million. '[E]xcessively parsimonious'.
(N&B) (RS) (BR)

*LYTTELTON; The Revd Charles (1714–68) [*the Rev Charles Littleton, Doctor in Divinity, Dean of Exeter*]
FRS (1743); FSA (1740); PSA 1765–d.
Antiquary and Bishop of Carlisle. Third son of Sir Thomas Lyttelton, 4th Baronet. Called to the Bar (Middle Temple) 1738 but abandoned the law for the church. Ordained 1742. 1747 chaplain to George II. Dean of Exeter Cathedral 1748. Bishop of Carlisle 1762. Contributed to *Archaeologia*. His papers on Worcestershire formed the basis of the later histories. Younger brother of Sir George Lyttelton (q.v.). 'His manners were genial, he was very hospitable to his friends, and he was lauded by Dean Milles for his knowledge of antiquities and his retentive memory'. Walpole, who heartily disliked the Society of Antiquaries was stung to special fury by the election of the Bishop whom he called 'Goody Carlisle'.
(*DNB*) (BR) (MN)

*LYTTELTON, Lord (George) (1709–73) [*George Littleton, Esq*]
FRS 1744; Elected British Museum Trustee 1753.
MP (Okehampton 28 March 1735 – 18 November 1756).
5th Baronet, eldest son of Sir Thomas Lyttelton, 4th Baronet. 1st Baron Lyttelton. Politician, poet, writer and patron. Secretary to Frederick, Prince of Wales 1737–44; Lord of the Treasury 1744–54; Cofferer of the Household March 1754 – November 1755; Privy Counsellor 21 June 1754; Chancellor of the Exchequer November 1755 – November 1756. Useful family political connections with the Grenvilles and Pitt. A liberal patron of literature. Fielding dedicated *Tom Jones* to him. '[A] good scholar, a dull historian, an amiable man, but a miserable politician' (Shelburne).
(*DNB*) (N&B) (BR) (RS)

METHUEN, Sir Paul (c.1672–1757) [*Sir Paul Methuen*]
MP (Devizes 1708–10; Brackley 1713 – 20 April 1714, 1715–47)
Diplomatist. Grandson of a wealthy clothier. Deputy to his father as envoy to Portugal 1694–5 and 1696–7; envoy to Portugal 1697–1706, to Spain 1705–6, to Turin 1706; Ambassador, Portugal 1706–8; Lord of Admiralty 1709–10; Lord of Treasury 1714–17; Privy Counsellor 29 October 1714; Ambassador to Spain 1715; Secretary of State 1716–17; Comptroller of the Household 1720–5; Treasurer of the Household 1725–30. Possessed a considerable knowledge of foreign languages and of the best authors in the chief European countries. During his stay abroad formed a fine collection of pictures which he left to his cousin Paul Methuen of Corsham House, Wiltshire. '[R]omantic . . . to the highest degree of absurdity; odd, impracticable, passionate, and obstinate; a thorough coxcomb and a little mad' (Hervey).
(*DNB*) (RS)

*MILES, The Revd Henry (1698–1763) [*the Rev. Henry Miles, Doctor in Divinity*]
FRS (1743)
Dissenting Minister and scientific writer. Educated for the dissenting ministry, ordained 1731. Contributed articles on natural history, meteorology and electricity. 'In private life he bore the character of great amiability'.
(*DNB*) (BR)

MILNER, John [*John Milner, Esq*]
Not traced.

*OGLETHORPE, General James (1696–1785) [*General James Oglethorpe*]
FRS (1749)
MP (Haslemere 1722–54)
General, philanthropist, and founder of the colony (later state) of Georgia which he successfully defended against Spain. Member of a Jacobite family then became a Government supporter. In 1730, with twenty associates, obtained a royal charter and financial assistance to a body of trustees

empowered to settle poor persons in a new colony of Georgia. 1736–43 engaged in defending the colony against Spain. Returned to England to raise funds. Court-martialled after the 1745 rebellion for aiding the Jacobites; acquitted. In 1752 he ceased to play a prominent part in public life. A friend of Walpole, Goldsmith, Burke and Dr Johnson. 'An attitude of sturdy independence towards Hanoverian ministers and a tendency to look with disfavour on all authority'.

(*DNB*) (RS) (BR)

*PAPILLON, David (1691–1762)   [*David Papillon, Esq*]
FRS (1720); FSA (1735).
MP (New Romney 1722 – 29 April 1728, 13 May 1728–34; Dover 1734–41)
Called to the Bar (Inner Temple) 1715. Bencher 1744. Commissioner of Excise 1742–54. A practising lawyer. Supporter of the Administration. Schoolfellow and lifelong friend of Lord Hardwicke.

(RS) (BR) (MN)

*PEARCE, The Rt. Revd Zachary (1690–1774)   [*The Right Rev. Zachary Lord Bishop of Bangor*]
FRS (1720)
Son of a rich distiller. Obtained the patronage of Thomas Parker, Earl of Macclesfield and lived with his family for three years, receiving rapid preferment. Ordained 1718. Vicar of St. Martin in the Fields 1723–4, Dean of Winchester 1739, Dean of Westminster 1756–68. Bishop of Bangor 1748/9, Bishop of Rochester 1756. Scholar. Published theological and classical works including editions of Cicero *De Oratore* (1746), *De Officiis* (1745), *Longinus* (1724). Bequeathed his library to the Dean and Chapter of Westminster.

(*DNB*) (BR)

RANBY, John (1703–73)   [*John Ranby, Esq*]
FRS (1724)
Surgeon in Ordinary to the King's Household 1738, Sergeant Surgeon to George II 1740, Principal Sergeant 1743 (present at the Battle of Dettingen), 1745 First Master of the newly founded Surgeons' Company (distinct from the Barbers), re-elected 1751 and 1752. Surgeon to Chelsea Hospital 1752. Lived there until his death. Promoter of Peruvian bark (quinine). Mentioned in Fielding's *Tom Jones*. Responsible for the unsuccessful operation on Queen Caroline. 'A man of strong passions, harsh voice and inelegant manners'.

(*DNB*) (BR)

REUS[S], Henry 28th, Count   [*Henry xxiixth Reus, Count and Lord of Plauen, Count of the Roman Empire, Lord Deputy or first Commissioner for executing the office of the Advocate of the Unitas Fratrum*]
(17 June 1752)
Member of the Moravian Church. Mentioned by Walpole in his letter to Sir Horace Mann (see above). Brother-in-law

of Nicolaus Ludwig, Count Zinzendorf, whose first wife, Erdmute, was Count Henry's sister. See also note 13.

*SAVILE, Sir George (1726–84)   [*Sir George Saville, Bart*]
FRS (1747); Vice-President Society of Arts
MP (Yorkshire 3 January 1759 – December 1783)
Member of an old Yorkshire family with estates in Ireland. Spoke frequently and soon became one of the most respected men in the Commons. Advocate of religious toleration and other reforms. 'A staunch Whig of unimpeachable character and large fortune. He devoted the whole of his time to public affairs and was greatly respected by his contemporaries for his unbending integrity and his unostentatious benevolence'.

(*DNB*) (N&B) (BR)

SHAW, The Revd Thomas (1694 – 15 August 1751)   [*the Rev. Thomas Shaw, Doctor in Divinity*]
FRS (1734)
African traveller, scholar, antiquary and natural historian. Son of a shearman dyer. 1720 went as chaplain to the English factory in Algiers and lived there for thirteen years during which time he visited Egypt, the Sinai Peninsula and Cyprus (1721), Jerusalem, the Jordan and Mount Carmel (1722), Tunis and Carthage (1727), in addition to expeditions to Algeria, Tripoli and Morocco. Returned to England 1733. Vicar of Godshill, Isle of Wight. Author of *Travels or observations relating to several parts of Barbary and the Levant* (Oxford, 1738). 1740 Principal of St. Edmund Hall, Oxford and 1741 Regius Professor of Greek. Vicar of Bramley, Hants. The genus Shawia in botany is named after him.

(*DNB*) (BR)

*SLOANE, William (d. 1767)   [*William Sloane, Esq*]
FRS (1722). Elected British Museum Trustee 1753
Son of Sir Hans Sloane's elder brother, also called William, who had likewise settled at Chelsea. BR quotes GM 37 (1767), p. 96 which records the death on 18 February of Wm. Sloane, Esq., Bloomsbury Square.

(BR) (GM)

SMITHSON, Hugh (Duke of Northumberland) (1715–86)   [*Sir Hugh Smithson, Bart*]
FRS (1736); FSA (1736, withdrew 1740). Elected British Museum Trustee 1753.
MP (Middlesex 15 May 1740 – 7 February 1750)
High Sheriff Yorkshire 1738–9; Lord of the Bedchamber 1753–63; Lord Lieutenant Northumberland 1753–d; Lord Chamberlain to the Queen 1762–8; Lord Lieutenant Middlesex 1762–d; Vice Admiral North America 1764; Master of the Horse 1778–80. Privy Counsellor 1762. Initially a Tory, which persuasion he gradually abandoned. 1729 succeeded grandfather as 4th Baronet. Married the Percy heiress, succeeded to Earldom of Northumberland 1750. 1766 1st Duke of Northumberland of the 3rd creation. 1763 Lord Lieutenant of Ireland. Interested in art,

science and literature. 'He had great talents and more knowledge than is generally found amongst the nobility'.
(*DNB*) (RS) (BR) (MN)

SOTHEBY, William (d. 1766)   [*William Sotheby, Esq*]
(17 June 1752)
Presumably Colonel William Sotheby FRS (1744); FSA (1743). Elected British Museum Trustee 1753.
Colonel of the Coldstream Guards. Married Elizabeth (d. 1790), daughter of William Sloane of Stoneham, Hampshire. GM 36 (1766), p. 103, records that on 7 January he died 'on the road from Bath'.
(BR) (MN) (*GM*)

SOUTHWELL, Edward (1705–55) [*The Right Hon. Edward Southwell, Esq*]
MP (Bristol 12 December 1739–54)
Joint Clerk of the Crown and Protonotary of King's Bench 1715–17; joint Secretary of the Council 1720–30, sole Secretary 1730–d. Member of an Anglo-Irish family. '[A] very sober, virtuous man' (1st Lord Egmont); 'a weak man. Has an affectation of being supposed to act according to his conscience . . .' (2nd Lord Egmont).
(RS)

*STANHOPE, Charles (1673–1760) [*Charles Stanhope, Esq*]
FRS (1726)
MP (Milborne Port 6 July 1717–22; Aldborough 1722–34; Harwich 1734–41)
Called to the Bar (Inner Temple) 1703. Under-Secretary of State Southern Department 1714–17; Secretary to Treasury 1717–21; Treasurer of the Chamber 1722–7 under George I but refused office by George II. Accused of profiting from dealings in South Sea stock but acquitted with the support of the Walpoles and George I.
(*DNB*) (RS) (BR)

*STANLEY, Hans (1721–80)   [*Hans Stanley, Esq*]
British Museum Sloane Family Trustee 1753.
Grandson of Sir Hans Sloane, whose elder daughter Sarah married Hans Stanley's father, George Stanley of Paultons, Hampshire.
MP (St. Albans 11 February 1743–7; Southampton 1754–12 January 1780).
Lord of the Admiralty September 1757 – July 1765; envoy to Paris May–September 1761; Privy Counsellor 26 November 1762; Governor and Vice Admiral Isle of Wight 1764–6, 1770–d. Ambassador-designate to Russia 1766–7; Cofferer of Household December 1766 – March 1774, October 1776–d. Travelled frequently to France and resided for two years at Paris. Tory. Committed suicide as did his father. 'He has good parts, much knowledge, and good breeding, but his manner is not agreeable' (Walpole).
(*DNB*) (N&B) (RS)

*STUKELEY, The Revd William (1687–1765)   [*the Rev. William Stukeley*]

FRS (1718); FSA (1709, 1717) Secretary, Society of Antiquaries
Antiquary. MB 1709. Started practice at Boston, Lincolnshire 1710, but in 1717 moved to London. Involved in the establishment of the Society of Antiquaries 1718. MD 1719, FCP 1720. In 1726 moved to Grantham and undertook considerable journeys throughout England studying antiquities. Ordained 1729. Incumbent of All Souls, Stamford. Returned to London 1748. Wrote some medical works but chiefly known as an antiquary. Publications include *Stonehenge* (London, 1740); *Abury* (London, 1743). Collection of coins (chiefly Roman), fossils, pictures and antiquities sold 1760. 'A learned and honest man . . . but a strange compound of simplicity, drollery, absurdity, ingenuity, superstition and antiquarianism' (Warburton).
(*DNB*) (BVR) (NM)

TAYLOR, [?]   [— *Taylor, Esq*]
(17 June 1752)
No first name is given in any of the sources. A Charles Taylor, Deputy Remembrancer of the Court of the Exchequer was elected FRS 1 November 1722, died 1766. Another possibility is Robert Taylor, elected FRS 23 June 1739, MD 1737, practised in Newark but moved to London under the patronage of Lady Burlington. FCP 1749, Censor 1751, Harveian orator 1775. Physician to the King. A third candidate might be John Taylor, FSA 1748, Director, Society of Antiquaries 1759 (d. 1766), a lawyer.
(BR)

*THEOBALD, James (d. 20 February 1759) [*James Theobald, Esq*]
FRS (1725); FSA (1726), Secretary 1727, VPSA 1750.
Contributor to the first volume of *Archaelogia*. BR assumes he was probably the James Theobald of Surrey Street, London who died 20 February 1759.
(BR) (MN)

*THOMPSON, Sir Peter (1698–1770) [*Sir Peter Thompson, Knt*]
FRS (1746); FSA (1743)
MP (St. Albans 1747–54)
Sheriff Surrey 1745–6. An eminent merchant engaged in the Hamburg and Newfoundland trade. Friend of James West (q.v.) and Joseph Ames (q.v.). Collector. Formed a valuable library and museum in his house at Poole. United 'the industry and intelligence of commerce with a love of literature'.
(*DNB* s.v. Ames, Joseph) (RS) (BR) (MN)

*WALPOLE, (Horatio [Horace]) (Lord Orford) (1717–97) [*the Hon. Horatio Walpole jun Esq*]
FRS (1746); FSA (1753)
MP (Callington 1741–54; Castle Rising 1754 – February 1757; King's Lynn 24 February 1757–1768)
Author, wit, letter writer and collector. 1791 succeeded as 4th Earl of Orford, 3rd Viscount Walpole. Third son of the

great Sir Robert. Creator of the Gothic Revival house 'Strawberry Hill' near Twickenham. Usher of Exchequer 1738, Comptroller of the Pipe 1738, and Clerk of Estreats 1738–d. Noted for his posthumous Memoirs of the reigns of George II and George III. '[E]minently fit to be the chronicler of his age'; 'A rich and complex personality, acutely sensitive to moods and impressions, vulnerable and touchy, he found relief from inner tensions in incessant writing'.
(*DNB*) (N&B) (BR) (RS) (MN)

*WATSON, Sir William (1715–87) [*Mr William Watson*]
FRS (1741). Elected British Museum Trustee 1753
Physician, naturalist and scientist. Son of a City tradesman, apprenticed to an apothecary then commenced business himself. After being disfranchised from the Apothecaries' Company began to practise as a Physician. LCP 1759. 1762 elected physician to the Foundling Hospital. FCP 1784. Contributed articles on natural history, electricity and medicine. Devoted much of his time to experiments in electricity. 1747 and 1748 with Folkes (q.v.) and other Royal Society members carried out a long series of experiments on the velocity of electric matter. Maintained a large foreign correspondence. Involved in the establishment of the British Museum's botanical garden at Montagu House which opened to the public in 1757. 'He was a man much liked'.
(*DNB*) (BR)

WATTEVILLE, Baron [*The Hon. the Baron of Watteville*]
Not listed in any printed version of the Will, Codicils or 1752 note but appears in the *London Daily Advertiser* of 30 January 1753.
Member of the Moravian Church. Three de Wattevilles are mentioned in Benham (see note 13) – Frederick, Johannes and Nicholas. In ibid p. 238 Frederick is referred to as the senior Lord Baron of Watteville.

*YORKE, Philip (Lord Hardwicke) (1720–90) [*the Hon. Philip York, Esq*]
FRS (1741); FSA (1745). Elected British Museum Trustee 1753
MP (Reigate 1741–47; Cambridgeshire 1747–6 March 1764). In 1754 styled 'Viscount Royston'. 2nd Earl of Hardwicke (succeeded 1764). Lord Lieutenant Cambridgeshire 1757–d; Teller of the Exchequer 1738–d; Privy Counsellor 17 December 1760; High Steward Cambridge University 1764–d. Eldest son of the 1st Earl of Hardwicke, Philip Yorke (1690–1764), FRS 1753, who was Lord Chancellor 1737 to 1756.
Brother of Charles Yorke (1722–70), second son of the 1st Earl who was himself appointed Lord Chancellor in 1770, FRS 1750, ex officio British Museum Trustee. 'Of a reserved disposition and in poor health, his main pleasure was in literature'.
(*DNB*) (N&B) (RS) (BR) (MN)

ZINZENDORF[F], Count (1700–60) [*Adolph, Count Zinzendorff and Potendorff, Count of the Roman Empire and great huntsman by inheritance of the arch-dukedom of Austria*]

(17 June 1752)
The leader of the Moravian community to whom Sloane sold the grounds of Beaufort House in 1750 was Nicolaus Ludwig, Count Zinzendorf (1700–60), the German religious and social reformer. Benham (see note 13) makes no reference to 'Adolph'. Count Zinzendorf offered asylum on his estate to the Moravian Brethren in 1722 and took over control of the group. The movement spread and he travelled widely in its interests, spending time in London. Grandson of Catherine von Gersdorf, he married Erdmute Dorothea, sister of Count Henry 28th of Reus; his only son died in 1752. 'An eager seeker after truth . . . he had an exceptional talent for talking on religious subjects even with those who disagreed with him . . . his dress was simple, his personal appearance gave an impression of distinction and force'. (*Encyclopaedia Britannica*, 11th edn. (1910–11), s.v. Zinzendorf, Nicolaus Ludwig.)

A number of ex-officio Trustees are also listed (the name of the incumbent in 1753 is given in brackets)

*THE PRESIDENT OF THE ROYAL SOCIETY
(PARKER, George, 2nd Earl of Macclesfield) (c.1697–1764)
FRS (1722); PRS 1752–64; FSA (1752)
MP (Wallingford 1722–7)
President of the Royal Society 1752–64. Married to the daughter of 'an eminent Turkey merchant'. A distinguished astronomer, largely responsible for the adoption of the 'New Style' Calendar in 1752. One of the Tellers of the Exchequer 1719–64. Styled Viscount Parker 1721–32.
(*DNB*) (RS) (BR)

*THE TREASURER OF THE ROYAL SOCIETY
(WEST, James, Esq (1703–1772))
FRS (1726), Treasurer 1736–68, PRS 1768–72; FSA (1726), VPSA 1750–d. Elected British Museum Trustee 1753
MP (St. Albans 1741–68; Boroughbridge 1768 – 2 July 1772)
Member of Inner Temple, called to the Bar 1728. 1738 admitted to Lincoln's Inn. Secretary to Chancellor of the Exchequer December 1743 – May 1752; Joint Secretary to Treasury May 1746 – November 1756, July 1757 – May 1762; Recorder, Poole 1746–d., St. Albans April 1758 – July 1760; High Steward, St. Albans 1759–d.; bencher Inner Temple 1761, reader May – November 1767, Treasurer 1767–8. As a young man travelled in France and the Low Countries and acquired a taste for antiquities. Through his marriage he added a fortune of £100,000 to an annual income of £1,000 from his father. Friend of Edward Harley and one of his trustees. In this capacity helped to arrange the sale of the Harleian manuscripts to the British Museum. Collected books, manuscripts, pictures, medals etc. Amateur scientist. His collection was dispersed by sale over twenty-four days on his death, some items reaching the British Museum. '[A]ble and well connected, industrious and perseverant, he eschewed a political career'.
(*DNB*) (N&B) (RS) (BR) (MN)

*THE SECRETARY OF THE ROYAL SOCIETY (1)
(BIRCH, Thomas (1705–66))
FRS (1735); Secretary 1752–65; FSA (1735). Elected British
Museum Trustee 1753
Historian and biographer. Son of a coffee mill maker.
Ordained deacon 1730 and priest 1731. Publications
include *A General Dictionary. Historical and Critical* (1734),
Memoirs of the Reign of Queen Elizabeth (London, 1754),
History of the Royal Society (London, 1756), biographies of
Tillotson, Robert Boyle, *et al.* Active British Museum
Trustee. 'Few have had more difficulties to surmount . . .
and more honourably surmounted them.'
(DNB) (BR) (MN)

*THE SECRETARY OF THE ROYAL SOCIETY (2)
(DAVALL (or DUVAL), Peter (d. 1763))
FRS (1740), Secretary 1747–59; VPRS 1759–62; FSA (1746)
Member of Lincoln's Inn (BR) or (MN) Middle Temple. A
Master in Chancery and Accountant General of that Court.
Consulted in the dispute about elliptical arches when Batter-
sea Bridge was built. 'He was well skilled in mathematical
and philosophical knowledge' (Royal Society Journal Book).
(BR) (MN)

Appendix 2
Visitors to the Museum appointed under the Will
of Sir Hans Sloane
* Denotes a Trustee appointed, *ex officio*, by the British
Museum Act 1753;
† Denotes a Trustee elected under the Act

Codicil 10 July 1749
His Majesty the King
His Royal Highness The Prince of Wales
His Royal Highness William, Duke of Cumberland
The Archbishop of Canterbury*
The Rt. Hon. Philip, Lord Hardwicke (*as Lord Chancellor
1754)
The Lord High Chancellor
The Lord President of the Council*
The Lord Privy Seal*
The Lord Steward of His Majesty's Household*
The Lord Chamberlain of His Majesty's Household*
His Grace Charles, Duke of Richmond (deceased – codicil
18 September 1750)
His Grace John, Duke of Montague (deceased – codicil 18
September 1750)
His Grace Holles, Duke of Newcastle
His Grace John, Duke of Bedford
The two Principal Secretaries of State*
The Rt. Hon. John, Earl of Sandwich
The Lord High Admiral or the First Lord Commissioner
of the Admiralty*

The Rt. Hon. Henry Pelham Esq
The Lord High Treasurer or the First Lord Commissioner
of the Treasury*
The Chancellor of the Exchequer*
The Lord Chief Justice of the King's Bench*
The Lord Chief Justice of the Common Pleas*
The Lord Chief Baron of the Exchequer*
The Lord Bishop of London*
The Lord Bishop of Winchester
The Rt. Hon. Archibald, Duke of Argyll†
The Rt. Hon. Henry, Earl of Pembroke (deceased – codicil
18 September 1750)
The Rt. Hon. Philip, Earl of Chesterfield
The Rt. Hon. Richard, Earl of Burlington
The Rt. Hon. Henry, Lord Montford
The Rt. Hon. Arthur Onslow, Esq
The Speaker of the House of Commons*
The Hon. Lord Charles Cavendish†
The Rt. Hon. Charles, Lord Cadogan*
The Rt. Hon. John, Earl of Verney
The Rt. Hon. George, Lord Anson

Codicil 18 September 1750
The Rt. Hon. the Earl of Macclesfield* (as President of the
Royal Society)
The Earl of Shelburn
The Rt. Hon. Sir John Strange, Master of the Rolls
Master of the Rolls

Appendix 3
Trustees appointed under the British Museum
Act, 1753

Principal Trustees (first incumbents shown in brackets)
The Archbishop of Canterbury (Thomas Herring
(1693–1757)
The Lord Chancellor or Lord Keeper of the Great Seal of
Great Britain (Philip Yorke, 1st Earl of Hardwicke)
The Speaker of the House of Commons (Arthur Onslow,
who became an elected trustee in 1761 following his retire-
ment from the Speakership)

Others, ex officio
The Lord Treasurer of Great Britain or the First Commis-
sioner of the Treasury
The Lord President of the Council
The Lord Privy Seal
The Lord High Admiral of Great Britain or the First Com-
missioner of the Admiralty
The Lord Steward of His Majesty's Household
The Lord Chamberlain of His Majesty's Household
The Bishop of London

Each of the Principal Secretaries of State, being a Peer or Lord of Parliament
Each of the Principal Secretaries of State, not being a Peer or Lord of Parliament
The Chancellor of the Exchequer
The Lord Chief Justice of the Court of King's Bench
The Master of the Rolls
The Chief Justice of His Majesty's Court of Common Pleas at Westminster
His Majesty's Attorney General
His Majesty's Solicitor General
The President of the Royal Society
The President of the College of Physicians

Sloane Family
The Rt. Hon. Charles, Lord Cadogan
Hans Stanley Esq.

Cottonian Trustees
Samuel Burroughs Esq.
Thomas Hart Esq

Harley Family
William, Duke of Portland
The Rt. Hon. Edward, Earl of Oxford and Earl Mortimer

Trustees elected under the provisions of the British Museum Act 1753

(Extract from General Meeting Minutes, 11 December 1753, p. 1)
* Denotes a Trustee of Sir Hans Sloane's will

Archibald, Duke of Argyll
Hugh, Earl of Northumberland*
Lord Charles Cavendish
Hugh, Lord Willoughby of Parham
The Hon. Philip Yorke*
Sir George Lyttelton Bart*
Sir John Evelyn Bart.*
William Sloane*
James West*
Nicholas Harding
Charles Gray*
William Sotheby*
Thomas Birch D.D.*
John Ward L.L.D.
Mr William Watson*

Notes and References

1. Edward Edwards, *Lives of the Founders of the British Museum with Notices of its chief Augmentors and other Benefactors 1570–1870* (London, 1870, reprinted 1969), p. 9.

2. J. Mordaunt Crook, *The British Museum: a case-study in architectural politics* (London, 1972), p. 39.

3. Sir George Francis Hill (1867–1948), joined the British Museum 1893, Keeper of Coins and medals 1912–30, Director and Principal Librarian 1931–6. Numismatist. The first non-librarian to be appointed to the Directorship since the eighteenth century.

4. Unpublished anonymous typescript, 'The British Museum: its History and its Work', British Museum Central Archive. Comments therein date it to 1936 and the note that the author has worked in the Museum for forty-three years ties in with Hill's starting date.

5. A full version of Sloane's will and codicils was published as follows: *The Will of Sir Hans Sloane, Bart. Deceased* (London, 1753), printed for John Virtuoso, and *Authentic Copies of the Codicils belonging to the Last Will and Testament of Sir Hans Sloane, Bart. Deceased, which relate to his Collection of Books and Curiosities* (London, 1753), printed by order of the Executors by Daniel Browne. References to Sloane's will are taken from these versions which are bound together in the British Library collections (see also notes 7 and 31). Thomas Faulkner, *An Historical and Topographical Description of Chelsea and its Environs* (Chelsea, 1829), gives an abridged version (pp. 363–73). *London Magazine* (January 1753), p. 44, refers to 'five sheets of paper, all written with the deceased's own hand, and witnessed by four persons in the year 1739, and again published and signed by the testator in the presence of three other persons, in the year 1751. There are nine codicils to it, the third of which is two large skins of parchment.'
There is also a copy in the Public Record Office, PROB.11/799/28. In fact, as the copy in the PRO indicates, a will and eight codicils only were proved in London on 13 and 22 January 1753. (There was double probate because there were four executors.) Sloane's final disposition of his collection, 17 June 1752, which names additional Trustees including the Moravian Brethren (notes 7, 13 and Appendix 1) was not witnessed. Since, however, those named are included in contemporary lists of Sloane's Trustees, his Executors must have complied with his wishes.
Much of the will is taken up by bequests to family and servants and provisions subsequent to the decease of first-named beneficiaries.

6. 'Will', op. cit. (note 5), p. 13.

7. The printed version of the Will and Codicils, cited above (note 5) is arranged as follows: 9

October 1739, Will, pp. 1–13; 18 October 1747, pp. 14–15; 5 July 1749, pp. 15–16; 10 July 1749, pp. 16–35 and Codicils pp. 3–28; 21 July 1750, pp. 36–8; 18 September 1750, pp. 40–1 and Codicils pp. 29–31; 14 April 1751, pp. 43–5; 22 September 1751, pp. 46–8; 26 December 1751, p. 45 (previous provisions also reconfirmed); unwitnessed note of 17 June 1752, Codicils p. 32.

8. 'Will', op. cit. (note 5), p. 4.

9. Sloane had been elected a member of these Academies as follows: Paris 1708 (or 27 March 1709 ?OS); Berlin 1712; St. Petersburg 1735; Madrid 1735. See Faulkner, op. cit. (note 5), pp. 345, 347); Gavin de Beer, *Sir Hans Sloane and the British Museum* (London, 1953), pp. 94–5.

10. 'Will', op. cit. (note 5), p. 5.

11. For lists of Trustees and biographical notes see Appendices.

12. 'Will', op. cit. (note 5), p. 23.

13. The Unitas Fratrum, (also known as the United Brethren or the Moravian Church) originated from the groups that followed John Huss in the 15th century. In 1722, after persecution, they crossed from Moravia to Saxony and settled at Herrnhut on the estate of Count Zinzendorf (q.v.). He established a common order of worship in 1727 and afterwards a common organization. The movement spread to Denmark, Russia and England and became particularly notable for its missionary activities. (*Encyclopaedia Britannica*, 11th edn., s.v. Moravian Brethren and Zinzendorf, Nicholas Ludwig).

The group was recognized by Parliament as 'an ancient Protestant Episcopal Church' in 1749. An account of their stay in Chelsea is given by Faulkner (op. cit. (note 5), p. 78) who states that in 1750 they hired a plot of ground on which to erect a large building for 300 families and to carry on a manufactory. They also purchased the Duke of Ancaster's old mansion, Lindsey House, and part of the gardens of Beaufort House from Sir Hans Sloane for a burial ground, together with its stables (to convert into a chapel) and an access route. Most of the remaining site of Beaufort House was also leased from Sloane. Members of the Society lived in Lindsey House for a time although this was relinquished for financial reasons in 1774. The Brethren were particularly active in North America and had been involved with General Oglethorpe (q.v.) in Georgia. Daniel Benham, *Memoirs of James Hutton* (London, 1856) includes references to Brethren listed by Sloane. An account is also given in Peter Kroyer, *The Story of Lindsey House Chelsea* (London, 1956).

14. Mordaunt Crook, op. cit. (note 2), p. 47.

15. Geoffrey Grigson (ed.), *Art Treasures of the British Museum* (London, 1959), p. 19.

16. The Cottonian library consisted originally of some 958 volumes of manuscripts, With this was a coin cabinet now in the British Museum.

For a discussion of other material see Colin G. Tite. 'A catalogue of Sir Robert Cotton's printed books?', *British Library Journal* 17 no. 1, (Spring 1991), pp. 1–11. In page 9, note 4 it is suggested that Cotton's printed books as a group never reached the British Museum.

The Cottonian library was begun by Sir Robert Bruce Cotton (1571–1631), continued by Sir Thomas Cotton (1594–1662) and Sir John Cotton (1621–1702). Sir John Cotton made arrangements for the donation to the nation after his death of the collection, with a house and garden. The arrangements are set out in an Act of Parliament ('An Act for the better Settling and Preserving the Library kept in the House at Westminster, called Cotton-house, in the Name and Family of the Cottons, for the Benefit of the publick', 12 and 13 William III, c.7). Trustees were appointed (the Lord Chancellor, Speaker and family representatives). By this Act the collection was to be 'kept for publick use and advantage'. Following Sir John Cotton's death in 1702 his grandson, Sir John Cotton (1679–1731) carried out his grandfather's wishes.

Sir Robert Bruce Cotton had made it his life's work to collect, study and make available to others as many ancient manuscripts and particularly historically important documents, not necessarily ancient, as he could come by, with a particular emphasis on English history, literature and related subjects. Much of his collection had survived the dissolution of the monasteries but Cotton also acquired state papers to which he had access as a consultant on procedures and precedents.

After its donation to the nation the collection was neglected and parts were lost or damaged following a fire in Ashburnham House (to which it had been transferred) in 1731 (see Arundell Esdaile, *The British Museum Library, a short history and survey* (London, 1946), pp. 26, 228–9). Among its treasures, the collection includes the Lindisfarne Gospels, Beowulf and two copies of Magna Carta.

An account of the library and of the 1731 fire is included in Sheila Lambert (ed.), *House of Commons Sessional Papers in the Eighteenth Century*, (Wilmington, 1975), vol. XII, pp. 111–321: *A Report from the Committee Appointed to view the Cottonian Library . . .* (London, 1732). Much of the credit for the library's survival in the aftermath of the fire was given to Speaker Onslow.

17. Mordaunt Crook, op. cit. (note 2), p. 28.

18. Ibid., p. 37. On Sloane and the Ashmolean, see Chapter 1, note 213.

19. Thomas Birch, 'Memoirs relating to the Life of Sr Hans Sloane Bart formerly President of the Royal Society' (BL, Additional MS 4241), fol. 14.

20. 'Will', op. cit. (note 5), p. 2.

21. Ibid., pp. 16–17.

22. *Gentleman's Magazine* 23 (1753), pp. 51–2.

23. *London Magazine* (January 1753), p. 7.

24. 'Will', op. cit. (note 5), pp. 28–9.

25. *The Record of the Royal Society of London* 3rd edn. (London, 1912), pp. 41–2.

26. *Gentleman's Magazine* 18 (1748), p. 301.

27. A.W. Franks, 'The Apology of my Life', unpublished MS in the possession of his family. See also David M. Wilson, *The Forgotten Collector. Augustus Wollaston Franks of the British Museum* (London, 1984).

28. BM, Original papers I, fol. 44.

29. See Appendix.

30. Frank Francis (ed.), *Treasures of the British Museum* (London, 1971), p. 11.

31. This version of the Will, op. cit. (note 5), 'found in a Curiosity Shop at Sevenoaks', is at BL pressmark C.61.b.13.1–2 and consists of *The Will of Sir Hans Sloane, Bart. Deceased* (London, printed for John Virtuoso, 1753) (price one shilling) and *Authentic Copies of the Codicils belonging to the Last Will and Testament of Sir Hans Sloane, Bart, deceased, which relate to his Collection of Books and Curiosities* (London, printed (by order of the Executors) by Daniel Browne, 1753). As James Empson was appointed secretary to the Trustees it is possible that the notes are his but the hand appears to differ from examples in the British Museum and British Library. It is quoted extensively by de Beer, op. cit. (note 9), pp. 143–50.

32. Accounts of the first meeting of Sloane's Trustees are given in the Curiosity Shop account op. cit. (note 31) and also: *Gentleman's Magazine* 23 (1753), p. 50; *London Magazine* (February 1753), p. 89; *London Daily Advertiser* (30 January 1753). The *Gentleman's Magazine* notes 'above 40' present (as does the *London Magazine*) but lists all those mentioned in Sloane's will. The Curiosity Shop account gives an abbreviated list, presumably those actually there, and an annotation against three names – Samuel Clarke, Dr James Bradley, Richard Arundell – 'was not there'. Sir William Heathcote Bart, Sir Thomas Burnet, Thomas Shaw and Henry Gough had predeceased Sloane. De Beer (op. cit. (note 9), p. 184) adds Siegmund (Baron Gersdorff) to this group.

33. The name of two small principalities of the German empire, part of the complex of Thuringian states. The male members of both the elder and younger branches of the family were all called Henry (Heinrich). In the elder branch the enumeration continued until the number one hundred was reached, when it began again. In the younger the first prince born in a new century was numbered I and the numbers followed on until the end of the century when they began again (*Encyclopaedia Britannica*, 11th edn. (1910–11), s.v. Reuss).

34. Walpole to Horace Mann, 14 February 1753, quoted in *The Letters of Horace Walpole*, ed. Mrs Paget Toynbee (Oxford, 1903), vol. III, pp. 142–3.

35. Edward Southwell (1705–55), MP for Bristol, 12 December 1739–54. See Appendix.

36. Henry Pelham, (1695?–1754) MP for Seaford

28 February 1717–22, Sussex Spring 1722 – 6 March 1754. Following other government appointments he became First Lord of the Treasury 25 August 1743–d. and Chancellor of the Exchequer 12 December 1743–d. Although recognized as 'the premier' he made no attempt to become 'sole minister'; the Ministry consisted of him, his brother and Hardwicke. One of Sloane's 'Visitors'. Described as 'A timid and peace-loving politician, without any commanding abilities or much strength of character ... a good man of business and both an able and an economical financier ... an able debater and an excellent parliamentary tactician' (DNB, s.v. Pelham, Henry).

37. Curiosity Shop account, op. cit. (note 31).

38. Arthur Onslow, (1691–1768), Speaker of the House of Commons 1728–61. MP for Guildford 15 February 1720–27, Surrey 1727–61. Elected Speaker 23 January 1728, re-elected in subsequent years until 1754 – for thirty-three years in five successive Parliaments. Retired from Parliament 18 March 1761 and elected a Trustee of the British Museum in June that year. The first career Speaker. 'A man of unblemished integrity and much ability' (DNB, s.v. Onslow, Arthur).

39. The Harleian manuscripts, some 8,000 volumes, 14,256 original rolls, charters, deeds and other legal documents, were part of the great library formed by Robert Harley (1661–1724), Earl of Oxford (of the second creation) and Mortimer, and Edward Harley (1689–1741), the 2nd Earl. Following Edward's death they were sold to Parliament by the 2nd Countess and her daugher and heiress the Duchess of Portland, for £10,000. The books, estimated to number some 50,000 volumes and over 250,000 pamphlets and 41,000 prints were dispersed in 1743 following their sale by his widow to a bookseller Thomas Osborne. Robert Harley, a skilled politician was a literary patron with a particular interest in English historical and political material including genealogy and heraldry and was also fond of books of sermons and theological controversy. Edward's agents acquired early printed books from Continental presses and his distinctive contribution was an interest in oriental manuscripts far ahead of his time.

40. Arthur Edwards, died 22 June 1743, by his will dated 11 June 1738 bequeathed to the Cotton Trustees his own library of some 2,000 volumes of antiquarian books and £7,000 'to erect in a proper situation such a House as might be most likely to preserve that Library as much as can be from all Accidents'. Were a proper building already to have been erected, then the money should be 'employed to purchase such Manuscripts, Books of Antiquities, ancient coins, medals and other curiosities as might be worthy to increase and enlarge the said libraries'. A Mistress Elizabeth Milles had a life interest which did not fall in until 1769.

41. Edwards, op. cit. (note 1), p. 311.

42. 26 George II c.22: 'An Act for the purchase of the Museum or Collection of Sir Hans *Sloane*. and of the *Harleian* Collection of Manuscripts,

and for providing one General Repository for the better Reception and more convenient use of the said Collections of the Cottonian Library and the Additions thereto'. This was supplemented a year later by 27 George II c.16. The Act of 1753 and subsequent provisions were repealed by the British Museum Act 1963, cap 24.

43. This session of Parliament is referred to in *Gentleman's Magazine* (June 1753), p. 291, and *London Magazine* (June 1753), p. 291. The Curiosity Shop account records a detailed debate on Monday, 19 March 1753 at which James Empson was called into the House. The *Journals of the House of Commons*, vol. XXVI, p. 701 (19 March) note that the House resolved itself into a Committee with the Speaker relinquishing his chair to Yorke who reported some progress. The House agreed to sit in Committee the following Wednesday and to include the Cottonian library in their discussions.
On 6 April (p. 747) are recorded the Parliamentary resolutions to acquire the Sloane and Harleian collections and to join to them the Cottonian collection. The Bill was to be prepared by Mr Yorke, Sir George Lyttelton, Mr Gray, Mr Hampden, Mr Horatio [Horace] Walpole of Callington, the Lord Duppin, Mr Attorney General, Mr Solicitor General, Mr Charles Yorke, Mr Clarke, Mr Hardinge and Mr West.
References to Sloane's collection in the *Journals of the House of Commons* are: pp. 647 (6 March), 672 (13 March), 695 (16 March), 701 (19 March), 707 (21 March), 729 (29 March), 747 (6 April).
The Royal Assent is recorded in *Journals of the House of Lords*, vol. XXVIII, pp. 153–4 and *Journals of the House of Commons*, vol. XXVI, p. 838.

44. See Appendix.

45. British Museum Act, op. cit. (note 42), section I, p. 333.

46. Ibid., section IX, p. 339.

47. Ibid., section XX, p. 341.

48. Ibid., section I, p. 333.

49. For a history of lotteries see John Ashton, *A History of English Lotteries now for the first time written* (London, 1893), while C. L'Estrange Ewen, *Lotteries and Sweepstakes ...* (London, 1932), pp. 152–3 gives a brief note on the British Museum lottery.

50. *London Magazine*, reproduced in *The Parliamentary History of England from the Earliest Period to the Year 1803* (London, 1813), vol. XV, cols. 192–3.

51. The debate on the conduct of the British Museum lottery is covered in: *The Parliamentary History of England from the Earliest Period to the Year 1803* (London, 1813), vol. XV (1753–65), cols. 192–249; *The History, Debates and Proceedings of both Houses of Parliament of Great Britain from the Year 1743 to the year 1774*, vol. III, pp. 201–2; *The Debates and Proceedings of the British House of Commons. From 1751 to 1760* (London, 1770), pp. 126–7.

52. 'Report from the Committee, Appointed to examine the Book, containing an Account of the Contributors to the Lottery 1753; and The Proceedings of the House thereupon. Published by Order of the House of Commons, 1754'; in Sheila Lambert (ed.), *House of Commons Sessional Papers of the Eighteenth Century*, vol. XIX, 1842–60, (Wilmington, 1975), pp. 209–54. Also reproduced in *Journals of the House of Commons*, vol. XXVI, pp. 987–1001. Further references to the Inquiry into the lottery appear as follows: pp. 807 (12 December 1753), 872 (13 December), 872 (14 December) (appointment of Committee), 874 (17 December), 879 (19 December) (additions to Committee), 979 (5 March 1754).

53. Peter Leheup (1699 – 4 May 1777) of Steeple Morden, Surrey, Purchased lands in Norfolk 1729. Married Clara daughter of the influential William Lowndes (1652–1724) (see DNB, s.v. Lowndes, William) who was Secretary to the Treasury and who arranged for Leheup's appointment to the Treasury (Newcastle Papers, BL, Additional MS 32,968, fol. 100). Leheup was one of the four Chief Clerks and Controller of Exchequer Bills. In Henry Roseveare, *The Treasury* (London, 1969), pp. 105–6, it is noted that he represents a rare instance of dismissal at this period.

54. Edwards, op. cit. (note 1), pp. 309–10.

55. Edward Miller, *That Noble Cabinet: A History of the British Museum* (London, 1973), p. 47.

56. 'Report from the Committee ... to examine the Book', op. cit. (note 52), p. 9.

57. *Gentleman's Magazine* 23 (December 1753), pp. 587 and 588.

58. Nicholas Fazakerley (?1685–1767). MP for Preston 24 January 1732 – February 1767. A Tory, opposed to the Administration.

59. *Parliamentary History*, op. cit. (note 51), col. 202.

60. Henry Fox (1705–74). At that time MP for Windsor (1741–61). A Whig.

61. *Parliamentary History*, op. cit. (note 51), col. 206.

62. Horace Walpole to Richard Bentley, 19 December 1753, quoted in Edwards, op. cit. (note 1), p. 310.

63. BL, Additional MS 32,735, fol. 320; 32,856, fol. 1; 32,855, fols. 385, 467; 32,871, fol. 178; 32,926, fol. 39; 32,968, fol. 100 (Newcastle papers) and also 35,593, fol. 158 (Hardwicke papers).

64. For an account of the Huguenot family of LeHeup see Gery Milner-Gibson-Cullum, *Pedigree of Wittewronge of Ghent in Flanders* (London, 1905). Peter Leheup's will is reproduced on pp. 36–7.

65. Sampson Gideon (1699–1762). Financier who on his death left a fortune in landed estates estimated at £580,000. Among his financial assistance to the Government was to raise a loan

of £1,700,000 in 1745 to meet the Jacobite advance. In 1756 at the beginning of the Seven Years War he paid a recruiting bounty and was almost wholly relied upon by the government for finance of the war in 1758–9. Described as 'of strong natural understanding, and of some fun and humour' (*DNB*, s.v. Gideon, Sampson), no doubt with some justification given the fiasco of the lottery.

66. A cockpit was built in Whitehall in the time of Henry VIII. In the seventeenth century the building was used as a theatre. It was demolished c.1675 and at the end of the seventeenth century the buildings on the Cockpit site were used as government offices and lodgings. The term 'in the Cockpit' came to mean usually no more than in one of the buildings lying between the street and the park. (London County Council, *Survey of London*, ed. Montagu H. Cox and Philip Norman (London, 1931), vol. XIV, pp. 23–30).

67. BL, Additional MS 36,269 (Hardwicke papers), fol. 4.

68. See Appendix.

69. BM, General meeting, Minutes 11 December 1753, p. 1.

70. BM, Standing Committee Minutes 19 January 1754, pp. 1–3 and General Meeting, Minutes 12 February 1754, p. 18.

71. BM, Standing Committee, Minutes 22 January 1754, pp. 3–4 and General Meeting, Minutes 2 February 1754, pp. 11–17. A brief report of the collection's arrangement was given by James Empson (pp. 5–6) – Rooms 1–7 The Library; Room 8 The Gallery with 33 cabinets and many things placed in the spaces between them and on them, above them continued all round 4 shelves of books arranged by size (2 of folios, 2 of quartos, 1 of octavos); Room 9 Books of Drawings etc; Room 10 Bedchamber with 3 cabinets; Room 11 3 cabinets of medals; Room 12 2 cabinets. On the Ground Floor: Rooms 13 and 14 the Halls containing the Horns of different Animals with Indian and other Weapons; Room 15 Skeletons etc; Room 16 Antiquities; Room 17 things in spirits of wine etc; Room 18 stuffed skins of Animals with Indian and other Habits etc.

72. BM, Standing Committee, Minutes 5 February 1754, p. 9 and General Meeting, Minutes 13 February 1754, p. 24.

73. BM, General Meeting, Minutes 2 February 1754, p. 18; Standing Committee, Minutes 19 January 1754, pp. 1–3.

74. British Museum Act, op. cit. (note 42), section I, p. 333.

75. For a description of Montagu House see Mordaunt Crook, op. cit. (note 2), pp. 54–61.

76. The standard general histories of the British Museum are: Edwards, op. cit. (note 1), Esdaile, op. cit. (note 16), Francis, op. cit. (note 30), Miller, op. cit. (note 55), Mordaunt Crook, op. cit. (note 2); Marjorie Caygill, *The Story of the British Museum* (London, 1981, revised edn. 1992).

77. Birch, op. cit. (note 19), fol. 25.

78. Thomas Gray to Palgrave, 24 July 1759, quoted in Paget Toynbee and Leonard Whibley (eds.), *Correspondence of Thomas Gray*, vol. II (Oxford, 1935), pp. 631–2.

79. Marjorie Caygill, in *British Museum Society Bulletin* 51 (March 1986), pp. 37–8. The design, by Richard Yeo (d. 1779) is now engraved on the glass above the entrance to the British Museum.

80. BM, General Meeting, Minutes 1 June 1754, pp. 44 and 45.

81. Edward Maunde Thompson, 'Draft History of the British Museum', BL Additional MS 52292, fol. 111.

82. BM, General Meeting, Minutes 17 January 1756, pp. 77–8 and Birch's Diary, BL, Additional MS 4478C, entry for 17 January 1756.

83. Dr John Mitchell (d. 1768). MD. Botanist. Emigrated to America. Author of *Dissertatio brevis de principis botanicorum* (Norimbergae, 1769), dedicated to Hans Sloane. Returned to England 1747 or 1748, FRS 1748.

84. Dr Gowin Knight (1713–72). MB. Practised as a physician. Involved in magnetical research. FRS 1745. Developed an improved compass. Inventor of dwarf venetian blinds. Principal Librarian 3 June 1756. Knight's application is to be found in BL, Additional MS 36,269 (Hardwicke Papers), fols. 29, 31. Knight stressed the relevance of his medical qualifications to care of a collection which included the Sloane library and anatomical specimens.

85. Dr Charles Morton (1716–99). MD Leiden. Practised in London for several years. 1750 Physician to the Middlesex Hospital, 1754 Physician to the Foundling Hospital. FRS 1752. Appointed to the British Museum 1756, Principal Librarian 22 November 1776 to death.

86. Dr Matthew Maty (1718–76). Born Utrecht. MD Leiden 1740. Practised in London from 1741. 1750 began publication of *Journal Britannique*. FRS 1751. Appointed to British Museum 1756. 1765 Secretary, Royal Society. Principal Librarian 31 July 1772.

87. British Museum Act, op. cit. (note 42), sections X and XI, p. 339.

88. BM Original Papers, vol. I, fols. 39–45, 27 August 1756.

89. BL, Additional MS 36,269 (Hardwicke Papers), fol. 44, 22 June 1756.

90. Edwards, op. cit. (note 1), p. 5.

3 Humana

Anatomical, pathological and curious human specimens in Sloane's museum

Michael Day

*This section of the Sloane collection naturally owes a great deal to the fact that Sir Hans Sloane was a trained and practising medical doctor for the greater part of his long and productive life. His propensity for collecting human material began early in his career and he brought back a number of specimens of this kind from his travels in the West Indies. Later some specimens were retained from his own medical practice but many more were given to him by his colleagues and friends in the professions of medicine and surgery; prepared specimens and curios of medicine were acquired in other ways. The catalogue comprises 760 numbered entries under this heading and in some ways seems a small number when compared with the many thousands of specimens collected in other fields. It is possible that, like many, Sloane was so familiar with the material of his own profession that he discounted some interest in its collection; on the other hand the human collection ranges so widely from the banal to the bizarre that it is hard to deny the catholicity of his tastes in medical memorabilia.

The Entries

The list of specimens designated 'Humana' appears incongruously as the final section of a catalogue volume titled 'Coralls, Sponges, & some other submarines', with the entries numbered consecutively 1–760. Each new entry number is usually preceded by a hyphen; where it is omitted it is hard to see whether this is simply an error or if there is indeed some significance in its omission. There are four missing entries but otherwise each number is assigned to a specimen. The entries each take the form of a brief description of the specimen and some indication of its provenance, both of these items of information being nearly always present. Other information presented may include a brief case history of the condition that led to the specimen. In some instances the name and age of the patient or the deceased is given; sometimes the date of the occurrence is recorded and in others the date of acquisition of the specimen. Finally, and often most interestingly, some 'gossipy' details are recorded relating to the provenance. There are also some tantalizing blanks left here and there where a name or an age has been omitted; it is not always clear whether this was a matter of medical etiquette or simply that the information was not known. A number of the entries are cross-referenced in the index.

The entries are for the most part in Sloane's hand, the majority in English but some in Latin. Towards the end of the catalogue his writing deteriorates and the legibility is less than perfect. Six entries are indecipherable to my reading.

21f/1–760

21f/469, 696–8

The Collections

It is clear that while Sloane made use of his own medical practice for his collection, from time to time he was given single specimens and small groups of specimens, or he acquired whole collections by gift, purchase or legacy. Notable contributors include Dr Edward Browne[1] [21f/95–9; 101–12; 114–24], Dr Jean Rodolphe Lavater[2] [21f/186–203; 359–69], Dr Groenvelt [21f/373–414; 417–26], Dr Cyprianos [21f/427–39], Dr Frederic Ruysch[3] [21f/441–7]; Mr Ranby [21f/470–2; 508–10; 547–69; 589–607; 628–40], Mr Dupuys [21f/473–505], and Dr Grew [21f/641–59]. The largest single collection was acquired from William Cowper (1666–1709)[4] the English anatomist and surgeon, and comprised no fewer than 135 specimens [21f/223–358] consecutively entered and thus, one imagines, all acquired at the same time.

Dates

Throughout the catalogue of 760 entries, only on twenty-nine occasions was a date recorded. The earliest concerns 120 gallstones from the gall bladder of Sir Robert Jawdie of Claxton with the date 1638;[5] this was the gift of Sir Thomas Browne. Two of the more recent 'The hairy scalp of Mrs. Robinson murdered by Ellen Lewis 1735 . . .' and, in 1739 'Two kidney stones taken out of the pelvis . . . of a child . . .' were inserted into the sequential acquisition of specimens and probably relate to Sloane's own practice which, for the reasons suggested above, does not form the major part of his collection.

21f/113

21f/750

21f/741

Topics and Subtopics

It is clear that the collection is fortuitous in its order of acquisition other than in the groupings of donated specimens. It was necessary, therefore, for the purpose of this analysis to sort the entries into some order that would allow an evaluation of the collection. At a first reading it was clear that the material was anatomical, embryological and pathological; that is, that it contained examples not only of normal anatomy but also of the results of pathological processes defined in the broadest terms, in almost all parts of the human body. In addition there were groups of specimens that required categories of their own.

A series of Topics and Subtopics were devised that would serve as indexes when the entries were put on to a standard data base (DBASE IV) and would permit the catalogue as a whole to be rearranged under headings that provide information as to its content that is not otherwise apparent. The following Topics and Subtopics were chosen;

the respective numbers of entries are given in brackets.

Anatomy (275)
Arm (4), Bladder (1), Breast (3), Ear (9), Eye (3), Foot (2), Genitalia (24), Glands (1), Gonads (12), Hair (3), Hand (6), Head (3), Kidney (1), Leg (2), Bones (77), Skin (9), Teeth (3), Vessels (52), Viscera (60).

Anthropology (10)
Race (10)

Bezoars (39)
Foreign bodies (31), Phytobezoars (7), Trichobezoars (1)

Embryology (60)
Foetuses (41), Foetal osteology (10), Placentas (5), Foetal vessels (4)

Lithiasis (234)
Bladder (156), Gallstones (17), Idiopathic (35), Kidney (23), Salivary (3)

Pathology (91)
Joints (4), Bladder (2), Eyes (2), Feet (2), Foreign bodies (1), Gonads (1), Hair (7), Infestations (5), Kidney (2), Membranes (1), Hand (1), Bones (26), Skin (9), Substances (2), Teeth (1), Tumours (4), Vessels (15), Viscera (6).

Teratology (18)
Anencephaly (3), Hydrocephaly (3), Monsters (6), Siamese twins (6)

Zoology (21), Indecipherable (6), Missing numbers (4), Unclassified (2)

The categories chosen may seem a little strange to medical doctors of today who would look askance at some of the headings that have been used and even more so at those that have been left out. However, I would like to emphasise that they have been chosen solely for the purpose of dealing with this catalogue and should be taken only in the broadest sense as any guide to the anatomical and pathological interests of the medical profession in the late seventeenth and early eighteenth century.

Anatomy
Under this heading I have assigned 275 specimens that at first glance appear to represent an entirely eclectic choice by Sloane but within which three strands become apparent.
1) Anatomical specimens and preparations of medical educational value.
2) Clinical anatomical specimens that are explanatory in terms of embryological abnormality or disease process.
3) Anatomical specimens solely of curiosity or notoriety value.

Educational or Research Specimens
Among the factors that clearly affected the collection were those of ease of acquisition, ease of storage without deterioration, the advantages of dry specimens and the disadvantages of heavy, bulk wet specimens that would need very large jars or tanks and immense quantities of spirit of wine.[6] (Formalin was unknown as a preservative at that time.) Bearing this in mind, it can be seen that dry and dried specimens seem to predominate and that the wet specimens were of limited size.

The educational or research specimens are typified by:

A preparation of the parts abᵗ the External ear, viz. the Salivary gland wᵗʰ its two ducts etc.   *21f/173*

The uterus of a girl wʰ the hymen appearing & the vessels injected with mercury prepared by [Mr Cowper].   *21f/264*

The kidneys of a malefactor hang'd at Tyburn wherein appear two ureters & two basons in each kidney which ureters Join before their insertion into the bladder, given me by Dr Rutty.   *21f/534*

The last example couples the interest of the hanged malefactor with the embryological abnormality disclosed at the dissection of the corpse. Similarly 'The skeleton of a man made by Mr Vernier of the body of a Highwayman executed at Tiburn & bought by me. 3.4.6.'   *21f/14*

Other osteological specimens that come into the category of educational materials include 'The Skull of an Irishman brought from Ireland for medicall use'; 'The skeleton of the head of youth made at Paris to take to pieces given me by Mr. Fotheringham' [now in a different hand] 'who was Surgeon to Alexander Fraiser & from whom I think he had it.' Several preparations of the auditory ossicles and some of the temporal bone dissected to show the auditory apparatus are recorded from the collection acquired from Sir Thomas Browne of his son Dr Edward Browne.   *21f/17* *21f/24* *21f/109, 111,133*

The injection of parts of the vascular system with warm coloured waxes and with mercury was a popular method of displaying the blood supply to various organs, viscera or even whole limbs.

The arteries of the arm of a man injected with red wax was given me by Mr. Bussiore.   *21f/16*

The Carotid arteries, injected with the anastomoses of them wʰ the vertebrals etc.   *21f/164*

The amnios of an abortive calf with its vessels fill'd with quick silver.   *21f/184*

The placenta or secundine with the vessels injected with red wax, green wax and mercury prepared by Mr Cowper.   *21f/262*

Amongst the items that particularly caught the eye of Sauveur Morand on his visit to Sloane's museum in 1729 (see Chapter 1, Appendix 2) were 'many preparations by Ruysch', one of the most famous exponents of the injection technique.[7]

It was not invariable for the vascular anatomy to be displayed by injection: on occasion the dissecting skills of the operator alone were sufficient to produce a preparation worthy of a place in the collection.

21f/271 The ductus chyliformis from its origination to its insertion etc. prepared by Mr. Cowper.

This dissection is particularly taxing since it necessitates the exposure of the upper part of the abdomen, the posterior mediastinum and the root of the neck; a task to which Cowper was eminently suited.

21f/145–6, 231, 266–70, 341, 640, 290, 320–1, 726 Viscera form a valuable addition to an anatomical museum collection since they are easily obtained, relatively easy to dissect and often of clear clinical significance. Preparations of the stomach, the bladder, the heart, the small gut, the colon, the omentum, the liver, the lung, the rectum were clearly then, as now, the stock-in-trade of anatomical museums, preserved for the instruction of students and practitioners alike.

Specimens of Clinical Anatomical Interest

What is now termed clinical anatomy comprises that body of anatomical knowledge that relates to, and illuminates, the practice of medicine and surgery. While the term was not used by Sloane, he was well aware of the implications of anatomical knowledge in medical and surgical practice.

21f/99 The basis of the scull and upper mandible wherein appears a tooth out of its place in the palate . . .

21f/140 Halfe of the superior maxilla with the sinus in it and the roots of the teeth bared . . .

21f/272 The gall bladder of Mr. Walter Charleton full of angular stones. The end of it was joined to the peritoneum from whence gall was discharged by a tumour which turn'd to an ulcer on the side. From Mr. Cowper.

Specimens of Anatomical Curiosity or Notoriety

Here the curiosity may relate to the specimen itself or to its provenance and the circumstances of its acquisition. The former is exemplifed by:

21f/705 The monstrous large femur & leg bones of a man giant found in a coffin under the foundations in St. Martins Lane . . .

and the latter by:

21f/108 Pars ossis amici Ambrosii Gilberti qui formidabili combustione mortuus est die 27 Dec. 1662 circa horam 2am. – matutinam Dr Br[owne].

21f/3 A womans breast after being buried [blank] years taken up given me by Mr. Walpole.

The latter specimen may represent a case of adipocere.[8]

21f/85 A piece of the breast of Queen Katherine out of the chest at Westminster abby 7ber [September] 1667 had out of Mr. Giffords collection.

21f/93 The head of an Egyptian mummy dried in the sands brought from Egypt by Mr. Sandys.[9]

21f/23 Part of the occipital bone of a man taken from the tumuli Sepulchrales near Amesbury on Salisbury plain in Wiltshire.

Anthropology

Relatively few entries relate to what is now termed physical anthropology; rather there was some interest in specimens that were obtained from black individuals. Most of these seem to derive from travels in the West Indies undertaken by Sloane early in his career, or from slaves in Virginia. The foetus of a negro is recorded, and several specimens *21f/678* that relate to skin colour.

The skin of the hand of a black? *21f/155*

The skin of a negro w[h] the black corpus mucosum partly taken *21f/527* off from the true skin and partly sticking to it. [From Mr Ranby]

All of the black corpus mucosum taken off. [Ibid.] *21f/528*

The few remaining specimens of foreigners include 'Part *21f/572* of the hide of a Bashaw that was strangled in Turkey given me by Dr. Varim . . .'

Bezoars

Bezoars can be defined as an agglomeration of food or foreign material in the intestinal tract causing blockage. It may be of vegetable matter (phytobezoar), foreign material of any kind or of hair (trichobezoar). All three types were encountered by Sloane and examples retained in the collection.[10]

Of the phytobezoars several were stones from plums, *21f/52, 87, 90–1* cherries, gooseberries, mulberries, currants, raspberries and the like, and were passed successfully.

A substance w[ch] occasioned a great colick in a woman voided *21f/716* by her likely the fibrous parts of nettles from spring potage.

Others were not so fortunate:

A ball of bezoar taken out of the gutts of a Schoolmaster in *21f/50* Lancashire who suffered seven years of the colic by it notwithstanding the attempts of Physicians. The center is a plumbstone stuck there with gathered [f]omentum about it w[ch] was found in opening his body by his own direction after death to find out the cause of so great a Distemper. Bought of Dr. Lough.[11] [See Fig. 9a].

The other halfe of the same. *21f/51*

Foreign bodies causing intestinal blockage are usually swallowed, sometimes inadvertently:

A small tumour of fatt voided by a person excessively troubled *21f/517* w[h] the colic who had swallowed a nail being nailing some laths upon a ceiling. He endeavour'd to gett it up by a whalebone and had a pain in his side about a year when by bleeding & the help of an electuary of conf. ref. bals. Locatell & fl. sulph. w[h] pectorall drink he brought it up w[h] a small cough.

The nail w[h] coagulated blood round it. *21f/518*

Sloane's modesty about his own practice occasionally breaks down when he is clearly pleased with a success.

Is a rib of beef that was swallowed w[h] some greens at dinner *21f/749* by a woman that seldom used to chaw her victuals. It stuck low in the Oesophagus, I got it out with a piece of sponge introduced on a whalebone While it was in the throat she could not take

Fig. 9 *a*: Half of a phytobezoar [21*f*/50] taken *post mortem* from the intestines of a schoolmaster; the plum stone had gathered layers of deposit and later had become impacted causing severe colic. *b*: Calculus from the bladder of a woman, with a bodkin about which it had formed [21*f*/44]. From J. & A. Van Rymsdyk, *Museum Britannicum* (1778), tab. xix, figs. 5 and 1.

any sustenance & what she endeavoured to swallow returned and made great noise putting her to vast pain.

Trichobezoars are common in domestic veterinary practice but less so in medical practice; they do occur, however, often in the mentally disturbed. One case is recorded (seemingly accompanied by case notes) which may combine both hair and vegetable matter in the bezoar:

21*f*/577 Two balls of a furry matter round, one covered w^h a black substance the other white within which are a cherry & plumb stones sent me by Dr. Short and the letter.

Finally the occurrence of intestinal stones is recorded on a number of occasions, two being worthy of note:

21*f*/453 A stone which was drawn out of a womans anus nigh this place, she had been afflicted w^h colic pains for some years before the stone was taken from her to that degree that she was perfectly emaciated. She has ever since enjoyed perfect health & is now ab^t 50 years old. Dr. Richardson near Bradford Yorkshire.[12]

21*f*/466 A part of a human bezoar occasioning great colic in [blank] the Mayor of Derby w^h showed stria from a common center being found in two like the stria of a pyrites. In it are shining particles like talc. given me by himself when he consulted me ab^t his colick

21*f*/216 like to 216 in its structure.

The origin of such stones as these is always a matter of some doubt. Some are swallowed, some inserted *per rectum* and some may be gallstones or bladder stones that have eroded into the gut. There is no clear indication here as to which category these stones belong.

Embryology

The normal human embryological material in the collection is almost all that of aborted foetuses of various ages. The majority are simply recorded with their supposed ages. No indication is given as to how these age estimates have been arrived at and it is likely that they derive from the case history. In one case the foetus is supposed to have been *in utero* twenty-six years! In another the foetus was taken from the Fallopian tube by Dr Cyprianos after twenty-one months. 21*f*/689 21*f*/429

An insight into the belief that experience during pregnancy can affect the form of the foetus is shown by the following specimen:

A foetus of seven months old resembling a monkey w^h a cloak which the woman saw playing tricks at Rochester. Given me by Dr. Gregory. 21*f*/662

Another insight into obstetric practice may be obtained from the sad story of a specimen contributed by Mr Dupuys:

The body of the child of the little woman or dwarfe that was shown about town. Sir David Hamilton laid her with much difficulty whereby the head was lost. 21*f*/478

The embryological collection also comprises several placentas and an injected amnion as well as two foetal specimens with injected vessels. 21*f*/325, 442, 522, 526, 286, 163, 283

Lithiasis

The second largest category of specimens is the collection of human stones derived from the bladder, the kidney, the gall bladder and the salivary ducts, as well as a large collection of idiopathic stones. Yet others are attributed to the uterus and the lungs. The occurence of stones within the urinary system was undoubtedly common in the eighteenth century and medical science of the day was much concerned with 'the stone'. In truth so were patients, since the threat of being 'cut for stone' was a terrifying prospect when the science of anaesthesia was unknown and the analgesics available were of limited efficacy. It is not surprising that patients hoped to pass them *per urethram* while they were still small enough and why some of them attained enormous size if this was not possible. On occasion patients took matters into their own hands:

21f/44   A silver bodkin on the larger end of wch is fastened an oblong stone as on a comber. This bodkin was thrust up the meatus urinarius of a woman on London bridge troubled with strangury to ease her where lying it gathered this stone.[13] [See Fig. 9*b*].

On another occasion the stones were not what they seemed at first:

21f/62   Two stones, like freestone, the one pretended to be voided by the penis, the other by the fundament of a boy of 13 years of age found to be afterwards an Imposter.

Some stones were those of celebrated people and here rather more detail tends to be recorded:

21f/222   A flatt human calculus weighing 4 ounces taken out of the bladder of Dr Hickes the late dean of Worcester. It is prickly the prickles sett at distances each of which had made a hole in the bladder corresponding to it so that it look'd like a honey comb. This was left me by him. He had been searched and judg'd to have a stone too large to be cutt out w^hout danger of his life. He enjoyed months of ease between whiles and when in great pain was helped with opium.

21f/675   A human calculus taken from the bladder of Mr. Hallingburgh tapestry maker to K. Charles at Mortlake, he found a weight on turning, voided stones till within 20 years of his death wch was at 73.

One stone at least was recorded because it was successfully removed and worthy of the making of a replica:

21f/132   The modell of a calculus spinosus cutt out of the bladder by Frere Jaques which person survived the operation.

The consequences of surgery, when survival was achieved, were not always entirely felicitous:

21f/583   This stone was extracted out of the bladder [presumably *per urethram*] of a woman in St. Bartholomews hospital by Mr. Salter. She lived sev^ll years after but could never hold her water. [From Dr. Woodward]

Pride in the production of stones was clearly common then as now. Many patients today insist on having stones kept for them post-operatively:

21f/758   To human calculi w^h silver hoops and chain on wch engraved These Were Extracted from Mr John Tunnicliffe he being 57 years of age by S P of Carswill June 17th 1706: from [Dr Stack].

One example must surely have pride of place in the record books:

21f/33   The modell of a stone taken out of the bladder of Mr. Bi[...]d given by Mr. Povey waying 32 ounces [...] 0.2.6.

Gallstones were also of interest and often recovered as an incidental finding at *post-mortem*, or were recognized when voided at stool:

21f/79   Gallstones about 20 taken out of a womans gall whose abdomen contained much limpid water and also [...] the duplication of the mesenterium & in severall hidatides were limpid water and some like washings of beef. Her testicles [*sic*] were each of them of a monstrous bigness and contained a white viscous matter like well concocted pus. Mr. Handisyde.

21f/646   A stone voided by stool from the gall bladder after some years great indisposition of Mrs Ducane a merchants wife in Pancras Lane in London. Dr Grew was her physician after many others. 1708 [From Dr Grew].

Renal stones were also common apparently at all ages:

21f/741   Two kidney stones taken out of the pelvis [of the ureter?] with fabulous matter of a child [blank] years old who dyed Oct 11th 1739 of a total suppression of urine from the two ureters being stopd by them from Mr Bell.

Combinations of renal and bladder stones also gave serious problems which could be compounded when attempts were made to pass them *per urethram*, often later necessitating surgical attempts at removal with dire results:

21f/204   A triangular smooth stone as bigg as a very small chestnut cutt out of the urethra of one Spurrit near Leeds in Yorkshire. He had voided three large ones & had 5 cutt out of the urethra whereof this was one. He had 6 lodged in the urethra when he dyed of a mortification of it & he had likewise 2 large ones in the bladder & 2 in the right kidney the left one being degenerated into a mucilage. Mr. Thoresby.[14]

Finally, and less commonly a salivary calculus from Wharton's duct that runs in the floor of the mouth from the submandibular gland to its opening under the tongue:

21f/125   An oblong rugged stone taken out of the ranula under the right side of the tongue of Frank Williams. There was some part cut to make way, it was extremely foetid, had been 12 years breeding, some pain at first coming.

Pathology

The variety of pathological specimens represented in the collection is extremely wide and it contains many specimens from Sloane's own practice as well as from those of his colleagues and friends. There are ankylosed joints, massive onychogryphotic[15] toe nails, perhaps the original *Plica polonica*[16] since it came from Poland, and several others.

21f/21, 707–8, 715, 569, 612, 28, 68, 673

Fig. 10 A sebaceous horn from a Mrs French of Tenterden, Kent, purchased from her by Sloane for four guineas when it broke off by accident. Sloane's catalogue entry [21f/519] omits her name but gives the place and describes the specimen and the circumstances of acquisition. The account by the Van Rymsdyks (p. 58) confirms the details of the purchase and its generous terms. It may be suggested that the omission of the name from the entry was on the grounds of medical etiquette rather than lack of knowledge. From J. & A. Van Rymsdyk, *Museum Britannicum* (1778), tab. xxiv, fig. 1.

21f/79, 703   Infestations were common, including worms of various kinds and hydatid cysts.

21f/142, 210, 305, 355, 448, 647, 677, 710–11   Carious bones were collected but not clearly defined as to the cause of the caries, some of which may have been fracture calluses. Once again Sloane's justifiable pride in his practice shows through when he tells of one of his own successes:

21f/748   One large bone which is part of the tibia of a grown girl under my care, the bone is intirely tubular, she had many convulsions from the pain. The case was four years in hand. I was resolutely bent not to perform the amputation of the leg to which I was much pressd. It is long since intirely cured.

21f/434–5   Untreated wens (sebaceous cysts) were also common and on occasion these split to permit the growth of sebaceous 21f/519 horns sometimes of great length, one no less than ten inches (see Fig. 10). Similarly untreated tumours tended to grow 21f/737 very large.

Vascular disease features strongly in the collection with specimens of hearts with hardened vessels; of the sixteen specimens, one seems of particular interest:

21f/506   A piece of bone found in the divarication of the great artery making as it were a ring, in a man publickly dissected at Padua. March 1st [n] A.D. 1659/60.

Teratology

The subject of monstrous births is one of peculiar fascination and has given rise to much speculation and research. We now know that genic and chromosomal abnormalities, perhaps influenced by environmental circumstances, are the root cause of maldevelopment and this often results in the spontaneous abortion of non-viable foetuses. A monstrous birth means that whatever the defects of development may be they are consistent with life *in utero* in its sense of passive growth. (Put another way a baby is a form of benign tumour of the mother which, after birth, is prepared for, and capable of, independent existence). The ability of the monster to maintain life *ex utero* is usually limited to days or weeks, with some notable exceptions such as Siamese twins with little tissue in common.

Sloane's collection of eighteen monstrous births contains six sets of Siamese twins (not termed as such at that time):

A monstrous child with 4 arms and 4 leggs.   21f/64

An human monster being two bodies of children joined together in one head it hath 4 arms & 4 leggs From Staffordshire.   21f/458

Two children growing together by the breast. [From Mr Dupuys]   21f/504

A human child w^h 2 heads and one body. The mother dyed in Westminster 10 days after she was delivered of it.   21f/537

Two female infants join'd by their abdomina given me by Sir Thomas Lyttleton in Sp V.   21f/676

A monstrous foetus from Yorkshire bought of a Surgeon who calld it a Janus or a foetus born alive having one Head, two Faces, perfect four arms & hands two bodies, four thighs Legs and feet.   21f/752

This condition is known as craniopagus and is not amenable to surgical separation.

The equally distressing conditions of anencephaly and hydrocephaly, being the absence of a properly developed head and the possession of a massive head respectively, are also represented.

Amongst others they include: 21f/366, 436

A foetus born at full time w^h the back part of the scull & brains wanting given to me by Mr. Chapman a man midwife or surgeon.   21f/679

A cranium of a child born at full time sine cerebro from Dr. Monot. The monstrous head of a child.   21f/738

   21f/13

Two further deformities can be identified, from the descriptions given, as the failure of development of the fronto-nasal process and the premature fusion of the maxillary processes in the development of the face.

A monstrous child w^h its 2 eyes growing together in the place of its nose & one nostril like a proboscis over them. It was born at full time in Mr Gibbs's parish and lived three days & then dyed.   21f/505

A monstrous foetus w^h the leggs cross'd like a tailors, a proboscis & turban on the head from La nouer collection   21f/700

Zoology

Some zoological material is recorded in this catalogue principally, it would seem, as the specimens relate to the anatomy of the animals concerned. Many of the dissections are the work of William Cowper and seem to pertain to the anatomy of the tortoise or the frog. One entry seems to encapsulate the spirit of the man himself:

21f/428   A case wherein are contained many stones cutt out of the bladder by the same great operator of sev[ll] forms and shapes, among which are the skeleton of a parrot, a squirrell, a chameleon, green snake & a bladder of urine in which also are to be seen lodged sev[ll] human calculi. [From Dr Groenvelt].

Curios

Two entries relate to inanimate objects that both deserve mention.

21f/704   This hinge was of the coffin of Queen Mary daughter of King Henry 8s taken off by a labourer that was mending the vault to make cramp rings. Nov. 9. 1733 Ed. Barnard

21f/691   A leaden bullet which was shott into the right side of Dr. Ding's skull near the orbit of the eye & came out 29 years after near the pomum Adami of the left side of the neck [. . .] and may be seen in the [. . .] given me by his son.

Conclusion

The entries in the catalogue under the heading 'Humana' offer a fascinating insight into Sloane's professional life and underline once again his overriding interest in curiosities and their derivation, both natural and unnatural. At a time when medicine was neither well advanced nor readily available to large sections of the population, the bizarre, the exaggerated and the gross were common in the untreated. These form an interesting part of his collection but there are also those that illustrate the normal condition and were the research specimens of the time; new knowledge emerged with improvements in injection techniques, dissection and gross observation.

Sloane never wrote a comprehensive medical text but was occasionally moved to publish when he had good results from a remedy.[17] Insights into his thinking come mostly from the *Philosophical Transactions of the Royal Society*, in which he published the results of experiments and medical curiosities from time to time.

Little of the collection of Humana seems to be extant. It is indeed unlikely that the wet specimens would have survived the vagaries of curation over time, since spirit needs to be constantly replenished in jars and bottles. Dry materials may have fared better but few have been traced.

Sloane was a monumental figure in British eighteenth-century intellectual, scientific and medical circles but his own monument must be the British Museum that was founded with his collection and of which these catalogues form a record.

Notes and References

1. Son of the notable collector and author, Sir Thomas Browne.

2. On Lavater, see Chapter 7.

3. For Ruysch, see below and note 7.

4. William Cowper (1666–1709), English anatomist and surgeon, was particularly interested in the organs of generation and many of the specimens reflect this interest. He described several organs and ligaments, including the bulbo-urethral glands in man, that still bear his name in those texts that make use of eponymous terminology.

5. Sir Robert Jawdie of Claxton (Norfolk) was a patient of Sir Thomas Browne as shown by the entry in Sloane's catalogue [21f/113]: 'Calculi 120 ex Vesica fellea equitus Roberti Jawdie de Claxton desumpti prater 30 aut 40 deperdos. 1638'.
    Another early specimen is represented by the following entry under the same number [21f/113]: 'Item calculi fellei duo per sedem ejecti a Domina Holt de Thaxton que portea a sapius recurreubo ictero convaluit 1648. Sir Thomas Browne.'

6. The costliness of this method of preservation was impressed upon Horace Walpole during his service as a Trustee of Sloane's will, when he observed; 'It is a rent-charge to keep the foetuses in spirit!' (Walpole to Sir Horace Mann, 14 February 1753). See further, Chapter 2.

7. See F.J. Cole 'The history of anatomical injections', in C. Singer (ed.), *Studies in the History and Method of Science* (Oxford, 1921), vol. II, pp. 285–343. Directly or indirectly, these specimens may owe their presence in the collection to James Petiver's visit to the Netherlands at Sloane's behest in 1711, when he made the acquaintance of Ruysch: see R.P. Stearns 'James Petiver, promoter of natural science, c.1663–1718', *Proceedings of the American Antiquarian Society* new ser. 62 (1952), pp. 282–5. See also above.

8. Adipocere: a grey-white substance with a cheesy or waxy consistency, formed by slow decomposition of the soft tissues of bodies that have been buried in moist environments or immersed in water. Also known as 'grave wax'. *International Dictionary of Biology and Medicine* vol. I (New York, 1986), p. 48.
    The number of years that the breast tissue had been buried is not recorded by Sloane but the condition of the specimen, and the fact of its exhumation, seems to have warranted its retention in the collection. The conversion of fatty tissue to wax-like adipocere is one of the few ways that buried soft tissue may preserve its form without the aid of embalming.

9. On Sandys, see Chapter 11.

10. The term is applied here in its everyday usage as distinct from that commonly encountered in earlier collections where bezoars (originally derived from the Persian wild goat) were treasured for their supposed amuletic or medicinal properties. See further, Chapter 4.

11. Noted and illustrated by John and Andrew Van Rymsdyk, *Museum Britannicum* (London, 1778), p. 48, tab. xix, fig. 5.

12. On Richardson, see Chapter 1.

13. Noted and illustrated by Van Rymsdyk, op. cit. (note 11), p. 47, tab. xix, fig. 1.

14. On Thoresby, see Chapter 1.

15. Onychogryphosis is a thickening of the nail (usually the great toe nail) in the elderly with curvature and elongation that can reach remarkable size if untreated. It is known colloquially as ram's horn nail.

16. A *Plica polonica* is a matted and often infested mass of head hair such as is found in vagrants and untended people who are mentally ill and destitute: *Dictionary of Biology and Medicine* (op. cit., note 8), vol. III, p. 2226.

17. Hans Sloane, *Account of a most Efficaceous Medicine for Soreness, Weakness, and several other Distempers of the Eyes* (London, 1745).

4 Vertebrate Collections

Juliet Clutton-Brock

* In the discussion following a lecture given at The Natural History Museum in London in 1991, someone asked whether it would ever be admissible to return certain biological specimens to museums in their countries of origin. One participant responded, perhaps mischievously, that the return of material objects might be no great loss to the Museum as long as the labels and all other information about the specimens were retained. This reflects precisely the situation of almost all of the 4,500 or so vertebrate specimens listed in the published works and handwritten catalogues of Sir Hans Sloane. Over the years the specimens have either been dispersed without trace, have perished or have been destroyed and although their loss is tragic, the evidence provided by Sloane's individual accounts of the animals remains of very great value. These accounts provide a unique record of contemporary knowledge of the natural world over the period of seventy years when Sloane was compiling his collections, from the 1680s until he died in 1753 aged ninety-two.

The main published sources of Sloane's descriptions of vertebrates are in the second volume of his *Natural History of Jamaica*, published in 1725, and in scattered papers in the *Philosophical Transactions of the Royal Society*. His collections of vertebrate specimens are described and indexed in his manuscript catalogues, which are listed (as with all Sloane's collections) according to a numerical sequence, but it is difficult to count the exact numbers in each class of animals since they are often mixed and some numbers are left unallocated. Fortunately, Sloane had all the entries indexed with marvellous neatness and accuracy by an amanuensis and this makes searching for an individual record relatively easy. The great majority of the original entries are in Sloane's handwriting but some are by his assistants, notably Cromwell Mortimer (see Chapter 1) whose script is very clear; other hands are less legible, and one is a barely decipherable scrawl. Most of the descriptions are in English but some are in Latin. Sloane was scrupulous in quoting publications that referred to any detail concerning his specimens and these are included in the descriptions given below, where appropriate.

Volume 25 of the catalogue contains the following numbers of vertebrate entries:
Fish

25a 1–1563 entries, which include parts of whales, a description of the manatee from the West Indies, a unicorn's horn, some fossils and many sea horses (designated as hippocampus).
Birds

25b 1–907 entries, ending with a shark's tooth.
Eggs

25c 1–272 entries, although some numbers are unallocated.

Includes reptile eggs as well as those of birds. There is an alphabetical index of the eggs at the end of this section.   *25d*
Quadrupeds
1–1903 entries.   *25e*

Sloane's *Natural History* of Jamaica

As recounted in Chapter 1, Sloane spent fifteen months in Jamaica, arriving on 19 December 1687 (at the age of twenty-seven) and leaving on 16 March 1689, during which time he amassed huge collections of plants and animals. An illustrator was employed by Sloane to make drawings of many of his specimens and these are reproduced in the *Natural History*, as engravings (see Figs. 11–13, 15; page numbers quoted in the following text refer to the same work.

Fishes from Jamaica

Sloane admitted that his observations on the fishes of Jamaica were very imperfect, partly because he was based six miles from the sea and the collected fishes rotted so quickly, and also because he was otherwise occupied. He observed that the Indians were expert at spearing fish during the daytime, and also at night which they did by having wax lights (*cerei*) on their boats that attracted the fish. The Indians also soaked the bruised bark of the Dog-wood tree (probably *Piscidia piscipala*) in standing water, which intoxicated the fish so that they could be speedily taken [p. 275].

The descriptions of fish are grouped in eight short chapters according to their physical appearance, such as flat-fish, eel, smooth-skinned, prickly and so on. Reproduced here in Fig. 11 is an example of the eight double pages of drawings of fish as included in volume II of the *Natural History*. The text records that the stomach of the Toad-fish (probably *Lagocephalus* sp. or *Sphoeroides* sp.) had under it 'two wind bladders', by which it puffed itself up [pp. 279–80]. The *Cugupuguacu Brasiliensibus* (a grouper, *Epinephelus* sp.) had been taken in the sea near Port Royal and was drawn natural size at Jamaica, but through lack of time Sloane had made no descriptions of the fish [p. 280]. About the Barracuda (*Sphyraena* sp.) he had observed quite correctly that its flesh was sometimes poisonous:[1]

According to its feeding on venemous or not venemous Food, 'tis wholesome or poysonous to those who eat it; 'tis also noxious in some Seasons of the year, and in some Places, and innocent in others, I suppose according to its nourishment, by which now and then, it acquires so much poison as to kill immediately. It was taken at *Old Harbour*, and notwithstanding its supposed poisonous Qualities sold in the Markets [p. 285].

---

* Marginal numerals in this chapter refer to Sloane catalogues listed on pp. 291–4

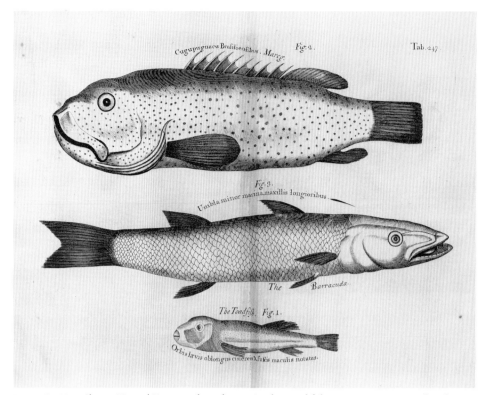

Fig. 11 Sir Hans Sloane, *Natural History*, vol. II, tab. 247. '*1*: the Toad-fish; *2*: *Cugupuguacu Brasiliensibus*; *3*: the Barracuda.'

Like those figured here, the rest of the fishes described by Sloane appear to be the locally common species caught for eating.[2]

Quadrupeds and Serpents from Jamaica

This chapter includes a tree frog, reptiles, and mammals. There is a detailed account of a crocodile (*Crocodylus acutus*) that reached a length of nineteen feet, and was common on the coasts and in the deep rivers of Jamaica [p. 332]. It is now very rare.[3]

In his account of the yellow snake (see Fig. 12), which he named *Serpens major subflavus* and which today is called *Epicrates subflavus*, Sloane recorded that 'An Indian brought this figur'd here and several others to me, he us'd to take them behind the necks, so that they could not bite him' [p. 335]. Sloane further commented that:

... the European Nations inhabiting the Countries producing Sugar, do not molest these Creatures, because they destroy the Rats (which came originally from ships cast away on the Coast, &c.) [which] multiply strangely there, and do infinite Mischief to the Sugar Canes, not only by eating them, but spoiling the Juice of those they gnaw [p. 346].

Unfortunately the endemic reptiles could not keep pace

with the rats and in 1872 four pairs of the small Indian mongoose (*Herpestes auropunctatus*) were brought from Calcutta to Jamaica. This had a lethal effect on the live-bearing yellow snake (now an endangered species) and on the populations of lizards that were devoured in great numbers by the mongooses.[4]

Sloane's most important contribution to knowledge of the Jamaican vertebrates was probably his drawing and description of the giant galliwasp, named by him *Scincus maximus fuscus* (see Fig. 13, no. 9), now called *Celestus occiduus*. This large anguid lizard, which has been extinct since before 1870, was described in detail by Sloane:

This appear'd in all things to be a great *Scinc*, it was eleven Inches long from Head to Tail, and six inches about the middle, where bigest, it was almost round every where from a sharp round Snout, increasing to the middle, and from thence decreasing to the Tail, which ended in a Point; the Back was hard and a little compress'd, and so was the Belly, it had two round *Spiracula* or Nostrils in the two corners of the snout. About half an inch behind them were the Eyes, and near an Inch further two oblong Holes for the Ears; about three Inches from the beginning of the Snout towards the Tail were the fore Feet, which had two Joints, and were not over an Inch and a half long, with five Toes like those of a Lizard, the hinder Legs were of the same Length, &c. and

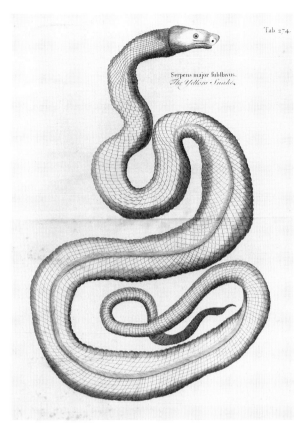

Fig. 12 Sir Hans Sloane, *Natural History*, vol. II, tab. 274. 'The yellow snake.'

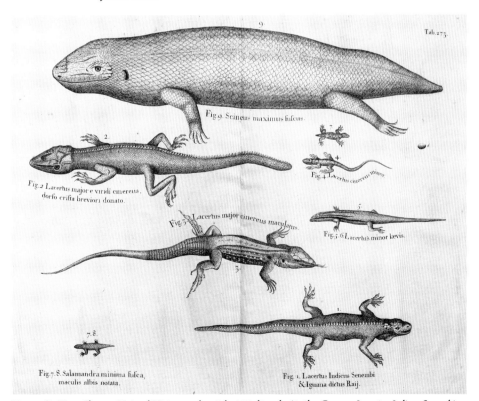

Fig. 13 Sir Hans Sloane, *Natural History*, vol. II, tab. 273: lizards. '1: the Gwana, *Lacertus Indicus Senembi & Iguana dictus Raih*; 2: *Lacertus major e viridi cinereus, dorso crista breviori donato*; 3: the Great Spotted Lizard, *Lacertus major cinereus maculatus*; 4: the least light Brown, or, Grey Lizard, *Lacertus cinereus minor*; 5: *Lacertus minor laevis*; 6: the egg of the previous; 7–8: the Wood Slave, *Salamandra minima sulca, maculis albis notata*; 9: the giant galliwasp, *Scincus maximus sulcus*.'

Fig. 14 *Ameiva dorsalis*. This could be a Sloane specimen although it is not the individual lizard described and figured by Sloane (see Fig. 13, no. *3*). It is labelled as the holotype of *Ameiva sloani*. NHM, spirit collections, III,10a. Reproduced by courtesy of the Trustees of The Natural History Museum.

beyond them the *anus*, cover'd with a transverse Flap, the back or upper parts were all cover'd over with Rhomboidall small rowes of scales of a brown colour with spots of Orange colour, and the Belly with the latter only.

It had a short Larinx, Lungs not altogether membranaceous, the Heart as of other Animals, the Stomach not at all muscular, but made not sack Fashion, but of several wide Circumvolutions, with Cells like those of the Colon in other animals, and with all very thin and wide, containing the smallest Crabs, the liver was great and very black, and there were two whitish colour'd Bodies of Likeness in Substance to the Lungs, made up of several Lobes plac'd long Ways on each side of the Pelvis, which I took for the Kidneys.

It is to be found in marsh Grounds, in several parts of the Island.

It is reckon'd very poisonous in the Bite, and I was told one had his thigh bit by this Creature and dy'd the next Day. It is amphibious, and lies both in water and on Land.

It flyes from a Man, but loves to feed on the Remainder of his Victuals.

It feeds commonly on the smallest sort of sea crabs [pp. 334–5].

This must be one of the most comprehensive descriptions of the anatomy of an extinct species of vertebrate written during the seventeenth century. It shows that Sloane, despite his very wide interests, was prepared to make and record careful observations on individual specimens.

Six other lizards were described and are shown in Fig. 13: these include the Gwana, *Cyclura collei* (Fig. 13, no. 1), about which Sloane wrote:

They are very common in *Jamaica*, and are eaten there, and were of great Use when the *English* first took this Island, being as I was assur'd by the first Settlers, commonly sold for Half a Crown a Piece in the publick markets [p. 333].

For the last forty years this iguana was believed to be extinct but it has been recently 'rediscovered'.

Another green lizard, *Anolis garmani* (Fig. 13, no. 2) was described as follows:

. . . found frequently in the Woods of Jamaica, it differs very little from the Guana, but in being greener, less, and having a shorter Crest or Comb along the Back. it lays Eggs less than a Pigeon's Egg [p. 333].

The Greatest Spotted Lizard, *Ameiva dorsalis*, shown here in Fig. 13, no. 3, is similar to but not identical with the specimen labelled as the holotype of *Ameiva sloani* in the spirit collections of The Natural History Museum (Fig. 14). It was described by Sloane as:

about eight inches long, of the shape of other Lizards, reddish under the Chaps, light brown on the Back and Tail, with one yellowish green Line along it, it is blue all under in the Abdomen, &c. It is very common about old Walls [p. 333].

The least light Brown, or, Grey Lizard, shown in Fig. 13, no. 4, may be identified as *Anolis lineatopus*. It was described as loving 'moist Places and Stones, where it is to be found leaping from one to another, not only here but through all the Caribes' [p. 333].

The description of *Lacertus minor laevis*, today named

Mabuya mabouya [p. 333], as having a great many brown Spots on it, does not match the drawing, shown in Fig. 13, no. 5 with its egg as no. 6.

The Wood Slave, (Fig. 13, nos. 7, 8), is a gecko, *Sphaerodactylus argus*, which is still widespread and common. Sloane wrote that 'it lodges it self in old rotten Timber, and peeps out frequently frisking up and down in hot Weather' [p. 334].

Besides these reptiles Sloane described an unidentified tree frog [p. 331], a land tortoise (*Testudo denticulata*) [p. 331], and two species of turtle, the Hawk's-bill (*Eretmochelys imbricata*) [p. 332], chiefly valued for the provision of tortoise-shell and the best or Green turtle (*Chelone mydas*):

The best or green Turtle or tortoises come to the *Caymanes* once a Year to lay their Eggs in the Sand, to be hatch'd by the sun, and at that time the Turtlers take them in great Numbers; at other times the Turtles go to the south Cayes of *Cuba*, there to feed on the Sea Grass growing under Water, wherefore the turtlers go thither in quest of them, and it may be four Men in a Sloop may bring in Thirty, Forty, or Fifty Turtles, worth seventeen or eighteen Shillings a piece, more or less, according to their Goodness. The Female with Egg is reckon'd the best, they sometimes get their Loading in a Day, but are usually six weeks in making the voyage; they feed on Turtle, Bisquet, Bread, and Salt, they catch the Turtle with Nets of Yarn larger than Whipcord. When they come home they put them into the sea in four square Penns or palisadoed places, where they keep alive till there be occasion to kill them, which will be very long sometimes, tho' the sooner they are kill'd after taking, they are the fatter. The Callipee, or under Part of the Breast and Belly bak'd, is reckon'd the best Piece, the liver and Fat are counted delicacies, those who feed much upon them sweat or discharge at their Pores a yellow Serum, especially under the Arm Pits. The Fat is yellow, tastes like marrow, and gives the Skin a yellow Hue [p. 331].

Birds from Jamaica

It is a common Opinion, that the hot Parts of the World abound most with Birds of fine colour'd Feathers, and that they want those who sing: The first of which is true and the latter false, for there are many sweet singing Birds to be found here, and those of as pleasant Notes as any in *Europe* [p. 293].

Sloane described seventy-five species of bird from Jamaica, including the introduced Guinea fowl, peacock, pigeon, common fowl, goose, and ducks [pp. 294–325].

About the Green Sparrow, or Green-humming Bird (*Todus todus*)[5] (Fig. 15, no. 1) he wrote 'It loves low melancholly Places, and scarce will stir from any one till they take it. It is one of the most beautiful Small-birds I ever saw' [p. 307].

No. 2. in Fig. 15 shows a small bittern (*Ixobrychus exilis*) drawn after death and so described:

It feeds on *Libellas*, Cray Fish, Shrimps, and other Insects haunting watery places. It loves watery places. I know not but that some part of the odd Position of the Neck may be owing to the carrying of it, after it was kill'd [p. 315].

Fig. 15 Sir Hans Sloane, *Natural History*, vol. II, tab. 263: birds. '1: Green Sparrow, or Green-humming Bird, *Rubecula viridus elegantissima*; 2: A small bittern, *Ardea stellaris minor*; 3: The black gaulding or blew gaulding, *Ardea coerulea-nigra*.'

Sloane was careful about measurements:

The birds were drawn life-size, the Green humming-bird being four inches from the end of the Bill to the end of the Tail, about twice as much from the end of Wing to Wing expanded, the head was large in proportion to the Body. It had a broad flat Bill three quarters of an inch long . . .

Clearly, he also inspected the gut contents of all the animals he collected and he wrote of the black gaulding or blew gaulding (the little blue heron, *Egretta caerulea*) (Fig. 15, no. 3), that 'the Oesophagus was wide, the Stomach hanging like a sack, and very well fill'd with Shrimps, young Crabs, spiders, Field Crickets &c. It loves ponds and watery places [p. 315].

Mammals from Jamaica

Mammals introduced to Jamaica were listed by Sloane as horse, ass, mule, cattle, sheep, Guinea goats and hair sheep, fallow deer, pig, monkey, dog, cat, rat (the black or ship rat, *Rattus rattus*), and mouse [pp. 327–9]. The only wild mammals listed are two species of bat (although Allen[6] records thirty-one species from the West Indies); one Sloane called a common bat, or flutter Mouse, *Vespertilio*, and the second he called *Vespertilio rostro* because it had an ear-like process over its snout, and fed on prickly pears. This was probably the Jamaican fruit bat (*Artibeus jamaicen-*

Fig. 16 J. & A. Van Rymsdyk, *Museum Britannicum* (1778), tab. vi: birds' eggs and a hair ball from Sir Hans Sloane's museum, later in the British Museum. '6: Parrot's Egg, form beautiful oval, colour reddish white, laid in September 1724, after the Parrot had been nine years in *England*, without a mate. *Vid.* for an entertaining Account like this, in the incomparable Dr. *Harvey* on Generation. *Exer*, v. *p.* 24; 7: A Hair Ball. found in an Ox's stomach, from Jamaica; colour brown ochre, the hair proceeding as it were from the center, the same at the posterior part; the inside solid of a hard glewey substance.'

sis.[7] Sloane also recorded a racoon (*sic*) or coati (*Procyon* sp. or *Nasua* sp.) which he claimed was common in the mountains, from where it made paths to the sugar cane which was its only food [p. 329]. There are no raccoons or coatis living wild on Jamaica today, but they were also described by Brown[8] who claimed that raccoons were occasionally brought to the island as captive animals.

The only aquatic mammal described by Sloane was the manatee or Sea-Cow (*Trichechus manatus*) which he wrote about at length:

This is sometimes taken in the quieter Bays of this Island, tho' rarely now a Days: They have formerly been frequent, but are, by the multitude of People and the Hunters catching them, destroy'd. They are caught by the *Indians* who are reckon'd the best Hunters, knowing the Haunts and customs of their Game, and being very dexterous at it, especially those of the *Musquitos*, or *Costa Ricca*. The *Manatis* are reckon'd extraordinary Food and are likewise salted as Beef, and eaten as Provision . . .

They lye towards the Surface of the Water in Rivers and Bayes, have two fins like Arms, are struck with Arrows having Cords fastened to them with a Buoy at their Ends. They are so large as to require a pair of Oxen in a Cart to carry them, the best

Fish in the World and appear like Beef or Veal. Their cur'd Flesh keeps long without Corruption, is brought from *Espanola* to *Spain*, and is like to English Beef at sight, and to Tunny Fish in Taste. *Manatis* feed on Grass growing under Water, they have Stones in their Heads, good for the Diseases of the Liver burn't and powder'd, taken in the Morning with white Wine, it takes away the Pain in the Kidneys, breaks the Stone . . . [p. 329].

As with the 800 plants (see Chapter 8) and much else, Sloane probably brought back to England many of the vertebrate animals that he collected, preserved in spirit or as skins. It is, however, difficult to distinguish, in the catalogues, the specimens that Sloane gathered personally from those that he purchased or was given during the sixty years that he continued adding to his collections after his return from Jamaica. He also attempted to bring back some living animals, a yellow snake, a crocodile, and a 'guana' (lizard) [p. 346]. The snake was shot on board ship by servants of the Duchess of Albemarle after it escaped from the jar in which it was kept. The guana fell overboard and was drowned, and the crocodile, which was fed on the same food as the snake, died in its tub on 15 May 1689. Sloane remarked: 'Thus I lost, by this time of the Voyage, all my live Creatures, and so it happens to most People, who lose their strange live Animals for want of proper Air, Food, or Shelter' [p. 346].

Other Exotic Animals brought to England alive or reared in Captivity

Sloane did, however, manage to keep many live animals in the garden of his Chelsea home and when they died they were added to his museum, as were exotic animals which lived and died in captivity elsewhere. The catalogued examples of exotic animals bred in England include the following.

Birds and Eggs

An ostridges egg. These are eaten in Barbary. Sir Nicholas Garret had one tame which laid eggs at his house at West Ham beyond Stratford & he commended them as admirable victuals. Oeuf's d'Autruche. Il faut observer que eux, qui ont ete pondu dans l'Afrique, ont la coque incomparablement plus epaisie queles oeufs des Autriches de la Menagerie du roi Biron p. 277.[9] · · · · · · · · 25c/136

Parrots eggs laid in [month?] 1724. after the parrot had been nine years in England & never bred, given me by Mr Harris (see Fig. 16, no. 6).[10] · · · · · · · · 25c/186

The egg of a Guana [lizard] laid in England after it was brought from Antigua & lived a few days. · · · · · · · · 25c/216

A vulturs egg laid in the Tower given me by Mr Doyly. · · · · · · · · 25c/245

The skin of the head & hock of the red headed crane from Bengall [probably the Common crane, *Grus grus*]. given me by Mr Dubois. this crane lived in my garden severall years, & died by swallowing a brass linked sleeve button. · · · · · · · · 25b/684

. . . a smaller sort of Bustard from Moca in Arabia. It lived in my garden many years and ate flesh & other foods as it had done at Mitcham in Mr Dubois' garden. who gave it me & had it brought over by one of the coffee ships. · · · · · · · · 25b/853

Fig. 17 *Chauliodus sloani*, NHM, 1978.9.11.1. Reproduced by courtesy of the Trustees of The Natural History Museum.

Quadrupeds

25e/253 A piece of the lyons skin that dyed in the Tower in K. James's reign.

25e/677 The horns of a Spotted East India deer or stagg [probably *Axis axis* but possibly the now endangered spotted deer from the Philippine islands, *Cervus alfredi*]. They shed them here in England at all times of the year. If the horns are not hardened ere winter they gangrene & the stagg dyes. These were given me by the Earl of Abbington.

25e/856 A hawks bill turtle or tortoise from the coast of Guinea where it was taken & brought to me by Mr. Harris I kept it in a tub of fresh water and made salt by the addition of 40th. part of bay salt. It fed on whitings which it would eat wᵗ its bill, it would come up to breath freqᵗˡʸ. & [?] itselfe in the water according to its pleasure. it was killed wᵗ the cold weather as was the following.

25e/857 A small land tortoise from Virginia of wᶜʰ I could not find the food.

25e/1284 A large grayish green lizard from Malaga. It would eat flies & drink water. It would likewise drink milk but vomited it curdled & died towards the latter end of Sept. at London.

25e/1428 The case [skin] of a beaver I kept alive in my garden for some time.

25e/1429 The inward parts in spirits.

25e/1462 The claw of an old Lyon that lived from K. Charles 2d. reign to 1711. Id. sticking to the bone.

25e/1519 A young lyon pupp whelped in the Tower. This is one of 3 of the same litter 2 whereof died the 3rd lived. The same lyon also brought a litter of 2 or 3 before. from Mr Marly a keeper of his Majesty's rough game.

25e/1779 Two cataracts taken out of the eyes of a blind small fox from Greenland [the arctic fox, *Alopex lagopus*]. He lived many years wᵗ me in my garden was brown in summer & turned white in winter. In April generally the fox shed the white hair unless [until] the last year of its life when being sick the white furr continued till its death not changing as usually.

25e/1864 The trunk eyes etc of the Elephant that died of a Consumption in the year 1741 at Mile end in Middlesex.

The Catalogue of Vertebrates

The entries of vertebrate specimens in volume *25a–e* of the manuscript catalogue present a kind of synopsis of the knowledge and attitudes of Sloane and his contemporaries to the natural world. A selection of these entries, under Sloane's divisions of fish, birds, and quadrupeds is therefore given below, using Sloane's spelling and abbreviations, and including his references to other published works either on that particular specimen or to the subject in general.

The first page of the volume has a note stating that in his garden Sloane had the skeleton of the spermaceti whale, or 'Cashalot' (*Physeter catodon*), which had been stranded on the Essex coast. The sperm whale is an inhabitant of warm equatorial waters, but old males quite often extend their range northwards and then they are occasionally stranded on the British coasts.

Fish

There are 1,563 entries of fishes amongst which are a number of fossils and other classes of animals. Many of the descriptions are in Latin. Marine mammals from manatees to whales are counted as fish.

One fish that has survived from the Sloane collection is the holotype of *Chauliodus sloani*, a deep sea fish collected from the Straits of Gibraltar (Fig. 17). The old label on the specimen bottle gives the fish the name 'viper mouth', presumably from the fish's habit of swallowing other fish whole. An entry from this fish has not, however, been found in Sloane's catalogue or index.

Birds

There are 907 entries, the last being a glass case with flycatchers, titmouse, and humming birds.

Amongst the birds indexed in volume 26d are:

Bird	No. of specimens
Birds of paradise	10
Canary	4
Cornish chough	3
Humming birds	52
Macaw	5
Toucan	11
Turkey	5
Upupa (hoopoe)	4

Selected entries of birds from the catalogue include the following:

Exotic birds

Feathers from birds of paradise (which are restricted to north Australia and New Guinea) had been brought to Europe since the Spanish explorers reached the Moluccas, the southern islands of Indonesia, in 1522. Sloane's collection

25b/530 included 'Remains of the Ring paradyse bird from Japan . . .' Presumably this bird of paradise had been imported to Japan by local traders. Many other birds (sometimes alive) and their eggs were brought as curiosities from all parts of the world, and Sloane must have been one of the first Englishmen to learn about the delights of bird's nest soup, as described below:

25b/140 Edible birds nest. /nidus avium Indicarium. Navarette voyages in Spanish page 45[11] ayuna ospecie de Golondrinas &c. Translated in Churchills Collections of voyages Vol 1 page 46.[12] In the Island of Calimianianes, belonging to Manila, & in others of that Archipelago, there is a sort of Swallows not much unlike ours, they swim upon the sea, & build their Nests in the rocks along the shore. These Nests are mightily valued in Manila among the Natives, & much more in China, where they give great Rates for them. Those Birds make them of the foam of the sea; when dry they look like a piece of ash-colour'd clay, but being boil'd w^t flesh they are excallent meat, & very nourishing, as they all say. Marry'd men, & those that have weak stomachs use it; it is no good food for those that are didicated to God's Service; but it is wonderful so delicious a Morsel, as they who eat it think can never be sufficiently commended, should be made of such matter.

Examples of birds from the Americas include the following:

Bill of the Toucan of Condamine p. 172 who says that its tongue is said to have great virtues.   25b/154

There are five genera of toucans belonging to the family Ramphastidae. Toucans all come from South and Central America.

Feather of the condor from ye. coast of Chili.   25b/214

This feather, which was 2 ft. 4 ins. long, was described together with details of the Condor (*Vultur gryphus*) and how this bird was killed by seamen while it sat on the cliffs. They ate the bird, thinking it was a kind of turkey.[13]

A white swallow from Buenos Ayres.   25b/702
Feathers made up to fright the slaves . . .   25b/724

Sloane's description of the booby (*Sula* spp.) indicates that this bird came from the West Indies but there are many species of this sea bird around the world including the gannet (*Sula bassana*), known to Sloane as the Soland goose, which is found in Britain:

A booby? The booby is a water fowl, somewhat less than a Hen   25b/720
of a light greyish colour, it hath a strong Bill, longer & bigger than a Crows, and broader at the end; her feet [are] flat like a Ducks feet. It is a very simple creature, and will hardly go out of a Mans way. In other places they build their nests on the Ground but here (the Isle of Aves [north west of Domenica in the Caribbean Sea]) they build on trees; wch I never saw anywhere else; tho' I have seen of them in a great many places. Their flesh is black & eats fishy, but are often eaten by the Privateers. Dampier voyag. Vol. 1. p. 49.[14]

A young Flamingo or phenicopher [now called Phoenicopteridae]   25b/814
from Mr Theobalds from the continent of America. vid Dampier's Voy Vol 1. p. 70. The flesh of both young & old is lean & black yet very good meat, tasting neither fishy nor any way unsavoury. Their tongues are large, having a large knob of fat at the root, wch is an excellent bit. a Dish of Flamingo's tongues being fit for a Princes table.[15]

The back part of the eye of an ostrich [with its] muscles prepared   25b/572
by Mr Ranby.

The latter specimen presumably came from an ostrich that was kept alive in England.

The Dodo

There is no mention of the Dodo (*Raphus cucullatus*) in Sloane's works, probably because it was already extinct by his time, but he did own an oil painting of this giant, flightless pigeon from Mauritius (Plate 5).

Birds from England

White hern [heron] top. an such as belongs to the black topping   25b/174
of the knights of the garter?[16]
The leggs & beak of the Cornish Chough? from the Isle of Wight.   25b/254
A Cornish chough, a sort of Jackdaw w^t a red crooked bill & red   25b/353
leggs . . . Charlton p. 75.[17] Tho. Killegrew.
A white hen pheasant.   25b/365
A white Canary bird.   25b/367
A milk white swallow from Lincolnshire given me by Mr Heneage.   25b/616

Birds from Scotland

In addition to a few carcasses of whole birds, there is listed:

25b/153 'Oil from a bird in the N. Isles of Scotland w^t wch the Inhabitants cure the Rheumatisme etc.' – probably oil from the
25b/523 Fulmar (*Fulmarus glacialis*) – and 'Eider down used for coverlets to beds in Denmark & other cold countries? taken from a sea fowl'. The eiderdown, a quilt filled with the down of the female Eider duck (*Somateria mollissima*) was obviously not yet a common form of bedding in Britain in Sloane's time.

Martin Martin, who had visited the islands of St. Kilda in the Outer Hebrides in the early 1690s, was one of the collectors from whom Sloane obtained a number of birds and their eggs that were otherwise little known south of
25c/118 the border. Examples includes the broken egg of a Soland
25b/213 goose, and a Goar fowl from St. Kilda. The Goar or Gar fowl were alternative names for the extinct Great auk (*Pinguinus impennis*) which nested on the islands of St Kilda, the Orkneys, and elsewhere until the last bird was killed in 1840.[18] The nesting habits of the flightless Great auk and its exploitation by the St. Kildans in the seventeenth century are described by Martin.[19]

Martin also presented Sloane with some examples of
25e/13 Scottish ram's horn, one of which was made into a ladle as used in the Western Islands of Scotland.

As people are today. Sloane and his contemporaries were intrigued by birds that were occasionally sighted as vagrants in the British Isles and he collected them when he could. A favourite was the hoopoe:

25b/790 Upupa the Dung-bird the Hooper. Charlton p. 98. From Cambridgeshire by my Grandson Cadogan. [also] Upupa, hoopoo or hoopoe from Hampshire in Sp. V. [spirit of wine].

Eggs

There are 272 entries (although some numbers are not assigned), with the index following, all in volume 25c and d. Some examples are given below, in order of their accession numbers, to show what a medley of scientifically valuable specimens and curiosities must have been contained in Sloane's museum:

25c/15 Fulmers egg perfectly white.
25c/20 An Scotch honey buzzard . . .[20]
25c/89 Land tortoises egg.
25c/117 Crocodiles egg.
25c/119 A salamanders egg from the East Indies. The young one seen in it.
25c/121 Awks egg.
25c/125 An egg w^t a horse shoe naild on it.
25c/141 An ostriches egg? from Mr. Burnett from Buenos aires? much lesser an Condors? a smaller sort of Ostridge, whose feathers are of no value.[21]
25c/148 A Kings fishers egg.
25c/155 The small bird without a name like the stopparola Aldrovandi. Willughby's ornithology. p. 217.[22] eggs w^t a nest.
25c/220 A humming bird large mantis & scorpion. Mr Maidstone.
25c/229 A Maccaws egg.
25c/233 The egg of a large Duke owl [?] laid in my garden.

A common hens egg shell wch was said to have had 2 yolks from 25c/234 Dr Grews collections.[23]
Four eggs from the China pheasant. 25c/240
An ostridges egg from Sir Nicholas Garrards in Essex, smooth. 25c/241 They were eat by that family as other eggs given me by Lady Garrard.
A very odd furrowed guinea hens egg given to me by my 25c/243 daughter Cadogan.[24]

Quadrupeds

There are 1,903 entries. The following numbers of specimens are selected from the index of quadrupeds in volume 25e:

Taxon	Number of specimens
Armadillo	5
Bezoars	49
Calculi	10
Chameleon	21
Crocodile	21
Elephant	68
Frog [incl. Rana]	24
Gall bladder	12
Hair ball	14
Hippopotamus	8
Iguana	6
Lizards [incl. Lacerta]	248
Lion	15
Manati	10
Monkeys	20
Porcupine	4
Orang Outang	3
Rabbit	10
Rats	10
Rhinoceros	20
Salamander	29
Scaly lizard	16
Sloth	4
Snake	5
Snake stones	3
Stones	44
Tortoise [incl. sea tortoise]	67
Tree frog	3
Unicorn	3
Water lizard	15

Some examples of quadrupeds from volume 25e of the catalogue:

A cane made of turned & joined ivory wth ye fig: of a shepherd 25e/26 tempting a naked woman wth an Fruit, carved on ye Head.
The head of a staffe of unicorns horn. 25e/111
A white boar's foot. 25e/44
The underchap of a fallow deer wherein the grinders appear gilded 25e/140 with armatura or pyrites. This was given me by the Lady Thanet who brought it from her park in ye North of England, where the deer feeding on one side of it have their teeth so encrusted the others not.
The skin of a tartar lamb, being an abortive lamb in Tartay of 25e/174 wch are made caps in China.[25]
A ratt which was starved to death in a wall given me by Mr 25e/194 Fowler.

25e/198   The skeleton of the head of the Babyroussa [the Babirusa, *Babyrousa babyrussa*] given me by Mr Courten.[26]

25e/222   The bone in an oxes legg taken up at Pauls & supposed to be of those sacrificed in time of the Romans when it was an heathen temple [see further, Chapter 12].

25e/404   A tigers tooth.

25e/408   Musk.

25e/459   The skin of the wild asse called Zebra from the cape of good hope, given me by Mr Charles Dubois.

25e/534   Small Cameleons from the cape of good hope. from [Dr Dolney]. One has a larger crest over the head than the others. Seba. tom. 1. p. 135.[27]

25e/634   Mus Indicus major . . .

25e/635   Mus Indicus minor . . .

25e/636   Mus Indicus striatus . . .

25e/716   A straight rams horn an the 4 horn'd one.[28]

25e/717   The same.

25e/730   A white Mole. Seba tom. 1. p. 51. Tab. 32. fig. 1.

25e/766   Hair ball from the stomach of a cow or ox . . .[29]

25e/864   A ratt with the foreleggs very short & the hind leggs long wch burrows in the deserts of Arabia from Mr Tanner.[30]

25e/1045   The skeleton of a Kama [hartebeest from southern Africa, *Alcelaphus caama*].

25e/1055   A very large Sea horses tooth. Id. vid. 1081.[31]

25e/1081   An Hippopotamus's tooth. Id cum 1055.

25e/1183   The hair of the urus lofar [?]. Commontar [?]. taken from between the horns & upper part of the neck wch smells of musk given to me as a rarity by the order of his Majesty King George [1 added in pencil] being taken from 2 A bull & cow from Prussia sent from Coningsberg by the K. of Prussia. They were sent in wooden coops & were 12 weeks in their passage.[32]

25e/1192   A large molar tooth said to be of an alogator from Dr Houston. but Alogators have no molar tooth.

25e/1197   The skin of a black fox from Carolina where they are very rare & found only on the mountains. Mr Catesby.

25e/1198   The skin of a polecatt, they all vary in their marks – two being never seen alike, some almost all white others mostly black w^t but little white which forms a sport of nature peculiar to this little beast, at least I know of no wild beast but what are all of the same colour.[33]

25e/1201   A white mouse catch'd in a trap in Hannover square.[34]

25e/1202   A white mole catchd about London given me by Mr. [ ] perish'd.

25e/1257   A dogg w^t one head & two bodies.

25e/1258   A dogg with 2 heads & one body.

25e/1311   Sea horse beard bristles to make a ring for the cramp.[35]

25e/1326   A whole hoofed boars foot a breed of which is in Leicestershire & Oxfordshire said to be better for food than the other kind. from Mr Cripp.[36]

25e/1329   Small bones (of froggs) sent as bones of some small birds, of which there is an Hill full, at Neither-Jossa. 7 German miles or 14 hours travelling from Hesse Cassell.

25e/1338   The bufalos horn of America from Mr Dering.

25e/1484   The backbone of a horse w^t sevll. protruberances upon it from a collar [. . .] by Mr Ranby.

25e/1731   An hydatis from the viscera of a sheep in sp. V.

25e/1861   A beavers tail from Hudson Bay by Mr Potts.

25e/1862   Two scent baggs of a Beaver or Castorium from the same.

25e/1869   The case [skin] of a Porcupine from Hudson Bay in North America its much larger than the common Porcupine tho' the Prikkles are smaller & all cover'd w^t hair or furr as long & of the colour of a Beaver probably designed by the Authore of Nature to keep it warm in that very cold climate from Dr Massey.

25e/1889   A large Philander or the Opossum w^t its young ones from Brasil belonging to the Duke of Richmond and bought at the sale of his Museum. by J.S. M.D.

25e/1890   A Persian cat . . .

Primates

It is evident from the entries on primates given below that Sloane was not sure whether these creatures were animals or some sort of primitive human.

25e/204   The skeleton of an Orang Outang or wild man from Sumatra in the East Indies by Capt. Aprice. the hands and feet were thrown overboard in coming from the East Indies when this creature died. It was given me by Mr. Maidstone. vid No 1851.[37]

25e/994   Simia tardigrada? Id. Animalculum Cynocephalum, Ceilonicum, tardigradum dictum Simii species, Seba tom. 1. Tab. 35, fig 1. page 55.

25e/1851   The homo sylvestris, Orang outang, or Chimpanzi from Borneo. It dyed in China and was put into rack & brought over to rot [?]. Charles Lockyer who gave her to me. She is covered w^t longer hair.

25e/1895   The fore Paws of an Orang Outang or Chimpanzi from the Duke of Richmonds Sale by Dr. Stack.

Rhinoceroses

The rhinoceros horns owned by Sloane are amongst some of the very few specimens in his collections of quadrupeds to survive. There is a pair of horns of the African white rhinoceros (*Ceratotherium simum*) and a pair of horns of the black rhinoceros (*Diceros bicornis*) in The Natural History Museum.[38] They are described and figured in the long letter on the natural history of the rhinoceros by Parsons[39] (see Fig. 18). The white rhino horns are described in Sloane's catalogue as:

25e/1262   Two horns of a rhinoceros joined together by the skin of the snout where they grow. One of them is straight, the other crooked. from Lagoa on the Continent of Africa N of Madagascar & taken by the person who made a present of them to Mr Lockyer who gave them to me. Vid. Cosman.

In addition, Sloane made the following comments on the horns:[40]

These Horns were given me by my worthy and ingenious Friend and Acquaintance *Charles Lockyer* Esq; who was (as I have been told) sent in a Ship of Strength with a Power given him by the *East-Indian* and *African* Companies, to go on their Affairs to that unfrequented Coast [south east Africa] which common Travellers have been afraid to go to because of the Barbarity and Cruelty commonly said to belong to its Inhabitants, and with which the *Egyptians*, and from them the *Greeks* and *Romans*, had a greater Intercourse and Knowledge than with the Southern Parts of *Asia*, where the Animal is generally found with only one Horn.

The two double-horned species of African rhinoceros, the black and the white, were little known and Sloane did not know whether the double horns were an abnormality or

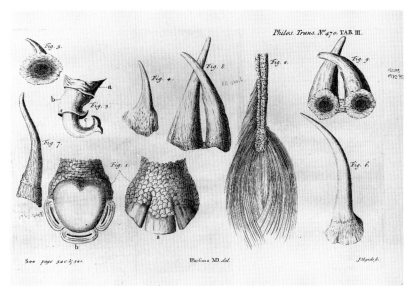

Fig. 18 Various parts of different species of rhinoceros. From J. Parsons, in *Philosophical Transactions* 40 no. 470 (1743), pl. ii. '*1*: Two views of the feet [*Rhinoceros unicornis*]; *2*: The tail of an old rhinoceros, in the Museum of the Royal Society; *3*: The penis in an erected state; *4*: A horn of rhinoceros, said to be six years old, being about 10 inches long; *5*: The bottom or concave basis of the same, to shew the cavity is very superficial; *6*: A beautiful horn in Dr Mead's museum, being about 37 inches long; *7*: The horn of a rhinoceros [*Ceratotherium simum*, NHM, 1972.748/1167d] in the museum of Sir Hans Sloane which (as those of oxen are sometimes liable to distortions in their growth) differs from the common form; it is 32 inches long; *8*: The double horn mentioned above [*Diceros bicornis*, NHM, 1972.753/1520b and 123a] belonging to Sir Hans Sloane: Whether they crossed each other on the Animal, is uncertain: It is most likely they did not, but that by drying they were crossed by the Corrugation of the Skin that joins them together: However, I have drawn them as they appeared to me. The strait Horn is 25 Inches long, the curved one somewhat shorter, and the Two Diameters of the Bases 13 Inches; *9*: The concave Bottoms of the above double horns, as they adhere to the same Piece of skin.'

Fig. 19 The young Indian rhino (*Rhinoceros unicornis*) exhibited at Eagle Street, London, in 1739. From J. Parsons, in *Philosophical Transactions* 42 no. 470 (1743), pl. i.

whether these rhinos were distinct from the one-horned Indian rhino (*Rhinoceros unicornis*).[41]

In addition to his collection of whole horns and objects made of rhino horn Sloane owned the drawing made by Dürer in 1515 of an Indian rhino (see Chapter 16, Fig. 94). Parsons[42] recounted the story of this first rhinoceros to reach Europe, but he criticized the drawing and published his own drawings of a young Indian rhino that was exhibited in Eagle Street near Red Lion Square in London in 1739 (Fig. 19). He also made an oil painting of this rhino which is in The Natural History Museum.[43]

Other specimens in the catalogues show that it was not only rhinoceros horns that were supposed to have medical properties but that other parts of these unfortunate animals were also believed to cure human ills:

25*e*/270   A plain cup of a rhinoceros horn.

25*e*/518   Shavings of a rhinoceros horn for a counter poyson.

25*e*/1003   Rhinoceros's hyde. Id. [note] le Rinoceros Biron. p. 183 the Blood is used to fortify the heart & in all Contagious diseases causing the Sweat very plentifully Stops the flux of the Belly and purifies the Blood & stops Bleeding. Of the Horn are made Cups against the bad air in time of Contagion. The teeth are used for the tooth ache applying it against the aching tooth.

25*e*/1046   A very large rhinoceros horn.

Stones and Bezoars

From the Middle Ages onwards, the various kinds of calcitic deposits called stones, bezoar stones,[44] and snake stones[45] that are found in the body cavities of humans and animals were of intense interest to the medical world and to ordinary people who believed that eating the powder from ground-up stones would cure them of innumerable ills, and act as an antidote to poisons. Some examples are:

25*e*/1454   A stone from the kidney of a mare 3 years old weighing 8 ounces cut out by a huntsman from the mare which dy'd in Hertfordshire of a totale suppression of water given to me by Dr Quinton.

25*e*/184   Orientale bezoar from Suratte. Thevonet Edit 1696 tom. 1. Bezoard d'Orient Biron. pag. 20 of Franc. Polsart w^t the Tarters of Urbek the animal is call'd Pazard whence come, by corruption of the word Bezoar.

25*e*/763   A [Four written above] rhinoceros bezoars made up of severall solid bezoars after the manner of the calculus humany Spinosus. This is of a darker colour than 5 others brought by Mr Moores wch are w^t 2 others marked 25. & 26. pretended to be had from Snakes heads vid. serpents. It is used in India as other bezoars. One given to the Russian Librarian. one rattles like an aetites & one split in the center of wch is seed or fruit, an Acorn?

25*e*/444   Manati stones.

25*e*/436   Buffalos bones calcined & halfe calcined for making the Snake Stones of India, from Dr Stuart.

25*e*/606   Snake stones of severall sorts from the East Indies. Dr Sam Brown.

25*e*/1334   Serpent stones wch are the bones of buffalos calcin'd by their own dung in Persia. Pet.[46] India Snake stones.

Elephants

Sloane was fascinated by the huge bones and teeth found underground in Europe and he wrote two accounts of them.[47] He described a great many of these finds from many parts of Europe, including Russia, where parts of frozen mammoths were quite commonly washed out of periglacial deposits and where mammoth tusks were already being collected for their ivory. Sloane recounts the legends of the time concerning these remains: that they were the carcasses of huge animals which lived underground in Siberia, or carcasses that had been washed northwards by the Deluge. Those in Germany and other parts of Europe were thought by some to be the remains of elephants that died during Roman manoeuvres and were thrown into water, 'as it is still practised to this Day with the Carcasses of Horses and other Beasts, to prevent the Distempers and other Inconveniences, which their putrefaction might otherwise occasian.'[48]

Sloane believed, probably correctly, that the very widespread myths and legends about the existence of giants owed much to the finding of ancient remains of elephants. The most intriguing of these concerns an elephant's skeleton that was found in Sicily, the skull of which was considered by some to be from one of the mythical Cyclops.[49] And herein could lie the origin of the Ancient Greek legend of the Cyclops, a race of men of huge stature, inhabitants of Sicily, who had only one central eye, as described by Homer in the *Odyssey* (c.850BC). For if the skull of an elephant is looked at from the front, the large cavity of the nasal orifice could very well be taken as a central eye socket.

There are sixty-eight entries for elephant teeth, ivory, and other parts in the catalogue of Quadrupeds, including two pieces of ivory that remain in The Natural History Museum (Figs. 20–1). These are described as:

A leaden bullet or slugg lodg'd in an Elephants tooth about which 25*e*/561 grows ivory or what is called lachryma elephanti bought of a Cutler who was sawing the tooth to make hafts for knives [bracketed and on the right side is the [?] price 00.05.00 on the left in pencil is the number 220.1].

Lachryma elephanti, a piece of ivory wherein by sawing to work 25*e*/854 it was found a long bullet or slugg which had many years before been shot into the tooth & had made its selfe a bed there given me by Mr. Smith of Tower hill. vid No. 1783.

These descriptions match exactly two pieces of ivory incorporating bullets in The Natural History Museum collections.[50] It is recorded in the register that these pieces were presented to the British Museum, along with other specimens, by the India Museum, presumably on its closure which took place in 1879. It is not improbable that the ivories formed part of the foundation collections of the British Museum. They would then have been handed over to the India Museum sometime after it was founded in 1801, and were then returned after the demise of that institution in 1879.[51]

The manner in which the bullets would have become embedded in the tusks was described correctly in 1856 by Richard Owen.[52] He explained how a bullet shot into the

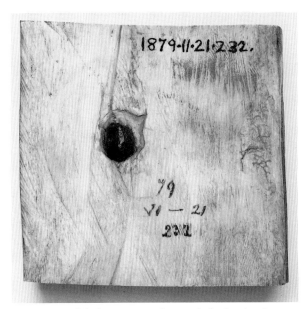

Fig. 20 Piece of elephant ivory enclosing a bullet [25e/561].
Reproduced by courtesy of the Trustees of The Natural History
Museum.

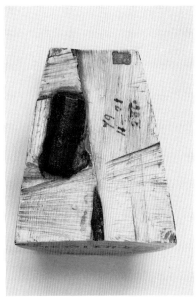

Fig. 21 Piece of elephant ivory enclosing a bullet [25e/854].
Reproduced by courtesy of the Trustees of The Natural History
Museum.

head of a young elephant could enter the pulp cavity of
the tusk; it would there become surrounded by an irregular
growth of dentine and with subsequent growth would
remain in the centre of the tusk. Even today, among some
people in India, the cysts or ivory 'pearls' surrounding a
bullet, which are sometimes found in tusks, are considered
to have magical properties.

25e/116   Included in this section is: 'The Tusk or *dens exertus* of
an elephant or ivory dugg up 12 foot deep among loam
in a gravelle pitt near the Pindar of Wakefield by Grays
inn. Mr Conyer' (see also Chapter 12). This fossil elephant
tusk was described in detail by Sloane[53] who recorded how
the separated 'cone-in-cone' structure of the degraded ivory
was 'tied about with Whale-bones and Tape by Mr Conyers, an ingeneous Apothecary, and a great Collector of
Curiosities of all kinds'. The piece of tusk was about five
inches long by nine inches circumference by three inches
diameter.

Other entries list many fragments of tusks and bones
25e/1491–   of elephant as separate items: 'found not far from the via
1514   Appia abt. 6 foot down near Rome from the Cardinall
25e/1716   Gualtieris collection'. Also listed is a growth from an
elephant's brain in a gold case. This was obviously considered by Sloane to be of considerable value, since the
printed list of the sale in Amsterdam whence it was bought
in 1737 is bound into the catalogue together with a handwritten certificate in Dutch and an English translation,
which states:

We the under Written Directors of the East India Company for
this Chamber, do Certify for Truth that the Growth out of the
Brains of an Elephant, Contained in a gold case, was sold at our
sale the 13th May 1737, And Sent to the General East India Company as a present by the Zery Sultan of Iamby. [Signed] B. Scott
G.V. Hoven 2d July 1737.

Water Buffalo Horns

'A very streight wreathed large pair of horns of a black   25e/1562
colour', may be the catalogue entry for probably the best-
known and certainly the largest of Sloane's quadruped
specimens, being the horns of the water buffalo, *Bubalus
arnee* (Fig. 22). As described by Sloane,[54] they were found
by Mr Doyly (who gave his name to the cotton mats,
known as doylies) 'in a cellar in Wapping where they had
lain so long that noone knew where they had come from
or when'. Doyly refused many large payments for them
but gave the horns to Sloane on recovery from a sickness
from which he believed Sloane had cured him. After describing the horns Sloane commented:

The Commander of an *East-India* Merchant ship upon seeing them,
told me, that he had seen such in the *Indies* on a large *Bufalo's*
Head. I am inclined to think, that they must belong to a very
large sort of Bulls or Cows, who are Natives of *Aethiopia*, and
other of the midland Parts of *Africa*, and are mentioned by many
of the Ancients, perhaps not without some fabulous additions,
though, which is strange, very few of the Modern Writers take
any notice of them.

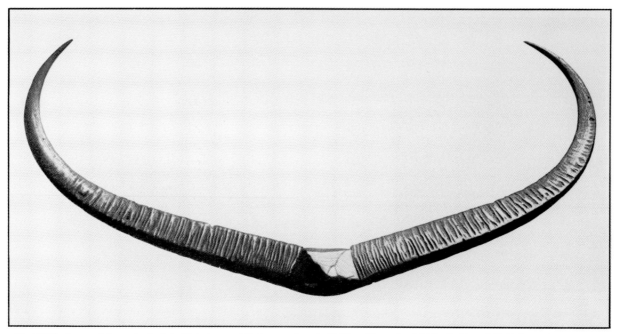

Fig. 22 The horns of the water buffalo (*Bubalus arnee*) that were given to Sir Hans Sloane by Mr Doyly. From J.G. Dolman, in *Natural History Magazine* 2 no. 12 (1929), fig. 4.

Each horn has a length of about 77 inches (196 cm) and for many years it has been accepted that the pair holds the world record for length in the species of buffalo.[55] Recently, however, a most interesting account has been made known to me of the way in which the horns of domestic water buffalo can be induced to grow longer than their natural length.[56] Wegner[57] described how the people of the island of Sumba in Indonesia used to castrate their male water buffaloes at the age of two years and then they would cut a notch about one inch in length on the dorsal side of each horn, right in the middle of their long axis. This notch had to be deep enough to draw blood. Nothing else was done and the wound healed quickly. When combined with castration this small operation was enough to make the buffalo's horns grow extra-long and very straight, turning up only at the ends. This is exactly the appearance of the Sloane horns and therefore it may be postulated that they are not from a wild water buffalo but from a domestic buffalo, *Bubalus bubalis*, that has been operated on in this way.

Conclusion

Sloane was a polymath and probably the most prolific collector in British history. His writings lie in a direct line of descent from Pliny's *Natural History*: they have exactly the same mixture of vast knowledge, correct observation, medical superstition, and empathy with the natural world. If he was intellectually the descendant of the classical polymaths such as Diodorus Siculus, Strabo, and Pliny, Sloane was also the forerunner of Joseph Banks and Charles Darwin.

Sloane's intense interest in natural history, as with Banks and Darwin, was fuelled by his travels across the world. His passion for collecting was made possible by his wealth, his social connections, and the world-wide explorations of the times. That his name is so much less well-known than those of other great figures in the history of natural history must be due only to the fact that his observations remain largely unpublished, being expressed mainly in his handwritten catalogues. Even today, these would present difficulties in printing and making available to a wide public. None the less, they deserve to form an essential part of the literature on the history of ideas concerning the natural world during the long period of Sloane's working life from about 1680 until he died in 1753.

Notes and References

1. I am grateful to Oliver Crimmen, Gordon Howes, and Alwyne Wheeler (NHM) for identifying and commenting on the fish from Sloane's *Natural History* of Jamaica.

2. O. Crimmen, personal communication (1991).

3. The maximum length recorded for this species of crocodile at the present day is 23 ft (7 m), A. Wheeler, personal communication (1993). I am grateful to Nick Arnold, Colin McCarthy, and Garth Underwood (NHM) for identifying and commenting on other reptiles from Sloane's *Natural History* of Jamaica.

4. G. M. Allen, 'Mammals of the West Indies', *Bulletin of the Museum of Comparative Zoology* 54 no. 6 (1911), p. 217.

5. I am grateful to Peter Colston (NHM, Bird Section at Tring) for identifying and commenting on the birds from Sloane's *Natural History* of Jamaica.

6. Allen op. cit. (note 4), p. 180.

7. Ibid., p. 234.

8. P. Browne, *The Civil and Natural History of Jamaica* (London, 1756), p. 484.

9. C. Biron, *Curiositez de la Nature et de l'art, aportées dans deux voyages des Indes, etc.* (Paris, 1793), pp. xxiii, 282.

10. Illustrated in John and Andrew Van Rymsdyk, *Museum Britannicum*, 2nd edn. (London, 1791), tab. vi, fig. 6.

11. F. Dominick Fernandez Navarrette on travels in China, translated by Awnsham and John Churchill, *A Collection of Voyages and Travels* (London, 1704), vol. I, pp. 1–424.

12. Churchill, op. cit. (note 11).

13. Hans Sloane, 'An account of a prodigiously large feather of the bird Cuntur, brought from Chili, and supposed to be a kind of Vultur; and of the Coffee-Shrub', *Philosophical Transactions* vol. 18 no. 208 (1693–4) pp. 61–4.

14. Capt. William Dampier, *A New Voyage Round the World* 7th edn. (London, 1729), vol. I, p. 49 [anno 1681]. Sloane's text is taken almost verbatim from this book, the observations being entirely those of Dampier.

15. Ibid., p. 71 [anno 1683]. The comments concerning the eating qualities of flamingo are again those of Dampier.

16. Sloane was the provider in 1705/6 of a 'Large fine Naturall Herne Topp' for the Garter headgear of the Prince Elector of Brunswick-Lunenburgh, for which service he received payment of £60 (PRO, LC5/44, 270; Royal Archives, Windsor Castle, 80825v; references kindly supplied by Lady de Bellaigue, Registrar of the Royal Archives). Later the Prince Elector, as George II of Great Britain, was to appoint Sloane his Physician in Ordinary (see Chapter 1).

17. Probably this was a manuscript catalogue of the Charlton (Courten) collection, which Sloane inherited: see Chapter 1.

18. R. Whitlock, *Rare and Extinct Birds of Britain* (London, 1953), pp. 32–3.

19. Martin Martin, *A Late Voyage to St. Kilda, the Remotest of all the Hebrides, or Western Islands of Scotland* (London, 1698), pp. 48–9.

20. *Pernis apivorus*, a rare summer visitor at the present day.

21. Sloane was very familiar with the ostrich, but this appears to have been his first sight of a Rhea (*Rhea americana*), the large flightless, ostrich-like bird from South America.

22. *The Ornithology of Francis Willughby*, ed. John Ray (London, 1676).

23. Nehemiah Grew, author of the Royal Society's museum catalogue, whose collections Sloane acquired; see Chapter 1.

24. The domestic Guinea fowl (*Numida meleagris*) may have been in Britain since Roman times and certainly since the sixteenth century; see P. Mongin & M. Plouzeau, 'Guinea fowl', in *Evolution of Domesticated Animals*, ed. I.L. Mason (London, 1984), pp. 322–5.

25. The modern so-called Persian lamb which has been a valuable commercial pelt for making fur coats and hats.

26. This wild pig is found only in the Celebes; the specimen was probably brought back by the Dutch spice traders.

27. Albertus Seba, *Locupletissimi rerum naturalium . . .* (Amsterdam, 1734–65).

28. The origins of the several breeds of four-horned sheep in the British Isles are unknown but records of their presence in park flocks goes back at least to the eighteenth century; see H.J. Elwes, *Guide to the Primitive Breeds of Sheep and their Crosses* (Edinburgh, 1913), reprinted by The Rare Breeds Survival Trust (Kenilworth, 1983).

29. This hair ball would have resembled the one shown in Fig. 16, no. 7.

30. This would have been a species of Jerboa, *Jaculus* sp.

31. This must be a muddled entry, as the hippopotamus is a river-horse not a sea horse and sea horses do not have teeth!

32. References follow that are very difficult to read. This sample of hair may have come from the European bison (*Bison bonasus*), which still lives in the forests of Poland, or from the aurochs (*Bos primigenius*), of which the last individual is said to have died in Poland in 1627; see F.E. Zeuner, *A History of Domesticated Animals* (London, 1963), p. 203.

33. Sloane was correct in his observations that there is seldom any variation in colour in any species of wild carnivore. The 'polecatt' skins that he saw were probably not from the wild polecat (*Mustela putorius*) but from ferrets (*Mustela furo*), the domesticated form of the polecat. This is an earlier use of the term 'sport' [mutation] than the date of 1768, given in the *Oxford English Dictionary*.

34. This was probably an escaped domestic mouse (*Mus domesticus*).

35. Probably these were hairs from a hippopotamus, see note 31 (above).

36. This abnormality, in which the two hooves are fused on each foot, is a mutation that occurs sporadically. A breed of solid-hoofed pigs was favoured in North America at the beginning of the nineteenth century, see R. Lydekker, *A Guide to the Domesticated Animals Exhibited in the Central and North Halls of the British Museum (Natural History)* (London, 1918), p. 26.

37. A note follows in Latin with references and mention of the Drill.

38. The horns of *Ceratotherium simum* in the NHM have the numbers 1857.2.5.2/1167c and 1972.748/1167d. The horns of *Diceros bicornis* have the numbers 1972.753/1520b and 123a.

39. J. Parsons, 'A letter from Dr. Parsons to Martin Folkes, Esq; President of the Royal Society, containing the Natural History of the Rhinoceros', *Philosophical Transactions* 42 no. 470 (1743), pp. 523–41, 2 figs.

40. Hans Sloane, 'A Letter from Sir Hans Sloane Baronet, late Pr.R.S. to Martin Folkes Esquire Pr.R.S. containing accounts of the pretended serpent-stone called Pietra de Cobra de Cabelos, and of the Pietra de Mombazza or the Rhinoceros Bezoar, together with the figure of a rhinoceros with a double horn', *Philosophical Transactions* 46 no. 491 (1749), p. 188, 1 fig.

41. Parsons does suggest (op. cit. (note 39), p. 538) that the African rhinos might have two horns.

42. Ibid., pp. 524, 539.

43. Oil painting on canvas of a young rhinoceros, no. 113. See J.C. Thackray, *A Catalogue of Portraits, Paintings, and Sculpture at The Natural History Museum, London* (London, 1992).

44. Bezoar stones were most commonly found in the gut of wild goats as described by Sloane [25*e*/184]. See Jessie M. Sweet, 'Sir Hans Sloane: life and mineral collection', *Natural History Magazine* 5 no. 36 (1935), pp. 156–8; see also Sloane, op. cit. (note 40), p. 118.

45. Ammonites were also known as snake stones. See Peter Dance, *Animal Fakes and Frauds* (Maidenhead, 1976), pp. 103–5.

46. For Petiver, see Chapter 1.

47. Hans Sloane, 'An account of elephants teeth and bones found under ground', *Philosophical Transactions* 35 no. 403 (1728), pp. 457–71; idem, 'Of fossile teeth and bones of elephants; part the second', *Philosophical Transactions* 35 no. 404 (1728), pp. 497–514.

48. Ibid., p. 510.

49. Ibid., pp. 500–1.

50. NHM nos. 1879, 11.21.232 and 231.

51. Ray Desmond, *The India Museum 1801–1879* (London, 1982), pp. 215.

52. Richard Owen, 'The ivory and teeth of commerce', *Journal of the Society of Arts* 5 no. 213 (1856), p. 69.

53. Sloane, op. cit. (note 47), p. 459.

54. Hans Sloane, 'An account of a pair of very extraordinary large horns found in Wapping some years since, with a probable account, whence they came, and to what animal they belonged', *Philosophical Transactions* 34 no. 397 (1717), p. 222–9.

55. Rowland Ward, *Records of Big Game*, 4th edn. (London, 1903), p. 407.

56. G.B. Corbet, personal communication (1991).

57. A.M.R. Wegner, 'The cause of the enormous proportions and the extraordinary shape of some buffalo horns from the island of Sumba', *Hemera Zoa*, Buitenzorg, Bogor, 57 (1950), pp. 708–10.

5 Invertebrate Collections

Kathie Way

* In the fifteenth and sixteenth centuries the establishment of trading posts in the East and West Indies and in America, the sea routes to India, and missionary activities in the Far East, brought Europe into contact with the astonishing wealth of natural objects to be found in remote lands. Such items proved to be desirable additions to cabinets already containing statuary, paintings, coins, medals, gemstones and other curiosities, both man-made and natural. As the content of such collections expanded to include increasing amounts of natural history, so we see the advent of the first printed books dealing with animals and plants.

At the time of Sloane's birth in 1660, there were already a number of such volumes, most notable of the earliest being the *Historia Naturalis* of the Frankfurt physician, Adam Lonicer, published between 1551 and 1555,[1] and Pierre Belon's *De Aquatilibus* of 1553.[2] Conrad Gessner's *Icones Animalium*[3] appeared in the same year, and Gessner illustrated many invertebrates in the fourth volume of his massive *Historia Animalium* in 1558.[4] In 1554, Guillaume Rondelet, professor of anatomy at Montpellier, where Sloane was to spend time in 1683 (see Chapter 1), published his *Universa Aquatilium*,[5] illustrating over 100 molluscs and other invertebrates. The first half of the seventeenth century saw the publication of two important works which discussed invertebrates, mainly molluscs. In 1606, Aldrovandi's *De Reliquis Animalibus* appeared,[6] and while much can be said for the quality of the text, the illustrations, both here and in all the volumes already mentioned were quite execrable. One almost universal fault in early illustrations of molluscs in particular was that the engravings of gastropods were not reversed before printing, making all the shells appear sinistral, or left-handed. A great step forward, both in text and illustrations, came with the publication in 1616 of the works of Fabio Colonna,[7] a Neapolitan naturalist.

Worthy though the efforts of all these authors were, the study of invertebrate animals in the mid seventeenth century had not advanced significantly since the discussions of Aristotle and Pliny.

By the time Sloane settled in Fleet Street 'for the Exercise of his profession' (see Chapter 1), the Italian Jesuit priest Filippo Buonanni (1638–1725) had published his great work *Ricreatione dell'occhio e della mente, nell'osservation' delle chiocciole* ('Recreation of the eye and for the mind through the observation of Snails'). Published in 1681,[8] with a second edition in 1684,[9] it therefore anticipates both in time and subject the *Historia Conchyliorum* (1685–92)[10] of Martin Lister (1638–1712), and is undoubtedly the first book to be entirely and specifically dedicated to shells. The *Ricrea-*tione is divided into four parts. The first and third are devoted respectively to the knowledge then available to, and the problems which faced, the naturalists of the day. The second part is composed of notes for the 319 shells (407 in the second edition) depicted in the fourth part. The engravings contained in the last part have been said to be some of the most significant examples of graphic art applied to scientific illustration in Italy. A facsimile edition of this work was published in 1985,[11] following the discovery of Buonanni's original pen and water-colour designs for the book in May 1984, after they had lain unnoticed for three centuries.

Sloane certainly had a copy of Buonanni's work to hand when he eventually catalogued his shells, and referred to it in many entries: He also received material from the priest, either directly 'From F. Bonanni' or from him via other collectors 'Mr Petiver had it from F. Bonanni J.' In fact Petiver, in volume II of his *Gazophylacium*[12] includes a list of thirty-three 'Shells Fossils and Corals sent me from the Reverend F. Philip Bonann , S. I. at Rome.'[13]

When Sloane accepted the Duke of Albemarle's invitation to accompany him to Jamaica as his physician, Lister had already begun work on his *Historia Conchyliorum*,[14] and a copy of the first part of this work, with the earlier title of *de Cochleis*[15] was presented to Sloane before his departure. The flyleaf of this copy, still extant in the British Museum, bears this inscription in Lister's hand:

For his honoured Friend Dr Hans Sloane. M. L.

He is desired to collect & transmitte hither ye land snailes & such shells as shall be found in ye Fresh water rivers or ponds of Jamaica wch will verie much oblige his most humble servant – Martin Lister.

Also to observe, whether there are any naked snailes in Jamaica, I meane such as are naturallie without shells at Land as with us.[16]

Incidentally, Sloane certainly found some 'naked snailes', one being figured on pl. 233 of his *Natural History* of Jamaica,[17] described as '*Limax nudus, cinereus, terrestris.*'[18] Sloane's collaboration with Lister was to be of great benefit to them both and is discussed in greater detail later in the chapter.

Sloane's long-time friend, John Ray (1627–1705) also encouraged him to make the journey, and despite Dr Sydenham's conflicting advice that 'No, you must not go to Jamaica; you had better drown yourself in Rosamund's pond',[19] Sloane finally set sail on 19 September 1687.

Sloane's own account of his voyage provides us with a remarkable insight into the great enthusiasm and curiosity that characterized his long life. His notes and observations,

22/1844, 2478;
23/2568, etc.
23/3711, 3855,4288
23/4121

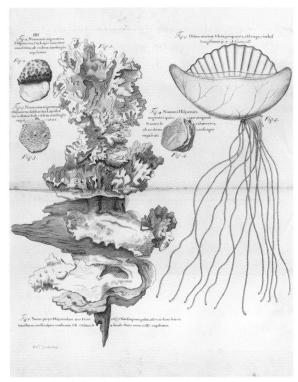

Fig. 23 Jellyfish described by Sloane on the outward journey to Jamaica; from Sir Hans Sloane, *Natural History*, vol. ɪ, tab. iiii.

both as physician and naturalist, show a clarity and attention to detail remarkable under the circumstances, not least of which being that he succumbed to seasickness on Day 1. Nevertheless he found time to describe the symptoms:

This first appears as a great uneasiness and a load about the Stomach, disorder and aching in the Head . . . and after the Liquors vomited up, as after a Natural or Artificial vomit, the persons generally from desponding and not caring what happens to them, come to be very easie.

This poignant passage is followed by the description of an emetic remedy, and the next day sees Sloane bird-watching with undiminished interest.[20]

During the three months of the voyage, Sloane's observations and conjectures ranged over much of the animal kingdom, and the meticulous detail which characterized his diary of the voyage is very well illustrated by the following description of a jellyfish seen on 11 October (see Fig. 23):

On Tuesday 11, when we were in about Forty Six degrees of Northern Latitude, I first saw what the Seamen call a Caravel or Portugese Man of War, which seems to be a Zoophytum, or of a middle Nature between a Plant and an Animal; it is of that kind of soft Fishes called *Urticae* from their Stinging quality, and to me seems different from any describ'd by any Natural Historian.

I shall call it *Urtica Marina, soluta, purpurea, oblonga, cirrhis longissimus.*

It is taken notice of by Stevens apud Hakluyt p. 99, where it is called a Ship of Guinea, and by de Lery p. 399 under the name of Immondicites Rouges. Martins calls it the other sort of Sea-Nettle in the Spanish Seas that weighs several Pounds, of a Blue, Purple, Yellowish and White colour, that burn more violently than those of the North Sea, they do suck themselves so close to the skin that they did raise Blisters, and cause sometimes St Anthony's Fire. He says further that one sort of this is called Sea-Spider, and is the Food of Whales, which may, by the way, explain a passage of Peyrere in his Anonymous Book, called Relation de Groenland, where the Author tells us, that Whales feed on Aranees du Mer. Ligon calls it Carvile, and observ'd it Five Hundred Leagues from Land, and where they are named Grandes Urticae by de Laet, who takes notice of them in Brazil.

This floated on the Surface of the Water, and consisted of two parts, the one was an oblong cylindrical Bladder not so big as a Turkey-egg, it was as it were blown up, and full of Wind, almost like the Swim of a Fish, widest at the bottom, and grew straiter or narrower to its top, where round about was a corrugated or curled Ledge or Band, something like a Cocks-Comb, Convex on one side and Concave on the other, which Seamen said was for its more convenient sailing; all this part of it was of a purple and bluish colour and Pellucid, the other part was a great number of blackish and Red Fibres, Strings or Cirrhi; they were long and White, here and there Purple, having several knots like Nits on it, taking their original from the bottom of this Bladder, which if stretched were several Feet long, but if curled up were very short, stinging much worse than Nettles, Whence it is by some reckoned Poisonous. They are very often to be met with at Sea, and Seamen do affirm that they have great skill in sailing, managing their Bladder or Sail with judgement, as may be most for their purpose, according to their different Winds and Courses; allowing them more Reason, than I, am willing to do of Life, there appearing to me no other parts than the Bladder and Cirrhi above-mentioned.[21]

This rather lengthy entry is worth quoting since it forms such an excellent example of Sloane's great curiosity about the natural world. He minutely describes the physical characteristics of the animal, has patently taken great trouble to find references to it in contemporary works, he discusses its distribution, its position in the food-chain, and offers an opinion about its intelligence.

The outward-bound diary incudes numerous observations of animals and birds seen, descriptions so detailed as to make it very easy today to make reliable identifications. The following passage refers unmistakably to the Purple Sea Snail, *Janthina*.

We had near, but before we came in sight of Barbados, a sort of Sea-Snail with Barnacles sticking to it, floating in the Sea. There were several of them, and their Apertures were filled with a Froth all standing in Bubbles. The Snail I described thus.

It was more flat or compressed than most of the *Cochleae Marinae* consisting only of Circumvolutions around the Columella or Axis of the Shell. It had some visible Oblique striae on the Circumvolutions, was brittle and thinner than any marine Shell I ever saw; it was of a very fine Violet or Purple colour. These shells floated on the Surface of the Sea, and had many Bullae of a Viscid Froth came out of them such as is raised from sope and water. They were more compressed than that of the Streights of Magellan, or Mediterranean, as also smoother. Wherefore I have chose to call it *Cochlea Marina e caeruleo purpurascens, compressa, laevis, tribus volutis constans*. It is the *Cochlea Marina Vicesima tertia caruleo-purpurascens* of Dr Lister Hist. Conchyl. Tab. 572.

There grew to this shell on every side that particular kind of Pluri-valved Shell-Fish made of several Shells called *Concha Anatifera*, figured in Dr Lister's Historia Conchyl. Tab. 439 and 440, which sticks to, and Breeds on anything floating on the Sea, by a hollow Neck somewhat resembling a Wind-Pipe. It looks somewhat like a Cockle, and it has some Cirrhi which have been taken for the budding feathers in the Wings of your Barnacles or Brent Geese which were supposed to Breed out of Trees. These Birds used to come yearly to Scotland, and other Countries in great numbers from the North in Winter, and go away in the Spring. They used in Northern Countries to have drift Wood come from the North with these Shell-Fish sticking to them, and never observing the Barnacles Breed as other Fowles, thought they bred so, till the Dutch in their attempts for a North-East Passage found these Barnacles sitting on Eggs as other Geese. I shall not say anything further, but refer the Reader to the Authors following, where he will find them treated of.[22]

There follow fourteen further references to goose barnacles in contemporary works.

Arriving in Port Royal Harbour, Jamaica, on 19 December 1687, Sloane devoted himself for fifteen months to an exhaustive study of the island and its flora, fauna and human inhabitants. During this time, the Duke of Albemarle became ill and died; the Duchess wished to return to England, and Sloane was to go with her. They sailed on 16 March 1689, this time also accompanied by Sloane's huge collections.

As on the outward journey, the return voyage provided the indefatigable naturalist with further opportunity for observation, again it is a jellyfish which catches his attention on:

April 8 1689. In the morning we had a Calm, and a current which set us about a Mile N.E. in an Hour. We were in N. Lat 26 23min. We had here a great many small Zoophytes or Blubber Fishes of that Kind, which are call'd by Natural Historians *Urticae Marinea*, floating about us, they resembled in their Shape small Snails, their Body was Gelly, they had some ferrugineous Spots and Streaks on them, their Motion was chiefly in their Circumference, and they had Eight redish Lines in their Insides.[23]

After returning from Jamaica, Sloane first continued in the Duchess's service; then, during the next six years he married, set up home in Bloomsbury and founded a successful medical practice. During this period he also began to publish accounts of his travels, mainly in the *Philosophical Transactions*,[24] which at this time were the responsibility and property of the Secretaries of the Royal Society. Sloane had been elected as such in 1693, becoming first Secretary in 1695. At around this time began the acrimony between Sloane and Dr John Woodward which continued for several

years, and culminated in an undignified public wrangle in 1710.[25] Despite considerable provocation, including being publicly lampooned,[26] Sloane seems to have behaved on the whole with some restraint, confining himself in the main to pithy comments such as that to be found in his catalogue of Echini:

Dr Woodward ... makes a new genus of them by the name of *Pentaphylloides*, but how he came to rank it among those with a single aperture seems amazing in a man of his accuracy, and so very apt to find fault with the inadvertency of others. *27d/21*

Apart from this involvement with the Royal Society, Sloane was preparing the first volume of his observations and findings from his trip to Jamaica, an undertaking to which his friend Ray had been urging him for several years: 'I have been importunate with you to hasten the publication of your discoveries in the history of nature, as well for the advancement of real knowledge, and gratification of the learned and inquisitive, as for your own deserved honour, that some other man might not prevent you, and by some means or other intercept what is yours.'[27] A year later: 'I hope you will so soon as may be gratify and oblige the curious in publishing of your labours.'[28] A later letter, whilst praising Sloane's meticulous preparation, returns to this theme:

I cannot but admire your patience turning over so many voyages and relations of travellers, besides herbarists and other authors, and making collections out of them, and that to so good purpose, to correct mistakes, to clear up difficulties and obscurities, and to contract the number of species. Your method is good enough, for I suppose you intend not to be very critical and exact in that. In your next be pleased to tell me how far the press hath proceeded in this previous work, and by what time you think it will be wrought off and published.[29]

Alas, Ray had been dead for three years when volume I of Sloane's *Natural History* appeared in 1707. This first volume contained, apart from the lengthy preface and diaries of the voyages quoted earlier, a number of plates figuring invertebrate material. In chapter I of the 'Plants of Jamaica', Sloane discusses what he calls 'Submarine Plants', and includes here corals and sponges. Plate xix depicts a glass bottle covered with what Sloane calls *Corallium asperum candicans adulterinum* (see Fig. 24):

One sort of it I have growing all around a common Glass Bottle, this Bottle was by Chance or Earthquake, thrown into the Sea in Port-Royal Harbour, and thence taken up by a diver, who the Reverend Mr Scambler sent to the bottom of the Sea to take up Money and Goods he had lost in the Great Earthquake.[30]

This may be the item mentioned in the Coral Catalogue thus: 'A glass bottle covered wth the *Corallium porosum album latissimum muricatum* Cat. Jam. growing on it fish'd up in the harbour at Port Royall & given me by M. Barham. It hath shells on it & is full of seawater.' However there are three other coral-covered glass bottles listed. *21a/646* *21a/9,121, 1380*

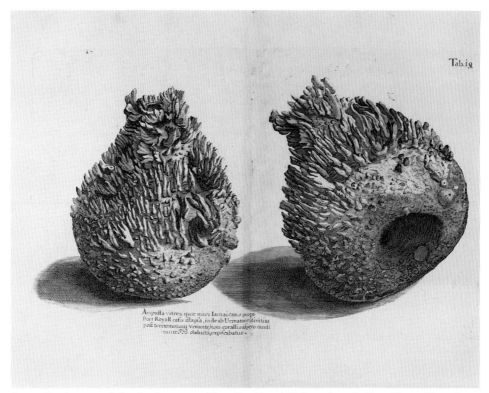

Fig. 24 Coral-encrusted glass bottle recovered from Port Royal Harbour; from Sir Hans Sloane, *Natural History*, vol. i, tab. xix.

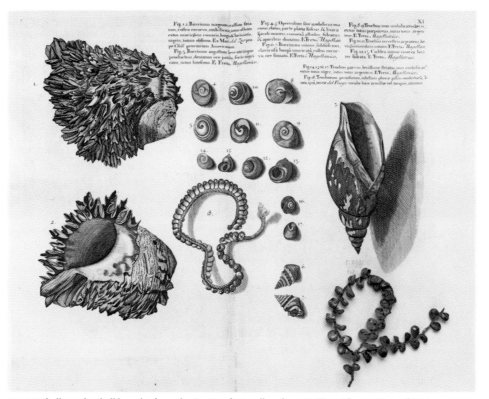

Fig. 25 Shells, and a shell bracelet from the Straits of Magellan, from Sir Hans Sloane, *Natural History*, vol. ii, tab. xi, together with a similar bracelet found in the collections of the NHM (bottom right). Reproduced by courtesy of the Trustees of The Natural History Museum.

Plate 1 Attributed to John Vanderbank [formerly attributed to Sir Godfrey Kneller], *Portrait of Sir Hans Sloane*. Reproduced by courtesy of the Trustees of the British Museum.

Plate 2 John Michael Rysbrack, *Terracotta bust of Sir Hans Sloane*.
Reproduced by courtesy of the Trustees of the British Museum.

Plate 3 John Michael Rysbrack, *Statue of Sir Hans Sloane*, formerly
placed in the Chelsea Physic Garden. Reproduced by courtesy
of the Trustees of the British Museum.

Plate 4 The British Museum's first home, Montagu House in Bloomsbury. Erected by Ralph, Duke of Montagu and designed by Robert Hooke (1635–1703), Montagu House was gutted by fire in 1686 and rebuilt to a similar design. Reproduced by courtesy of the Trustees of the British Museum.

Plate 5 Attributed to Roelandt Savery; painting of the dodo. According to G. Edwards, FRS, who gave the painting to the British Museum in 1759, it had previously been in the collection of Sir Hans Sloane, who had recorded that 'this picture was drawn in Holland from the living Bird, brought from St. Maurice's island in the East Indies, in the early times of the discovery of the Indies by the way of the Cape of Good Hope'. Reproduced by courtesy of the Trustees of The Natural History Museum.

Plate 6 Sloane catalogue numbers in his own hand on six shells. Reproduced by courtesy of the Trustees of The Natural History Museum.

Plate 7 Sloane catalogue numbers written on slips of paper and glued into the apertures of five shells. Reproduced by courtesy of the Trustees of The Natural History Museum.

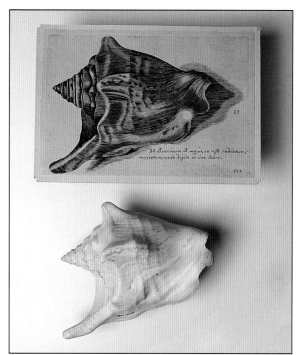

Plate 8 Sloane's specimen of *Strombus tricornus* Lamarck, together with Lister's engraving prepared from the specimen for his *Historiae . . . Conchyliorum* (1685–92), lib. IV, pl. 873, species 29. NHM, 23/2816. Reproduced by courtesy of the Trustees of The Natural History Museum.

Plate 9 Sloane's specimen of *Cassis (Phalium) strigata* Gmelin, together with Lister's engraving prepared from the specimen for his *Historiae . . . Conchyliorum* (1685–92), lib. IV, pl. 1014, species 78. NHM, 23/3924. Reproduced by courtesy of the Trustees of The Natural History Museum.

Plate 10 The holotype of *Dipsas plicatus* Leach. The valves were catalogued by Sloane as 'A pearl muscle with 4 pearls in it' and 'A pearl muscle with 8 pearls in it'. The engraving of the right-hand valve by J. & A. Van Rymsdyk in *Museum Britannicum* (1778), reproduced here in Fig. 27, shows that two pearls had already been removed or had become detached by 1778; as can be seen here, two are also missing from the left valve (top). NHM, 22/886–7. Reproduced by courtesy of the Trustees of The Natural History Museum.

Plate 11 Glove (one of a pair), 'made from the beard of the Pinna marina', together with an engraving of it from J. & A. Van Rymsdyk's *Museum Britannicum* (1778), tab. XII, fig. 2. NHM, 24/4912. Reproduced by courtesy of the Trustees of The Natural History Museum.

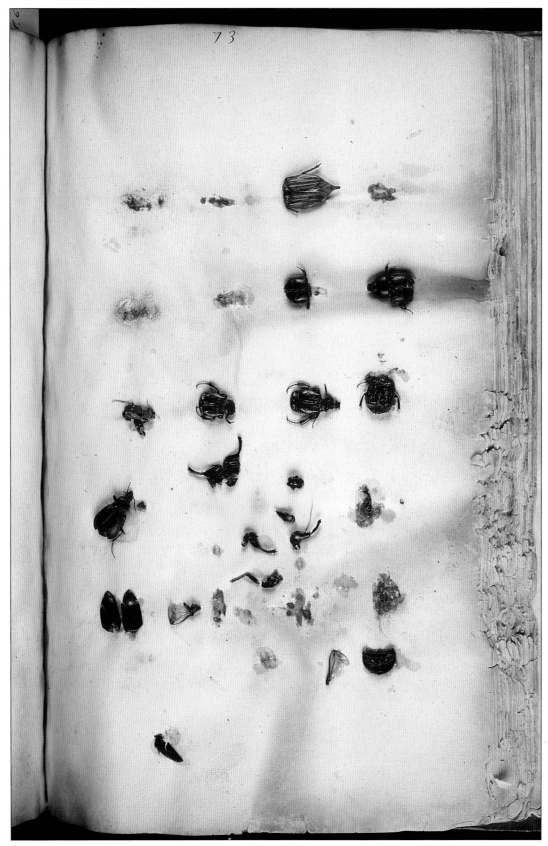

Plate 12 Folio 73 from the volume of insects prepared by Leonard Plukenet. These specimens are all large, heavy beetles and have suffered some damage. Most on this page are scarabs (dung beetles and chafers), together with a tiger beetle and a large ground beetle. Reproduced by courtesy of the Trustees of The Natural History Museum.

Plate 13 Folio 20 from the first volume of Petiver insects preserved between sheets of mica. The butterflies on this page are mainly 'milkweeds' (Danainae). Reproduced by courtesy of the Trustees of The Natural History Museum.

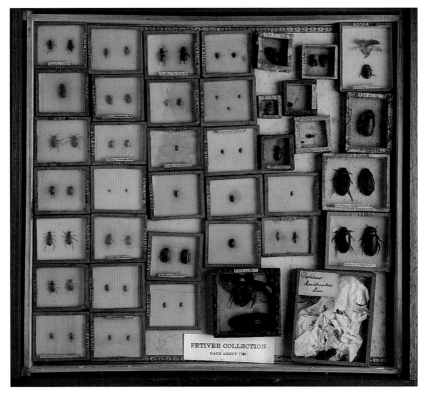

Plate 14 A drawer of beetles preserved in small glass-topped boxes. They are not solely from the Petiver collection as was once supposed: in fact, the majority of the boxes in this drawer, with Sloane drawer numbers (roman numerals) in the range I to XCVI, are from Joseph Dandridge's collection. The labels giving latin binomials are more modern additions. Reproduced by courtesy of the Trustees of The Natural History Museum.

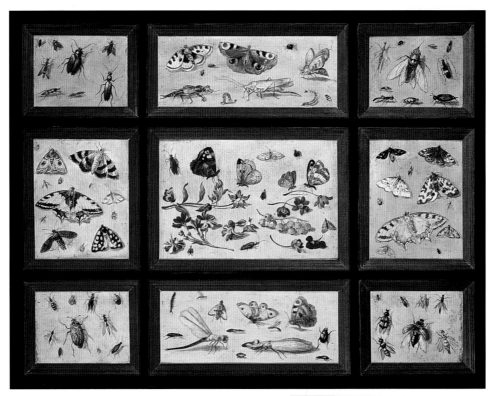

Plate 15 Attributed to Jan van Kessel (1626–79), a variety of insects, undated. Oils on copper panel, 57 by 43 cm (excluding frame). Reproduced by courtesy of the Trustees of The Natural History Museum.

In all Sloane describes and figures thirteen varieties of coral in volume I (pp. 50–8; pls. 17–20), together with a number of sponges (pp. 62–4; pls. 23–4). The invertebrate fauna of Jamaica is dealt with more extensively in volume II of the *Natural History*, which for a number of reasons was not published until 1725.[31] Echinoderms appear in this volume (pp. 267–8; pls. 242–4), as do Crustacea and jelly-fish (pp. 269–73; pl. 245).

Despite evidence from the catalogues that quite large amounts of coral and sponge material survived the homeward journey to be incorporated in Sloane's collection, none of these specimens have yet been identified among the present-day collections of the Natural History Museum.[32]

Sloane made an extensive collection of shells in Jamaica, and these are described in the second volume (pp. 227–65). Because the work did not appear until 1725, many of the species, and in some cases the specimens he collected, had already been described and figured by Lister and Petiver; perhaps this is why Sloane devotes only three of his many plates to shells. Full reference to the figures in these previous publications, and copies of Lister and Petiver's Latin descriptions, were given for each species, followed by additional locality notes and descriptions in English. At the end of the introduction to volume II, the author includes a series of plates, following consecutively from a similar series at the end of the introduction to volume I. Plate xi is devoted to shells, and bears the following caption:

Shews some shells I had from the Streights of Magellan, the Coast of Chili and the Tierra del Fuego, amongst the rest a small black *Trochus*, which being Strung by the Natives on Fish Guts, or Nerves, and Worn as Bracelets and Necklaces, come to an extraordinary fine Colour, even beyond that of the finest Oriental Pearl. I thought to have given a farther Account of this Voyage to the Streights of Magellan and the South-Sea, and of natural Things from these Places, but must leave them for another opportunity.[33]

Sloane does not mention the donor(s) of the shells, but at least some were probably sent by 'Mr Handisyd,' who sent Sloane other specimens from this locality in about 1702–3. There is an entry in the shell catalogue which may refer to the specimens mentioned above:

23/1385; 24/2920, etc.

23/2911 This is the Shell of which they make in the Streights of Magellan bracelets. The Shells differ in bigness as do the bracelets. The bracelets are black when first worn and turn of an oriental pearl colour after being worn. 12 hours lying in juice of lemon eats off this outward skin / The same strung on seal gutts of wᶜʰ they likewise make netts / Lesser and larger shells.

A bracelet similar to that depicted in pl. xi has been found in the collection of the Natural History Museum, and whilst there is no concrete evidence to link it with Sloane, it certainly dates from the very origins of the collection (see Fig. 25). In book II of volume II, 'Insects of such as suffer no Change in their Forms, and have no Feet', Sloane refers to the 'naked snaile' mentioned earlier, calling it the 'Naked White Snaile'.

It looked almost like a Leech, was three Inches and a half long, one broad, convex on one Side, and was plain on the other, it had Horns three quarters of an Inch long, was all over white, or ash-coloured, with some black spots, they leave shining Marks after them, shewing their March as our Snails do. Tab. 232 Fig. 3 shews the under side of this Snail after it had been preserved in Spirit of Wine several years, where on the Belly, or near its whole length is a remarkable Rising, made up of many Rings, on which I believe it creeps when alive. They feed on Herbs, and are to be met with after Rain; their excrement is round, long and Black. Lopez de Gomara says, that after beating the Indians, the Spaniards found these among other Provisions for Merchandize, for the Inland country.[34]

In the same chapter Sloane reports the sighting of a sea-slug, or nudibranch as follows:

Limax nudus e cinereo fuscus maritimus sub aquis, herbae marinas uti fucos etc. Tab. 233 Fig. 4,5. This Snail, while under Water, appear'd to be about three quarters of an Inch long, it was roundish, somewhat compressed on the under side, one long, narrow, yellow Line, the Back was roundish and light brown coloured, the Belly was compress'd and more whitish. It was feeding upon a *Fucus marinus* growing on the Rocks under Water near Don Christopher's Cove ... When I saw it first it had divers Motions in the Water, and after I took it out, altho' it shew'd sufficient Signs of Life, yet it put it self into such Shapes, as you may see by the Figures, the two Postures it lay in.[35]

It is of interest to note that all the shells figured in volume II, although quite well engraved, have been reversed in the printing. It seems strange that Sloane could have overlooked this two-hundred-year-old error.

Twenty-five of the shells collected by Sloane in Jamaica have so far been recognized among the collections of the Natural History Museum.[36]

Sloane's collections of invertebrate animals total over 8,000 entries in five catalogues, with indexes in a sixth. Fossil and recent acquisitions are listed together and at random, making it often quite impossible to separate these two categories of material and so to provide any really accurate assessment of the true numbers of recent species involved. The real figure must certainly be considerably larger than that obtained by simply adding together all the entries for each group, since Sloane employed a multiple-entry method, sometimes listing more than ten additional items under one number (e.g. 23/4011: see Fig. 26). The invertebrates were divided into the following groups:

21–4, 27, 26

23/4011

Coralls and Sponges	141 entries	21a: fols 2–108, fols. 1–6; index 26f: fols. 280–304
Crustacea	304	21d: fols. 226–57; index 26i: fols. 338–46
Echini	855	21c: fols. 157–219; 27: fols. 1–84; index 26h: fols. 322–55
Shells	5,846	22–24; part index 24b & c: fols. 210–62
Starrfishes	174	21e: fols. 277–360; index 26j: fols. 350–4

Because of the size of the original collection, and the relatively large numbers of specimens still extant, Sloane's shells are perhaps the most interesting part of the invertebrate collections. They formed the nucleus of the present day holdings of Mollusca at the Natural History Museum, a collection now estimated to have grown to over ten million specimens.

The date when cataloguing of the shells began is uncertain, but may have been as early as 1702, when Sloane acquired the collection of William Courten (1642–1702). There are three catalogues of shells, 22, 23 and 24, ending

24/5846   with entry no. 24/5846. This final entry can be reliably fixed
24/5843   at shortly after September 1747, since one entry records the gift of a fossil *Anomia* from E.M. da Costa and is dated 17 September 1747. At the end of the third volume a list of fossil material from the first two volumes up to October 1728 is given, totalling 1,757 specimens; the last
23/4911   entry in that volume gives a total of 3,154 recent shells in the collection in October 1728.

Some 500 of Sloane's shells have been traced in the general collections and among the exhibits at the Museum. The location of a large number of these specimens prompted the finder, Guy L. Wilkins, to publish his excellent account of the Sloane shell collections[37] upon which I have drawn freely in these pages. Many of the specimens bear Sloane's catalogue numbers, in his hand, either written directly on to the shell (see Plate 6) or on strips of paper gummed to the shell's surface (Plate 7). During the preparation of his paper, Wilkins examined the Huddesford edition of Lister's *Historia Conchyliorum* in the Radcliffe Science Library, Oxford. This copy, once the property of a Dr Combe, contains a number of watercolour drawings, originals of some of the final engravings. The volume also contains manuscript notes in Lister's own hand, often indicating the source of figured specimens and confirming that he had borrowed material from contemporary collectors, including Sloane, Courten and Lhwyd, as well as copying from Buonanni and other authors. The notes also serve to reinforce da Costa's statement that: 'Dr Lister, to complete his intended work, carried home all the shells singly to his daughters, to engrave on single or detached copper plates.'[38] Lister's daughters, Susanna and Anna, drew and engraved over 1,000 shells for the *Historia*, and it may prove that the Sloane specimens are the only shells figured in this important early work which are still in existence (see Plates 8–9). So far, forty-two such specimens have been located, and these are listed by Wilkins.[39]

The first part of the *Historia* bears a dedication to 'That illustrious and excellent man William Courten, of the Middle Temple, London', as an appreciation of Courten's help in lending parts of his collection for illustration. Lister pursues this sentiment in a Latin preface praising Courten:

Both on account of the extreme industry with which he collects these specimens at great cost, stores them neatly and preserves

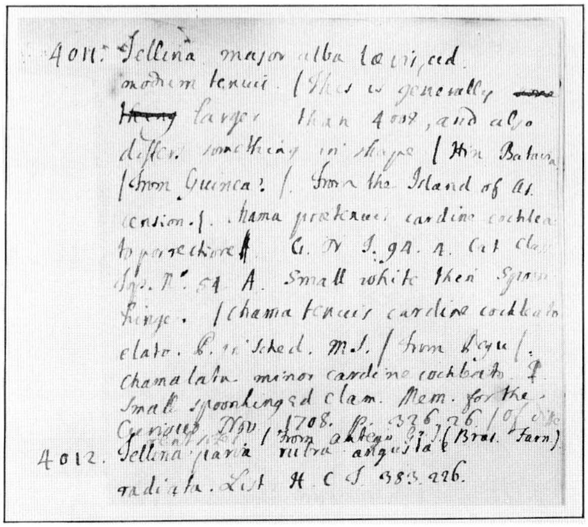

Fig. 26 An entry from Sir Hans Sloane's manuscript catalogue of shells [23/4011], illustrating his practice of making multiple entries. There are twelve entries under this number. Reproduced by courtesy of the Trustees of The Natural History Museum.

them carefully, and on account of his remarkable kindness in giving easy access to myself and other research workers in natural history, and in affording the opportunity of drawing and describing these and other objects of the same kind from his abundant resources.[40]

When Courten died in 1702, his collection was bequeathed to Sloane; John Evelyn, in his diary for 16 December 1686 (see Chapter 1) described a visit to Courten's rooms and opined that the collection was estimated at £8,000. Certainly these specimens must be among the oldest yet recognized among the Natural History Museum collections, since Courten, although a contemporary of Sloane, was eighteen years his senior, and had begun collecting in the 1660s. A small manuscript catalogue of his 'Curiosities' in the British Museum[41] lists purchases made from the widow of John Tradescant the Younger in 1667, before Tradescant's collection, his 'Ark', went to Elias Ashmole, the founder of the Ashmolean Museum, Oxford.

1705 saw the publication of the *Amboinsche Rariteitkamer*[42] of Georg Eberhard Rumpf (or Rumphius) (1627–1702). Rumphius was employed by the Dutch East India Company and spent much of his life on the island of Amboina (Ambon), observing and describing the local fauna. At the time when Sloane was adding the Courten material to his collection, it is evident that he possessed a copy of this remarkable work, and he made frequent reference to it in the invertebrate catalogues.

A search of the catalogues has not revealed any material specifically marked by Sloane as coming from Courten. However, a series of specimens for which no localities or donor's names were listed may well have originated with Courten; for example:

22/1895 *Buccinum admodum crassum ingens leviter purpurascens* a Surinam viparum. List. hyst. tab.23.

It appears that the specimens figured by Lister were received by Courten from Surinam in 1690. The figures show an adult *Strophocheilus oblongus* (Müller) with a large egg and a recently emerged snail;[43] these specimens engendered a lively correspondence: Lister apparently first mentioned them in a letter to Lhwyd dated 4 April 1690,[44] and Lhwyd wrote to Ray on 14 April: 'Dr Lister acquaints me that Mr Charlton has lately received a land-snail from Surinam, not bigger than a hen's egg, which yet lays eggs as big as those of a sparrow; and the snails that are hatched of them are, he says, twice as large as the eggs.'[45] Ray wrote in similar terms to Tancred Robinson a month later, seeking confirmation of the facts,[46] and he also replied to Lhwyd: 'The snail you write off, received by Mr Charlton from Surinam is very strange and remarkable. But how ye young snayl hatch't of ye egges should come to be twice so big as ye egges, I understand not.'[47]

Meanwhile Lhwyd had written to Lister in similar vein: 'I thank you for y[r] account of ye shell from Suranam. Its strange if ye young snayles be hard and twise as big as ye shell immediately upon exclusion.'[48] Robinson's letter to Ray seems to close the subject:

Mr Charlton has such a snail-shell as you mention, with eggs and young ones, which are the wonder of our philosophers here; but I being naturally too jealous, do almost suspect (though I durst never declare my suspicion), the young ones have been severally, and very artificially added to the snail, though indeed the snails are oviparous, and peradventure perfect-shelled animals may be observed in the eggs themselves; so that I may be under unreasonable doubt.[49]

This lively curiosity is a prevalent feature of the correspondence of Sloane and his contemporaries; it characterized a generation of men of science no longer content to regard natural objects as decorative items or mere 'curiosities' but who began to ask important questions which were to lead to the formation of theories on evolution, adaptation, zoogeography and the fossil record which still pertain today. Thus we see that as early as 1702, Sloane, with his own West Indian material swelled by Courten's huge collections, was amassing a museum of considerable magnitude.

Some years later, in 1718, Sloane purchased the collections of James Petiver (1651–1718), making an extremely important addition to his holdings of invertebrates. Petiver was the apothecary to the Charterhouse and an enthusiastic collector of natural objects. John Ray said of him that: '... he hath the greatest correspondence both in East & West Indies of any man in Europe; I think I may say, th[a]n all Europe besides.'[50] Elsewhere he wrote: 'Another great contributor ... is Mr Petiver, a man of greater correspondence in Africa, India & America than any one I know of besides.'[51] Sloane himself said that: '... he had taken great pains to gather together the productions of England and by his correspondents and acquaintances all over the world procured, I believe, a greater quantity than any man before him.'[52]

Petiver was elected to the Royal Society in 1695, the year of publication of the first part of his *Musei Petiveriani Centuria Prima*.[53] This was to be a list of his collection, issued in a series of 'centuries' of 100 specimens; the foreword acknowledges Sloane and other collectors. Ten parts of this work had been finished by 1703, when Petiver began work on the *Gazophylacium Naturae et Artis*,[54] to be published in ten parts, each containing ten plates, over the next six years. In an editorial published in the *Philosophical Transactions* for 1703 (pp. 1411–12) the completion of the first of these 'Decades' was announced. The writer (Petiver himself?) states: 'One advantage will accrue, by publishing these things in Decades, that of presenting them entire, which are too often mangled scatter'd or absconded by change of hands.' Regrettably, this was just what happened when Sloane acquired the collection, since as he catalogued it, he incorporated it piecemeal into his own cabinets. The fact that Petiver's own curatorial treatment of his specimens left something to be desired was commented upon by Sloane: 'Mr Petiver put them in heaps, with sometimes small labels of paper, where there were many of them injured by Dust, Insects, Rain etc.'[55]

As with Lister's *Historia*, Sloane makes copious references to Petiver's works throughout the five invertebrate catalogues. Entries are followed by 'P.' or 'Pet.' with a reference to 'Mus. Pet.' or to the contributions to the *Philosophical Transactions*. The phrase 'designed by Mr Petiver for his Gaz. Nat.' occurs frequently.

In 1711, Sloane commissioned Petiver to go to the Netherlands, where the collection of Paul Hermann was to be sold at auction, and to make purchases on Sloane's behalf. Petiver does not seem to have been sanguine about his prospects of surviving the trip, and wrote to Sloane before he left: 'Hon Sir, – In case I should dy before my return from Holland, I make you sole possessor of all my collections of naturall things whatsoever ...'.[56] However, return he did, and with a sizeable collection, as evinced by the still extant Bill of Lading for 'Three cases and one casket'.[57] From the original catalogue, preserved in the British Library,[58] it has been possible to trace two lots of shells bought for Sloane from Hermann.

'*Rhombus angustus tenuis punctatus.* List. hist. tab.737.no.32. 22/1611
Terebella sex Een Ruypers booren. Herm. p. 49, no. 426.'
'*Rhombus angustus tenuis fasciatus.* List. hist. tab.736.no.31? 22/1612
Terebellum Een Ruypers booren. Mus. Herm. p. 49. no. 426.'

Thirty-nine further shells traceable to Petiver and figured or described by him are still extant, and these are listed by Wilkins.[59]

Apart from his early visit to Jamaica, Sloane did not venture far afield, and both he and Petiver depended for specimens upon friends and acquaintances travelling abroad. Several of these were surgeons or officers in the service of the Dutch East India Company in China and India. Among the most significant of Sloane's acquisitions of invertebrates were those from the collection of Dr Engelbert Kaempfer (1651–1716), sometime physician to the Dutch East India Company in Japan (see Chapter 18), bought by Sloane after Kaempfer's death. An account of Kaempfer's time in Japan was published posthumously at Sloane's expense.[60]

21a/776 A round deep small [*fungus saxeus*] from Japan by Dr Kempfer.

21d/258 The joint of a claw of a Crayfish 5/8 of an ell long. From Japan by Dr Kempfer.

27b/13 The second species figured by Rumph. as belonging to a species of his *Echinometra* . . .

27b/13a Another of the same, something less . . . Likewise from the East Indies by Mr Kemfer.

The molluscan catalogues include a great many references to Kaempfer, and some of his shells are still extant.[61]

James Cunningham (or Cunninghame) (d. ?1708), also a surgeon with the British East India Company, sent Chinese specimens to Sloane and Petiver from Emuy in 1698, Chusan in 1700 and 'Pulo Condore' in 1702–3. Petiver referred to him as 'A learned and most industrious promoter of Natural Philosophy, and extremely well qualified for such a design',[62] he also reported on the specimens he received in the *Philosophical Transactions* for 1698[63] and 1701.[64] Cunningham never returned to England and is thought to have perished at sea in 1708.

21d/119 The body of the same wth 99 [*Cancer totus spinosus cinereus*] from the Island – Pulo Condore by Mr Cunningham.

27a/13 This beautiful *Echinus* hath not been hitherto described by any author . . . it was sent me from China by Mr Cunningham, an ingenious surgeon.

Cunningham also donated large numbers of shells, some of which are still to be found in the Natural History Museum collections.[65]

Mr Fawcett, also of the East India Company, sent numerous invertebrate specimens to Sloane from Fort St. George (Madras) in 1705:

21a/741 Part of a . . . sea fann from Fort St. George or China by Mr Faucett.

21d/245 A sea crab very like the land one of Jamaica. From China. Fawcet.

21d/250 A small cornered bodied crab echinated round the edges wth depressions on the shell of it. From China or Fort St. George Faucet.

Fifteen of Fawcett's shells survive from the many entered in the catalogues.[66]

Other frequently occurring names throughout the invertebrate catalogues include Father Kamel (or Cammelli), a Jesuit priest living in Manila; Samuel Brown, a surgeon in Madras; Sylvanus Landon and Rowleston Jacobs from the Moluccas; the Revd Hugh Jones from Maryland; Mr Campbell (another 'ingenious surgeon') and William Brown, both from Jamaica; and William Clerck (later Clark) of Newfoundland.

A rather romantic name from the catalogues is that of William Dampier (1652–1715), known as a navigator and buccaneer who showed considerable interest in the natural history of the countries he visited. In 1699 he wrote this account of the molluscs of Sharks Bay:

Of shell fish we got here muscles, periwinkles, limpets, oysters cockles etc. The shore was lined thick with many other sorts of very strange and beautiful shells, for variety of colour and shape, most finely spotted with red, black or yellow etc., such as I have not seen anywhere but this place. I brought away a great many of them but lost all except a very few, and those not of the best.[67]

There are no donations from Dampier in any of the invertebrate catalogues apart from the shells, and the specimens still extant were catalogued as being from 'Dampier's 2nd. circumnavigation'. This was probably the voyage undertaken in 1708–11 to harass Spanish shipping in the South Seas.[68]

Nearer home, donors include John Salvatore, an apothecary of Barcelona; Dr Oliver, Tangier; Dean Hickes, Scotland; Dr Preston, Orkney; and Mr Wynne, Wales.

A later contribution to Sloane's collection was that of Mark Catesby (d. 1749), author of the *Natural History of Carolina*. Catesby received financial support from Sloane during his stay there from 1722–6, and he acknowledged this both by paying tribute in his book to '. . . that great Naturalist and Promotor of Science Sir Hans Sloane, Bart. to whose goodness I attribute much of the success I had in this undertaking',[69] and by numerous gifts to his benefactor's museum.

Tethitis x *virginia* . . . a marine body called here commonly Couhage from its having when burnt powdered, the tormenting stinging quality of the true East India Couhage. I take it to be what is called by Botanists *Alcyonium*. from Mr Catesby.[70] 21a/154

Corallium album porosum maximum muricatum catal. Jamaic. p.1. from the Bahama Islands by Mr Catesby. 21a/823

Frutex marinus elegantissimus . . . cat. Jam. p.3. wth the crust rubd off from the Bahama Island by Mr Catesby. 21a/825

A small sphericall crab from Providence by Mr Catesby. 21d/273

A square one from the same. 21d/274

A painted one from the same. 21d/275

A small *squilla lata* long shaped from Gibraltar where it was taken amongst prawns by Mr Catesby. 21d/344

Only six shells from the large number sent by Catesby from the Bahamas and Carolina are still extant.[71]

At the time of these donations from Catesby, Sloane's collections were still at his home in Bloomsbury. In 1742 the whole museum was removed to his manor-house in Chelsea, where it remained until he died in 1753, when it became national property and was opened to the public in 1759. In this way large amounts of hitherto unknown material were made available to the authors and illustrators of the late eighteenth and early nineteenth centuries; there began an era of popular and scientific publication, and many of the great works which date from this time cited or illustrated Sloane's specimens.

Following the milestone of Linnaeus's *Systema Naturae*,[72] introducing binomial nomenclature, came Pallas's *Elenchus zoophytorum* in 1766,[73] and da Costa's *Conchology* in 1770;[74] the latter is, as far as is known, the only scientific work ever to cite a Sloane catalogue number in the text.

J. and A. Van Rymsdyk's *Museum Britannicum* followed in 1778,[75] and contains numerous figures and descriptions of Sloane's material (see Fig. 27, Plates 10–11). *The Natural History of Many Curious and Uncommon Zoophytes*, published in 1786 by Ellis and Solander[76] dealt in detail with some invertebrate groups which had been largely ignored up to that time, namely the corals, sponges and bryozoans. A recent study of this work concludes that Sloane's specimens were used in its preparation;[77] one of the corals illustrated, *Madrepora lactuca* (Pallas, 1766) is extant in the Natural History Museum collection and it has been suggested that this may be a Sloane specimen.[78]

Between 1813 and 1817, Dr W.E. Leach, an assistant keeper at the Museum, published his *Zoological Miscellany*, illustrated by H. Nodder.[79] Sloane shells were used in this work, and several of them were new to science. Three of these have been recognized in the present-day collections: the holotype of *Dipsas plicatus* Leach (Fig. 27, Plate 10); 22/886–7 and two without Sloane numbers: the holotypes of *Voluta subnodosa* Leach and of *Strombus sloanii* Leach.[80]

Two early nineteenth-century works also refer to Sloane's specimens: William Wood's *Index Testaceologicus* 1825,[81] with a Supplement in 1828,[82] and Edward Griffiths' 1825 edition of Cuvier's *Animal Kingdom*.[83] Between 1779 and 1849, fifteen new invertebrate species were described bearing the name *sloanii* or *sloaniana*. Five of these (all molluscs) are preserved in the Natural History Museum collections.

By 1837, less than eighty years after the opening of the British Museum, the Sloane invertebrate material had become largely unidentifiable, having been merged with recently acquired collections (Royal Society, 1781; Cracherode, 1799; Tankerville, 1825; Banks, 1827). As far as the shells were concerned, the purchase of the W.J. Broderip collection in 1837 meant that many of the Sloane specimens were removed from display and replaced with the brighter, cleaner, new material. It is likely that many of the Sloane shells were disposed of at this time; the remainder were assiduously cleaned, with the result that the catalogue numbers were often wholly or partially obliterated.

Given that there had been a tradition of collecting shells for their beauty and rarity, in contrast to the more random collection of other invertebrates, it is certain that many of Sloane's corals, crustaceans and sponges were also disposed of at this time. They had been on display for some years and must have looked faded and dusty against new, fresh

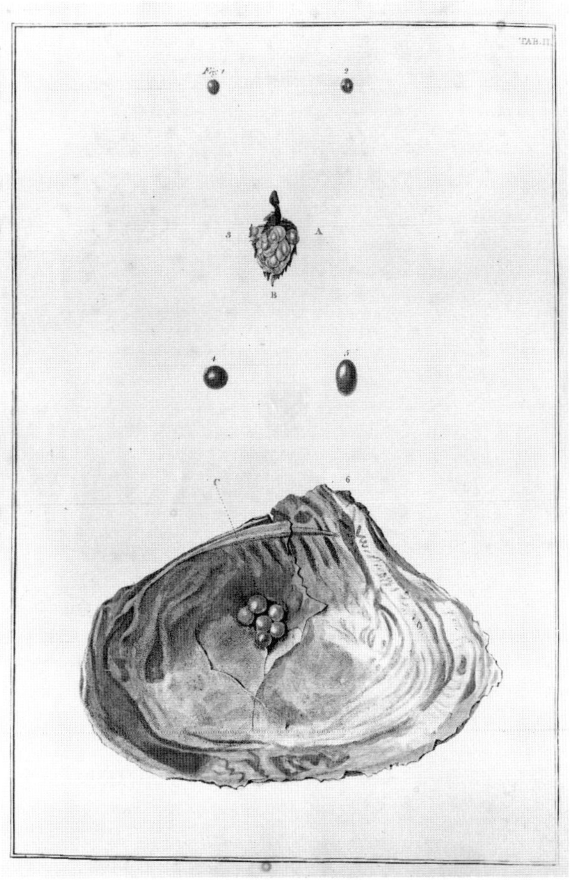

Fig. 27 J. & A. Van Rymsdyk, *Museum Britannicum* (1778), tab. ii: 3: 'An *Oriental Pearl*, resembling a bunch of grapes, set in vine-leaves'; 6: 'A Bohemian River *Horse-muscle* with six *Pearls*, sticking to the shell', is the right valve of the holotype of *Dipsas plicatus* Leach.

specimens. This probably explains why shells seem so far to be the only invertebrate group from Sloane's museum to survive. However, it should be noted here that some of the entries in the coral catalogue indicate objects of considerable intrinsic value, also now untraceable but perhaps for different reasons:

A branch of red corall sett upon a brass silver gilt pedestall sett 21a/439 with turcoises.

A piece of rock with red corall growing on it wherin on its broad 21a/598 basis is cut the Virgin Mary with her babe. from Naples.

A branch of red corall the ends of which are cut into hands to 21a/599 prevent thunder?

In contrast, a large pearl from Sloane's collection, figured by the Van Rymsdyks (see Plate 10), is still extant, and indeed is on public exhibit at the present time. It is described thus:

An original pearl, resembling a bunch of grapes set in vine leaves . . . Lord Donegal honoured me with a sight of his curious Pearl, modeled by nature in the shape of a bunch of grapes; embellished with the line of beauty, polished to a great degree of light, and in excellent preservation – in short it is a perfect Beauty.[84]

22/60,62, 1880
Sloane also had some rare and exquisite carved and engraved *Nautilus* shells: these still exist and have been figured and described in a British Museum publication.[85]

One of the most curious items connected with the invertebrate exhibits is a glove made from the byssus of a *Pinna* shell. This glove, once one of a pair, was also figured by the Van Rymsdyks (see Plate 11).

24/4912
A pair of men's gloves made of the beard of the *pinna marina* in Andalousia in Spaine sent me by His Grace the Duke of Richmond.

There is another byssus glove, of a different style, in the collection:

24/5711
Glove made of it, Id. from the Duke of Richmond.

A twelve-year-old boy's account of a visit to the British Museum in 1780 tells:

The next room was filled with all kinds of serpents and lizards once alive, and some of them with wings. There was a pair of gloves made from the beards of mussels, also some snakes and rattlesnakes and swordfishes etc., and a crocodile, which was such a monstrous great thing, he could have eaten three or four men for a breakfast . . . There were thousands of other things, which I have not time to enumerate, and indeed, we could not stay to look at half of them.[86]

This then was the great strength of Sloane's collection; the fact that on one level the material could excite the curiosity of a twelve-year-old, on another provoke discussion and interest among his learned contemporaries, and on yet another provide the basis for significant taxonomic work and the naming of species new to science. Sloane's contribution to the foundation of our current knowledge of the invertebrates was undeniably considerable.

Notes and References

1. A. Lonicer, *Historiae naturalis opus novum etc.* (Frankfurt, 1551–5).

2. P. Belon, *De Aquatilibus, libro duo, etc.* (Paris, 1553).

3. C. Gessner, *Icones animalium . . . quae in Historia animalium C. Gesneri describuntur etc.* (Zurich, 1553).

4. C. Gessner, *Historia animalium. Liber 4 qui est de piscium et aquatilium animantium natura, etc.* (Zurich, 1558).

5. G. Rondelet, *Libri de piscibus marinis, in quibus verae piscium effigies expressae sunt, etc.* (Leiden, 1554–5).

6. U. Aldrovandi, *De reliquis animalibus exanguibus libri quatuor post mortem ejus editi . . . de Mollibus, Crustaceis, Testaceis, et Zoophytis* (Bologna, 1606).

7. F. Colonna, *Fabii Columnae Lyncei Purpura etc./ Aquatilium et terrestrium aliquot animalium, etc.* (Rome, 1616) [these two treatises are usually bound together].

8. F. Buonanni, *Ricreatione dell'occhio e della mente nell'osservation' delle chiocciole proposta a'curiosi delle opere della natura* (Rome, 1681).

9. F. Buonanni, *Recreatio mentis, et oculi in observatione Animalium Testaceorum curiosis naturae inspectoribus. Italico sermone primum proposita . . . nunc denuo ab eodem Latine oblata, centum additis Testaceorum iconibus, circa quae varia problemata proponuntur* (Rome, 1684).

10. M. Lister, *Historia sive Synopsis Methodicae Conchyliorum, etc.* (London, 1685–92).

11. Buonanni, op. cit. (note 8), facsimile edn. with nine additional plates (Milan, 1985).

12. J. Petiver, *J. Petiveri Opera, historiam naturalem spectantia; or Gazophylacium, etc.* (London, 1764).

13. Ibid., vol. II, 'Petiveriana seu Naturae Collecteana Domi Forisque Auctori Communicata', p. 1, comm. II.

14. Lister, op. cit. (note 10).

15. M. Lister, *De Cochleis* (London, 1685).

16. Ibid., flyleaf inscription.

17. Sloane, *Natural History* (London, 1707–25).

18. For a discussion and synonymy of this slug see T. Cockerell and W. Collinge, 'A checklist of the slugs', *The Conchologist* 2 (1893), p. 217.

19. J.F. Payne, 'Thomas Sydenham', in *Masters of Medicine* (London, 1900), pp. 190–1.

20. Sloane, *Natural History*, vol. I, pp. 2–3.

21. Ibid., vol. I, pp. 7–8, pl. IIII, fig. 5.

22. Ibid., vol. I.

23. Ibid., vol. II, pp. 343–4.

24. E.g. *Philosophical Transactions* 21 no. 251 (1699), p. 113.

25. G. R. de Beer, *Sir Hans Sloane and the British Museum* (London, 1953), p. 89.

26. Ibid., pp. 90–1.

27. E. Lankester (ed), *The Correspondence of John Ray* (London, 1848), pp. 249–50 [Ray to Sloane, 25 May 1692].

28. Ibid., p. 259 [Ray to Sloane, 31 January 1693].

29. Ibid., pp. 286–7 [Ray to Sloane, 12 February 1695].

30. Sloane, *Natural History*, vol. I, p. 51.

31. Ibid., vol. II.

32. Pers. comm. with members of staff, Zoology Dept., NHM.

33. Sloane, *Natural History*, vol. II, p. viii.

34. Ibid., vol. II, p. 191.

35. Ibid., vol. II, p. 191.

36. G. Wilkins, 'A catalogue and historical account of the Sloane shell collection', *Bulletin of the British Museum (Natural History) Historical Series* 1 no. 1 (1953), pp. 1–47.

37. Ibid.

38. E. da Costa, *Elements of Conchology, or an Introduction to the Knowledge of Shells* (London, 1776), p. 34.

39. Wilkins, op. cit. (note 36), pp. 13–22.

40. Lister, op. cit. (note 10), pls. 4, 5.

41. W. Courten, Manuscript catalogue. BL, Sloane MS 3988.

42. G. Rumpf, *D'Amboinsche Rariteitkamer etc.* (Amsterdam, 1705).

43. Lister, op. cit. (note 10), pl. 23.

44. Wilkins, op. cit. (note 36), p. 21.

45. Lankester, op. cit. (note 27), p. 212 [Lhwyd to Ray, 14 April 1690].

46. Ibid., pp. 214–5 [Ray to Robinson, 16 May 1690].

47. R. Gunther (ed.), *Further Correspondence of John Ray* (London, 1928), p. 207 [Ray to Lhwyd, 7 May 1690].

48. R. Gunther (ed.), *Life and letters of Edward Lhwyd* (Early Science in Oxford 14) (Oxford, 1946), p. 102.

49. Lankester, op. cit. (note 27), p. 214 [Robinson to Ray, 17 May 1690].

50. Gunther, op. cit. (note 47), p. 279 [Ray to Lhwyd, 30 April 1701].

51. Ibid., p. 281 [Ray to Lhwyd, 11 June 1701].

52. Sloane, *Natural History*, vol. II, p. iv.

53. J. Petiver, *Musei Petiveriani, centuria prima (secunda-decima). Rariora Naturae Continens* (London, 1695–1703).

54. Petiver, op. cit. (note 12).

55. Sloane, *Natural History*, vol. II, p. 4.

56. De Beer, op. cit. (note 25), pp. 110–11.

57. Bill of Lading dated 5 August 1711: BL, 1044, C.4. [bound with 58] J. du Vivie, *Register van het Indiaanse Cabinet bestaande uit Veeldehande vreemde dieren en gewassen, etc.* (Leiden, 1711).

58. Du Vivie, op. cit. (note 57).

59. Wilkins, op. cit. (note 36), pp. 22–6.

60. E. Kaempfer, *The History of Japan ... translated by J.G. Scheuchzer, etc.* (London, 1727).

61. Nos. 22/749, 983 [part], 1113 [part], 1244, 1487, 1516; 23/3845, 4029.

62. Petiver, op. cit. (note 12), vol. III, p. 44.

63. J. Petiver, in *Philosophical Transactions* 21 no. 255 (1699), p. 295.

64. J. Petiver, in *Philosophical Transactions* 22 no. 271 (1701), p. 843.

65. Nos. 22/200, 234, 983, 985 [part], 1113 [part], 2303; 24/5191.

66. Nos. 22/197 [part], 209 [part], 1114 [part], 1119 [part], 1252, 1467, 1561 [part], 1579 [part], 1841 [part]; 23/3342, 3849.

67. W. Dampier, 'Account of ... Observations ... on the Coast of New Holland, in 1699, being an extract from "A Voyage to New Holland" etc.', *Hakluyt Society* no. 25 (London, 1859), pp. 134–64.

68. W. Rogers, 'Voyage round the World ... in 1708–1711', in R. Kerr, *A General ... Collection of Voyages and Travels* vol. x (London, 1824), pp. 337–8.

69. M. Catesby, *The Natural History of Carolina, Florida and the Bahama Islands; containing the figures of Birds, Beasts, Fishes, Serpents, Insects and Plants, etc.* (London, 1731–43), vol. I, preface, pp. v–vi.

70. Couhage/ Cowhage/ Cowitch: a leguminous plant of the genus *Stizolobium* having crooked pods covered with sharp hairs which, penetrating the flesh, cause irritation and itching. It is sometimes used as a vermifuge.

71. Nos. 22/748 [part], 1443 [part], 1482 [part], 1894 [part]; 23/2815 [part].

72. C. Linnaeus, *Systema Naturae ... Editio decima, reformata* (Holmiae, 1758).

73. P. Pallas, *Elenchus zoophytorum* (The Hague, 1776).

74. E. da Costa [and G. Humphreys], *Conchology or Natural History of Shells etc.* (London, 1770).

75. J. and A. Van Rymsdyk, *Museum Britannicum* (London, 1778).

76. J. Ellis and D. Solander, *The Natural History of many curious and uncommon Zoophytes, collected from various Parts of the Globe* (London, 1786).

77. P. Cornelius and J. Wells, 'Ellis & Solander's "Zoophytes", 1786', *Bulletin of the British Museum (Natural History) Historical Series* 16 no. 1 (1988), pp. 17–87.

78. Anon, 'An eighteenth-century coral', *Report on the British Museum (Natural History) 1984–1986* (London, 1987), p. 20.

79. W.E. Leach, *The Zoological Miscellany; being descriptions of new, or interesting animals*, vols. I–III (London, 1814–17), illustrated with coloured figures by R. P. Nodder.

80. NHM, registration nos. 1952.5.10.2 and 1952.5.10.3 respectively.

81. W. Wood, *Index Testaceologicus; or a Catalogue of Shells, British and foreign ... with the Latin and English names, references to figures, and places where found* (London, 1818).

82. Ibid., Supplement (London, 1828).

83. E. Griffiths and E. Pidgeon, *The Animal Kingdom ... by the Baron Cuvier, with supplementary additions to each order* vol. XII (London, 1834).

84. Van Rymsdyk, op. cit. (note 75), p. 5.

85. H. Tait, *Catalogue of the Waddesdon Bequest in the British Museum*. vol. III: *The 'Curiosities'* (London, 1991), pp. 100–3.

86. C. Hutton Beale (ed.), *Catherine Hutton and her Friends* (Birmingham, 1895), p. 112 [John Coleman to C. Hutton, 1780].

6 Insect Collections

Mike Fitton and Pamela Gilbert

* 'Is the entomological collection which was left by Sir Hans Sloane, in a perfect state at present?'
'There is hardly any of it remaining.'

The question had been put to Charles Koenig (1774–1851) by a Parliamentary Select Committee investigating the conditions in the British Museum in 1835.[1] Koenig, who had worked in the Library of Sir Joseph Banks and was successor to George Shaw (1751–1813) as Keeper of the Department of Natural History and Modern Curiosities, was questioned in some detail by the Select Committee:

'How does it happen that the collection has been lost?'
'When I came to the Museum most of these objects were in an advanced state of decomposition, and they were buried or committed to the flames one after another; Dr Shaw had a burning every year; and he called them his cremations.'
'Is there any single insect remaining of the 5439, which were presented by Sir Hans Sloane?'
'I should think not.'
'Do you think that so great a destruction of specimens can solely arise from Natural Causes?'
'Sir Hans Sloane had a method of keeping his insects which was very injurious to them. He squeezed them between two laminae of mica, which destroyed the specimens in most cases, even the wings of the butterfly.[2] A few specimens of these insects remained, and we considered them as rubbish, and such were destroyed with other rubbish.'

In 1806 Shaw had been appointed Keeper of the Department of Natural History and Modern Curiosities at Montagu House, the early home of the British Museum. Immediately it became clear to him that many of the zoological specimens were in an advanced state of deterioration, and not least among them the Sloane insect collections. He quickly began a clearing operation and reported accordingly to the Trustees.

This seemingly drastic exercise caused some concern to the Trustees and in 1809 they directed 'that Sir Joseph Banks be requested to consider Dr Shaw's Report, respecting the Articles on the Basement Story, as read this day and to give such directions as may appear to him proper relating to any of the articles suggested by Dr Shaw as fit for destruction, or to be disposed of; and that no article be removed without the approbation of Sir Joseph Banks'.[3]

In spite of Shaw's determined efforts to burn the rubbish, and contrary to Koenig's evidence to the Select Committee, some of Sloane's insects survive to this day and form part of the collections in the Entomology and Botany Departments in The Natural History Museum, London. The remnants are, however, small. It is a tragedy that these fine collections were allowed to rot away, but that in itself has helped a little in understanding the entomology practised

by Sloane and his contemporaries. It will become obvious that we are able to give only a rather superficial review, because little work has been done, even with the surviving material. Our own major discovery is that the origins of one section of the surviving collections are entirely different from what has been supposed for a hundred years and more. And in another way we are fortunate: some of the surviving Sloane material is in the form of discrete, if not complete, collections which have continuing scientific importance as well as antiquarian interest. In addition to still being available for study by entomologists they tell us something of the attitudes of early workers to the formation and maintenance of insect collections and of the techniques they used.

Our survey, then, is divided into a consideration of Sloane's entomological activities; the scope of his insect collection; the major collections acquired by Sloane, with particular reference to the special features of the surviving material; how information relating to the Sloane collections throws light on the problems of keeping insect collections in the eighteenth century; and a note on an insect painting.

Sloane's Entomological Activities

Sloane's interest in entomology lagged far behind his interest in botany. Like most contemporary naturalist-collectors he concentrated on plants, though he undoubtedly paid attention to 'other Parts of Nature' from an early age.[4] He brought back large numbers of insects from his voyage to Jamaica, where he had collected extensively during fifteen months spent as physician to the Governor, the Duke of Albemarle.[5] Back in London these exotic specimens formed the core of Sloane's growing insect collection. Entomological work, however, can have been only a small part of the collecting activity that seems at times to have threatened to overtake his professional medical career. While Sloane was once described as collecting everything and anything, his primary activity as a physician probably put an end to any fieldwork on insects. However, his huge reputation as a collector continued to bring him vast quantities of 'desiderata'.

Sloane did continue some work on insects and he must have known his collection well, but it is difficult to know to what extent his activities rose above the level of mere accumulation of material. That they did so is fairly easily demonstrated: for example, in 1704 John Ray remarked on Sloane's particular knowledge of flies.[6] His general understanding of entomology is well shown in volume II of his *Natural History* (Fig. 28), where the insects collected in Jamaica are described in detail. There are field observations

 * Marginal numerals in this chapter refer to Sloane catalogues listed on pp. 291–4

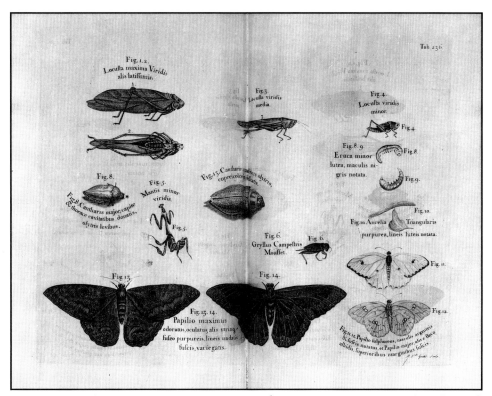

Fig. 28 A variety of insects, from Sir Hans Sloane, *Natural History*, vol. II, tab. 236. Amongst those illustrated, in figures 11 and 12, is a butterfly to which Linnaeus gave the name *Papilio sennae*. Pupae, probably of this species, survive in the collection (see p. 117 and p. 122 note 23). Reproduced by courtesy of the Trustees of The Natural History Museum.

and records of life-histories, and Sloane's own observations are cross-referenced to the entomological works of authors such as Merian, Petiver and Swammerdam and include data from Europe and mainland America as well as the West Indies.

His knowledge as well as his aptitude placed Sloane at the centre of a large circle of persons interested in the study of natural history;[7] for many it was a secondary interest, but others such as Ray were among the most advanced biologists of their day. Systematizing nature was the main concern of the serious naturalists of the late seventeenth and eighteenth centuries and possession of a large cabinet of specimens was essential. Such collections also had a social function: something to talk about amongst one's friends, even perhaps to boast a little on the acquisition of a particular specimen, and many had the financial ability to employ collectors or at least to buy specimens from unusual localities. And, of course, the serious natural history collectors were no secret society: quite the opposite, it was the universality of the collection that gave it a high reputation.[8]

Sloane's material was referred to by Carolus Linnaeus (1707–78) in his great works.[9] The famous Swedish naturalist, founder of modern biological nomenclature, came to London in 1736 where he met Sloane and saw his collections. It is said that Sloane was not over-enthusiastic in his welcome for Linnaeus (see Chapter 1), but he must have had some respect for him, for he arranged to have read before the Royal Society Linnaeus's description of how gadflies attack reindeer.[10] The surviving insects include type specimens of some species named by Linnaeus in 1758. Linnaeus's references are to the publications of Petiver and Sloane and although he saw the specimens it is probable that he did not examine and draw descriptions directly from them. He may, in any case, have concentrated on Sloane's plants during his visit: like Sloane, Linnaeus's first love was botany, and he was also a medical man.

The Scope of the Collection

Since so little of the collection survives, we must rely on the catalogue for much information. After his return from Jamaica and his establishment in London society, Sloane's collections continued to grow.[11] Many of the notable collections of the time went to Sloane on the death of their respective owners. Some were bequeathed to him, others were purchased, often through some earlier agreement to fulfil other legacies. More specimens arrived from sources around the world. Sloane's large circle of correspondents, including travelling traders, ministers of religion and doctors, were requested to collect. The data in the catalogue

Brief Directions *for the Easie Making, and Preserving* Collections
of all NATURAL Curiosities.
For IAMES PETIVER *Fellow of the Royall Society* LONDON.

ALL *small* Animals, *as* Beasts, Birds, Fishes, Serpents, Lizards, *and other* Fleshy Bodies *capable of* Corruption, *are certainly preserved in* Rack, Rum, Bandy, *or any other Spirits; but where these are not easily to be had, a strong* Pickle, *or* Brine *of Sea Water may serve; to every* Gallon *of which, put 3 or 4 Handfulls of* Common *or* Bay Salt, *with a Spoonful or two of* Allom *powderd, if you have any, and so send them in any* Pot, Bottle, Jarr, &c. *close stopt, Cork'd and Rosin'd. N.B. You may often find in the* Stomachs *of* Sharks, *and other great* Fish, *which you catch at Sea, divers strange* Animals *not easily to be met with elsewhere; which pray look for, and preserve as above.*

As to Fowls, *those that are large, if we cannot have their* Cases *whole, their* Head, Leggs, *or* Wings *will be acceptable, but smaller* Birds *are easy sent entire, by putting them in* Spirits *as above, or if you bring them dry, you must take out their* Entrals; *which is best done by cutting them under their* Wing, *and then stuff them with* Ockam *or* Tow, *mixt with* Pitch *or* Tar; *and being thorouhly dried in the* Sun, *wrap them up close, to keep them from Moisture, but in long Voyages, you must* Bake *them gently, once in a Month or two, to kill the* Vermin *which often breed in them.*

All large pulpy moist Fruit, *that are apt to decay or rot, as* Apples, Cherries, Cowcumbers, Oranges, *and such like, must be sent in* Spirits *or* Pickle, *as* Mangoes, &c. *and to each Fruit, its desired you will pin or tye a sprig of its* Leaves, *and* Flowers.

All Seed *and dry* Fruit, *as* Nutts, Pods, Heads, Husks, &c. *these need no other Care, but to be sent whole, and if you add a* Leaf *or two with its* Flower, *it will be the more instructive, as also a piece of the* Wood, Bark, Root, *or* Gum *of any* Tree *or* Herb *that is remarkble for its* Beauty, Smell, Use, *or* Vertue.

In Collecting PLANTS, *Pray observe to get that part of either* Tree, *or* Herb, *as hath its* Flower, Seed, *or* Fruit *on it; but if neither, then gather it as it is, and if the* Leaves *which grow near the* Root *or any* Herb, *differ from those above, be pleased to get both to Compleat the Specimen; these must be put into a* Book, *or* Quire *of* Brown Paper *stitch'd (which you must take with you) as soon as gathered; You must now and then shift these into fresh* Books, *to prevent either rotting themselves or Paper. N.B. All* Gulph-Weeds, Sea-Mosses, Coralls, Corallines, Sea Feathers, Spunges, &c. *may be put altogether into any old* Box, *or* Barrel, *with the* Shrimps, Prawns, Crabs, Crawfish, &c. *which you will often find amongst the* Sea weeds, *or on the Shoar with the* Shells, *which you may place in layers; as we do a Barrel of* Colchester *Oysters. All* SHELLS *may be thus sent as you find them, with or without their* Snails *in them, and wherever you meet with different sizes of the same sort, pray gather the fairest of all Magnitudes; the Sea shells will be very acceptible, yet the* Land, *and* Freshwater *ones, are the most rare and desirable. In Relation to* INSECTS, *as* Beetles, Spiders, Grashopper, Bees, Wasps, Flies, &c. *these may be* Drowned *altogether, as soon as Caught in a little wide Mouth'd* Glass, *or* Vial, *half full of* Spirits, *which you may carry in your Pocket: But all* Butterflies *and* Moths, *as have mealy* Wings, *whose Colours may be rub'd off, with the Fingers, these must be put into any small Printed* Book, *as soon as caught, after the same manner you do ỹ* Plants.

All Metals, Minerals, Ores, Chrystals, Spars, Coloured *Earths, Clays, &c. to be taken as you find them, as also such formed* Stones, *as have any resemblance to* Shells, Corals, Bones, *or other parts of* Animals, *these must be got as intire as you can, the like to be Observ'd in* Marbeld Flints, Slates, *or other* Stones, *that have the Impression of* Plants, Fishes, Insects, *or other Bodies on them: These are to be Found in* Quarries, Mines, Stone *or* Gravel Pitts, Caves, Cliffs, *and* Rocks, *on the Sea shour, or wherever the* Earth *is laid open.* NOTE *If to any* ANIMAL, PLANT MINERAL *&c. you can learn its* Name, Nature, Vertue *or Use, it will be still the more* Acceptible.

N.B. As amongst Forreign Plants, *the most common* Grass, Rush, Moss, Fern, Thistle, Thorn, *or vilest* Weed *you can find, will meet with Acceptance, as well as a scarcer Plant; So in all other things, gather whatever you meet with, but if very common or well known, the fewer of that* Sort, *will be acceptible to*

ỹ most Humble Servant

Aldersgate street
LONDON.

IAMES PETIVER.

BOOKS &c. Printed for ỹ AUTHOR.	GAZOPHYLACIUM NATURÆ & ARTIS.
Musei PETIVERIANI Centuriæ X. FIG.	Containing above 1200 Figures, in 100 Folio Copper
Labells for Medicinall Plants.	Plates, with their Names &c.
Labells for English Wild Plants.	The Catalogue & Descriptions Seperate.
FIGURES to Mr RAY's English Plants.	Aquatilium Animalium AMBOINÆ Icones &
with References to his History & Synopsis, Nº 600	Nemua, Containing near 400 Figures in 20
in 50 Folio Copper Plates.	Folio Copper Plates.
An ENGLISH Catalogue Engraved	The Printed Catalogue Seperate.
A Latine Catalogue Engraved	Directions for Collecting Naturall Rarities.

Fig. 29 James Petiver published this single sheet of *Brief Directions* to encourage and instruct collectors. Although brief indeed, they are remarkably comprehensive and give a good idea of the methods used by collectors at the time Sloane was active. The date of publication has not been established with certainty, but was probably about 1700. Reproduced by courtesy of the Trustees of The Natural History Museum.

(see below) give some idea of the range of individuals who contributed insects to the collection and the wide geographical range from which they came. One of the most regular donors in London was James Petiver (see Chapter 1). Petiver, like Sloane, had a large number of contacts and even issued a sheet of *Brief Directions*[12] giving instructions on methods to be used for various groups of plants and animals (Fig. 29). For insects:

... as Beetles, Spiders, Grasshoppers, Bees, Wasps, Flies, &c. these may be Drowned altogether, as soon as Caught in a little wide Mouth'd Glass, or Vial, half full of Spirits, which you may carry in your Pocket. But all Butterflies and Moths, as have mealy Wings, whose Colours may be rub'd off, with the Fingers, these must be put into any small Printed Book, as soon as caught, after the same manner you do ye Plants.

Sloane also knew of the disordered chaos of Petiver's collection and this, as much as anything, may have determined Sloane's ambition to order and catalogue his own collections, and then to keep his catalogue up to date.

In 1725 the Sloane collection is recorded as containing some 3,824 insects, and this total included the specimens he brought back from Jamaica.[13] By the time of his death in 1753 it had increased to 5,439.[14] It is perhaps worth noting here that in Sloane's day 'insects' included several groups of animals, such as spiders, millipedes and scorpions, which are now classified separately. The collection was certainly the largest at that time and possibly included representatives of more species than any other. For comparison, Linnaeus's insect collection totalled some 3,200 specimens at the time of his death in 1778, and he had gone to great lengths to obtain material from all parts of the world.

Sloane's Manuscript Catalogue

Two folio volumes of the catalogue are devoted to the insects.[15] The title page, in the first volume, reads thus:

INSECTS
contained
in Cabinet no.234.
English Insects, collected by Mr. Dandridge. Draw[ers] 1 to 96.
English Insects from various persons. Drawer[s] 97–126.
in Cabinet no.235.
Foreign Butterflies. Draw[ers] 127.–148.
in Cabinet no.236.
Foreign Moths. Draw[ers] 149.–156.
Miscellaneous Insects. Draw[ers]. 157. 161. 162.
Foreign Caterpillars & Nests. 158–160.
Miscellaneous Insects preserved in Books. 163. 164.
in Cabinet 237.
Foreign insects of all the other Classes, (except Butterflies & Moths) Nests &c. Dr[awers]. 165.–232.
Fossil Insects. Draw[er]. 233.
in Bottles in Spirit of Wine, in the Gallery

Miscellaneous insects on shelve r. 1.–8.
s. 1.–8.
t. 1.–8.
w. 1.–5.
in Cabinet no. 181. Insects used in the Materia medica.

Following the title page there is a tabular synoptic classification of the insects, covering five sides and evidently prepared by Cromwell Mortimer (see Chapter 1). Then follows 'An Explanation of several Abbreviations & notes made use of in the Catalogue of Insects'. The main body of the catalogue, entered on the recto pages, comprises a series of entries which refer to individual (or sometimes a small number of) specimens. The entries are serially numbered, have a brief diagnosis (usually in Latin), and information on the origin of the insect. Additional information includes supplementary entries on the verso pages and numbers in pencil adjacent to the continuing series numbers. The supplementary entries, which are in ink, have the same number as the main entry opposite, sometimes with a suffix, for example, '3512.*.' and '3512.a.', and mainly refer to Petiver specimens. The pencil numbers are either drawer numbers or relate directly to the folios of the volumes of insects from the Petiver collection (see below). The 'Tabula Synoptica Insectorum in Classes distributorum à Cromwello Mortimero M.D. R.S. secr.' is apparently in Mortimer's own hand, and the 'Abbreviations', most supplementary entries and several annotations match this handwriting. The main catalogue entries are in a number of hands, although they are fairly uniform up to 4,205; these are presumed to be in the hand of Sloane himself. The added pencil numbers through the two volumes are quite different and may have been inserted at a later date. Catalogue entries end with number 5,447 (which is on fol. 326 of the second volume). This is followed by the word 'End' and in the same hand 'A hornets nest found in Yorkshire given by Mr. Burroughs', seemingly an early acquisition to the newly-established British Museum (see p. 54). At the back of the second volume, on page 376 and its reverse is a list, 'Numbers of Insects not found on the review made by C. Mortimer.' The list has ninety-four entries (plus some others which have been struck out). A few are marked '2-' in the margin, which is explained 'Those markt 2- are suspected to be in ye drawers tho' not markt.'

The 'Tabula Synoptica' is important because each entry in it ends with one or more roman numerals which are drawer numbers, for example, 'Insecta Fossilia, petrificata. CCXXXIII.' which corresponds to the entry in the list on the title page. More importantly the table provides, in several entries, links to the two bound volumes of insects from Petiver's collection (see below), for example 'Vespae, XL. XLI, CXI. CLXVI. V.II.f.23' and the general 'Insecta inter folia cartacea in Libris conservata. Vol.I.II. & Dr.CLXIII.'

Collectors and Localities

The catalogue entries use a number of abbreviations for

both collectors and localities. As already noted these were gathered at the beginning of the first volume, by Mortimer, and we reproduce some of the list here because it forms a sample of the sources of insect specimens. We have added more details (in square brackets) which will make it of more general interest to entomologists.

Antrob. i.e. Mr. Antrobus.
[Contributed British specimens to Petiver.]
B.H. (English) Mr. Benj[amin] Harris.
[Little is known; most of his specimens are from Croydon. It has been suggested that he might be related to Moses Harris.¹⁶]
B.3. Goff.
[Mr Goff, sent specimens from the 'East Indies'.]
Bengal H.S.
Cap. BS. – cape de Bona Speranza, or Cape of good Hope.
Carolin. W.
[Carolinas]
Cun./D.J.Cun. – Dominus Johannes Cunningham. a Scotch Surgeon
[James Cunningham¹⁷ (or Cunninghame) proved to be important to both Sloane and Petiver. A Scottish surgeon and a great traveller. On a journey to St. Helena and the Cape of Good Hope in 1696 he collected a considerable number of specimens. He returned to England and was elected to the Royal Society. He later went to the Far East and continued his collecting; whilst in Cochin China most of the English there were massacred and he was imprisoned for two years. He escaped and wrote to Petiver 'I question not but before now you have lamented . . . that you lost one of your Butter-flie catchers, but a Singular Providence has . . . preserved me . . . [I] now send you some Cochinchina Butterflies'.]
C. – Mr Courten.
[William Courten (1642–1702). Best known as a collector of medals and antiquities. He had an interest in natural history but did not rise above the level of accumulation. His collections, valued at £50,000, were bequeathed to Sloane and included many insects.]¹⁸
Dan. – Mr. Sam[ue]l. Daniel, Surgeon
[He contributed some specimens from Turkey.]
D. – Mr. Dandridge.
[(1664–1746).¹⁹ See below.]
E.B. fort St. Geo. – Edward Bulkley at Fort St. George
[He sent specimens from Fort St. George (Madras) to Sloane and Petiver].
E.B. p. CL. Luz.
GLAN. Mrs. Glanvil?
[Eleanor Glanville²⁰ (c.1654–1709) was one of England's outstanding early entomologists. She collected widely, particularly butterflies and moths, and she reared species from larvae and kept careful records. She was in contact with Petiver, Ray, Dandridge, Buddle and Vernon. William Vernon wrote 'A lady came to town with the noblest collection of butterflies . . . which has sham'd us'.

At least three of the specimens she gave to Petiver, a butterfly and two moths, still survive in the Sloane collection. She is immortalized in the name of the butterfly the Glanville Fritillary (*Melitaea cinxia*), of which she collected the first British specimens. See also p. 193, note 3.]
G.Sk. – George Skeen.
[Some of his specimens from 'Annamabon' survive.]
Gof. mont. Ch. Italy.
G.I. Camel. – Georg. Joseph. Camelli, e Soc. Jesu.
[Otherwise Kamel, Jesuit missionary, at some time in Manila. See Chapter 8.]
G.I.C. – the same.
H.J. Maryland
[Revd Hugh Jones, Christ Church, Calvert County from 1696 to 1702.²¹]
K. or, KAM. – Kamel or Camelli, q.v.
Lisbon I.F.
L. – Lister.
[Martin Lister]
Livonia N.M. – Livonia Nic. Martini
[see below]
Malacca H.S.
Maurit. H.
MER. – Maria Sybilla Merian.
[(1647–1717) Entomologist and painter. First to describe and illustrate life-histories of many butterflies. Her most important work being on the insects of Surinam, where she did important fieldwork. See also Plate 34.]
Martini, 4. – Dr. Nich. Martini. £0:0s:4d. his Insects sent form Livonia, & the prices put to them thus . . 3. . . 6. . . 1. .
P., Pet. Petiv. – Mr. James Petiver.
[His insects made up a high percentage of the Sloane insect collections (see below.)]
R.P. & R. Planer – Richard Planer.
[Ship's surgeon, Cartagena.]
R.E. – Robert Ellis.
[see next entry.²²]
R. Ellis. Carolina S. Robt. Ellis, South Carol. (vid. no. 5111.)
Robert Rutherford W.
[of the Edinburgh Society of Apothecaries, contributed specimens from America to Petiver.]
S.B. – Sam. Buckley [crossed out] / Samuel Brown.
[The latter a surgeon with the East India Company at Fort St. George (Madras).]
St. X. – Santa Cruz.
Surin. – Surinam.
Stonest. – Stonestreet. [William Stonestreet (d.1716). See Chapter 1]
WAT. – Mr. Watt.

Descriptions of the Collection

A selection of entries from the catalogue is given below. In the absence of the greater part of the collection itself, the catalogue gives some idea of the range of material, Sloane's diagnoses, and his attempts to systematize the collection and information by referencing.

13e/108 Triangular aurelias from whence the yellow butterfly of Jamaica. [Added later:] fasten'd to a twig of – Sena Spuria.[23]

13e/238 The largest Brazilian horned Beetle. From Mrs. Rider who had it from her Grandfather Dr. Wright's collection who was physician to Oliver Cromwell.

13e/246 Ichneumons generated in the small hard shelled Galls underneath oakleaves. from [Mr Derham][24]

13e/556 Locusta major viridis mas 1a. Mouf. p. 117. D.[25]

13e/690 Formica maxima. The horse ant. Ray. p. 69. D.[26]

13e/795 Scarabaeus capricornus dictus maximus compressus pedibus anterioribus longissimus, ventro cinereo, dorso & fusco & coccineo pulcherrimo-variegato. From the river of the Amazons. C.

13e/1177 Scarabaeus hemisphaericus major e rufoflavescens, singulis elytris maculis nigris 4or. notatus, capito nigro – duabus maculis flavescentibus notato. D. [and added later:] one with 2 black spots only and a little lesser. R. Mark'd 21. [and added later:] Scarabaeus alber niger, alarum thecis miniabulis in quibus maculae nigrae et in humoris & albi macula alba. Lady Cloak Anglice. List. R. p. 382. L.[27]

13e/1307 Scarabaeus haemisphaericus minor totus ex atro violaceous splendens. L.

13e/1397 Papilio fritillarius minor. Pet. Mus. no. 234. Mr Vernon's Small fritillary. Gaz. nat. tab. 16. no. 10. Ray. p. 422. D. Mark'd 9.[28]

13e/1615 Chrysalis sive aurelia triangularis ex qua exit papilio sulphurea no. 1336. descripta. C. from Jamaica Many of them sticking together. vid. 108.

13e/1620 Phalaena media alis exterioribus oblongis, albicente & viridis fusco coloribus pulchre variegatis, intercoribus coccineis cum maculis nigris. D / R. larger & variet[illegible] an femina?[29]

13e/1983 Phalaena minor tota sulphurea. From Mr. Lawson from Carolina.

13e/2330 No.1177. With its Chrysalis resembling cochineel lying in a white thorn or hawthorn leaf rouled up. D.

14a/3563 Araneus major. from Lady Katherine Windham.

14a/3742 Vespa ichneumon major bipennis [later altered to quadripennis] tota caerulea splendens. I brought it from Jamaica.

14a/3910 A scorpion from Fort St. George in the E. Indies. I have received this species from Barbados & Jamaica by the name of the Surinam scorpion. Dr. Woodw'd.[30]

14a/4120 A very large curculio studded with black spots from Madagascar.

14a/5438 Locusta maxima cinereo purpurea maculis brunis Nat. Hist. Jam. p. 29. Vol. 2. p. 202 several of which came into England Scotland &c in the year 1748. of which there are some that were taken in Chelsea & the streets of London they lived several months in a Glass bottle, fed upon Grass which they eat greadily and which was given them every day.

14a/5439 The Eggs of the same.

Just as the bare facts in the catalogue help little in any detailed scientific assessment of Sloane's collection, so, neither do the accounts of the collection as left by others. However, these accounts include interesting details. For example, Zacharias Conrad von Uffenbach remarks that 'He also had a handsome collection of all kinds of insects, which are kept in the same fashion as those we saw at Herr Dandridge's house, except that here, instead of glass, moonstone or Muscovy glass is used, which is much more deli-cate and light but more costly'.[31] So we know that by 1710 Sloane was covering his specimens with mica, and that Dandridge used glass to similar effect, but exactly how the mica and glass were used is not clear.

In 1748 Per Kalm the Swedish naturalist-traveller and pupil of Linnaeus visited Sloane whilst in England on his way to America. He gives a very clear account of Sloane's collections.[32] By this time, just five years before Sloane's death in 1753, the collection had received its last major accession – the insects of Joseph Dandridge. Again Kalm's description includes little which helps in assessing the collection, but it does have the following details:

... A large number of various kinds of insects which filled many cabinets. They were all mounted in large drawers. Each species or individual was laid in a rectangular box the bottom of which was wooden. But among them, some had both the cover and the bottom of the box made of a crystal-clear glass, while some had only a transparent glass lid. At the joints where the glass ran up to the sides of the box it was sealed tight with paper in such a way that no air let alone any moth or other insect could get inside to damage the contents. Where the box had a glass bottom, the insects were firmly fixed to it.

This describes accurately part of the surviving collection (see below). Kalm implies that all the insects were housed in this way.

Major Insect Collections acquired by Sloane

Leonard Plukenet[33] (1642–1706) was a distinguished botanist who became Superintendent of the Gardens at Hampton Court in 1690 and was known as Queen's Botanist (see Chapter 1). His entire collections were purchased by Sloane following their acquisition by Dr Moore, Bishop of Norwich. Plukenet's insect collection, at least, is a survivor of the bonfires and may be the oldest insect collection still surviving largely intact. The collection as we know it comprises a single bound volume[34] of about 140 leaves, with the specimens mounted on the sheets of paper in true botanical style – being pressed rather like flowers and glued in place (Plate 12). A section at the back of the volume, possibly blank and unused pages, between leaves 105 and 138, appears to have been removed at some time. The relatively good state of preservation of most of Plukenet's specimens testifies to the effectiveness of his 'botanical' technique. Colours, for instance, have faded little. However, some specimens, particularly of the larger and heavier species, have come unstuck from the pages over the years and are broken, and some are missing entirely.

Most of the sheets bear specimens, often twenty or thirty, and there are examples of the orders Orthoptera (grasshoppers and crickets), Dermaptera (earwigs), Odonata (dragonflies), Hemiptera (bugs), Mecoptera (scorpion flies), Megaloptera (alder flies), Neuroptera (lacewings), Coleoptera (beetles), Diptera (flies), Lepidoptera (butterflies and moths), Trichoptera (caddis flies) and Hymenoptera (bees, wasps, ants and sawflies). There are specimens of immature stages as well as adults, and in addition to the insects there are some arachnids (spiders) and crustaceans (woodlice, etc). The arrangement of specimens is not haphazard and they are laid out in groups of related species, few pages, for example, having representatives of more than one order (as now recognized). Altogether there are about 1,700 specimens, all apparently British species.

Among the Sloane manuscripts is a single sheet of paper entitled 'Number of genera in a collection of insects, 18th cent.'; apart from this title it is, apparently, in Plukenet's hand.[35] It lists categories of insects of various kinds, with the number in each category in a column to the right. A few figures are also in a left-hand column. The list is reproduced below, its main interest being the English names and the classificatory system used, which approximates to the grouping of specimens in the collection. The total is not much larger than the collection as it survives and the numbers of specimens of each group are also more-or-less consistent. The one large discrepancy is in 'moths'.

3	Butterflyes	093
9	Moths	446
3	Fether'd Moths	006
	Lybellids	035
	Bees	095
	Moth Bees	007
	Waspes	041
	Icknumens	081
	Taild Icknumens	022
	Icknumen Flyes	031
	Flyes	208
	Bank Flyes	042
	Ants & Ant Flyes	013
	Father Long Leggs	031
1	Grass-hoppers	042
1	Beetles	134
1	Snap Beetles	011
1	Cappricornes	056
1	Pipers	047
1	Stafilines Turntails	012
+	Lady Cow	025
1	Tortiles	004
1	Buggs or Cymax	074
1	Frog hoppers	023
1	Wood Lice	010
1	Other creeping things	010
	Water Beetles	024
	Water Buggs or Cymax	017
	Other things of the Water	012
	Land Caddises	015
	Water Caddises	024
	Cressleses	142
	in all	1850

The Sloane catalogue makes no obvious reference to this volume or to any Plukenet insect specimens. It is at least possible that it was originally among the plant collections

(and had thus been overlooked by Koenig). On the spine it is marked 'III' and 'Insects III' on the title page. This numbering is almost certainly not Plukenet's and volumes 'I' and 'II' form part of the Petiver collection (see below). There is no documentation definitely associated with the Plukenet volume, but a notebook has been identified among the Sloane manuscripts which to all intents and purposes is an entomological field notebook and would seem to relate to the collection.[36] The notes date from 1696 and 1697 and the localities mentioned are all in the London area. Although it is clear that most specimens were collected from obvious situations, the presence of certain species in the collection has helped in making deductions about changes in the British insect fauna since then. Of the 106 species of beetles represented, several are absent from or scarce in the London area today.[37]

The Revd Adam Buddle[38] (c.1660–1715) is not widely known as a collector of insects, but his plant collection was important (see Chapter 8) and was bequeathed to Sloane on Buddle's death-bed. At the time of his death, Buddle's manuscripts and collections were in the hands of James Petiver and Sloane had some considerable difficulty in obtaining the material to add to his own collection. Many of the plant sheets are interspersed with insects and these have remained intact. It seems likely that neither Koenig nor Shaw knew of the existence of the relatively small numbers of insect specimens within the botanical collections and there is no evidence that Sloane regarded them as part of his insect collection: they are not mentioned in his catalogues of insects. Because of the loss of most of the other insects these now represent a valuable resource.

Another collection which remains to this day, at least in part, is that of James Petiver[39] (1658–1716). Petiver was an apothecary who is said to have procured a greater quantity of natural rarities than any man before him (see Chapter 1), but in the course of time his collections overpowered his means, or his industry. When at the collector's death, they passed into the possession of Sloane they were in chaos. The due classification and ordering occupied many hands over several months.[40] In Sloane's own words, 'I have taken as much Care as I can to bring his Collection and Papers out of the Confusion I found them in, and will take farther Care, that what he hath gather'd together ... shall not be lost ...'.[41] As we know, most of it was lost, eventually. However, as well as amassing collections, Petiver was an active entomologist and contributed greatly to the early development of the subject in Britain.

The remains of Petiver's insect collection have been preserved in two distinct styles. Part of it is to be found in two large folio volumes.[42] The specimens are flattened and pressed in the volumes, in botanical style, but are individually enclosed between two sheets of mica which are held together and sealed around the edges with paper strips (Plate 13). No doubt these are similar to the specimens described by Koenig, but again, perhaps because they were, by the 1800s, either among the bound volumes of botanical specimens or considered to be books, they escaped destruction in the Shaw and Koenig purge. As noted in the discussion (above) of Sloane's catalogue they are the volumes of 'Miscellaneous insects preserved in Books' kept in drawers 163 and 164 of cabinet 236. The title page of volume I reads 'Insects collected cheifly by Iames Petiver F.R.S. having References to His Description of Them in his Museum and Gazophylaceum Naturae, wrote by His own Hand: Methodized by Cromwell Mortimer, M.D. secr. R.S. VOL. I. Containing Butterflies. Anno MDCCXXXVIII.'. In the second volume 'II' replaces 'I' and 'Moths, &c.' replaces 'Butterflies'. Then follow un-numbered folios (one and three respectively) with a classification-cum-contents list.

The individual mica envelopes are attached to the pages by a paper hinge, enabling the undersides of the specimens to be examined. The paper edging of the envelopes bears a range of handwritten data. All have a Sloane catalogue number, presumably added by Mortimer. Other information varies, but that, such as, 'Pet. G.N. Tab.3. fig.3', 'Cochin china. 1706' and 'Mr T[h]ompson Collect. of insects caught on ye coast of Guinea & Calabar' is perhaps mainly in Petiver's hand. The two volumes originally included 633 and 281 specimens respectively, of which a total of 444 survive. The envelopes of the missing specimens often seem to have been neatly cut from the pages.

A puzzle remains — were the insects preserved in this way by Petiver? Koenig in his reply to the Select Committee had described the mica envelopes as Sir Hans Sloane's curious way of pressing his insects, but he was speaking more than eighty years after Sloane's death and we have no idea where he got this information. It is possible, even likely, that Sloane and Petiver used the same method. However, it is just possible that Mortimer was put to work in placing the insects in their envelopes before arranging the two volumes, under Sloane's direction. Certainly the time and trouble it would have taken to prepare specimens in this way does not fit with the general chaos that Sloane found when he took over the collection on Petiver's death. Petiver's other surviving specimens are preserved differently.

The rest of the surviving Petiver material is housed in small, shallow, glass-topped containers (Plate 14), as described by Per Kalm (see above). A collection comprising some 322 of these containers with specimens is kept in seventeen shallow, glass-lidded drawers and traditionally it has been known as the Petiver collection, on the assumption that all the specimens originated from Petiver. The glass-lidded drawers themselves appear to date from the late eighteenth century and the cabinet which houses them is modern. However, we are now able to demonstrate that the material they contain comes from the collections of not just Petiver, but Dandridge (see below) and Sloane himself. Most of the individual specimen containers each bears two labels: one on the side with the Sloane catalogue number

(in the same hand as the catalogue entries — Sloane's own) and a second, narrow label on one upper edge (apparently in the hand of Cromwell Mortimer). The latter labels have two numbers — one in arabic and the other in roman numerals. The arabic numbers are duplicates of the catalogue entry numbers and the roman numerals are drawer numbers. This is easily confirmed by reference to the catalogue entries and the 'Tabula Synoptica'. A preliminary investigation has revealed that much of the so-called 'Petiver collection' is material from Dandridge's collection. There are also specimens from Jamaica (apparently collected by Sloane); others given to Sloane by Ray and Lister; and others from Courten's collection. Obviously, a more detailed investigation is needed, but it seems that Petiver, Sloane and Dandridge all prepared specimens in a similar way in glass-faced containers (see below). And, the specimens present us with another, only partly-solved mystery: on close examination some of the insects in the sealed boxes can be seen to have holes in them — they were once impaled on pins like specimens in more modern collections!

The important part that Joseph Dandridge[43] (1664–1746) played in the development of the science of entomology in England has only recently been recognized. By profession a pattern designer for silk weavers in Moorfields, he was one of the greatest insect enthusiasts of his time. He was an active field worker and gathered together an important collection, thought until now to be entirely lost. Dandridge's knowledge of the subject was second to none, and perhaps more importantly, he was ever ready to impart that knowledge to others and to show his collection to contemporary naturalists and insect hunters. However, he did not publish anything and whilst many of his colleagues with similar interests were elected Fellows of the Royal Society, he was not. Dandridge was also an artist of some merit. Eleazar Albin (born before 1690–1741), who was to produce the first extensive work on British insects illustrated in colour, *A Natural History of English Insects*, acknowledged the help he received from Dandridge, which probably included guidance on how to paint insects.[44] Ninety-six drawers of insects from Dandridge's English insect collection went to the Sloane collection, together with paintings of spiders and caterpillars.[45] Dandridge's will does not mention Sloane, however, and the collection and paintings were purchased.

Problems of keeping Insect Collections at the Beginning of the Eighteenth Century

Insect specimens are fragile. However, with a means of handling them safely, such as the humble pin, upon which so many of them are impaled, they can be preserved more-or-less indefinitely in collections. The real enemies of insect collections are light, 'museum' beetles and other pests, and damp. The results of all three are aptly described by Eleanor

Glanville in a letter to James Petiver, dated December 1702:[46]

I being not at home . . . and so long neglecting to clean my butter-flys being almost 2 years ye mites have done me much m[is]chefe, I have lost above a 100 Species of my finest wch if I had not known [MS damaged, few words missing] to ye description in my booke ye colers are so cut of [faded] I could not my Self have known what they had been, and this has happened most to my finest, wch I put up closest and safest for fear of spiders or mice[.] I believe for want of aire not being [fresh] ye mites breed ye more, and ye Bettles was molded over wth a whit crusty mould wch when I went to clean broke al to peeces[.]

Light is simply excluded from collections and they can easily be kept properly dry to prevent the growth of mould. Museum beetles and other insect pests present a more diffi-cult problem, and one that has not yet been fully solved.

None of the surviving Sloane specimens is preserved on a pin and we are not aware of any reference to pinned insects in the collection. If the survivors are a representative sample of the collection, then one might conclude that the technique of pinning insects had not been introduced to England. But, we do know that pins were in use because some of the specimens preserved in glass-topped boxes have pin holes and must once have been pinned. So, either the other surviving material dates from the period before pins came into use, or Sloane (and/or Petiver and others) rejected pins as not providing adequate protection for specimens. Most of what we know of contemporary seventeenth- and eighteenth-century methods comes from study of literary and manuscript sources.[47] We have seen that Petiver's *Brief Directions*, possibly issued about 1700, gives instructions to press some insects like plants and pre-serve others in spirit, and makes no mention of pins. How-ever, as early as the 1680s Courten gave Posthumus Salwey directions that butterflies were to be 'fastned with pinns to a box', although he also indicated that other insects were to be treated in other ways. In manuscript instructions dated 1690, Petiver stated that 'Insects as Spiders flyes Butterflyes and Beetles' should be preserved 'by thrusting a pin thr their Body and s[t]ick[ing] them in your ha[t] until you get a board then pin them to ye wall of your cabin or ye inside lidd of any Deal Box so yet they may not [be] crushed'. Petiver later described his own methods: how he put butter-flies into a 'Collecting Book' with plants, while 'thick bodied' moths were pinned and placed in a box; and other insects were drowned in spirits and brought home in bot-tles. All of these references are essentially to field tech-niques, although they do point directly to the use of a variety of methods of preservation once specimens reached the collection. In a letter to Richard Richardson in 1702, Petiver suggested putting butterflies 'into frames, with glas-ses over them, which you may cheap and easily procure in the country, they will keep for many years; and if at any time you find lice or worms in them, you may easily take out the glass and clean them'. This is clearly the method

used for some of the material which survives. Notes on the use of chemicals to kill or ward off pests are scarce. Petiver himself seems not to have used anything, but recorded that Albin rubbed 'ye bottom of ye Boxes . . . with Oyl of Spike'.

The evidence then, not least that provided by the Sloane material itself, is that in the late seventeenth and early eighteenth centuries naturalists were experimenting with ways of keeping insect collections. They undoubtedly needed to minimize the damaging effects of clumsy hand-ling, although once arranged in a collection direct handling of specimens was probably negligible, but their main con-cern then, as now, was undoubtedly to exclude museum beetles. The methods used to preserve those specimens which still survive – pressed in books, sealed between sheets of mica, or in little glass-topped boxes – have stood the test of time. Most pinned material of the period, includ-ing any which formed part of Sloane's collection, has perished. The inherent disadvantages: lack of flexibility in arrangement; problems associated with detailed exam-ination of specimens; and high cost per specimen, caused the methods of Plukenet, Petiver, Dandridge and Sloane to be abandoned in favour of pinning. By the time Joseph Banks (1743–1820), Johann Rheinhold Forster (1723–98) and other later-eighteenth-century naturalists were active, pinning insects and arranging them in cork-lined, glass-lidded drawers had become established as the standard methods. However, drawers in early cabinets for pinned specimens may not have been very pest-proof and attempts at chemical pest control inefficient. More-or-less constant monitoring was the price that had to be paid. Concern over shortcomings in care at the British Museum may have been the cause of many workers, such as Joseph Banks, leaving their collections to learned societies, such as the Linnean Society, and the lack of attention led, as we know, to Sloane's insect and other zoological collections

. . . mouldering or blackening in the crypts of Montagu House, the tombe or charnel-house of unknown treasures . . . moths, *ptini*, dermestes are busily employed amid the splendours of plumage, or roaring through the fur of animals, we do not know a single insect visible to the public, of all that have been in the British Museum.[48]

An Insect Painting

Although not strictly part of the entomological collections, we draw attention here to a painting portraying a variety of insects (Plate 15). At Bloomsbury it was, apparently, not regarded as part of the collection of paintings. It was 'Found in a store room in the British Museum in 1878, and trans-ferred to the Department of Zoology' and hence came to South Kensington.[49] The painting, 'From the collection of Sir Hans Sloane', is in oils on a copper panel and is attributed to Jan van Kessel (1626–1679) but undated. The panel is now in The Natural History Museum and today hangs in the offices of the Directorate.

The entry in Sloane's catalogue of paintings reads: 'Seven views of insects on copper bought of Kinsey'. In fact there are nine 'views' on the panel. The nine small paintings are similar to panels on a painted cabinet in the Smithsonian Institution.[50] With the exception of one or two obviously exotic forms the insects depicted on Sloane's panel appear to be European species.

Conclusion

The 'remains' today of Sloane's insect collection are meagre, about 770 specimens (excluding the surviving Plukenet and Buddle material which was not catalogued as insects). The huge investment made by Sloane and his contemporaries in collecting from around the world the rare, the unusual and the commonplace was, at least partly, wasted effort. Much of what they collected, preserved and arranged in their collections went unrecorded, apart from the brief entries in Sloane's manuscript catalogue. The exceptions are the insects described by Petiver in his various publications and Sloane's own account of insects from Jamaica. The material that survives includes historically important specimens and taxonomic types. Although it has been used to comment briefly on faunal changes in historic times and throws some light on the history of insect collection technology, it has not attracted a great deal of attention. Our main contribution, to demonstrate that it includes material collected by Dandridge, Ray and Sloane himself, further shows that it deserves to be better researched and documented.

Acknowledgements

We are grateful to our past and present colleagues at The Natural History Museum for freely sharing their knowledge of the collections and their history. The Museum's photographic unit prepared the illustrations used in this chapter.

Notes and References

1. House of Commons, *Report from the Select Committee on the conditions, management and affairs of the British Museum* (London, 1835). All the staff in charge were closely questioned on the state of the collections and it is clear that by this time most of the natural history collections, but particularly the soft-bodied invertrebrates were in a sorry state, and few had escaped destruction.

2. The insects that remain today in this style have been attributed to Petiver. See below for further discussion.

3. British Museum, Trustees minutes, 9 July 1809. It is clear from directives issued occasionally that permission was not always obtained or indeed sought: A.E. Gunther, *A Century of Zoology at the Museum throughout the Lives of two Keepers 1815–1914* (London, 1975), p. 60.

4. Hans Sloane, *Natural History*, vol. I, preface.

5. Ibid., vol. II, 'Book II. Of Insects', pp. 189–226.

6. See Chapter 1.

7. G.R. de Beer, *Sir Hans Sloane and the British Museum* (London, 1953), pp. 96–107.

8. D. Allen, *The Naturalist in Britain. A social history* (London, 1976), p. 19.

9. Linnaeus in his attempt to catalogue all animals and plants includes references to many earlier publications, including the works of Sloane and Petiver, and thereby to the specimens in Sloane's collection, making the latter type specimens of the species included in the 10th edition of Linnaeus's *Systema Naturae* (Stockholm, 1758). For example, Linnaeus's *Papilio sennae (Systema Naturae*, vol. I, p. 470): '72. P. D. alis integerrimis rotundatis flavis apice nigris singulis subtus puncto gemino ferrugineo argenteo. *Sloan. jam.* 2. *t.* 236. *f.* 11, 12. . . . Habitat in Cassia Americes.' See Fig. 28.

10. W. Blunt, *The Compleat Naturalist. A life of Linnaeus* (London, 1971), pp. 112–13.

11. See Chapter 1.

12. James Petiver, *Brief Directions for the Easie Making and Preserving Collections of all Natural Curiosities* (London, c.1700), a single, engraved folio sheet. Apparently two states of the sheet are known: R.S. Wilkinson 'English entomological methods in the seventeenth and eighteenth centuries. Part I: to 1720' *Entomologist's Record* 78 (1966), p. 146.

13. Sloane, *Natural History*, vol II, introduction, p. ii.

14. It is not clear if this total is for specimens extant in 1753, since the catalogue entries, including supplementaries, probably greatly exceed 6,000.

15. NHM, Entomology Library, S.B.q.S.8; see below, p. 292, nos. 13–14.

16. J.A. Thomas and A.M. Emmet 'Thecla betulae', in A.M. Emmet and J. Heath (eds.), *The Butterflies and Moths of Great Britain and Ireland* (Colchester, 1990), vol. VII pt. i, p. 126.

17. R.P. Stearns, 'James Petiver. Promoter of natural sciences c1663–1718', *Proceedings of the American Antiquarian Society* 62 (1952), pp. 268–9.

18. See Chapter 1. The abbreviation 'C.' appears after many entries in the Sloane insect catalogues.

19. W.S. Bristowe, 'The life and work of a great English naturalist, Joseph Dandridge (1664–1746)', *Entomologist's Gazette* 18 (1967), pp. 73–89; idem, 'More about Joseph Dandridge and his friends James Petiver and Eleazar Albin', *Entomologist's Gazette* 18 (1967), pp. 197–211; N. Rothstein, 'Joseph Dandridge – naturalist and silk designer', *East London Papers* 9 no. 2 (1966), pp. 101–18, concentrates on his professional activities in the silk trade.

20. W.S. Bristowe, 'The life of a distinguished woman naturalist, Eleanor Glanville (circa 1654–1709)', *Entomologist's Gazette* 18 (1967), pp. 202–11; R.S. Wilkinson, 'Elizabeth Glanville, an early English entomologist', *Entomologist's Gazette* 17 (1966), pp. 149–60. Together these two papers cover the 'sad story of a great entomologist who gained happiness from natural history in the midst of sorrow'.

21. Stearns, op. cit. (note 17), pp. 292–303. Jones worked with Edward Lhwyd, Keeper of the Ashmolean, and was recommended for the position of chaplain to the Governor of Maryland mainly to promote natural history interests: see Chapter 8.

22. Stearns, op. cit. (note 17), pp. 343–4.

23. These are among the surviving specimens and may have been collected by Sloane (or for him) during his stay in Jamaica.

24. This specimen, galls of a cynipid wasp (probably *Cynips divisa*) on an oak leaf, is one of those surviving; it is in one of the small glass-topped containers.

25. T. Moffet, *Insectorum sive minimorum animalium theatrum* (London, 1634), p. 117.

26. J. Ray, *Historia Insectorum* (London, 1710), p. 69. Ray applies this name to the 'largest British species' and his text certainly refers to the wood ant (*Formica rufa*).

27. Ray, op. cit. (note 26), p. 382. The reference is to a species described in Martin Lister's 'Appendix de Scarabaeis Britannicis' (pp. 377–398 of Ray's work). Sloane's multiple catalogue entry apparently relates to two specimens (one from Ray the other from Dandridge) which he has either identified with Lister's description or associated with a third specimen of Lister's species received from Lister himself. The beetles concerned are ladybirds, then known as lady-cows, cow-ladies or lady-cloaks.

28. This species, now known as the Duke of Burgundy Fritillary (*Hamearis lucina*), was first discovered in Britain by William Vernon, hence the name used by Sloane, Ray (op. cit. (note 26), p. 122 [the page number is incorrectly printed 422, and was accurately cited as such by Sloane]) and Petiver (*Gazophylacium Naturae et Artis* (London, 1702–6), pl. 16, fig. 10). According to Ray, Dandridge's specimen(s), of which Sloane's was one, came from Box Hill.

29. A surviving specimen labelled '1620.R/CLVI', a tiger moth *Arctia villica*, is presumably the specimen referred to in the latter part of the entry and given to Sloane by John Ray.

30. For Woodward see Chapter 1 and *passim*.

31. See W.H. Quarrell and M. Mare, *London in 1710 from the Travels of Zacharias Conrad von Uffenbach* (London, 1934), p. 186.

32. 'Pehr Kalm, Journey in England on his way to America', an unpublished translation by W.R. Mead of the transcript made by M. Kerkkonen from Kalm's original manuscript. See Chapter 1, Appendix 3.

33. H. Trimen and W.T.T. Dyer, *Flora of Middlesex: a topographical and historical account with sketches . . .* (London, 1869), pp. 374–6. Some account is given here in the Supplementary Appendices of the early botanical collectors. These include Buddle, Plukenet and Petiver. J.E. Dandy, *The Sloane Herbarium* (London, 1958), pp. 183–7. P.M. Hammond, 'Seventeenth-century British Coleoptera from the collection of Leonard Plukenet (1642–1706)', *Entomologist's Gazette* 26 (1975), p. 261.

34. NHM, Entomology Library, S.B. f.P.5, with vellum binding. In the course of recent conservation work many loose specimens were replaced in position on the pages and broken legs and antennae, which could not be reattached, have been preserved in envelopes.

35. BL, Sloane MS 4019, fol. 51.

36. BL, Sloane MS 2347: see Hammond, op. cit. (note 33), p. 263.

37. Hammond, op. cit. (note 33), pp. 261–8.

38. Trimen and Dyer, op. cit. (note 33), pp. 386–8 and Dandy, op. cit. (note 33), pp. 102–8.

39. Stearns, op. cit. (note 17), pp. 243–365. This full account of Petiver's life is also a good source for his collections. Petiver's collectors and correspondents were large in number. They included ships' captains, surgeons and traders. He was constantly in touch with many private individuals, ministers, doctors and members of staff of Governors' households. For example, he had correspondents in nine American states and five of the West Indian Islands.

40. E. Edwards, *Lives of the Founders of the British Museum with notices of its chief augmentors and other benefactors 1570–1870* (London, 1870), pp. 290–1.

41. Sloane, *Natural History*, vol. II, introduction, pp. iv–v.

42. NHM, Entomology Library, S.B. f.P.4, two volumes, leather binding.

43. See Bristowe, op. cit. (note 19).

44. E. Albin, *A Natural History of English Insects* (London, 1720), preface. This work first appeared entire in 1720, but was probably issued earlier in parts, beginning in 1713 or 1714 (see Wilkinson, op. cit. (note 12), pp. 147, 150).

45. BL, Sloane MS 3999. This is a volume of Dandridge's paintings of spiders, accompanied by descriptions and field notes, and a note about Sloane's purchase of it and the collection.

46. Quoted in Wilkinson, op. cit. (note 20), pp. 150–1.

47. A good general account is given by Wilkinson in *Entomologist's Record*, op. cit. (note 12), 'Part 1: to 1720' (1966), pp. 143–51; 'Part II: Wilkes and Dutfield' (1966), pp. 285–92; and 'Part III: Moses Harris' *The Aurelian*' 80 (1968), pp. 193–200. The quotations are taken from Wilkinson's papers.

48. T.S. Traill, in *Edinburgh Review* (May 1823), p. 397.

49. The information comes from a note pasted on the back of the painting.

50. P.C. Ritterbush, 'Art and science as influences on the early development of natural history collections', *Proceedings of the Biological Society of Washington* 82 (1969), pp. 572–6.

7 Mineral and Fossil Collections

John Thackray

The Background to Sloane's Collection

* The early part of Sir Hans Sloane's lifetime was a period of tremendous interest in the Earth, its origins and productions. In particular, the nature and origin of 'fossils', as all objects dug from the ground were called, was the subject of a protracted debate. By 1660, the year of Sloane's birth, there was already an extensive foreign literature on these fossil bodies, including the great illustrated museum catalogues of Ferrante Imperato of Naples, Ulisse Aldrovandi of Bologna and Olaus Worm of Copenhagen.[1] In Britain, on the other hand, rocks and minerals had attracted comparatively little attention, although they were mentioned by writers such as Christopher Merret (1614–95), and were present in the collections of Robert Hubert, John Bargrave (1610–80), the Tradescants and others.[2]

The situation changed with the founding and growth of the Royal Society. The Society provided a forum where facts could be presented and ideas discussed; it brought provincial observers into contact with metropolitan savants; it published and circulated digests of foreign publications, and it began to build up the first substantial collection of natural objects in Britain.[3] Robert Hooke (1635–1703) lectured to the Society on fossils, which he maintained were the remains of once-living animals and plants, at intervals between 1667 and the end of the century, and, in 1669, Henry Oldenburg, the Society's Secretary, translated and published a book on fossils by the Danish cleric Niels Stensen which made the same claim.[4] Interest was further raised in 1671 when the distinguished naturalist Martin Lister (?1638–1712) responded both to Stensen's book and to the review of it that had appeared in the *Philosophical Transactions* with a letter which was read and discussed at a Society meeting.[5] He raised a number of objections to the acceptance of fossils as organic, and asserted that they were in fact produced by forces at work within the Earth, that they were *lapides sui generis*.

By 1685, the year of Sloane's election to the Society, the arguments for and against the organic origin of fossils had been well-aired; detailed descriptions had been published of fossils from many parts of Britain, and a number of British naturalists were emerging as specialists in the study of the Earth. Private museums were becoming somewhat more focused in their scope, and Robert Plot (1640–96) in Oxford, Robert Sibbald (1641–1722) in Edinburgh and Robert Hooke in London all had substantial collections.[6] A consensus on the origin of fossils began to emerge only in the 1690s, as it became apparent that objects of many different origins were encompassed by the various ill-defined terms in use – fossil, extraneous fossil, figured stone, petrifaction and mineral. It became clear that there

was a broad spectrum between those specimens that were clearly organic and those that were clearly inorganic, and the question became where to draw the line. By 1700, most naturalists could agree on the placing of that line, though adjustments continued to be made as further specimens were reinterpreted.[7] A second phase of the debate now began, in which attention focused on the mechanism of fossil formation, and in particular on the way in which they became buried underground in their present positions.

It is clear from his writings and from the way in which he arranged his collection that Sloane believed that the fossil bones, shells and leaves that he collected were indeed the remains of once-living animals and plants. Equally, he recognized that crystals, earths and metals were natural and lifeless constituents of the Earth. However, in reaching these conclusions he simply followed the opinions of others, and made no original contribution to the controversy. In this, as in so many other areas, Sloane was not a controversialist. His collection was available to anyone who wished to consult it, whatever their views, and he corresponded equally with those of all shades of opinion on the subject. Sloane was clearly more attracted to the specimens themselves than to the theories to which gave rise. He wrote:

Knowledge of *Natural-History*, being Observations of Matters of Fact, is more certain than most Others, and in my slender Opinion, less subjected to Mistakes than *Reasonings, Hypotheses*, and *Deductions* are. . .[8]

The Size and Scope of the Collection

The synopsis published by Sloane's executors suggests that, at the time of his death, Sloane's collection included 9,942 minerals and rocks listed in seven catalogues, and 32,535 natural history specimens listed in thirteen catalogues.[9] The numbers quoted in the synopsis are, in most cases, those of the final entries in the relevant catalogues. To estimate more closely the number of specimens that would today be called 'geological', it is necessary firstly to adjust the given totals to take account of the blocks of numbers omitted or duplicated in different catalogues; secondly to sample the natural history catalogues to get an idea of the number of fossils present and thirdly to add the contents of the 'Catalogus Marmorum', which Sloane apparently 20 owned but did not register. From this, it seems that he possessed a minimum of 15,250 geological specimens at the time of his death. This total included about 8,750 minerals, 2,500 rocks and sediments, 150 fossil plants, 3,450 invertebrate and 400 vertebrate fossils.

In modern mineralogical and palaeontological terms, Sloane's collection was restricted in its scope. It was rich in the more common and showy mineral species such as chalcedony, quartz, calcite and a few other carbonates and sulphates, the chief metallic sulphides, and a few silicates such as garnets and micas. Rock specimens consisted mainly of the decorative marbles, together with a good range of sedimentary limestones and sandstones and a few volcanic rocks. Fossils were almost entirely Mesozoic and Caenozoic in age, with a few from the Carboniferous. Molluscs were very well represented, as were the echinoderms and corals, but fossil fish and a very narrow range of Quaternary mammal bones and teeth were the only fossil vertebrates in the collection.

The reasons for these restrictions are not hard to understand. Neither the chemical classification of minerals nor a knowledge of the geological column existed in Sloane's day. The bewildering variety of specimens that came easily to hand was enough to satisfy even the most acquisitive collector. Although in modern terms Sloane's hundreds of flints seem repetitive, for him they were not, as each had features of colour or form which distinguished it from the others. His names are often the same as modern names, but they were based on simple physical properties rather than chemical composition, and may not be 'correct' identifications in our terms. While so many new and unknown fossils were to be found in the soft rocks of south-east England, it is not surprising that few collectors, other than perhaps Edward Lhwyd, ventured into the hard and unpromising mountains of Wales to search for the tiny fossils that we now know are there.

The geographical scope of the collection is, in fact, very wide. British specimens probably comprise 40%, with specimens from the continent of Europe making up about another 40%. Of the remaining 20%, North America accounts for the major part, with the West Indies, the Far East, South America, India, and Russia all being represented in the remainder.

From about 1720 Sloane started to list his collection in a series of catalogues, each devoted to a particular category of material. These catalogues reveal the basis of his classification and also the physical arrangement of the specimens. He first separated the fossils — remains of once-living animals and plants preserved underground — from the minerals and rocks — earth materials produced by inorganic processes. His division was nearly, but not quite, that which we would make today. Sloane followed contemporary opinion when he included his belemnites, which we now know to be remains of an extinct cuttlefish, with the minerals. Likewise he included oolitic and pisolitic limestones with the fossils, believing them to be composed of the eggs or spawn of fish. Sloane's catalogue of 'Asteriae, Trochite, Entrochi etc', objects that we now place among the fossil echinoderms, is currently bound among his mineral catalogues. It is not clear whether this represents Sloane's understanding of their origin, or whether it is a later artefact.

Sloane listed and housed his fossils alongside his recent natural remains, and they occur in ten out of his thirteen zoological and botanical catalogues. They are identifiable as fossils only where the locality makes it obvious, as in the 'Pectunculites from Great Milton, Oxfordshire', and the 'Pectunculites ... out of the ruins of Wenlock Abbey, Shropshire', or where entries describe the preservation of the specimen, as in the 'very large smooth sulcated scallop filled with a yellowish stone', and the 'black slate with the impression of a fish upon it'. The classification of animals and plants was well understood by the end of the seventeenth century, following the work of the great synthesizers such as Conrad Gessner in the sixteenth century and Aldrovandi in the seventeenth. Building on their achievements, Sloane divided his fossils into nine categories:

Vegetables and vegetable substances	Echini
Coralls, sponges and other submarines	Starrfishes
Shells	Fishes
Crustacea	Quadrupeds
Asteriae, Trochite, Entrochi	

In addition there was a category of 'flints, fossils &c', which included a number of shells and fossil vegetables, together with otherwise unidentified 'figured stones' and 'curiously shaped stones'. Sloane was consistent in his classification of fossils, and few specimens are, when judged by the knowledge of the day, out of place. Within each of these categories Sloane did his best to name the specimens he received, using the long descriptive phrases in Latin that were the norm for pre-Linnaean terminology. Among the shells he includes Cornu ammonis, Buccinum, Conchites, Trochus, Nautilus, Planorbis, Pectunculites, and many others. However, many of his specimens are not identified, and simply listed as 'stone', 'shell' or 'bone'.

Not surprisingly, Sloane found much more difficulty in subdividing his mineral collection. No previous writer had provided the sort of unequivocal text that Sloane would have needed to sort out his collection in any detail. There was a consensus that four major classes were represented in the outer layers of the Earth: the 'earths', the 'metals', the 'salts' and the 'bituminous substances'. But classification within these classes was always changing, and there was no agreement as to the significance of physical form, such as crystal shape or arrangement in layers. Sloane generally followed prevailing opinion when he subdivided his minerals into six categories, as follows:

Pretious stones, agates, jaspers &c	Bitumens, Sulphurs, Ambers,
Chrystals, sparrs, &c	Ambergreese, &c
Metals, mineral ores, &c	Earths, sands, salts, &c
Talcs, Micas, &c	

In addition there was the category of 'flints, fossils &c' mentioned above, as well as two catalogues listing carved precious stones. Sloane clearly found the classification of his minerals more difficult than his fossils. There is a degree of overlap between the 'Pretious stones' and the 'Chrystals', in that the same minerals appear in both categories, and

22/306
22/457
22/255
25a/5

e.g. 15a/360
e.g. 25a/567

also between the 'Metals, mineral ores &c' and the 'Flints, fossils, &c'. In a number of places Sloane has noted that a specimen is the same as that in another category. As with the fossils, Sloane assigns his specimens a mineral name, such as jasper, agate, 'granat', 'lapis asbestus', osteocolla, ironstone, or lead ore, or else gives a descriptive phrase.

The standard of documentation revealed by Sloane's catalogues is very variable. A few entries give the identification and description of the specimen, with details of the precise locality and donor of the specimen, as, for example:

16/2528   Dark coloured antimony or lead ore from a hill which took fire in year 1738, 4 miles from Naples. given by Dr Massy

and again:

24a/4429   Cornu Ammonis From Northamptonshire by Mr Henry Heathcote. It was found in a gravel pit about six foot deep in the field of Branston a country town about two miles north from Daventry in Northamptonshire, in the year 1725

Many entries, however, are much less informative. In the mineral and fossil catalogues just under 25% of entries give a locality of some sort, just under 20% of entries record the donor of the specimen, and 5% give a literature reference.

The literature cited by Sloane gives an indication of the use he made of books in his library for curatorial work on his collection. For the fossils, three recently-published, illustrated works were cited regularly. These were Lhwyd's *Lithophylacii Britannici*, John Morton's *The Natural History of Northampton-shire*, and Lister's *Historia Conchyliorum*.[10] Occasional reference was made to books by Plot, Scilla, and Scheuchzer,[11] and to papers in the *Philosophical Transactions* by James Brewer, Samuel Dale, Lhwyd and others. Fewer references are given in the mineral catalogues, and those that appear tend to be older. Most numerous are references to the *Musaeum Metallicum* by Aldrovandi (1632) and to Worm.[12] In a few cases it is possible that Sloane's is the actual specimen figured in the work referred to, but this is rarely certain, as for example: 'Two joints of the nautilus figured by Dr Lister hist. conch. tab. mut. 1044'.

22/547

The chronological growth of Sloane's geological collections is not easy to establish. Few of his catalogue entries are dated, and few donations can be linked to dated letters in his correspondence. He was certainly interested in fossils as early as 1686, when he wrote to John Ray about a visit to the Isle of Sheppey, where he found 'a Buccinum petrified, and after that turned into a Pyrites; so that you might see everything in it as in a Pyrites, viz. weight, colour &c.'[13] This specimen has not been identified in the catalogues. Sloane noted and perhaps collected stones, earths, sands and minerals during his stay in Jamaica.[14] He particularly mentions a stratum of fuller's earth found when a well was being dug, which was no different from the fuller's earth of England, and he was clearly disappointed that he was unable to find any fossil shells.[15] Other early acquisitions

included the minerals of medicinal value from the East Indies that came from Dr Patrick Adare (*fl.*1674–97) before the end of the century, and the fossils from Robert Plot, Keeper of the Ashmolean Museum. The fossils from Derbyshire and Lancashire sent by Dr Charles Leigh (1662–1701) and the Central European minerals and metals given by Dr Edward Browne (1644–1708) were also early additions.

Sloane acquired the huge collection of William Courten or Charleton (1642–1702) on the latter's death in 1702, but, although Evelyn had reported 'Minerals, precious stones, vessels & curiosities, in Amber, Achat, chrystal &c.' when he visited in 1686 (see Chapter 1), only three specimens are identified in the geological catalogues as being from Courten. The huge collection of James Petiver (*c.*1663– 1718), which Sloane purchased in 1718, contained large numbers of fossils, minerals and rocks (see Chapter 1). It seems to have been the disorderly state of this material that spurred Sloane to start cataloguing his own specimens,[16] and by February 1721, when it was proposed that Johann Caspar Scheuchzer should work for him, he reported that 'As to ye Catalogue of my Museum, I have my Self near finished the catalogue'.[17] This cannot have been completely true, for in October 1721 he wrote to William Sherard that he had made a catalogue of his medals and was now busy upon the shells.[18] Sloane gave a numerical synopsis of his collection in the Preface to the second volume of his *Natural History* (1725) from which it appears that he had already registered nearly 5,500 minerals and rocks, just over half his eventual total.[19] In October 1728, when Sloane came to the end of the second volume of his catalogue of shells, he tabulated the numbers of the different genera of fossil shell that he owned, and totalled up 1,757 specimens out of his eventual total of 2,350.[20]

15/1, 119; 19f/12

From the late 1720s the catalogues were more like accessions registers, and the position of a collection gives an indication of its date of acquisition. Thus the fossils and rocks sent by William Brownrigg (1711–1800) of Whitehaven consistently occur in the last few pages of each register, as do minerals and fossils from Mr Mason in North Wales and the minerals and rocks from New England sent by John Winthrop (1681–1741). The last dated entry in the catalogue is 1747, when Emmanuel Mendes Da Costa gave a fossil shell from Derbyshire.

24a/5843

The Sources of the Collection

Few of the specimens detailed in the catalogues were definitely collected by Sloane himself. One exception is the flat astroites 'taken up by my selfe at Faringdon in Berkshire where stony matter is joined to it'. Two other catalogue entries show that he did venture into quarries from time to time. When registering a Pectunculites he wrote: 'I have seen these in the rocks about Badminton in Gloucestershire abt. 3 foot under the surface. They are almost diaphanous', and of an Alcyoniis he noted: 'I have observed in the perpendicular fissure of a limestone quarry near Fryar end in

21a/74

22/449

21a/579

Craven large pieces of this fossil filling up the vacancies & sticking close to both sides of the rock'. Such records must be treated with caution, as occasionally Sloane quotes in the first person from letters received with the fossils.

15a/2211   There are many other specimens that one would like to believe he collected himself. Surely the small brown jasper 'from my own garden wall' must have been picked out by
15a/2210   Sloane himself, as well as the previous specimen, 'a dark coloured jasper . . . from my gravell pitt at Chelsea'. An important locality that was not far from Sloane's home and which he must have visited was the great tile pit at Rich-
e.g. 25a/170   mond, Surrey, the source of many fossils and minerals.

In spite of these few examples, there is no doubt that the great bulk of Sloane's fossil and mineral collections were gathered by hands other than his own, and that Lhwyd was quite wrong in writing to Sloane about his collection:

Yet yours being (I presume) chiefly of your own collecting, will be more valuable [than specimens already in Oxford University's collection] on account of the information you may adde of their nature places &c . . .[21]

In this respect Sloane was similar to Petiver but very different from his chief rival in the field of geological collecting, Dr John Woodward (1665–1728), who is believed to have collected over 90% of his British specimens himself.[22] The comments that follow are based largely on the 20% of catalogue entries that bear the name of a donor or vendor. For the majority of the specimens there is no clue as to their origin.

Sloane acquired specimens in three distinct ways: he purchased or was given entire collections, generally after the death of the original collector; he exchanged or was given small numbers of specimens by friends and acquaintances, often in the course of correspondence; and he purchased individual specimens from dealers and others.

The three large and important collections that came to Sloane in their entirety have already been described (see Chapter 1). The earliest was that of Courten, who is known from the comments of Ralph Thoresby, who visited him in May 1695,[23] to have owned a fine collection of both fossils and minerals, an observation confirmed by John Evelyn, the diarist, who called in December 1686.[24] In the catalogues, however, only three specimens are credited to
15b/1   Courten's collection: 'A mountain of metals and minerals of Saxony with the ways of working the same, bought by
15b/119   Mr Courten of Dr Walraven's widow . . .'; a horseshoe
18b/12   encrusted with copper from Hungary; and 'A large log of oak wood petrified from Lough Neagh, Ireland. given to Mr Courten by Sir Arthur Rawdon'.

The second of these major acquisitions, the Plukenet herbarium, contained no fossils or minerals.

The case is very different with the greatest of all Sloane's acquisitions, the collection of James Petiver, which he purchased for £4,000 after Petiver's death in 1718. Many hundreds of catalogue entries bear the note 'Mr Petiver', 'Pet', 'P'.

or simply 'P'. Petiver specimens are to be found in the catalogues of Shells, Asteriae, Fish and Quadrupeds, as well as 'Pretious Stones', Metals, 'Chrystals', Amber, Earths, Talc and Flints & Fossils. They come from all over the world, and were themselves gathered for Petiver by many different collectors. They were registered by Sloane over a great many years. The shells, for example, first appear at no. 259 with a Concha from Lisbon, while the final entry is 4,785, a Pectunculus from Hampshire. Among many notable items are the fossil shells from Lisbon sent by Don Pedro   e.g. 23/4285
d'Almeyda, Count d'Azumar; the sharks' teeth and other   e.g. 25a/1281
fossils sent from Maryland by the Revd Hugh Jones   18a/513–15
(d. 1701); a number of Chinese drugs; and agates and other   15a/1327
precious stones taken up in the East Indies as ballast. The fossil fish on slate, figured by Petiver in his *Opera Historia Naturalem Spectantia*, can be identified with the 'large slate   25a/1273
with the impression of fish on it. Sent from Christian Maximilian . . . from Malta' in Sloane's catalogue of fishes.

Another important collection purchased by Sloane in its entirety was that of the German physician and surgeon, Engelbert Kaempfer (1651–1716), who travelled widely in Russia and the East, and who spent the years 1690–2 in Japan[25] (see Chapter 18). His collection was apparently not rich in minerals or fossils, and only two specimens are listed in the catalogues. One, 'A very large Alveolus from Japan   15a/2050
by Dr Kaempfer' still survives, while the gold ore from   16/1870
Japan does not.

Sloane's manuscripts include a number of catalogues that seem to represent sizeable acquisitions. The 'Catalogus fossilium Helveticorum'[26] arrived with a collection of specimens, eighty of which were registered by Sloane soon after   16/1437–
1725. Likewise, the 'Catalogus fossilium' of Dr Erhart of   1491;
Memmingen contains fossil shells, crystals and rock speci-   18/1053–
mens from different parts of Germany which were   1076
registered by Sloane about the same date.[27] The 150 or   18/1077–85
so minerals from Sweden and Lapland that comprised 'Mr Grainger's' collection were registered by Sloane later in the 1720s, as were the Italian fossils and minerals that came   e.g. 16/*1604–
to him in Cardinal Gualtieri's collection. Another substantial   88 25e/1491–
accession is represented by the 'Catalogus Marmorum'[28]   1517
(after 1731), a manuscript which lists 1,200 minerals and rocks from Germany and Austria. This undoubtedly belonged to Sloane, and the later addition of Sloane-type shelf locations suggests that it did accompany a collection of specimens. However, none of the entries can be matched with items in Sloane's own catalogues, so presumably he decided not to recatalogue the specimens.[29]

Large as these collections undoubtedly were, they were surpassed in size and scope by the myriad of smaller gifts that Sloane received from all over the world. The Sloane catalogues reveal the names of 198 individuals who gave, exchanged or sold geological specimens to Sloane during the sixty years that he was collecting. Many gave just a single specimen, while others contributed hundreds over many years. Among these 198 collectors were sixty-five fellows of the Royal Society; sixty-two medical men, including physicians, apothecaries and surgeons; fifteen members of the titled nobility, both British and foreign; thirteen clergymen, including four bishops and an arch-bishop; three sea captains and one army officer. Seventy-two of them provided material from Great Britain and Ire-land; forty-eight sent specimens from continental Europe; fourteen from North America, including the Arctic and Greenland; five from the West Indies; seven from South America; ten from the East Indies, including China and Siam; and three sent material from Russia and Siberia.

As mentioned above, it was the more common and obvious fossils and rocks of the well populated and acces-sible areas of England that are best represented in Sloane's British collection.

His most regular donor of material of this type was the Revd John Morton (1671–1726), Rector of Great Oxendon, Northamptonshire. He corresponded with Sloane from 1704 until 1716, and was author of *The Natural History of Northampton-shire* (1712), to which Sloane makes frequent reference in his catalogues. Almost 1,000 catalogue entries bear the name 'Morton' or, more usually the abbreviation 'M'. All come from England, and all but a few are from the central counties of Northamptonshire, Oxfordshire, Derbyshire and Bedfordshire. Many entries bear references to Morton's book, and it seems likely that many of the figured specimens were in the collection, though they are not identified in the catalogues.[30] As well as fossil shells, belemnites, echinites and entrochi, there are elephants' teeth, fish vertebrae, spars and stalactites, jet and amber, and a considerable number of building stones.

Many of the fossil shells that Morton sent to Sloane were not at all unlike those living in the sea. Rather more puzzling were some of the specimens sent up from Somerset by John Beaumont (d. 1731), a surgeon who lived at Stony Easton. He corresponded with Sloane from 1702 until 1730, and sent him metal ores, crystals and fossilshells, trochites, entrochi and screwstones from the Mendip Hills and else-where in Somerset on numerous occasions. These came from rocks that we now know to be substantially older than those of central England, and whose fossils are mostly of types unknown at the present day. Beaumont's own particu-lar interest was in specimens which he called 'rock plants', believing them to grow like plants in the solid rock, and which are now called crinoids and known to be related to starfish and sea urchins.[31]

e.g. 15b/649– 653

Somewhat similar fossils were sent to Sloane from the north of England by Dr Richard Richardson (1663–1741) of North Bierley, Yorkshire, who was introduced to Sloane by Ralph Thoresby in 1702, and corresponded with him until his death. Richardson was primarily a botanist, so it is not surprising that they first corresponded about coal plants, many of which Richardson sent to Sloane.[32] Later gifts included fossil shells, entrochi and 'starr stones' from Yorkshire, 'St. Columba stones' from Scotland, and marble

e.g. 18b/212

from Northumberland.

Many of Sloane's collectors were, like Richardson, men of wide interests and attainments. Edward Lhwyd, on the other hand, although a Celtic scholar and antiquary, was perhaps the first naturalist in Britain to specialize in the study of fossils. He was Keeper of the Ashmolean Museum from 1690 until his death in 1709, and published an import-ant catalogue of his fossil collection in 1699, with financial help from Sloane, and to which Sloane constantly refers in his catalogues.[33] Well over 100 catalogue entries bear Lhwyd's name, while a further 250 bear the letter 'L', which may indicate his gifts. These specimens given by Lhwyd are from central England, south and central Wales, and a few from Ireland. They include fossil shells, items in the fish catalogue, including toadstones and plectronites, belemnites, astroites, and various crystals, spars and stalac-tites. Many of the catalogue entries for specimens from Lhwyd bear prices in the margin but, as discussed below, it is not clear what these signify.

Sloane was lucky in having a number of collectors send-ing him material from Scotland. Chief of these was Dr Charles Preston (1660–1711) of Edinburgh. He cor-responded with Sloane between 1679 and his death, and sent him fossil shells from the Lowlands, fuller's earth, marcasite and other minerals from the Orkney Islands, and an item in the 'chrystall' catalogue described simply as 'petrified water'.

18a/596

Given Sloane's close connections with the *Philosophical Transactions* of the Royal Society (see Chapter 1), it is not surprising that he received many of the specimens that were described or cited in its pages. Whether he received the specimens first and encouraged the donor to write about them, or whether he received an account first and then soli-cited the specimens, we generally do not know. It is to be hoped that he gave the Royal Society's own museum first refusal. Dr James Brewer gave Sloane some of the oysters from Reading that he described in 1700, and Dr Francis Nichols gave minerals and metals which are described in the catalogue as 'ye pieces figured by him in Phil Trans no 401'. Similarly, The Revd De la Pryme, then a curate in Hull, sent the fossil shells from Lincolnshire that were described in a paper in 1700, and Mr Wilson sent a specimen of the asbestos 'lately found in Scotland'.[34]

22/266
16/1553
22/1162–72
15a/472

Sloane's foreign collections of minerals, rocks and fossils came partly from travellers, who sent or brought back large and varied consignments, and partly from overseas residents who collected in more detail from a restricted area.

Of the many Englishmen abroad in the seventeenth cen-tury, one of the keenest observers and collectors was Edward Browne (1644–1708), eldest son of the naturalist and antiquary Sir Thomas Browne. He travelled widely in central and eastern Europe between 1664 and 1673, and published accounts of his travels which give details of the mines and minerals in the regions he visited.[35] He gave Sloane precious stones, crystals, metals, earths and talcs from the mining regions of Germany, Austria and Hungary, as well as a smaller number of British specimens. Sloane also acquired Browne's manuscript journals and daybooks for his library.

Dr Jean Rodolphe Lavater was likewise a traveller. He was a native of Zürich, and first met Sloane in January 1706 when he and his brother visited England as young men. He sent consignments of fossils, rocks and minerals from Switzerland, Germany, Austria and the surrounding regions, as well as many British specimens which he seems to have carried on behalf of Edward Lhwyd (Fig. 30). Lavater corresponded with Sloane between 1705 and 1715, and it is clear from the positions of catalogue entries that e.g. 23/3371 Lavater's foreign specimens are almost all in Latin, and appear to be transcripts from catalogues or lists which are now lost.

In marked contrast to these two travellers was Phillip Henry Zollman of Soissons, in north-east France, who corresponded with Sloane between 1723 and 1730. He sent fossil shells, fish teeth and carbonized wood from the area immediately around his town, and he accompanied these gifts with detailed descriptions of the occurrence and characteristics of the specimens, all of which Sloane copied into his catalogues. A fossil gastropod, *Buccina*, bears the note: 'From yᵉ smallness of these shells Mr Zollman sup- 24a/4986 poses yᵗ they are not the remains of yᵉ Deluge, but rather generated in yᵉ Earth'. A specimen which Sloane named Porpites, perhaps a column ossicle of a crinoid, has the note: 24a/4992 'The most common (says Mr Zollman) & yet perhaps the most curious Species of figured stones found about Soissons ... I have gathered many of them in different places ...' Zollman was undoubtedly a careful local observer, whose specimens and observations Sloane valued highly.

Other naturalists had a particular interest in one or more types of natural object, which they then shared with Sloane. Dr Johann Philipp Breyne (1680–1764) was a physician and naturalist of Danzig, who corresponded with Sloane from 1704 until 1742. He was particularly interested in amber, and gave Sloane 'A small amber cabinet of s'v'll coloured 17a/254 ambers engraved', perhaps the one referred to in a letter

Fig. 30 Fossil bivalves and echinoids from Neuchâtel and elsewhere in Switzerland, given to Sir Hans Sloane by Dr Lavater [21/232, 629, 22/926–7]. NHM, palaeontological collection. Reproduced by courtesy of the Trustees of The Natural History Museum.

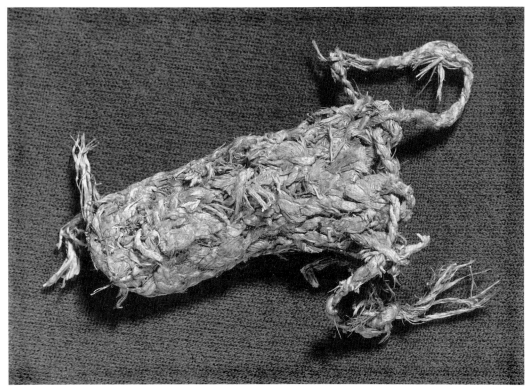

Fig. 31 Purse made from actinolite/tremolite asbestos from New England, sold to Sir Hans Sloane by Benjamin Franklin [28/1205]. NHM, mineral collection, BM 61063. Reproduced by courtesy of the Trustees of The Natural History Museum.

of 25 May 1718.[36] Breyne was a collector himself, but told Sloane that, compared to his treasures 'my poor collection . . . is as a little dish to a vast ocean'.[37]

Sloane acquired many specimens from the eastern states of North America, a large number via Petiver and others from a variety of smaller donors. His most significant acquisition from this area came late in Sloane's collecting career from John Winthrop, who was born in Boston, Massachusetts, and was the grandson of John Winthrop (1606–76), first Governor of Connecticut. He is named as donor of nearly 800 rocks and minerals from New England, including 'granats' (garnets), sulphur, sands and earths, talcs, selenites, sparr, limestone and crystals. These specimens appear to be those presented by Winthrop to the Royal Society on his election in 1734, and annexed by Sloane either then or later. However it is possible that Winthrop sent a separate collection of similar material to Sloane at the same time.[38] One of Winthrop's specimens which still 16/2029 survives, is the 'heavy black stone with golden streaks', which was used by Charles Hatchett (?1765–1847) in his original description of the new element, columbium, in 1802, and again by W.H. Wollaston (1766–1828) in his further researches into columbium and tantalum.[39]

It is difficult to be sure to what extent Sloane purchased specimens. Many of his catalogue entries bear figures in the right-hand margin which appear to be prices. This seems to be borne out by an entry such as this:

A small broad one [Astroites] of the same wt a crooked hole going 21a/66 through its surface for a solen or worm. Sold me by Dr Leigh of Lancashire where he said that 'twas a fossil . . . 0.7.6.

However, many entries seem to carry two prices, one in the body of the entry and a second, often double the first, in the right margin, as, for example:

A flint echinites Spatagus sticking to the flint & bruised 1sh . . . 21c/200 0.2.6.
Another high flint echinites sticking to the flint – 6d . . . 0.1.0. 21c/201

To add to the confusion, some items record both the name of the donor and a price in the margin. If however the prices are taken at face value as records of purchases, then it is clear that Sloane spent a considerable amount of money on precious stones, and a fair amount on his other categories of material. The most expensive single item was 'a large 15a/1317 hexangular piece of water topaz, out of wch triangular pieces for seals had been cut', which cost 5 guineas. But a number of items cost several pounds, including a 'hexangular 15a/1294 whitish semi diaphonous short sparr in clusters w an inch & ½ long hexangular emerald lying upon it' for £3. 4s. 6d., and 'a rough diamond hexangular at both ends' which cost 15a/816 £2. 10s. and was probably quartz. The total sum represented by the prices marked in the precious stones cata-logue is £115. Among a number of mineral specimens listed by Sloane among his 'Miscellanies' is a notable item that he bought in 1725: this is a purse made from the fibrous mineral asbestos, brought to London from North America by the young Benjamin Franklin (1706–90) and sold to Sloane (Fig. 31). It has recently been suggested that the purse originated at Newbury, Massachusetts, some time around 1700.[40]

The Design behind Sloane's Collecting

Sloane's rival and sometime antagonist, John Woodward, railed against those who collected for collecting's sake:

Censure would be his due, who should be perpetually heaping up of Natural Collections, without Design of Building a Structure of Philosophy out of them, or advancing some Propositions that might turn to the Benefit and Advantage of the World.[41]

Sloane was clearly a comprehensive rather than a dis-criminating collector. Reading through the catalogue entries, it is hard to imagine him rejecting any item as too trivial or too commonplace. However, it is still possible to discern a number of areas where a 'Design' is revealed, and where he is indeed seeking for propositions that would be of benefit to the world.

Sloane used both his fossils and his rocks to make deduc-tions about the Earth and its history, particularly in relation to the great debate over the origin and significance of fos-sils. He followed Hooke and Woodward in accepting that fossil leaves, shells, teeth and bones really were the remains of animals and plants which had once lived in the places in which their remains are now found, and occasionally commented on his fossils as if they were still living:

25a/180 Palat or mandible of an orbis muricatus dugg up in England. This fish eats shell fish & grinds them between the upper & under mandibles w are like millstones.

From a study of materials in his fossil collection, Sloane recognized a similarity between the living animals and plants of Jamaica and the West Indies and the fossil speci-mens dug up in Britain. He first noted this in a paper in the *Philosophical Transactions*, and came back to it at greater length in the introduction to his *Natural History* of Jamaica.[42] He was clearly able to imagine that geography and climate had both changed in the past, though he did not seek to hide the fact that he considered the whole matter 'pretty strange'. On one occasion Sloane used a rock speci-men to report a similar sort of deduction:

15b/1090 A piece of red stone or mineral from St Helena seeming ironstone in wch are lodged some silver mica or talc. It looks as if it had been a volcano cinder. Dr Halley saith the most part of the island is of it & believes it cast up from the sea bottom.

This same interest in history and environment is dis-played in the one paper that Sloane wrote on his geological collections, his 'Account of elephants teeth and bones found

under ground'.[43] He prefaced his survey with the note that fossils of terrestrial animals are rare, and therefore worthy of study. He described specimens from London, North-amptonshire, Gloucester and Siberia, citing his own cata-logue numbers as appropriate. Apropos of the Siberian specimen, he repeated the account given in his catalogue, that 'some of the Russians believe yt to be the tooth of   25e/1185 the largest animal of the earth yt it lives underground'.

The one thing that is lacking from the understanding of the Earth at this period, is the concept of stratigraphy. Although Sloane recorded some specimens as 'from the Chalk' or 'from white limestone', he does not seem to have been aware of the succession of rocks in Britain. He certainly knew about strata in particular localities, as his catalogues include a very detailed account of the strata in a coal pit   17c/194–223 at Dudley, and in an ironstone mine in Sussex. There is   15b/1117–39 no sign that he saw the link between rock type and particu-lar types of fossils, or that he considered that some might be dramatically older than others. These ideas did not emerge until the end of the century.[44]

Sloane was, for many years, one of the leading physicians in London, and it is not surprising that his collection is strongly influenced by his interest in drugs and remedies of all sorts. Among a large number of medicinal powers noted in his catalogues are, for example:

Lapis Tiburonium from Mr Adams from Ireland. a specific for help-   25a/1424 ing women in travail.
A round christall ball. Perhaps such as were used to hold in the   15a/138 hands to cool them in fevers.
Pierre de Picote. Lapis variolosus, Aldr. having marks on it like   15a/268 the smallpox & therefore said to hinder that distemper from injur-ing the face if . . . about the person deseased.
Purging chalk from Bedfordshire.   17c/2

Finally, and most remarkable of all:

This is plompxci [?] a present from the King of Persia to the Czar   17a/257 of Muscovy. It was given by Dr Posnkove the Czar's physician to Sir John Colbatch who told him that it was good for everything. From Sir John Colbatch.

In one case at least, Sloane was not a sceptic:

A deep coloured green triangular lapis nephriticus wrote upon   15a/*1729 by Mr Wild. This is a tryed good spleen stone or lapis nephriticus, it will stick to the flesh.

Drugs from Siam were sent by Captain Uvedale,   18a/516 white sparr used as a drug in the East Indies came from   18a/508 Dr Adair, Chinese drugs from Mr Cunningham and many   14e/310 others. Still preserved in The Natural History Museum, are a number of drawers in which Sloane kept his pharmaceuti-cal specimens in small compartments (Fig. 32). The two drawers containing minerals and fossils are each divided into forty-nine compartments bearing legends such as 'Lap : Lincis' and 'Lap : Nephrit'. A total of 107 mineral speci-mens are preserved, including 'hyacinthus' (garnet and zircon), 'crystallus' (crystalline quartz) and Lapis nephriticus

Fig. 32 Minerals and fossils from Sir Hans Sloane's pharmaceutical collection, in their original drawer. NHM, mineral collection. Reproduced by courtesy of the Trustees of The Natural History Museum.

(nephrite jade). Included in the collection are a number of bezoar stones, calculi from animals such as the goat or, more highly prized, the rhinoceros, which were used as antidotes to poison.[45]

Closely related to Sloane's medical interests was his fascination with shapes and resemblances. Both the precious stones and the flints catalogue include pairs of items that were presumably housed side by side, such as:

15a/376 A stone resembling a dryed pear
15a/377 A dryed pear

Other items were shaped like an apricot, 'a makeroon biscuit', a small rhinoceros horn, 'a knotted Hercules's clubb', and so on. Related to these are stones which seemed to show a picture, such as:

15a/274 The Florence stone with a naturall landskip of ruins on it, such as are made use of for cabinetts
17e/254 A piece of common flint ... w a woman praying. Given me by Mr Bignall.

Shaped stones of this sort were described and interpreted, alongside petrified shells and bones, by the earliest writers on geological topics, such as Gessner, as well as contemporaries such as Athanasius Kircher.[46] There is no evidence that Sloane followed either of these authors in believing that any of his shapes were due to occult powers, or irradiations from the planets, but it is not impossible that he did so.

The most powerful of Sloane's 'Designs' in collecting was his desire to identify and classify the myriad of objects that made up the natural world, and to have examples of them within his own cabinet. He went to great trouble to identify his fossils, minerals and rocks as far as he could, using the literature that was available to him. Many catalogue entries have corrections to the original designation, showing that he was constantly working over his specimens, comparing them with incoming material. This is seen in an entry such as: 'Tellina. This shell is found fossil in Maryland & I believe [23/3721] is the same w no. 716'. In cataloguing precious stones, Sloane often had to be satisfied with a description, as: 'a [15a/134] piece of soft green stone from Turkey given me by Mr Lenoy ...' But, even here, he would hazard a name where possible: 'a stone made of fibres as if it had been wood. [15a/239] It is green capable of polish from Suratte sent by Dr Waldo to Mrs Hayes his sister. An sort of alumen plumosum or Lapis Amiantus?' He is often clearly sceptical of the identification passed on by the original collector, as: 'Round or [15a/473] sphaerical iron stones brought from Knowle in Kent & given me by Lord Dorsett who fancied they came from drops of water in great rains rouling down the sandy irony steep cliffs'. In just a few entries, he is close to giving up: 'I think [16/2572] this antimony I would be glad to know what it is. From Bengal. P[etiver]. lead ore?'

Sloane applied a number of chemical and physical techniques to learn more about his specimens. He had a chemical

131

15b/769   analysis made of 'a blackish mineral with yellow shining
15b/761   parts in it . . .', and he roasted 'a yellow shining pyrites w
severall cavities in it?'. Another specimen that was analysed
15b/634   was an ironstone from the Forest of Dean, from which 'Dr
Wall extracted his tincture which he gave w his diet drink'.
Another technique which Sloane seems to have used with
enthusiasm was to heat his specimens by focusing the rays
of the sun with a large concave mirror made by Monsieur
15a/1323   Villotte.[47] Some tests were hardly helpful: '[mother of
emerald] which being exposed to the focus of the great
burning concave speculum of Mr Villotte crackled & flew
to pieces'. A second trial was scarcely more informative:
17d/145   'Talc vitrified into a blackish glass by Mr Villott's burning
glass of 47 inches diameter'.

Sloane had an interest in and an understanding of both
natural history and natural philosophy – what we would
now call 'science' – that raises him above the level of the
mere dilettante, or undiscriminating collector. He was certainly not a great original scientist, but he did use his collection to further natural knowledge wherever he could, and
used scientific techniques to make the most of his
materials.[48]

Survival of the Geological Collections

Approximately 14,000 geological specimens were taken
into public ownership at the founding of the British
Museum in 1753. A system of registration was not set up
in the Museum until 1837, and, in the Mineralogy Department it was not possible to deal with the older specimens
until 1883. By this time, sales of duplicates, disposal of
unwanted material, and loss of provenance information had
dramatically reduced the number of recognizable Sloane
specimens and only 370 were registered as being from his
collection. When *The History of the Collections* was compiled
in 1903 these were critically reviewed by Lazarus Fletcher
(1854–1921), and their number reduced to fifty-eight.[49]
Leonard J. Spencer (1870–1959) and Jessie M. Sweet (1901–
79) both became interested in the Sloane collection in the
1930s, and increased the number to 161 definite, and a number of possibles.[50] Many of these specimens are carved
objects which were included by Sloane in his catalogues
28h, 28i   of 'Agate handles &c' and 'Agate cups botles spoons &c'
(see also Chapter 13). Removal of these leaves ninety-five
specimens from the Sloane mineral collection. Among the
survivors are forty 'pretious stones', including jasper, agate,
bloodstone, aquamarine and emerald; two 'metalls', including the heavy black stone with golden streaks sent by Mr
Winthrop and a proustite on arsenic from Dr Lavater. There
are seven specimens from the amber catalogue, and ten
'chrystalls', including three pieces of quartz and a petrified
human skull (Fig. 33), all from Cardinal Gualtieri's collection.
In addition, and not included in the totals given above, there
are 107 small mineral and fossil specimens, housed in three
divided drawers, that made up part of Sloane's pharmaceutical stock.

Charles Davies Sherborn (1861–1942) compiled a list of
the surviving Sloane fossils in July 1889, annotating the
original catalogues as he did so. His list comprised two fossil
vegetables, eighty-four invertebrate fossils, and ten vertebrate remains, and these figures were repeated in *The History
of the Collections*.[51] Surviving invertebrate fossils include a
good range of Caenozoic and Mesozoic sea urchins, molluscs and brachiopods from the 'Echini' and 'Testacea' catalogues. Although most of the specimens are British, there
are also specimens from Spain, Switzerland, Jamaica, Maryland, Hungary, Sweden and Russia, including a number sent
by Dr Lavater. Among the fossil vertebrates is part of a
fish tooth figured by Sloane in his 1697 paper,[52] a fine mam-   25a/289
moth tooth from Siberia (Fig. 34),[53] and a fossil turtle sent   25e/1807
from Turkey by Dr Massy, which is the type specimen of   25e/1821
Testudo sloanei Lydekker (Fig. 35).[54] These three important
specimens are some small consolation for the myriad that
have been lost.

Fig. 33 J. & A. Van Rymsdyk, *Museum Britannicum* (1778), tab.
iii, fig. 1: 'An Incrusted Scull and Sword, they were both found
in the Tiber at Rome, on the right side of the Scull (A) is the bone
or head of the humerus, and (B) the first rib adhering'.

Fig. 34 Tooth of a mammoth (*Mammuthus primigenius*), from Siberia [25e/1807]. NHM, palaeontological collection, 4 (Old Cat). Reproduced by courtesy of the Trustees of The Natural History Museum.

Fig. 35 Fossil turtle (*Testudo sloanei*) from Turkey, given to Sir Hans Sloane by Dr Massy [25e/1821]. NHM, palaeontological collection, R 1587. Reproduced by courtesy of the Trustees of The Natural History Museum.

Notes and References

1. Ferrante Imperato, *Dell'Historia Naturale di Ferrante Imperato Napolitano Libri xxviii Nella quale ordinamente si tratta della diversa condition di minere, e pietre* (Naples, 1599); U. Aldrovandi, *Musaeum Metallicum* (Bologna, 1648); Olaus Worm, *Museum Wormianum, seu Historia Rerum Rariorum, tam Naturalium quam Artificialium, tam Domesticarum, quam Exoticarum, quae Hafniae Danorum in Aedibus Auctoris servantur* (Lugduni Batavorum, 1655).

2. For early collections in Britain see Arthur MacGregor, 'The cabinet of curiosities in seventeenth-century Britain', in O. Impey and A. MacGregor (eds.), *The Origins of Museums* (Oxford, 1985), pp. 208–11.

3. Michael Hunter, 'The cabinet institutionalized: the Royal Society's "Repository" and its background', in Impey and MacGregor, op. cit. (note 2), pp. 158–68.

4. Hooke's lectures and the reactions they aroused are dealt with in R. Rappaport, 'Hooke on earthquakes: lectures, strategy and audience', *British Journal for the History of Science* 19 (1986), pp. 129–46. Niels Stensen, *The Prodromus to a Dissertation Concerning Solids Naturally Contained within Solids . . . English'd by H. O.* (London, 1671).

5. 'A letter of Martin Lister, written at York August 25 1671', *Philosophical Transactions* 6 no. 5 (1671), pp. 2281–4. The discussion that followed the reading of the letter on 2 November 1671 is reported in T. Birch, *History of the Royal Society* (London, 1756–57), vol. iv, p. 487.

6. The development of geological collections in Britain is described in H.S. Torrens, 'Early collecting in the field of geology', in Impey and MacGregor, op. cit. (note 2), pp. 204–13.

7. Among the naturalists who, after 1700, were unable to agree that any fossils were organic were John Beaumont (d.1731), and Robert Sibbald (1641–1722). John Ray (1627–1705) wavered from one point of view to the other, while Edward Lhwyd (1660–1709) developed a distinctive compromise.

8. Sloane, *Natural History*, vol. i, preface.

9. The synopsis is reprinted in Gavin R. de Beer, *Sir Hans Sloane and the British Museum* (Oxford, 1953), p. 160.

10. Edward Lhwyd, *Lithophylacii Britannici Ichnographia sive Lapidorum aliorumque* (London, 1699); John Morton, *The Natural History of Northampton-shire* (London, 1705); and Martin Lister, *Historia Conchyliorum* (London, 1685–92).

11. Robert Plot, *The Natural History of Oxford-shire, Being an essay towards a Natural History of England* (Oxford, 1677); Agostino Scilla, *La Vana Speculazione disingannata dal Senso* (Naples, 1670); Johann Scheuchzer, *Herbarium Diluvianum* (Zurich, 1709).

12. Aldrovandi, op. cit. (note 1); Worm, op. cit. (note 1).

13. Quoted in *The Correspondence of John Ray: consisting of selections from the philosophical letters published by Dr. Derham, and original letters of John Ray, in the collection of the British Museum*, ed. E. Ray Lankester (London, 1848), p. 186.

14. Sloane, *Natural History*, vol. ii, pp. 337–40.

15. Sloane, *Natural History*, vol. i, p. lxii.

16. Sloane, *Natural History*, vol. ii, p. i.

17. Quoted in M.E. Jahn, 'John Woodward, Hans Sloane, and Johann Gaspar Scheuchzer: a reexamination', *Journal of the Society for the Bibliography of Natural History* 7 (1974), pp. 19–27.

18. J.E. Dandy (ed.), *The Sloane Herbarium* (London, 1958), pp. 176–7.

19. Sloane, *Natural History*, vol. ii, p. i.

20. This *Musei Fossilium Conspectus* is in catalogue 24, fol. 262, and is dated *Medio Octobri 1728*.

21. Letter from Lhwyd to Sloane, 15 September 1701, BL, Additional MS 4038, fol. 236. Lhwyd is explaining why the University will accept Sloane's duplicates even though they have many of them already.

22. David Price, 'John Woodward and a surviving British geological collection from the early eighteenth century', *Journal of the History of Collections* 1 no. 1 (1989), pp. 79–95. For an account of Sloane's relations with Woodward, see J.M. Levine, *Dr Woodward's Shield. History, Science and Satire in Augustan England* (Berkeley, Los Angeles and London, 1977), pp. 84–92.

23. *The Diary of Ralph Thoresby*, ed. J. Hunter (London, 1830), vol. i, p. 298.

24. *The Diary of John Evelyn*, ed. E.S. de Beer (Oxford, 1955), vol. iv, pp. 531–2.

25. William T. Stearn, 'Kaempfer and the Lilies of Japan', *The Lily Yearbook* 12 (1948), pp. 65–70.

26. BL, Additional MS 3396, fol. 42.

27. BL, Additional MS 3396, fols. 45–54.

28. BL, Additional MS 4048, fol. 266; see p. 293, no. 20.

29. Sloane's acquisition of another large collection of German minerals is mentioned by Thoresby in a letter to Richardson of 21 June 1723: see D. Turner (ed.), *Extracts from the Literary and Scientific Correspondence of R. Richardson* (London, 1835), p. 196.

30. For Morton's debt to Sloane and the loan of the figured specimens, see Turner, op. cit. (note 29), p. 117. Woodward also received specimens from Morton, including at least four of the figured specimens, see Price op. cit. (note 22), p. 95.

31. John Beaumont, 'Two letters concerning rock-plants and their growth', *Philosophical Transactions* 11 no. 129 (1676), pp. 725–41.

32. Richardson sent a box of coal plants to Sloane in June 1702, and exchanged letters on their origin and significance throughout that year, see Turner, op. cit. (note 29), pp. 43–71. It was Richardson's gift of drawings of these fossils, which Sloane showed to the Royal Society, that led to a dispute between Sloane and John Woodward, (ibid., p. 46).

33. Lhwyd, op. cit. (note 10). Sloane's involvement is described in M.E. Jahn, 'A note on the editions of Edward Lhwyd's *Lithophylacii Britannici Ichnographia*', *Journal of the Society for the Bibliography of Natural History* 6 (1972), pp. 86–97.

34. James Brewer, 'Part of two letters concerning beds of oystershells found near Reading in Barkshire', *Philosophical Transactions* 22 no. 261 (1700), pp. 484–6; Francis Nicholls, 'Some observations towards composing a natural history of mines and metals', *Philosophical Transactions* 35 no. 401 (1728), pp. 402–7; Mr. Wilson, 'A letter giving an account of the Lapis Amianthus, Asbestos or Linum Incombustibile lately found in Scotland', *Philosophical Transactions* 22 no. 276 (1701), pp. 1004–6.

35. Edward Browne, *A brief Account of some Travels in Hungary, Servia, Bulgaria, Macedonia, Thassaly, Austria, Styria, Carinthia, Carniola and Friuli . . .* (London, 1673), p. 144; and *An Account of Several Travels through a Greater Part of Germany: in four Journeys . . .* (London, 1677), p. 179.

36. BL, Additional MS 4045, fol. 117.

37. BL, Additional MS 4048, fol. 110.

38. Many of Sloane's specimens appear to be identical to those listed in Winthrop's catalogue of the specimens he gave to the Royal Society. See John Winthrop, 'Selections from an ancient catalogue of objects of natural history, formed in New England more than a century ago', *American Journal of Science* 47 (1844), pp. 282–90.

39. Charles Hatchett, 'An analysis of a mineral substance from North America containing a metal hitherto unknown', *Philosophical Transac-*

tions 92 no. 1 (1802), pp. 49–66; William H. Wollaston, 'On the identity of columbium and tantalum', *Philosophical Transactions* 99 no. 2 (1809), pp. 246–52.

40. Clifford Frondel, 'Benjamin Franklin's purse and the early history of asbestos in the United States', *Archives of Natural History* 15 (1988), pp. 281–7.

41. John Woodward, *An attempt towards a natural history of the fossils of England; in a catalogue of the English fossils in the collection of John Woodward, MD . . .* (London, 1729), pp. xiii–xiv.

42. Hans Sloane, 'An account of the tongue of a Pastinaca Marina, frequent in the seas about Jamaica, and lately dug up in Maryland, and England', *Philosophical Transactions* 19 no. 232 (1697), pp. 674–6; and *idem., Natural History*, vol. I, p. lxiii.

43. Hans Sloane, 'An account of elephants teeth and bones found under ground', *Philosophical Transactions* 35 no. 403 (1728), pp. 457–71.

44. See general comments on the growing understanding of strata in Roy Porter, *The Making of Geology, Earth Science in Britain 1660–1815* (Cambridge, 1977), pp. 118–23.

45. Jessie M. Sweet, 'Sir Hans Sloane: life and mineral collections part III: mineral pharmaceutical collection', *Natural History Magazine* 5 (1935), pp. 145–64.

46. Conrad Gessner, *De Omni Rerum Fossilium Genere, Gemmis, Lapidibus, Metallis, et Huiusmodi, Libri Aliquot, Plerique nunc Primum Editi* (Zurich, 1565), and Athanasius Kircher, *Mundus Subterraneus* (Amsterdam, 1678), vol. II, p. 22.

47. This is presumably François Villette (1621–98), whose thirty-four-inch burning mirror is still preserved at the Paris Observatory. See M. Daumas, *Les Instruments Scientifiques au XVII et XVIII Siècles* (Paris, 1953), p. 112, note 8. See also D.L. Sims and P.L. Hinkley, 'Brighter than how many suns? Sir Isaac Newton's burning mirror', *Notes and Records of the Royal Society* 43 (1989), pp. 31–51.

48. Maarten Ultee, 'Sir Hans Sloane, scientist', *British Library Journal* 14 (1988), pp. 1–20.

49. British Museum (Natural History), *The History of the Collections contained in the Natural History Departments of the British Museum* (London, 1904–12), vol. I, pp. 355–6.

50. Jessie M. Sweet, 'Sir Hans Sloane: life and mineral collections part II: mineral collection', *Natural History Magazine* 5 (1935), pp. 97–116.

51. Dandy, op. cit. (note 18), p. 325.

52. Sloane, op. cit. (note 42), figs. 7 and 10.

53. R. Lydekker, *Catalogue of the Fossil Mammalia in the British Museum (Natural History)* (London, 1885–7), vol. IV, p. 204.

54. R. Lydekker, *Catalogue of the Fossil Reptilia and Amphibia in the British Museum (Natural History)* (London, 1888–90), vol. III, p. 89.

8 Botanical Collections

John F. M. Cannon

[*] It would be difficult to overstate the significance of the Sloane herbarium for the history of plant classification, as it represents by far the largest extant collection of plant specimens from the pre-Linnaean era. It is, indeed, almost certainly, the largest collection that was ever assembled during this early period. As such, it provides a remarkable demonstration of the state of botanical knowledge in London just before the the the dawn of today's systematic methods and nomenclatural procedures. These are the direct result of the introduction by the Swedish taxonomist Linnaeus, of the sexual system of classification and the binomial system of nomenclature.[1] Before Linnaeus initiated his pragmatic and highly practical system, plants were characterized by phrase names:[2] thus the plant we now know as *Heliotropium indicum* – the concise Linnaean binomial – was known to Sloane as *Heliotropium americanum caeruleum, foliis hormini angustioribus* – a phrase-name which was supposed to distinguish the plant from all other species with which it might be confused, in addition to providing a convenient 'handle' for everyday reference.

Thus the Sloane herbarium provides a unique and tangible snapshot of the scope of a very major collection and the curatorial techniques used in its management, at an important turning-point in the history of plant science, just before the introduction of binomial nomenclature freed taxonomists from the considerable tyranny of the old polynomial terminology[3] and paved the way for the subsequent flowering of plant taxonomy in the late eighteenth and nineteenth centuries. This new nomenclature was also directly related to the Linnaean sexual system of classification, which provided a simple means of arranging plants into major groupings: this greatly facilitated scientific inventory of the large number of new species which were then becoming known through travel and exploration but, since it was largely artificial and did not reflect the actual relationships of plants, it did not stand the test of time. None the less, the binomial sytem of nomenclature is likely to remain the internationally accepted standard for the foreseeable future.

For these reasons, the Sloane botanical collections represent a unique international resource for the history of science, and their place of honour in the national archive is more than justified. They have an additional significance and relevance for contemporary taxonomists, however, in that they contain a large number of specimens which must be regarded as the types which establish the ultimate identity of many plant species. In many ways this transcends their undoubted historical significance, at least in the eyes of Sloane's successors – the practical working taxonomists of the present day.[4]

Nearly all modern plant nomenclature (some lower plant groups excepted) stems from the publication in 1753 by Linnaeus of *Species Plantarum*. This was essentially a catalogue with descriptive phrase names and the highly convenient binomials, of all the species then known to science and, as such, it has been adopted as the starting-point for modern nomenclature. Since most scholarly interaction at that time took place in Latin, the internationally accepted, modern requirement for Latin descriptions was automatically provided by the phrase names. The type concept, however, is a later development which was unknown to Linnaeus, although it has been applied retrospectively to his works (and to those of the other early taxonomists) by the alignment of his numerous descriptions with specimens present in his own herbarium and others to which he had access. There remain, however, a number of species which were known to him only from descriptions, with or without illustrations, in the published works of other authors: in these circumstances, modern practitioners can only regard the earlier description, accompanied perhaps by an illustration, as the 'type' of the Linnaean species. Even in these difficult circumstances, it is sometimes possible to locate an original specimen that lies behind the author's description and, in the case of illustrations, the common identity of the specimen and the published plate is often very convincing. It is in this context that the importance of the Sloane herbarium for modern systematists actually lies. Quite a number of species in the works of Linnaeus were known to him only from earlier publications and the typotypes[5] of a significant number of these can be found in the Sloane herbarium. For example, Sloane's own descriptions in his *Natural History* of Jamaica are covered by specimens in the first eight volumes of the herbarium, while species originally recognized by early authors such as Plukenet, and otherwise unknown to Linnaeus, may be found in the later volumes. The herbarium also includes many collections made or accumulated by early botanists, which were subsequently acquired by Sloane and incorporated into his collections.

This rather lengthy introduction has seemed necessary, not least to establish the prime importance of the Sloane herbarium in the eyes of modern scientists and others responsible for the allocation of the resources upon which the proper curation and preservation of museum collections depend. The Sloane botanical legacy is not merely a musty pile of old dried plants of purely antiquarian interest: it represents one of the ultimate reference sources for the nomenclature of plants, upon which modern electronic data banks for the transmission of information on resources of vital importance to man ultimately depend.

The Herbarium

Unlike a modern herbarium, in which each specimen is mounted on a separate sheet of paper so that they can easily be sorted and rearranged – in ways similar to index cards in a file drawer – those in the Sloane herbarium are mounted

[*] Marginal numerals in this chapter refer to the *Hortus Siccus* numbers assigned to the volumes comprising Sir Hans Sloane's herbarium (see p. 137).

Fig. 36 General view of one of the nine cabinets which contain the Sloane herbarium. Reproduced by courtesy of the Trustees of The Natural History Museum.

(with a few smaller exceptions) on the pages of large folio-sized volumes (Fig. 36). Each page may contain one large specimen or several small ones. There is some internal evidence that, towards the close of his life, Sloane may have begun to assemble herbarium specimens on separate sheets. While the inconvenience of these volumes for ready reference is obvious, they did provide a means of curation and protection that has served the collection well over the years. Well-informed visiting botanists often express surprise at the remarkable state of preservation of the specimens, while lay visitors to the collection are clearly amazed that specimens of this age are still in such good condition. Dried plant specimens mounted in volumes are known as *horti sicci* and the Sloane herbarium consists of no less than 337 of them. In some cases two or more *horti sicci* have been brought together in one bound volume, so that the total number of separate units is now 265. The Sloane herbarium is not unitary, in the sense of a collection accumulated directly by one man through his own efforts in the field; rather it is a huge amalgamation of collections acquired by Sloane at different times during his life and incorporated with his own personal collections which formed the basis

of the herbarium as a whole. In this sense the herbarium can be compared to a library of books; perhaps analogy with the Bible is not too fanciful. Sloane's botanical collections can certainly be compared to the later development of the national collections of The Natural History Museum, in which the bringing together of countless collections, from many individuals from all over the world, resulted in an end-product in which the totality was of greater significance than the sum of the parts. As such the Sloane herbarium was very much a true forerunner of what was to develop into a major international botanical resource.

Unlike most of Sloane's natural history collections, the herbarium remains, for all practical purposes, as he left it, and is thus by far the largest extant part of the foundation collection of the national museum of natural history. Although apparently very delicate, dried plants, firmly attached to strong paper, are remarkably resilient, as is testified by the oldest material in the herbarium which probably originated in the late sixteenth or early seventeenth century. Provided specimens are protected from the ravages of insects and kept dry to prevent mould, it seems that they can be expected to have a virtually unlimited life, given reasonably careful handling.

Such a huge collection could have been amassed only by a man with very substantial financial means, and this is true both with regard to the acquisition of collections by purchase, and their subsequent accommodation and curation. While Sloane was undoubtedly a man of wide botanical knowledge and interests, we should not think of him primarily as a practical working scientist; it would be a mistake, for example, to equate him with his outstanding younger contemporary Linnaeus, whose significance has already been outlined and who had, incidentally, already adopted the separate sheet system of curation still in use today. Rather, we should think of Sloane as a well-informed, scholarly connoisseur and entrepreneur, whose enthusiasm acted as a catalyst for the promotion of scientific development within his very wide circle of friends and correspondents. Clear evidence from his letters and from the contents of the herbarium itself, demonstrates that Sloane was in no way regarded as a superficial dilettante by his contemporaries, and that his benign influence was very wide ranging.[6]

The great curatorial problem posed by collections arranged in bound volumes, as compared to those on individual loose sheets is that, with the passage of time, it becomes impossible to arrange the material in any scientifically useful manner. Some form of detailed index is essential so that, for instance, multiple specimens of one species, which may be represented in several volumes, can be located for comparison and other detailed studies. From internal evidence, it is clear that Sloane had such a catalogue and references to pages numbering up to 3,502 attest to its size. Unfortunately, the catalogue has not been located; we may perhaps hope for its rediscovery although, in the light of the vast amount of distinguished and painstaking research that has been undertaken on Sloaneana at both Bloomsbury and South Kensington, the prospects do not seem bright. An outline catalogue survives, listing only the titles given H.S.283 by Sloane to each volume in the herbarium: e.g. 'Plants from Cochinchina Carolina etc. collected by Mr Petiver'.

Two factors, one historical and the other a more recent development, facilitate our access to the herbarium. In Sloane's own time, it was customary for Sloane himself or his curators (notably Dr Johann Amman) to 'refer the specimens in the collections to Ray'.[7] This process consisted in using a large paper copy of Ray's *Historia Plantarum* as an index (Fig. 37).[8] As specimens were identified, the ample margins of the *Historia* were annotated as to the location of specimens in the collections. This system of indexing is nowhere near comprehensive, but it does at least provide a partial means of access to specimens of given species. Painstaking work by later curators culminated in the publication in 1958 of *The Sloane Herbarium*, edited by J.E. Dandy.[9] This does not set out to be a comprehensive catalogue of the collection, but rather attempts, with considerable success, to provide a key by which users can find their

way around the vast collection. It is itself a considerable publication, consisting of 246 quarto pages of text, followed by no fewer than ninety-six facsimile reproductions of the most important handwritings that appear as annotations in the herbarium volumes. The text falls into three main sections. The first provides a valuable and quite concise background to Sloane and his botanical collections; the second lists the *horti sicci* in their numerical sequence by H.S. (*Hortus Siccus*) numbers and, in addition to providing for each the full title allocated by Sloane, lists the collectors and/or herbaria included, with indications as to the volumes and folios in which individuals are represented. The third, and by far the largest section of the book, lists all the actual field collectors and accumulators of herbaria that have been identified as being represented in the Sloane Herbarium. Thus, under 'Dale (Samuel)' we find biographical information, followed by notes on Dale's botanical significance and relations with Sloane: by reference to letters preserved in the Sloane correspondence, interesting light is shed on aspects of the contemporary natural history scene. The H.S. volumes in which Dale specimens are to be found are

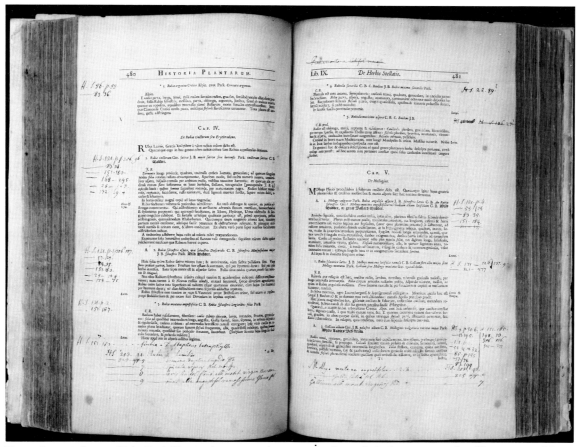

Fig. 37 Annotated copy of John Ray's *Historia plantarum* used as a partial index to the herbarium. Reproduced by courtesy of the Trustees of The Natural History Museum.

enumerated, together with some indication of their provenance and significance. Finally, we are reminded that *Dalea*, a large New World genus of the Leguminosae was named in his honour by A.L. de Jussieu, and reference is made to the facsimile reproduction of his hand.

Selections from the Herbarium

Most, probably all, of the volumes in the herbarium, have features of historical and contemporary interest, but in the space available it is impossible to provide a comprehensive survey of the whole vast collection. Indeed, this would scarcely be sensible in the light of the availability of the Dandy index mentioned above. It seems preferable in the present context, to provide relatively full information on a small number of examples and, in this way, to give a clear impression of the scope and interest of the collection, to whet the reader's appetite, and to encourage further detailed research by workers at present unaware of the opportunities that remain to be explored. In this respect, it may, perhaps, not be too fanciful to compare the Sloane herbarium and the related vegetables and vegetable substances collections, to vast quarries from which much valuable material has been extracted but which, since Sloane's day, have become somewhat overgrown. Research undertaken since Dandy's time on particular collections, however, has demonstrated the tremendous potential of important material that remains to be exploited. If this publication stimulates further scholarly excavations, the effort will have been well worthwhile. Let us then review some individual volumes, in the hope that the flavour and scope of the whole will become apparent.

Sloane's Own Collections

A large number of the somewhat heterogeneous volumes in the collection contain specimens collected by Sloane himself, either in the wild or in the gardens of his friends. For instance, he titled one 'Plants rare gathered by me H[ans] S[loane] in the fields and gardens about Montpeliers, Paris and in several parts of France, about the year 1683.' To this is added the rather plaintive suffix: 'Many not named, chiefly for want of leisure' (modern scholars will sympathize with his problem). Another is similarly titled: 'Plants gathered at Dr Uvedale's. Hampton Court, by me H[ans] S[loane] etc. The first and last part omitted to be named for want of time' – still the same problem. The Revd Robert Uvedale was a teacher and non-resident rector of Orpington, Kent. It must be assumed that he had ample private means, as he had a large garden at Enfield which was well known for its numerous exotic plants. His own large herbarium was later acquired by Sloane from his widow. It has been described as one of the best-preserved collections in the Sloane herbarium; James Edward Smith, who purchased the Linnaean collections and brought them to England, drew attention to its importance, along with that of Buddle.[10] These collections are of importance in the interpretation of Ray's pioneering *Historia Plantarum*, as Ray himself did

not make extensive herbarium collections. We can at least turn to those of his friends with whom he had frequent communication and who were well acquainted with his plants. Many other plants from Uvedale and his garden are scattered through numerous other volumes of the herbarium.

Interesting though such collections are, they are certainly eclipsed by eight volumes which may be regarded as the foundation of the whole herbarium (see Fig. 38). They contain specimens collected by Sloane during his voyage to Jamaica in 1687 and during his stay there until 1689, as physician to the Governor – the Duke of Albemarle. As with many other eminent naturalists, exposure to the immense riches of a tropical flora at an early stage in his career had a powerful effect in stimulating the development of his later work and interests. The majority of specimens are naturally from Jamaica, but material collected in Madeira, Barbados, Nevis and St. Kitts during the outward journey and from the Isles of Scilly on the way home is also included. The collection formed the basis of Sloane's *Natural History* of Jamaica (1707–25) in which the new species he found are described and figured. Interestingly, the illustrations can often be correlated very clearly with specimens in the herbarium and thus admirably meet the criteria for typotypes. At the time he was compiling his *Species Plantarum*, Linnaeus was familiar with Sloane's publication but lacked specimens of the latter's new species, so, following Dandy's dictum, we can look for specimens to typify the Linnaean concepts in the Sloane herbarium. We can thus locate the type of *Sloanea*, a genus named in Sloane's honour by Plumier (Fig. 39).[11] Swartz, in his *Prodromus* (1788),[12] a foundation work for the study of the West Indian flora, notes the importance of Sloane's work and makes references to it throughout his text. Unlike, Linnaeus, Swartz had access to the herbarium and to Sloane's annotated copy of the *Natural History* during the course of his work, which post-dated the establishment of the British Museum after Sloane's death.

One of the most interesting consequences of Sloane's stay in Jamaica was his introduction to chocolate (Fig. 40). This he found at first to be 'nauseous and hard of digestion, which I suppose came from the great oiliness' – hardly an encouraging initial meeting with a commodity that was to become a prime snack for today's often over-fed countries of the 'first' world. However, further experience with chocolate mixed with milk, demonstrated that it could be made much more palatable and even attractive. On his return to London, he gave the recipe to Nicholas Sanders of Soho, who manufactured chocolate and, in due course, passed on the trade to his successor William White, who sold it as 'Sir Hans Sloane's Milk Chocolate … Greatly recommended by several eminent Physicians, expecially those of Sir Hans Sloane's Acquaintance, for its Lightness on the stomach & its great use in all Consumptive Cases' (see Chapter 1, Fig. 2). In due course, during the nineteenth cen-

H.S.10

H.S.12

H.S.302–15

H.S.1–8

Fig. 38 *Malviscus arboreus* Cav., a typical specimen from Sloane's own collection, made in Jamaica [H.S.4:45]. Reproduced by courtesy of the Trustees of The Natural History Museum.

Fig. 39 Type specimen of *Sloanea emarginata* L., collected by Catesby [H.S.232:18]. Reproduced by courtesy of the Trustees of The Natural History Museum.

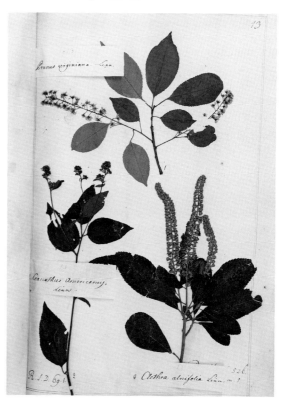

Fig. 40 Sloane's specimen of *Theobroma cacao* L., the source of chocolate [H.S.74:13]. Reproduced by courtesy of the Trustees of The Natural History Museum.

Fig. 41 Early specimens from Maryland [H.S.74:13]. Reproduced by courtesy of the Trustees of The Natural History Museum.

tury, the production of milk chocolate was continued by Messrs. Cadbury,[13] using Sloane's recipe and eventually resulting in yesterday's 'health food' — even medication would not be too strong a term — becoming today's highly popular confection. Were he here today, the good physician Dr Sloane might well wonder what he had started, and be concerned to prescribe a degree of restraint, lest his chocolate contribute to unhealthy obesity in some of his sweet-toothed patients.

Botanical Beginnings in Maryland

Not surprisingly, many of the earliest existing botanical specimens from North America are to be found in the Sloane collection (Fig. 41) and, during the past decade, these have been explored in great detail by Professor J.L. Reveal of the University of Maryland.[14] It is gratifying to know that study of these old collections is not merely of antiquarian interest (although this is in itself considerable), but are also of immediate contemporary significance for the light they can shed on changes in vegetation that have taken place since Sloane's time. In turn, this can contribute to current thinking on conservation, and the possible biological reconstruction of areas devastated by man's activities, currently neglected, but potentially capable of regeneration to provide both natural history interest and recreational opportunities, for today's inheritors of the colonial territories that were known to Sloane.

H.S.74   The first of these early Maryland botanists that we shall consider is Hugh Jones (died 1701). Jones was a young Welshman who had gone to Oxford on a scholarship and was trained by his distinguished fellow countryman Edward Lhwyd, who, as Keeper of the Ashmolean Museum, himself made major contributions to British natural history. The London botanical establishment of the time, otherwise referred to (somewhat inaccurately) as the Temple Coffee House Botany Club (see p. 13), was well aware of the botanical importance of North America, both for its purely scientific interest, and also for its undoubted potential for plants of economic value. The 'membership' was, no doubt, concerned that the death of the Revd John Banister (1654–92), an early and highly significant botanical correspondent of the London botanists of the day, had left them without representation in the American colonies. It seems likely that the Hon. and Revd Henry Compton, one of the membership who combined his natural history interests with weighty responsibilities as Bishop of London, may have seen a way of killing two birds with one stone: if a competent naturalist could be found who was also an ordained priest of the Church of England, he could be sent to Maryland to combat that colony's unfortunate predilection for the Roman Catholic version of the faith. Funding was needed for this somewhat Machiavellian scheme; the involvement of the Royal Society was sought, and eventually financial support was found through the Royal Governor of Maryland, a staunch Protestant who was keen to rid his colony of what he perceived as the Roman menace. Meanwhile, in Oxford,

Jones had completed his basic education as a naturalist and Lhwyd felt able to commend him in glowing terms to Compton.

So in 1695, Jones came to London for what we would now call a 'crash course' on the duties of an Anglican minister and, having made contact with the London botanists, set off for Annapolis, the newly established capital of the colony, which was then as described by Reveal, 'a city of less than 40 buildings and considerable mud'. The original intention was that Jones should be the Governor's chaplain, but he was soon assigned to the rectorship of one of the largest rural parishes. Once there, he seems to have set about his natural history collecting with some diligence, but unfortunately it appears that his enthusiasm was not matched by experience and practical skills in the collecting, labelling and packing of material for dispatch to England. In short, the members were deeply disappointed in their new biological chargé d'affaires in the colonies. For Jones, although well provided for as rector of one of the most wealthy parishes in Maryland, life in America was frustrating. The climate, often bitterly cold in winter and hot and humid in the summer, was debilitating, and the religious inclinations of his parishioners towards catholicism, coupled with Quaker incursions from Pennsylvania, made his official functions fraught with difficulties and rather unrewarding. However, he was not without support in London and James Petiver, apothecary and botanical activist, urged him to redouble his efforts, as moves were under way to seek alternative representatives in the colonies.

Eventually, William Vernon, a fellow of Peterhouse, Cambridge, was sent out under official sponsorship and David Krieg, a Prussian friend of Petiver's, also made the journey, supported by his own efforts as a ship's surgeon. The collections from these subsequent travellers are also represented in the Sloane herbarium. As is customary in botany, the collections were made up into duplicate sets and distributed to Krieg's supporters; Sloane's share of the treasure was sent directly to John Ray, where it proved a significant addition to the resources for his *Historia Plantarum*, an early and valiant attempt to encompass the entire world's flora. It only remains to follow Hugh Jones to a premature death in 1702, at the probable age of thirty-one — untimely, even for those days when life expectancy was so much shorter than today. It seems likely that tuberculosis, coupled with the climate and, no doubt, made worse by depression arising from disappointment in both his religious and natural history vocations, resulted in his early demise.

It must not be thought that Jones's sojourn in Maryland was entirely a failure and, indeed, the extended title given by Sloane to this volume includes the statement '. . . Extraordinary good specimens, well preserved, and the greatest part refered to Ray.' Some Krieg and Vernon specimens are also included in the volume, but it seems clear that in spite of the grumbles from London, the efforts of Jones were by no means all in vain. It is gratifying to report that in

1983 these early collections returned to Maryland for a short stay in association with the bicentenary of the State and the centenary of the University of Maryland.[15] Much space has been devoted to this one collection, and this is only a summary of the interesting information that is now available. It does, however, show very clearly the potential of the Sloane herbarium for modern research, as has been demonstrated by Professor Reveal using data from many sources, to present a fascinating picture of Anglo-colonial botanical life in the late seventeenth century.[16]

Philip Miller and the Chelsea Physic Garden

In addition to his association with the foundation of the national collections in the British Museum, Sloane was also intimately involved in the early development of the Chelsea Physic Garden, one of the oldest botanical gardens in the world. The Society of Apothecaries, in modern terms the organization responsible for the training of the physicans of the day, had established a scientifically-based garden for the cultivation of medicinal herbs and for the education of their students. In 1722 Sloane, who meanwhile had become landlord of the garden, settled the land on the Society, but astutely required a number of provisions, some of which were calculated to stimulate the effective management of the garden. In particular, he stipulated that each year the Royal Society should be sent fifty specimens that had been grown in the garden during that year and which were different from any sent previously, until no less than two thousand had been delivered. All gardeners will appreciate that, even for professionals, this requirement is rigorous and likely to stimulate vigorous activity. Philip Miller (1691–1771), a young man from Kent, was appointed to act as the superintendent, a function which he admirably filled, especially in his role as a taxonomic botanist. In particular, the publication of his *Gardener's Dictionary* (dedicated to Sloane) remains the most important single memorial to his diligence. The *Dictionary* is unusual, in that its various editions span the introduction, and gradual acceptance of Linnaean binomial nomenclature. Thus it is to the eighth edition of 1768 – the first with binomials – that modern botanists turn to find the validation of plant names published by Miller. The specimens that had been sent to the Royal Society, eventually numbering no fewer than 3,150, were transferred to the British Museum in 1781, where they were incorporated into the General Herbarium. There they were united with a large number of other Miller specimens from Chelsea that had been acquired by Sloane, and may be found in twelve of the herbarium volumes. Miller's numerous contacts throughout the world ensured that many new plants came to Chelsea, and consequently many specific names are today attributed to him. The modern process of retrospective typification means that Miller collections in the Sloane herbarium and elsewhere in the Museum, must be examined as the present location of potential 'lectotypes'.[17] A manuscript catalogue of Miller

specimens in the Sloane herbarium was prepared in 1960 by John Lewis, a senior member of the Museum's Botany Department, and this provides a convenient means of access to material of particular species.

Engelbert Kaempfer

Kaempfer (1651–1716) was the first European to investigate and make known the flora of Japan, both by the specimens he collected and by accurate drawings of the plants.[18] He was born in northern Germany and, after a thorough medical education, travelled widely including visits to Sweden, Russia and Persia. It may be that the unsettled state of central Europe on his return stimulated thoughts towards further travel abroad; eventually he entered the service of the Dutch East India Company, in the course of which he spent two years at the Company's outpost on the tiny artificial island of Deshima in Nagasaki harbour. The ultra-xenophobic Japanese policy of the day ensured that the foreigners were prevented for most of the time from crossing the bridge to the mainland. Under these frustrating conditions, and with commendable initiative, Kaempfer made full use of his contacts with individual Japanese to obtain specimens and information about the Japanese flora. Among other incentives, instruction 'in astronomy and mathematicks with cordial and plentiful supply of European liquors' stimulated the flow of information. As a part of the obligatory annual appearance of the Dutch ambassador at the court in Edo (now Tokyo), Kaempfer was able to see more of the country, but there can be no doubt that this early glimpse of the Japanese flora owed much to his

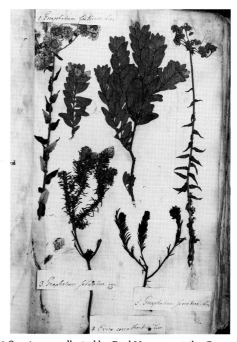

Fig. 42 Specimens collected by Paul Hermann at the Cape of Good Hope in 1672 [H.S.75:11]. Reproduced by courtesy of the Trustees of The Natural History Museum.

H.S.211
energy and persistence under remarkably restrictive and irksome conditions. One of the most important and frequently consulted volumes in the herbarium contains Kaempfer's very early collections from Japan; furthermore it seems that no other institution has any Kaempfer material to shed light on the numerous species figured and described in his *Amoenitates* (1712).

Kaempfer's collection was purchased by Sloane after Kaempfer's death in 1716 (see Chapters 1 and 18).[19] The Japanese specimens are supplemented by a manuscript in the British Museum, which consists of no fewer than 217 folios of plant drawings, mostly with Japanese names but without descriptions; however, an alphabetical list of Japanese names is included, with references to the *Amoenitates* etc.[20] Another Sloanean connection with Kaempfer is provided by the translation by Dr J.C. Scheuchzer, an amanuensis of Sir Hans, of the manuscript *History of Japan*, published in London in 1727.[21]

Paul Hermann

In his younger days, Paul Hermann (1646–95), later Professor of Botany at Leiden, was the first botanical collector at the Cape of Good Hope, the home of one of the richest and most remarkable floras in the world. One *hortus siccus* is devoted to plants collected there by Hermann (Fig. 42), though it is not clear how they came into Sloane's possession. According to Dandy,[22] they correspond with, but are more extensive than those included in the list by Bartholinus, which was given by Hermann to Hieremias Stolle, a surgeon whom he met at the Cape. The list has been described as probably the first ever published of African plants.

H.S.75

From the Cape, Hermann went to Ceylon (now Sri Lanka) where he practised as a physician and formed a remarkable plant collection. This was used by Linnaeus as the basis for his *Flora Zeylanica* (1747) and, consequently, is the location of many type specimens. The Sinhalese herbarium was eventually purchased by Sir Joseph Banks and so came into the care of the British Museum. It is not, of course, a part of the Sloane herbarium but, like it, consists of bound folio volumes and by reason of the historic links, merits brief mention here.

Georg Joseph Kamel

Georg Joseph Kamel (1661–1706), familiar to us through *Camellia* named in his honour and based on a variant spelling of his name, was born in Moravia and, after becoming a lay brother in the Society of Jesus, went to Manilla and became the pioneer investigator of the flora of the Philippines. Once established there, he studied the local natural history, moved by a concern to relieve the sickness of the poor who came to the dispensary that he founded. No doubt the tropical conditions and the ignorance of hygiene in those days, greatly stimulated his medical interests. Kamel was a competant botanist, an industrious collector and accomplished artist. He was in correspondence with Ray

and his *Historia Stirpium Ins. Luzonia et reliquarum Philippinarum* occupies no fewer than ninety-six folio pages in the appendix to the third volume of Ray's *Historia Plantarum* where it is reproduced. Today's botanists will appreciate the anguish when, in writing to Ray, Kamel mentions that his first consignment of drawings, 'a piratis intercepta fuit', and did not reach their destinations. Kamel specimens are to be found in several Sloane volumes and, in addition to their great historical interest, are important for present-day taxonomists, as the sole representatives of his remarkable botanical labours, under what must have been very exacting conditions.

Cryptogams in the Sloane Herbarium

Specialists on the various groups of cryptogams, i.e. the lower plants such as mosses, lichens, seaweeds and fungi, will look in vain in the foregoing account for mention of their particular concerns, and will complain that, as usual, the smaller and less obvious lower plants have been overlooked in favour of the more conspicuous and better-known flowering plants. The number of cryptogam specimens in the herbarium is very small compared to those of the flowering plants. This is not surprising, as clearly the more conspicuous and familiar groups attracted scientific notice and study before the relatively inconspicuous lower plants. In order to redress, at least partially, this imbalance, there follow notes on some cryptogamic groups in the hope that more specialists may be stimulated to explore the potential of this aspect of the collection.

The lower plant specimens in the Sloane herbarium are of considerable interest for the light they shed on the development of the taxonomy for these groups, but perhaps their special value for botanists today follows from the practical evidence they provide concerning actual plant localities some three hundred years ago. The lively interest in environmental conservation of the past few decades, and the related concern with the pollution of our atmosphere, fresh waters and the sea, have focused special attention on lower plants, especially algae and lichens, since these organisms are particularly sensitive to detrimental chemical changes in their environments. For this reason, specimens that provide hard evidence of past distributions are of special value. Unfortunately, a large proportion of the specimens are unlocalized, and one can only regret that the need for detailed label information did not become apparent earlier in the development of natural history collections. However, enough specimens are localized and have sufficient evidence of dates, to make study of the herbarium from this highly emotive modern standpoint a worthwhile exercise. Not surprisingly, although some foreign cryptogam specimens (e.g. coralline seaweeds from Jamaica) are present in Sloane's own collections, the vast majority originated from our own country. A large number of fern specimens are to be found but, since their size and conspicuous structures have always resulted in their study along with the higher plants, no further special mention of them will be made here. At the other extreme, the fleshy nature of fungi makes their preservation by normal methods rather difficult and they are not well represented in the collection. On the other hand, the mosses, lichens and seaweeds are quite numerous and their interest is demonstrated by the following examples.

The collections of the Revd Adam Buddle (c.1660–1715) were bequeathed by him to Sloane, although Sloane seems to have had some difficulty in getting them from Petiver who had them at the time of Buddle's death. The collection H.S.114–26 comprises no fewer than thirteen volumes (currently bound into four composite volumes). The quality of the specimens and their state of preservation is remarkably high and the collection has earned the comment 'undoubtedly the most trustworthy and accurately-named . . . of the period which H.S.115 exists'. In the present context one volume (Fig. 43) is of special interest to us, as it contains a significant series of lower plant specimens. Buddle was clearly held in high regard by his contemporaries as a cryptogamic specialist,[23] as is reflected by comments like: 'the most skilful in the knowledge of grasses and mosses of any in England'.[24] Jacob Bobart the younger, who succeeded his father as *Horti Praefectus* of the University Botanic Garden at Oxford provided the eulogy when returning this volume from loan, 'I am now to be thankful to God and my friends that I have not only seen, but had the perusal of (as I think) the best Collection of its kind in the World, and is as instructive as admirable: if the intellectuall is the best part of Mankind, certainly whoever contributes to that is the most amicable and performs the greatest part of humanitie . . .'[25] Some Bobart specimens and identification annotations are to be found in the Buddle collections. Finally, in somewhat more picturesque terms, we have the comment of Vernon, who describes Buddle as 'the top of all the moss-croppers'.[26] Practising taxonomists today could hardly aspire to better epitaphs, and it is fitting that such a man's reputation is enshrined by a very familiar garden shrub, even though the origin of the name and its distinguished progenitor, are unlikely to be known to many garden lovers.

The lichen collections in this volume include a number of specimens from Hampstead. Evidence from this and other sources has shown a considerable diminution of the lichen flora of Hampstead Heath, resulting from atmospheric pollution to which these composite algal/fungal organisms are especially sensitive.[27] One of the few localized foreign specimens (on p. 11) deriving from Vernon, 'In Terra Marianum' (i.e. Maryland), has been recognized as probably the earliest lichen specimen from North America. There are also some excellent moss and liverwort specimens in the collection which, like the lichens would certainly repay a critical modern study. These do not as yet seem to have attracted as much interest as those of the former group, possibly for technical reasons related to the later nomenclatural starting date for the bryophytes, which does not

Fig. 43 Lichens collected by the Revd Adam Buddle [H.S.115:10]. Reproduced by courtesy of the Trustees of The Natural History Museum.

stimulate so much bibliographical-related interest in very early extant collections.

The seaweeds are notably represented in the collections of Robert Plot (1640–96), first keeper of the Ashmolean Museum, Oxford, and those of his deputy and later successor Edward Lhwyd (1660–1709), whose activities we have already noted as the mentor of Hugh Jones prior to his journey to Maryland. Not surprisingly, many of Lhwyd's specimens are from his much-loved Welsh homeland, but there is also one especially noteworthy volume: *Plantae Aliq[u]ot marinae, ex Couno [Sheppey] Insula in Agro Cantiano*. These specimens provide a particularly interesting early picture of the seaweeds, which has recently contributed to a critical review[28] of the marine flora of Kent, made in the light of the contemporary environmental conditions.[29] A specimen of *Padina pavonica* labelled 'Harwich' (Fig. 44) provides another good example of the utility of these classic collections in modern research since this attractive brown seaweed is no longer to be found in Essex. It

H.S.113

H.S.113

H.S.114 is possible that the specimen collected by Buddle may have been found amongst the unattached drift weed on the shore, but this seems unlikely as this species usually disintegrates rapidly *in situ* and the record also correlates with a contemporary reference in literature from Dale, who records it from Harwich thus: 'grows plentifully upon the stones that lie before the Cliff, but not so far down as not to be seen but when the Tide is lowest . . .'[30]

The Collection of Vegetables and Vegetable Substances

The Sloane herbarium has already been compared to a huge, partially exploited quarry and, if this is an apposite metaphor, then the collection of vegetables and vegetable substances is more like a vast sand-pit of little-appreciated significance, that may well hold great treasures for a modern scholar with the appropriate historical and other skills to exploit its potential.

The collection is accommodated in ninety drawers (Fig. 45) arranged in five cabinets. Many of the specimens are still in the glazed boxes, of many different sizes, in which they were originally housed, while others had to be re-curated after minor damage suffered during an air-raid in the Second World War. Although adequately housed for its preservation, the collection is very poorly understood and this is probably due to its character. Its origin seems to lie in Sloane's professional concerns with *materia medica*, and this is clearly reflected in its contents, which include seeds, fruit, bark, roots, gums, resins and all manner of plant odds and ends. This is especially true of the earlier accessions, but in the later part of the collection one gets an impression of more generalized, purely scientific accessions. It seems probable that this is a real phenomenon, and that the collection developed as Sloane's increasing resources and expertise allowed him to diversify, from the more practical affairs of medicine to the wider fields available to a gentleman of means, with a truly catholic taste for all aspects of natural history.

Sloane's manuscript catalogue of this collection survives (NHM, unnumbered), unlike that which is believed to have covered the detailed contents of the herbarium. The catalogue comprises three volumes with the accessions listed in order of acquisition, bearing numbers 1 to a scarcely credible 12,523. So far as is known, the collection remains more or less complete. There is also a supplementary manuscript index in alphabetical order, that was made by listing the specimens, cutting the list into very small slips, rearranging the slips and pasting them into a book in the correct new order. The information in the catalogue for each specimen is very variable. For many only a simple botanical name is given, while for others pharmaceutical names, native vernacular names, localities or countries of origin, and donors or collectors are occasionally provided. In a few cases, figures which appear to be a purchase price (e.g. '0.2.3.') are present. Rarely, a museum-style description of the

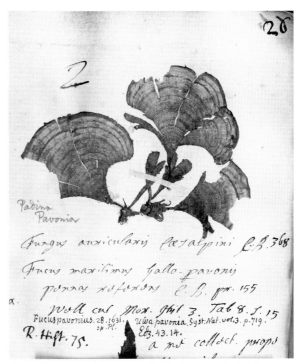

Fig. 44 Specimen of the Brown Alga *Padina pavonica* (L.). Lamour, collected by Buddle at Harwich [H.S.114:26/2]. Reproduced by courtesy of the Trustees of The Natural History Museum.

Fig. 45 A typical drawer from the Sloane collection of vegetables and vegetable substances. Reproduced by courtesy of the Trustees of The Natural History Museum.

Fig. 46 An imaginative evocation of the vegetable lamb of Tartary. Reproduced from *Natural History Magazine* 3 (1932), p. 195.

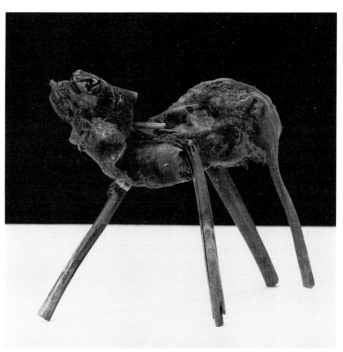

Fig. 47 Sloane's specimen of the vegetable lamb of Tartary, now much denuded of its originally woolly covering of scales. Reproduced by courtesy of the Trustees of The Natural History Museum.

object occurs; these generally relate to curios of a basically vegetable origin, e.g no. 642, 'a carv'd snuff box made of a small coco nut shell or fruit of a palm').

As has already been noted, the collection is vast, complex and vey poorly understood. It was apparently studied by a Mr T.E. Wallis[31] of the Pharmaceutical Society in the late 1930s and the years soon after the War. So far as is known, no publications resulted and we are not aware of any preserved working notes. There can be no doubt that this collection, which demands expertise beyond that normally possessed by modern scientific taxonomists, would richly repay detailed study by a scholar with an extensive background in the historical aspects of pharmacology, as it represents, in many ways, a 'fossilized' pharmacopoeia of Sloane's era in the development of medicine.

Sir Hans and the Vegetable Lamb of Tartary

In the Middle Ages, the known world and its contents, although much smaller than that familiar to us today, was, nevertheless, filled with objects that were a source of amazement and wonder to our forebears. It is easy, in our sophisticated times, to look on some of their beliefs with amusement and even incredulity, but we should be wary of adopting a patronizing attitude towards those in circumstances that are difficult for us to comprehend fully. The

limited communications of the day, coupled with a fervent faith that accepted miracles as everyday happenings, together with the decay of science during the Middle Ages from its highly promising beginnings in classical times, led to the ready acceptance of many myths and stories which to informed minds today seem literally unbelievable. Having said that, we should again pause, to recollect recent stories in the popular press about flying saucers and their crews of 'little green men', before we congratulate ourselves on the current state of society.

The story of the vegetable lamb of Tartary[32] seems to have come to England through Sir John Mandeville. In many ways, it parallels the much more widely known myth of the barnacle geese, which were believed to originate from trees growing somewhere in the north of Europe: the origin of that story is plainly the result of goose barnacles being found growing attached to twigs cast up on the shore, and their superficially goose-like shape and colouring (see further, Chapter 5). Sir John travelled in the realms of the Cham of Tartary and, on his return, reported that there was in that country a great marvel, through which certain plants produced living lambs (Fig. 46) that, when mature shed the umbilical connection with their vegetable parents and led a normal independent ovine existence. Even in Sloane's time this fable lingered on, and there is in the Vegetable and Vegetable Substances collection a specimen of the supposed lamb (Fig. 47).[33] Sir Hans showed it to a meeting of the Royal Society in 1698 and demonstrated his scientific acumen by identifying it as a scale-covered rhizome and associated leaf bases from a large sub-arborescent fern. It had been sent by a Mr Buckley from India, where it was known as the Tartarian lamb, but our present knowledge of the distribution of *Cibotium barometz* – the species concerned – tells us that it must have originated in China, where it occurs naturally. It is interesting to note that from very early times, information about this plant had been filtering through oriental bazaars and by camel caravans to medieval Europe. In such circumstances, it is scarcely surprising that garbled stories, enhanced by the speculations of unsophisticated minds, often resulted in remarkable traveller's tales. Although normal wear and tear over the years has resulted in the loss of most of the woolly covering from Sloane's 'lamb', we can perhaps see, if we try to put ourselves in our ancestors' shoes, how objects of this kind would have seemed tangible proof of the story. It has also been suggested that early reports on the cotton plant may have added to the confusion surrounding the vegetable lamb. In conclusion, it is pleasing to record that Sloane's lamb was included in the special exhibition at the British Museum in 1990 entitled *Fake? The Art of Deception*.[34] Although the misunderstandings surrounding the lamb were probably related to distance, credulity and a lack of understanding, rather than to deliberate calculated deception, it was very fitting that this small memorial to Sir Hans should have been included in a special exhibition in the Museum that is founded on his collections.

Conclusion

As we have seen, during the course of his long life, Sloane amassed botanical collections that were on a scale without equal at the time and, through his network of scientific friends and correspondents, he was in touch with leading botanical practitioners throughout the world. The collection remains an important resource for today's taxonomy and nomenclature, as well as a milestone in the history of botany. In spite of all this, one is left with a slight nagging feeling of anticlimax. Some further explanation is necessary, lest it be thought that such a conclusion is at best impertinent, and bordering on treason, coming from a lifetime servant of the Trustees of one of the great museums which stemmed directly from the acquisition by the nation of Sloane's collections, in 1753.

This feeling of unease stems, no doubt, from the author's professional background as a taxonomic scientist, whose prime concern is with the practicalities of plant classifications and floristics, rather than with main-stream history of science (although, of course, taxonomy rests, to a degree totally unknown in other branches of science, on an understanding of the classical literature of the subject). In this context, the whole matter hinges on the position of Sloane's collection which stands alongside the initiation by Linnaeus

of modern taxonomic methods and nomenclature. At a time of unprecedented change, when current taxonomic methodology is under challenge to a remarkable extent, due largely to the extraordinary new possibilities provided by the computer, it may be particularly timely to consider the impact of Linnaeus on Sloane and his times.

Linnaeus arrived in London in July 1736[35] and clearly lost no time in calling on Sloane, then aged seventy-six and the doyen of British naturalists who, during the course of his long life, had known personally or by correspondence, everyone worth knowing in science and especially in botany. The young Linnaeus, then aged twenty-nine, brought with him a letter of introduction from Herman Boerhaave (1668–1738), a physician and botanist of great distinction at the University of Leiden. The way had been further paved, a little earlier, when Gronovius and Lawson sent Sloane two copies of Linnaeus's *Systema Naturae* – one for himself and the other for the Royal Society. However, the letter from Boerhaave rather tactlessly said 'Linnaeus, the bearer of this letter, is particularly worthy of seeing you, and being seen by you. He who sees you together will look upon a pair of men whose equal is hardly to be found in all the world'. Such a eulogy was indeed prophetic, but its impact was scarcely likely to smooth the path of the then almost unknown young Swede, in his meeting with the President of the Royal Society, even though Sloane does not appear to have been unduly concerned with protocol and was ever helpful towards his younger contemporaries. The view that 'Sloane did not pay [Linnaeus] that respect and attention which his merits deserved',[36] may well be correct, though in the circumstances it would be difficult to fault Sloane for his failure to foresee the future. After Linnaeus returned to the Netherlands, his letter of thanks to Sloane referred to the 'incomparable Museum' – but did not mention his critical opinion as to its curatorial condition, which he described to others as a state of chaos.[37] Although Sloane appears to have been too set in his ways to understand the new methods introduced by Linnaeus, he did soon afterwards arrange for some of the young man's work to be read before the Fellows of the Royal Society.

We are now faced with the big question that assails the modern taxonomist in his contemplation of the Sloane collection. What if Sloane had fully appreciated Linnaeus's remarkable abilities and the drive that he brought to bear on all the work he undertook? Likewise we may wonder how Linnaeus would have reacted to the opportunity of being placed in charge of Sloane's collections and given the chance to bring methodical order out of the chaos that he perceived. Such a scenario is by no means fanciful, as is demonstrated by the employment by Banks, a generation later, of talented students and disciples from the Linnaean school of botany at the University of Uppsala. Assuming that the course of Linnaeus's work then followed the lines with which we are familiar, the Sloane herbarium would be today of paramount scientific significance as the foundation collection of modern taxonomy. It would, no doubt, have been greatly enhanced by numerous additions, through the international network that Linnaeus was himself to establish. The vast significance of this possibility is difficult to convey to anyone unaccustomed to the working methods of practical taxonomy. For Linnaeus, secure employment in London, a major centre of scientific endeavour and international connections, might well have promoted even further his extraordinary abilities and persistent energy. However, such was not to be and we are left contemplating the Sloane botanical collections as a mighty achievement, balanced somewhat precariously at a time of great change in taxonomy, between the Old Testament of the earlier botanists who stemmed directly through the herbalists from the classical authors, and the New Testament which has included almost all of us who have followed in the discipline of plant taxonomy since the time of Linnaeus.

Acknowledgements

I am grateful to a number of colleagues in the Department of Botany at The Natural History Museum for advice on particular topics. In particular to Jim Price and Ian Tittley for the marine algae, Jack Laundon for the lichens, Charlie Jarvis for aspects related to Linnaean typification and Eric Groves for the collection of vegetables and vegetable substances. The experience gained by Mr Groves as a young curator soon after the war, in bringing the Sloane specimens together again after previous dispersal in the general fruit collection, provides the only practical knowledge available today on this neglected Sloanean collection. I am also indebted to Prof J.L. Reveal of the University of Maryland, who has spent much time on early North American collections in the Sloane herbarium, for information and discussion on this aspect of the account.

Notes and References

1. As a consequence of the introduction by Linnaeus of the binomial system of nomenclature, every species is provided with a reasonably short and convenient name, consisting of two elements – generic and specific – by which it can invariably be distinguished from all other plants and, for practical purposes, from animals as well.

2. Phrase names not only provided a unique reference point for the species but, since they consisted of several words, served a second function by listing the characters by which it could be recognized and distinguished from its relatives.

3. Many phrase names were longer than the example cited and thus highly inconvenient for practical use in both scientific and popular literature.

4. For the benefit of readers who are not familiar with the working practices of international taxonomy, a brief description of the type method as applied to plant nomenclature may be helpful. When a botanist discovers a species that he believes to be new to science, two procedures are required to validate the name he proposes: a description must be published in Latin, and a specimen must be designated as the 'type'. The latter is then available for future purposes as a standard for ultimate reference, as to which plant the original author wished to be recognized under the name proposed.

5. The term 'typotype' was introduced by J.E. Dandy as a convenient concept to cover these circumstances. Thus, it is sometimes possible to discover early specimens that lay behind original descriptions and/or illustrations of species which were known, after the adoption of binomial nomenclature, only from the published works of earlier authors. The specimens can then be used to interpret the descriptions and illustrations that are technically the 'types' of the species concerned.

6. In all these respects, Sloane was a remarkable forerunner of Sir Joseph Banks (1743–1820) who, at a somewhat later time, similarly promoted the progress of botany and whose collections eventually joined those of Sloane, to form the dual foundation stones of the Museum's plant collections.

7. After 1736, when Amman became Professor of Botany at St. Petersburg, this useful practice became much diminished.

8. Ray's *Historia Plantarum* (London, 1686–93), an outstanding achievement in systematic botany, which remained a key work for botanical taxonomists until the publication by Linnaeus of *Species Plantarum* (Stockholm, 1753).

9. J.E. Dandy (ed.), *The Sloane Hebarium* (London, 1958). This volume, published by the Trustees of the British Museum (Natural History), is, in spite of a complex and difficult bibliographical gestation, a scholarly compilation and commentary of which the Museum may be justly proud. The accumulation of information on the Sloane herbarium was started by James Britten, for thirty-eight years an assistant in the Department of Botany. He established an extensive series of paper slips, on which he recorded the results of many detailed investigations, all of which are the result of everyday scholarly familiarity with the collection – an epitaph which may well appeal to all those with natural curatorial instincts. Although his work was incomplete at his death in 1924, the slips remained an appreciated working tool for botanists wishing to gain access to the collection. The work of others, notably William Carruthers (Keeper of Botany 1871–95) in his contributions to volume I of the *History of the Collections contained in the Natural History Departments of the British Museum* (London, 1904), had meanwhile provided further important historical background to the herbarium. In 1953, to commemorate the bicentenary of Sloane's death and the foundation of the British Museum, the then Keeper, George Taylor (later Sir George, Director of the Royal Botanic Gardens, Kew), recommended to the Trustees that the Britten catalogue should be published. Naturally, with the passage of time, further substantial work was needed to bring the work up to date and into a state fit for publication. Fortunately, Spencer Savage, who had been Librarian of the Linnean Society and who had an exceptional knowledge of the relevant period, was available. His contributions were of great value, especially those stemming from his familiarity with the handwriting of many of the botanists concerned, and he was responsible for selecting the samples that were reproduced as facsimiles. In spite of all this work, it became obvious that the account was still deficient in several respects. It fell to James E. Dandy (Keeper of Botany 1956–66) to undertake a final revision which involved a page-by-page critical examination of all 265 volumes. Those of us who were junior members of the Department at the time and were privileged to see Dandy at work, have the greatest confidence in the quality of the text that finally appeared in 1958. As in his other work, he set standards of precision that are equalled by few, if any, of our contemporaries.

10. Buddle's name is familiar to gardening enthusiasts today through the commonly grown genus of shrubs *Buddleja*. These are also commended by entomologists for their nectar-producing flowers which are particularly attractive to butterflies.

11. P.C. Plumier, *Nova Plantarum Americanarum Genera* (Paris, 1703), p. 49.

12. O.P. Swartz, *Nova genera & species plantarum seu Prodromus* (Stockholm, Uppsala and Cibo, 1788), p. 152.

13. Anon., *Nature stored nature studied* (London, 1981), pp. 17–19.

14. For detailed information see J.L. Reveal, 'Significance of pre-1753 botanical explorations in temperate North America on Linnaeus' first edition of Species Plantarum', *Phytologia* 53 (1983), pp. 1–96.

15. On this occasion, the Jones, Vernon and Krieg volumes of the Sloane herbarium were exhibited at the University of Maryland, the State Capitol and the present church of the parish that was served by Hugh Jones, where a tree was ceremonially planted in his memory. The limitations of the airline booking computer, resulted in a bizarre record that the seat occupied by the volumes on their way across the Atlantic was officially allocated to a hypothetical 'Mr Sloane'. Thus the limitations of current technology unintentionally provided recognition where it was certainly due. Fortunately, no crisis necessitated reference to the passenger list, otherwise a search for the non-existent Mr Sloane might have been prolonged and unsuccessful.

16. Ironically, the 'bio-political' manoeuverings of Sloane's time seem remarkably familiar and reminiscent of the present day, as will be recognized by all those who have spent time in the administration and promotion of scholarly activities. It seems that here, as in other spheres of human activity, *plus ça change* . . .

17. 'Lectotypes' are specimens which were available to the original author and on which he based his specific concepts, but which were designated formally by a subsequent author as nomenclatural types.

18. W.T. Stearn, 'Kaempfer and the lilies of Japan', in *The Lily Year Book* 12 (1948), pp. 65–70.

19. See also C.P. Thunberg, *Travels in Europe, Africa and Asia. Performed between the years 1770 & 1779* (London, 1796), vol. IV, p. 290. Thunberg inspected the collection in 1778.

20. BM, PD, Sloane MS 2914.

21. Another volume, H.S.213 contains specimens collected by Kaempfer in the botanical garden at Leiden; the specimens, however, are fragmentary and of little importance.

22. Dandy, op. cit. (note 9), p. 137.

23. Ibid., pp. 102–8.

24. Richard Richardson, quoted in ibid., p. 103.

25. Ibid.

26. Ibid.

27. D.L. Hawksworth and P.M. McManus, 'Lichen recolonization in London under conditions of rapidly falling sulphur dioxide levels, and the concept of zone skipping', *Botanical Journal of the Linnean Society* 100 (1989), pp. 99–109. Happily, there is now some evidence of improving environmental conditions, together with the rediscovery of some lichen species, probably related to recent legislation and generally improved public awareness.

28. I. Tittley and J.H. Price, 'An atlas of the seaweeds of Kent', *Transactions of the Kent Field Club* 7 (1977), pp. 1–80.

29. J.H. Price, I. Tittley and W.D. Richardson, 'The distribution fo *Padina pavonica* (L.) Lamour. (Phaeophyta: Dictyotales) on British and adjacent European shores', *Bulletin of the British Museum (Natural History)* Botany Series 7 (1979), pp. 1–67.

30. S. Dale, *The History and Antiquities of Harwich and Dovercourt* (London, 1730), p. 345.

31. J.M. Sweet, 'Sir Hans Sloane: life and mineral collection, part III, mineral pharmaceutical collection', *Natural History Magazine* 5 (1935), pp. 145–64.

32. The remarkable history of the vegetable lamb is well reviewed by A.W. Exell, 'Barometz: the vegetable lamb of Scythia', *Natural History Magazine* 3 (1932), pp. 194–200.

33. Specimen in the Sloane collection of vegetables and vegetable substances, but the original accession number is not known at present.

34. M. Jones (ed.), *Fake? The Art of Deception* (London, 1990), p. 85.

35. See W. Blunt, *The Complete Naturalist* (London, 1971), for a general review of the life and work of Linnaeus, including an account of his trip to England.

36. J. Lempriere, *Universal Biography* (London, 1805), *s.v.* Linnaeus.

37. Dandy, op. cit. (note 9), p. 11.

9 Coins and Medals

Marion M. Archibald

Ancient and modern coins and medals in gold and silver, the lasting monuments of historical facts.[1]

In these words the report of a royal visit to Sir Hans Sloane's house at Chelsea in 1748 captures the real importance of his coin collection, but it was its sheer size, 23,000 pieces at the time of his death, which most impressed the many learned and curious visitors to whom Sloane so readily made his collections available.

It is sadly no longer possible to make a full appraisal of the collection's range and importance (or even to be completely sure of its size) because the ten volumes[2] in which the coins were listed are now missing. They were last recorded in the Department of Coins and Medals of the British Museum in 1933,[3] but no evidence of their continued existence can be found after the 1939–45 war.[4] The conclusion seems almost inescapable that the Sloane coin catalogues were among the small number of losses of manuscript material sustained when the Coin Room was hit by an incendiary bomb on the night of 10 May 1941.[5] Thus Sloane's own careful record of his collection which provides a starting point for students in other areas of his interest is not available to the numismatic researcher.

Hopes have been expressed that it might be possible to reconstruct the Sloane coin collection directly from the British Museum trays,[6] but success here is likely to be limited. Comprehensive registration of coin acquisitions began only in 1838, so there is no independent record of what was acquired by the museum, and none of Sloane's original labelling survives. Nor is it possible simply to use the style of tickets belonging to known Sloane coins to identify others. The tickets under such coins are not uniform, but are made of different kinds of paper or card, and are inscribed with varying amounts of numismatic detail in several different hands. Tickets of exactly the same kinds are also to be found under coins securely attributed to other early collections (e.g. that of Sir Robert Cotton, 1571–1631). Further work in identifying the hands involved will help but is unlikely to resolve these problems completely.

Why there are no original tickets is partly explained by the circumstances of the coins' arrival in the British Museum. Sloane's coins were housed in the room next to his bedchamber at Chelsea.[7] When he died in 1753, it was clearly going to take some time for the provisions of his will to be negotiated with the government,[8] so his executors had to take measures for the security of the most vulnerable parts of his collections, principally the coins and medals. The coin cabinets, which were probably monumental pieces of furniture,[9] were emptied and the coins, still

in their trays, were packed with a number of other small items into one iron and ten wooden chests and deposited in the Bank of England.[10] They were eventually delivered to the British Museum at some time between 17 June and 12 July 1757.[11] On 12 November, it was noted that the work of sorting the coins would take some considerable time,

. . . it having appeared, upon opening of the boxes, that the medals were so loosely pack'd up, as to be shook out of their places.[12]

It would seem that any attempt to marry the mixed-up coins with their original tickets, or with Sloane's catalogues, was abandoned, and the coins were identified from scratch and new tickets written. Nowadays great care is taken to preserve pedigrees and provenances but in the eighteenth century this was not thought to be so necessary. James Empson, Sloane's curator and a trustee of his will, had urged in 1756 that the coins should be housed beside the other Sloane material as his former master had intended,[13] but the coins were integrated with the British Museum's holdings from other sources.[14] The Sloane coins thus lost their identity among the rest of the Museum's collection.

Before considering other sources from which sections of the Sloane collection can be reconstituted, it is necessary to mention one further problem with which the Trustees of the Museum had to contend: the vexed question of the duplicates. Sloane's daughter, Sarah Stanley, complained in a letter to Empson dated 26 January 1758 that the duplicate coins which she and her sister claimed, and had desired to be left in the manor house at Chelsea, had also been delivered to the British Museum.[15] These had arrived direct from Sloane's house, not by way of the Bank, and their state on receipt is not recorded, but the Trustees' minutes suggest that they too required some sorting out. The Museum soon conceded that the duplicates should be returned to the family but, in the circumstances just discussed, some time was needed before it could be decided just what was really duplicate. After a long correspondence between the Museum and 'H. Stanley', a half share of the duplicates was delivered to him on 17 October 1771.[16] Lord Cadogan, to whom the other half-share of the duplicates was due through Sloane's other daughter Elizabeth (but who had made no claim), renounced it in favour of the Museum.[17] This division was based on the list of duplicates, totalling 3,240 coins, compiled by Matthew Duane, after the collection had been sorted by Andrew Gifford, Thomas Snelling and himself.[18] The coins comprising half of the Sloane duplicates left in the museum were no doubt among the total of over 5,000 British Museum duplicates sold three years later,[19] but no pedigrees are given.

150

When John Evelyn visited Sloane's collections in 1691 (see Chapter 1) they were already extensive, but coins were not included among the areas of particular strength which he mentioned. Sloane had some coins[20] but there is no evidence that he had a systematic numismatic collection before 1702 when he inherited that of his friend William Courten.[21] Reports by numismatic experts who saw Courten's coin collection indicate that it was a large and impressive one,[22] but neither a list nor an estimate of the total number of coins it contained is extant.

In the absence of the catalogues, general descriptions in the British Museum records provide some idea of the range of Sloane's coin collection, but they are too vague to help to reconstitute the collection in detail in any series.[23] The evidence has to be found in miscellaneous sources of varying reliability which list or mention coins with unequal detail and at differing dates. Courten's papers describing his holdings can sometimes supply information about Sloane's collection which complement the latter's own records, for example his series of papal medals, listed in 1701.[24] He was, however, less well-off than Sloane and no evidence of any really large-scale purchases has been found. Unlike Sloane's papers which reveal relatively few single purchases, there are many among Courten's. His main method of acquisition was by regular – it might almost be said compulsive – small-scale acquisitions from a wide range of sources.[25] This illustrates an essential difference in the approach of the two men to collecting and also in their personal interest in coins.

Among the Sloane papers there are a large number of lists of coins, some in his own hand and some in Courten's. These vary very much in length, detail and usefulness. At their best they form a complete listing at a stated date of a section of the collection,[26] and some of them may well have formed the basis of the missing catalogues. Others are much less useful: they are scrappy, undated, quote only numbers of coins under general headings, often giving values (generally in bullion rather than in antiquarian terms). Sometimes the status and ownership of the coins in the lists is in doubt, especially those in other hands. Coins are mass-produced objects, so even with the best descriptions, it is often not possible to identify individual specimens in modern collections without additional evidence. Like all collectors, Sloane and Courten sold coins as well as bought them,[27] so there is no guarantee that any coin or group of coins survived in their respective collections until they died.

Sloane bought other collections, or major parcels from them, which included coins. The purchase of the ready-made Carteret collection, for example, greatly strengthened his holdings in the Roman series.[28] Coins were among the acquisitions from John Michael Wright and William Stonestreet,[29] and also from John Kemp whose collection incorporated material from several earlier antiquaries including Jacob Spon[30] and John Conyers. Conyers' collection was important because he acquired material found in the re-

building of London, and particularly of St. Paul's Cathedral, after the Great Fire of 1666.[31] Coins and medals were also present in the Gualtieri collection acquired in 1728.[32]

Coins were also acquired from site finds and hoards. We know of acquisitions from coin-rich sites[33] and of Sloane's offer to buy a hoard of Roman coins of unspecified period found at St. Leonard's Hill, Windsor Forest.[34] There is also indirect evidence for his purchase of hoards in the list of duplicates mentioned above[35] which records large numbers of coins of the Gallic Empire in the third century, and of the houses of Constantine, Valentinian and Theodosius in the fourth century, which must represent different hoards, and includes coins as late as Arcadius (383–408) and Honorius (393–423). Some of the coins of Victorinus (268–70) and Tetricus (270–3) in the same list were no doubt among the 'near halfe a bushell of coins' of these emperors found near Wisbech and given to Sloane by Dr Massy.[36] Hoard acquisitions can also be discerned in abnormal imbalances in representation among his holdings in other areas, for example in the two close-knit but isolated groups of coins of William I and William II.[37] Although a number of hoards of this period have been recorded from Sloane's time[38] none can be directly associated with coins in his collection. Once again the loss of his catalogues has probably deprived students of further identifications of both hoard provenances and details of site finds.

More fundamentally, the absence of the catalogues means that we lack the evidence which might have resolved the problem of the total number of coins which were in Sloane's collection at his death and hence, after the deduction of the duplicates, the total number which were acquired by the British Museum.[39] The summary list of his collections published as one of the codicils to his will in 1753 records that the coins numbered 'about 32,000'. This might seem to be a most reliable source: while it was not compiled by Sloane himself, but for his trustees after his death, it must have been produced with the knowledge of Empson. Unfortunately, the manuscript original of the list does not survive. A letter from the Revd George North of 26 July 1757 states 'Dr Ward observes the number of the coins to be very large (to the amount of 32,000 if I am not misinformed)',[40] but this statement is likely to have been based on the published list and to have no independent authority. No statement of the precise total of the coins has been found among the Trustees' Minutes and other official papers in the British Museum archives, where reference is made to the collection as listed in the catalogues. The condition of the coins on their arrival in the Museum mentioned above explains why the catalogues were the sole authority for some time afterwards. An official introduction to the Museum published in 1808 lists Sloane's coins as '23,000'. This figure was, it says, taken from the schedule which was handed over at the time of purchase of the Sloane collections, 'but as this document is by no means authentic we must request our readers to consider these numbers rather as approximations than as accurate enumerations.' The

Coins and Medals

1753 list, as noted above, in fact reads '32,000' not 23,000 and the statement of 1808 might appear to be merely an erroneous transposition of the first two digits. The very first official British Museum guide of 1761 however states that 'their number, as I have been credibly informed, is upwards of twenty thousand', which might suggest that there had been a mistake in transcription, or an uncorrected printer's error, in the hurriedly-produced codicil which was corrected in the first guide. It is just possible that the similarity of the figures is coincidental and that they are to be explained as the totals before and after the duplicates were subtracted. It is therefore necessary to look at earlier evidence for the size of the collection before Sloane's death.

In Sloane's own listing of his collections published in volume II of his *Natural History* in 1725 he records, with his usual concern for precision, that his coin collection amounted to 20,228 pieces. When Sauveur Morand visited the collection in 1729 he was told that it included 23,000 coins.[41] The similarity of the 'increase' of 2,772 between 1725 and 1729 with that of the 3,240 duplicates listed by Duane may be mere coincidence, but it could be that Sloane was counting only the systematic collection in 1725 (not including the multiple duplicates from late Roman hoards etc. which he also owned). If so, it would suggest that the collection might well have been largely complete by 1725.

Support for such an interpretation comes from the dates of the compilation of the Sloane coin catalogues. Sloane writes in a letter of 26 January 1725 concerning the possible employment of Scheuchzer, recommended as a 'good Medallist', that they had already been completed.[42] Scheuchzer did in fact produce the catalogue of 'Gold Coins Antient and Modern' and a section in another giving 'An Account of the Number of Medals in the Collection'.[43] This suggests that the rest of the coin catalogues were already complete by the beginning of 1725. (Scheuchzer in any case died in 1729). While the acquisitions after this date, such as the coins with the Gualtieri material in 1728,[44] and the medal of Empress Anne,[45] could have been interlined in the catalogues, there is no evidence of any major numismatic purchases in Sloane's later years. It appears therefore that his massive coin collection was acquired essentially between 1702 and 1725, and most of it certainly before 1729. While not conclusive, this evidence also favours the lower figure of 23,000 rather than 32,000 as the total of the Sloane collection.

Sloane was active in the Royal Society after his election in 1685.[46] He would have been familiar with the accounts of coin finds which regularly appeared in its journal the *Philosophical Transactions*, of which he was editor between 1695 and 1713. Whether he acquired any of the coins mentioned is uncertain.[47] Significantly, Sloane was not a Fellow of the Society of Antiquaries, but he gave generous access to his collections for its projected publication on the coinage of Great Britain.

Sloane's holdings in the principal areas of his coin collection will now be considered.

The earliest British Museum coin catalogue published in 1814 dealt with the Greek series.[48] Although the introduction mentions that the basis of the collection was Sloane's, and alludes to the ten volumes of his catalogue, the Sloane coins are not identified in the text. Neither are they cited in any of the volumes of the systematic series of British Museum catalogues of Greek coins.

A few Greek and Greek Imperial coins can be positively identified in the early eighteenth-century work by Nicholas Haym where the sources of the coins included are recorded.[49] Five of the coins can be identified in the British Museum today with absolute certainty because of the unusually accurate engravings in the plates prepared from Haym's own drawings; irregularities of outline, off-centre striking and illegible areas are all faithfully reproduced. Sometimes, however, a single drawing serves for a type of coin quoted from several sources including Sloane, so in these cases it is not possible to be certain from which collection the illustrated coin has been taken.[50] The identifiable coins are:[51] Antioch, Syria (Haym I, p. 22–3, no. 57 = BMC 11 TC, p. 219, 2: see Fig. 48, *i*); Commagene, Antiochus IV (Haym I, p. 48, = BMC 6 TC, p. 217, 3); Kings of Cilicia, Philopater (Haym I, p. 72 = BMC 1 TC, p. 189, 1); Carteia, Spain (Haym I, p. 126–7, no. III = Spain 1698 TC, p. 2, 6); and Lilybaeum, Sicily (Haym II, p. 48 = BMC 4 TC, p. 68, 1). Six more coins cited from Sloane's collection not in the British Museum are: Commagene, Antiochus IV, (two coins, Haym I, pp. 49 and 50); Caesarea ad Libanum, Phoenician, (Haym I, pp. 133–5, no. 13); Eleutheropolis, Judaea, Julia Domna (Haym I, pp. 139–40); and Kings of Pontus, Sauromates I (Haym II, pp. 17–18); Nicomedes II year 162 (Haym II, p. 47). Some of these coins may have been disposed of by Sloane in his own lifetime, but could have been included among those sent by the British Museum to its duplicate sales.

Sloane mentions '62 silver Greek Medals' of unspecified type, '12 of whose doubtful', on 22 April 1704.[52] Nine further Greek coins are listed by him in an undated manuscript and are identified by their numbers in one of the publications of Lorenz Beger.[53] It is possible that these coins might be found among the pre-1838 acquisitions in the British Museum trays, always bearing in mind the difficulties outlined above.

There is an excellent list in Sloane's hand dated 1706 entitled 'Catalogue of my coins of the Roman families extracted out of the two volumes of Vaillant'.[54] These are the later Roman Republican issues, mainly denarii. He describes the type of each coin and gives both obverse and reverse inscriptions in full. They are set out in Vaillant order under his numbers. In one case[55] he records a coin of the family Caninia in his collection against which he notes 'not in Vailant [*sic*]'. He has entered some Vaillant headings with a blank space left below where he had no such coin, thus

152

Plate 16 The Arreton Down Bronze Age hoard. Included in this view are all the items from the hoard surviving today in the British Museum, including the four spearheads and one axehead from the Sloane collection [28*b*/743–8]. Reproduced by courtesy of the Trustees of the British Museum.

Plate 17 Bronze Age copper alloy metalwork from the Sloane collection. *1*, low-flanged flat axe, Yorkshire [BM, PRB, Sl.249*]; *2*, palstave, Windsor [Sl.300]; *3*, palstave, Windsor [Sl.372]; *4*, palstave, Kent [Sl.101]; *5*, palstave, said to be from Wales [Sl.315]; *6*, palstave, near Brentwood [Sl.30]; *7*, socketed axe, Kiddall [Sl.238]; *8*, socketed axe, unprovenanced [Sl.237]; *9*, point, Windsor [Sl.251]. Note: the function of the latter item is obscure, no parallels for it have been found, and its dating is problematic. Reproduced by courtesy of the Trustees of the British Museum.

Plate 18 The 'Phoenix' Jewel, a gold pendant with a bust of Queen
Elizabeth I cut out in silhouette (English, c.1570–80) [4c/1778].
Reproduced by courtesy of the Trustees of the British Museum.

Plate 19 Ceramic bowl (one of three surviving) of Japanese Utsusugawa ware, early eighteenth-century.
BM, OA, Sl.1698. Reproduced by courtesy of the Trustees of the British Museum.

Plate 20 Soapstone figure of Guanti, the god of war; Chinese, late seventeenth- or early eighteenth-century. BM, OA, Sl.1174. Reproduced by courtesy of the Trustees of the British Museum.

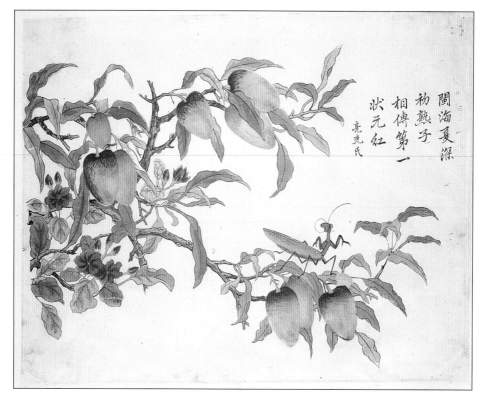

Plate 21 Ding Laingxian, woodblock print of fruit and praying mantis; made in Suzhou, mid seventeenth-century. The print was acquired by Sir Hans Sloane as part of Engelbert Kaempfer's collection. BM, OA, 1906–11–28–14. Reproduced by courtesy of the Trustees of the British Museum.

Plate 22 Unknown Persian artist, painting of wild asses. Acquired by Sir Hans Sloane as part of Engelbert Kaempfer's collection. BM, OA, 1974. 6–17.01(27). Reproduced by courtesy of the Trustees of the British Museum.

Plate 23 Persian planispheric astrolabe of brass, engraved and inlaid with silver, made for Shah Hussain in 1712 by Abd-al-Ali. Length 22 cm. BM, OA, +369. Reproduced by courtesy of the Trustees of the British Museum.

Plate 24 Knife of wrought iron with skin sheath from the Western Sahara/Sudan; [28a/1830] 'A Capashears *knife* from Guinea'. Length 29 cm. BM, Ethno, Sl.1830. Reproduced by courtesy of the Trustees of the British Museum.

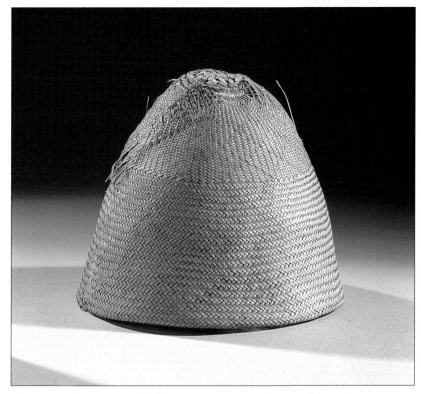

Plate 25 Hat of woven vegetable fibre. Nigeria. [28a/32] 'A straw or bent *cap*'.
Height 15 cm. BM, Ethno, Sl.32. Reproduced by courtesy of the Trustees of the
British Museum.

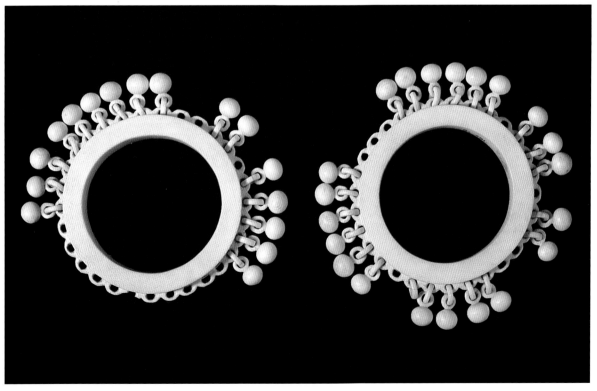

Plate 26 Two West African ivory bracelets. [28a/590] 'An [Indian crossed out] *bracelet* wᵗ. rattles to it cut out of the elephants tooth
(*ivory*) worn upon the arms in Guinea . . .'; [28a/591] '*Another* . . .' Maximum diameters 12–12.5 cm. BM, Ethno, Sl.590–1. Reproduced
by courtesy of the Trustees of the British Museum.

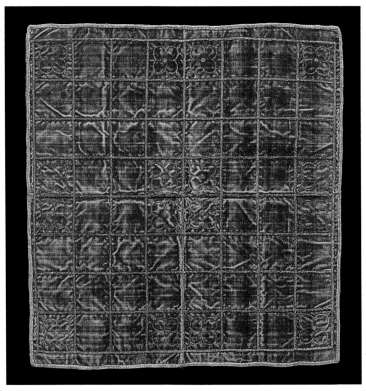

Plate 27 Chess board of velvet with metal thread, from India [?]. [28a/1122] 'A *chesse* play the board of silk & the twelve men wᵗ sevll. animals of ivory on elephants . . . sevll. ware like postures on elephants &c. as in the great Moguls country. given me by my nephew'. 52 by 50 cm. ʙᴍ, Ethno, Sl.1122. Reproduced by courtesy of the Trustees of the British Museum.

Plate 28 Saami drum, from Scandinavia. [28a/1103] 'A Lapland *drum*'. 39 by 33.5 cm. ʙᴍ, Ethno, Sl.1103. Reproduced by courtesy of the Trustees of the British Museum.

Fig. 48 Coins from the collection of Sir Hans Sloane. *1*, Bronze coin of Antioch, Syria, mid-second century BC (BMC vol. 20, A11) and the engraving of this coin from Haym (1719–20); *2*, Roman Republican silver denarius of the moneyer Marcus Sergius Silus, early first century BC (BMC Italy 514); *3*: Roman Republican silver denarius of the moneyer Caius Serveilius Caii Filius, mid-first century BC (BMC Rome 3817); *4*: Roman Republican silver denarius of the moneyer Manius Acilius Glabrio, mid-first century BC (BMC Rome 3946); *5*: Roman Imperial silver denarius of Augustus, 27BC–AD14 (BMC 345); *6*, Roman Imperial silver denarius of Caligula, AD37–41 (BMC 4); *7*: Roman Imperial gold aureus of Claudius, AD41–64 (BMC 5). Reproduced by courtesy of the Trustees of the British Museum.

Fig. 49 Coins and medals from the collection of Sir Hans Sloane. *1*, Roman Imperial orichalcum sestertius of Nero, AD54–68 (BMC 125); *2*, Silver penny of Cnut, 1016–35, Quatrefoil type, moneyer Oswi at Ilchester (BMC 209); *3*, Silver penny of Cnut, 1016–35, Short Cross type, moneyer Edred at London (BMC 438); *4*, Silver penny of William I, 1066–87, Two Stars type, of St. Stephen's, Launceston (BMC 326); *5*, Silver penny of William II, 1087–1100, Cross in Quatrefoil type, moneyer Wulfwine at Maldon (BMC 119); *6*, Silver penny of Henry I, 1100–35, Annulets type, moneyer Ordgar at London (BMC 9); *7*, Silver penny of Stephen, 1135–54, Cross Pommée type, moneyer Driv at Hereford (BMC 214); *8*, gold medal dated 1664 by Thomas Simon, 1623–65, of Thomas Wriothesley, Earl of Southampton, 1607–67. Reproduced by courtesy of the Trustees of the British Museum.

leaving room to insert one if he should have subsequently acquired it. There are 144 coins individually listed, but this is not the complete total as in the margin he sometimes notes 'multa',[56] for example beside the very common legionary denarii of Mark Antony. It should be possible to establish the identity of at least the more distinctive types among these coins if they survive in the British Museum trays (e.g. the coins in Fig. 48, nos. 2–4). There is no evidence of Sloane having had any of the very rare Republican gold coins, and if he had any of the earlier coins of the Republic there are no surviving details of them. Courten's records typically include '1 small consulary, 6d', acquired in 1688.[57]

Seventeen coins are cited from the Sloane collection in the first volume of the British Museum catalogue of Roman Imperial coins by Harold Mattingly, published in 1923. These citations were almost certainly based on the Sloane catalogues and may be accepted with confidence. There are two gold aurei, one tetradrachm, ten silver denarii, three orichalcum (brass) sestertii and one copper as, as follows. *Augustus*: denarii, Spain, BMC 345 (see Fig. 48, 5), 386, 397, 421; Lyons, BMC 455, 461, 465; tetradrachm: Ephesus, BMC 697. *Caligula*: denarius, Lyons BMC 4; as, Rome BMC 59. *Claudius*: aureus, Rome, BMC 5 (see Fig. 48, 7); sestertius, Rome, BMC 221. *Nero*: aureus, Rome, BMC 2; sestertius, Rome, BMC 125 (see Fig. 49, 1); sestertius, Lugdunum, BMC 304. *Vitellius*: denariius: Rome, BMC 21; denarius, Spain, BMC 96.

The later volumes of the British Museum catalogues published by the same author before the 1939–45 war, when the Sloane catalogues were still available, do not quote any coins as Sloane's. No explanation is offered for the departure from volume I, but it was perhaps that the Sloane catalogues were not so detailed for the later period.

A major purchase of Roman coins, mostly silver Imperial issues, from Lady Carteret[58] is recorded by Sloane on 22 April 1704.[59] The total number of coins acquired from her was 2,322 pieces; he then notes that he has sold 1,470, leaving 852 of her coins in his hands. The end result is summarized that 'of my own before' he had 291, so that with those 'of My Lady's' 852, 'all silver in my hands' now amounts to 1,143 coins. This means that in the field of Roman silver coins, the original collection of Courten (plus any other coins he may have acquired himself) was increased almost four-fold by the Carteret acquisitions.

Sloane himself compiled lists on 25 July 1709 of the number and value (in antiquarian terms) of his Roman Imperial coins under the headings of 'silver', 'great brass' and 'lesser brass'.[60] As this account is so comprehensive, there is no need here to resort to the earlier incomplete lists by Courten.[61] The coins are listed under emperors only, with no further details. They include, he says, '13 aegyptian silver Greek coins', i.e. billon tetradrachms of Roman Egypt whose inscriptions are in Greek, but they are not distinguished in the lists from the other coins of the same emperors. He totals the coins listed as 'great brass' 733,

'middle brass' 379, and 'silver' 392, making 1,504 in all, valued at £1308. 17s. 6d. Among the brass he lists a coin of Otho (AD69) which is a forgery as it is now known that Otho struck no base-metal coins. There may have been other forgeries in the collection not so immediately recognizable. These lists include only a few bronze coins of the fourth century, presumably those of follis size which qualified as 'middle brass'. The small very base silver and bronze coins of what was then known as the 'Lower Empire' do not feature in these lists. Sloane certainly had great numbers of them,[62] but they may have been acquired after 1709 or perhaps the comparable list, if ever made, has not survived. There is also no extant list of the Roman gold. The 1,504 coins listed in 1709 are therefore only a partial record of Sloane's Roman Imperial coins. A total of sixty-five 'Byzantines' appear in the list of duplicates.[63]

Sloane appears to have been less personally interested in his English coins, as no lists survive. Among Courten's papers there are just brief references to single English coins or to small groups as they are acquired. The Ancient British coins which appear in Taylor Combe[64] must have been largely from Sloane's collection, but are not attributed. Some can be identified in William Stukeley's notebook where he drew the coins from Sloane's collection in preparation for his section of the book on the coins of Great Britain planned by the Society of Antiquaries.[65] The coin group is biased in favour of issues from Eastern England and this may reflect a major acquisition from a collection formed in that area. A number of individual provenances are noted.

Gough says that eleven coins of Cnut (1016–35) in the British Museum were from the Sloane collection, although he lists only ten and one is in fact of Harthacnut.[66] With attributions corrected in line with modern scholarship they are *Exeter*: BMC 70, 74; *Ilchester*: BMC 209 (Fig. 49, 2); *Leicester*: BMC 269; *Lincoln*: BMC 308, 324, 342; *London*: BMC 438 (Fig. 49, 3); *Southwark*: BMC 541; *Thetford*: (Harthacnut) BMC 608. At that time the mint of London normally represents about half the coins in hoards, so the high proportion of Lincoln coins suggests that the group was possibly derived from a Lincolnshire find. In 1689 Courten mentions '18 small Saxon ps B of Mr Pinfold 18/−' (no further details) and '1 Saxon coine An Ethelred 1/−'.[67] His papers also include a reference dated 28 March 1695 to 'Saxon and English coins for my Ld Colrane' (no details).[68]

In publishing the British Museum Norman coins, Brooke did not discuss his sources, but clearly made use of the Sloane catalogues to attribute coins to the Sloane collection.[69] The tickets of the coins are annotated with their Sloane numbers in his hand. There are twenty-eight coins which Brooke was able to say were certainly Sloane, and seven which he cites as possibly Sloane. One of the latter, BMC 359, is in fact possibly from the collection of Sir Robert Cotton. The Sloane coins are: *William I*: type II: London, BMC 119, type IV: Lincoln, BMC 244(?); Nottingham, BMC 267; Thetford, BMC 277; York, BMC 292, 294; type V: Canterbury, BMC 304; Cricklade, BMC 308; Launceston, BMC 326 (Fig. 49, 4); Lincoln, BMC 330; London, BMC 337, 348; Wilton, BMC 385; type VII: Shaftesbury, BMC 472. *William II*: type II: Dover, BMC 84; Hythe, BMC 98; Lewes, BMC 103; London, BMC 106(?), 109; Maldon, BMC 119 (Fig. 49, 5); Thetford, BMC 157; type III: London, BMC 198, 202(?), 204(?), 205, 208(?); Salisbury, BMC 216; York, BMC 256. *Henry I*: type I: Dover, BMC 2; London, BMC 9 (Fig. 49, 6). *Stephen*: type II: Norwich, BMC 159; type VII: Norwich, BMC 206; Hereford, BMC 214 (NK = Thetford but see NC 1955, p. 243); Norwich, BMC 222; Two Standing figures type, BMC 262(?).

It is notable that within this series there are two very clear discreet groups; the first of William I types IV and V and the second of William II types II and III. At this period the types were changed about every three years and hoards generally contain, apart from a few possible earlier strays, only coins of the current and the immediately preceding types. This suggests that Sloane had obtained parcels from two different hoards. The first was buried *c*.1075, and the second *c*.1095. There are no known contemporary hoards with these profiles, but knowledge of their contents is often very sketchy.

Courten notes the acquisition of twelve coins of Stephen without further detail which also looks like a parcel from a hoard.[70] If the Sloane coins in BMC are from this source, it would appear to have been a hoard essentially of Stephen's last type, BMC VII. He also acquired in March–April 1689 '1 William Rufus, 1/6', although the attribution is not to be relied upon.[71]

Sloane's collection contained some later English coins. The list of duplicates records, very generally, coins from Edward I through 'siege pieces' (*temp.* Charles I, types unspecified) to 'Pewter money of James 2d', and 'Oliver's shilling cast' (i.e. a forgery) 'Tradesmens' halfpence etc' (the late seventeenth-century local copper tokens) and other 'counters, silver' (possibly including those of Simon Passe). Irish and Scottish coins also feature in the list of duplicates, in particular 109 pieces of Gunmoney which was for Courten and Sloane a contemporary issue.[72] Anglo-Gallic coins of Henry VI were on display for the royal visit in 1748.[73]

No lists by Sloane of his continental European coins survive. There are seventeen impressions of French, German, Italian (and English) coins of the fifteenth and sixteenth centuries with notes on their values.[74] Courten provides a record, in considerable detail, of his acquisitions in this area 'since 1670' (possibly just up to 1674). There are 110 coins valued at £129. 19s. including a few Roman pieces, but mostly relatively recent German and other continental issues, including '1 Spanish ps y^t I know not'. The latest is a gold ducat of Augsburg dated 1669.[75]

Descriptions of some of Sloane's medals were included in one of his catalogues still extant, and are discussed in Chapter 13. A list of several of Sloane's medals exhibited to the Prince and Princess of Wales on their visit to Chelsea in 1748 is preserved.[76] There are a considerable number of other, often quite explicit, references to medals in Courten's papers. Courten lists ninety-two papal medals giving the inscriptions in full but usually no descriptions of the designs.[77] Seventeen French 'medals' costing £25 are briefly noted, without a date and in an unknown hand, 'For Mr Charlton in Brick Court'.[78] In 1689 he buys a *Quatuor maria vindico* medal of Charles II for three shillings, and '1 other silver meddal model of ye gold ps g. to those y^t were touched for the King's Evil in K. Ch. ye 2^ds time *Soli deo gloria*' for the same price, and '1 meddall in block tin upon K. W^ms expedition for England 15 O^ber 1688, 3/6'.[79] The gold medal of the Earl of Southampton by Thomas Simon in the British Museum (Fig. 49, 8) was also almost certainly the one in Sloane's collection described by Vertue.[80] One of the few references to an isolated acquisition by Sloane is to 'a very fine medalion of her Imperial Majesty' (Anne, Empress of Russia, 1730–40), forwarded to him by Johann Amman in 1736.[81] Medals of Queen Mary and Queen Anne also feature without details in the list of duplicates.[82]

Although 'oriental' coins are included in Sloane's collection, little is known about them.[83] 'Hebrew' coins appear in the list of duplicates, but there are no descriptions.[84]

Even from the incomplete picture which can be built up of Sloane's coin and medal collection in the absence of the catalogues, it is possible to agree with the views of contemporaries that it was not only large but was wide-ranging and remarkably representative in many series. In the English and classical series other collections such as that of the Duke of Devonshire[85] probably rivalled Sloane's, but they did not have the range of other material which he possessed.

Coins were not among Sloane's principal interests and he was actively collecting coins over a relatively short period. He was not an expert and published nothing on the subject. There is no evidence that he ever engaged in the lively debates current in his day about attributions, nor that he had any appreciation of numismatic problems and ideas for their solution. The nearest he came to commentary is to note that his coins depicted columns ascribed to Trajan and to Hadrian.[86] When the Society of Antiquaries was planning its publication on the coinage of Britain, Sloane was not one of those selected to do the work (although he was not a Fellow, and was still a busy physician at the time). Sloane was proud of the size of his collection, always keen to discover exactly how many coins he had and what they were worth, and concerned for their security.

Sloane was, however, very much more than the man with a long purse buying up the cabinets formed by earlier antiquaries to impress his visitors. He did not buy collections blindly but selected those which would strengthen his holdings in areas of relative weakness. He acquired the best numismatic books, and listed his coins according to them; he read widely in the historical background and made extensive notes on the careers of the issuers. He had sufficient knowledge and application to work carefully through his coins of many series, evaluating them for authenticity, sorting out those which complemented his existing collection, and disposing of the rest. The use which modern scholars were able to make of his coin catalogues, while they survived, shows that they had been compiled with the acute observation and attention to detail which is the foundation of all numismatic studies. Sir Hans Sloane was not a compulsive coin collector or a numismatic scholar; he was the creator of a museum.

Acknowledgements

I should like to thank the following for their help: Andrew Burnett, Marjorie Caygill, John Cherry, Joe Cribb, Christopher Day, Ian Jenkins, Peter Murray Jones, Venetia Porter, Martin Price, Elizabeth Savage, Luke Syson, Janet Wallace and the staff of the British Library Department of Manuscripts.

Notes and References

1. From a newspaper report of the visit of the Prince and Princess of Wales to Sloane's house at Chelsea. See Chapter 1, Appendix 4.

2. BM, Central Archives, GM, vol. I, fol. 12 of 2 February 1756, (CE 1/1).

3. List of extant Sloane catalogues as of 27 July 1933 drawn up by L.J. Spencer, Keeper of Mineralogy at the British Museum (Natural History). He makes the following entry: '10 bound foolscap volumes mostly in Sloane's handwriting, and with indexes in several volumes. Bound in volumes according to countries, apparently *all* coins.' I owe this reference to Dr Peter Murray Jones. See in general P.M. Jones, 'A preliminary check-list of Sir Hans Sloane's catalogues', *British Library Journal* 14 (1988), pp. 38–51.

4. They were not available to R.H.M. Dolley and Mrs J.S. Strudwick (later Mrs Martin) who worked on the pedigrees of the British Museum Anglo-Saxon coins in the 1950s, especially for their paper 'The provenances of the Anglo-Saxon coins recorded in the two volumes of the British Museum Catalogue', *British Numismatic Journal* 28 (1955–7), pp. 26–59. Some corrections were published in J.S. Martin, 'Some remarks on eighteenth-century numismatic manuscripts and numismatists', in R.H.M. Dolley (ed.), *Anglo-Saxon Coins* (London, 1961), pp. 227–40 at pp. 237–40. Some further corrections are now required.

5. John Forsdyke, 'The museum in wartime', *British Museum Quarterly* 15 (1941–50), pp. 1–8, especially p. 7, and pl. Ia.

6. Dolley and Strudwick op. cit. (note 4), p. 34.

7. BM, Central Archives, GM, vol. I, fol. 11 of 2 February 1754 (CE 1/1). After noting what was in the bedchamber, 'The next room three cabinets belonging to the medals at the Bank'. In the eighteenth century, the term 'medals' was often used to denote currency coins as well as commemorative and other medallic issues.

8. See Chapter 2.

9. See note 7. All the coins had apparently been housed in these three cabinets, which were probably not dissimilar in size to the late seventeenth-century Browne Willis coin cabinet in the Heberden Coin Room, Ashmolean Museum, Oxford, although Sloane's may have been grander. They were not a matched set as Sloane describes one of them as 'my best cabinett' (BL, Sloane MS 3407, fol. 92 of 25 July 1709).

10. There are many references in the British Museum Central Archives to the deposition of the coins in the bank e.g. BM, Central Archives,

GM, vol. I, fol. 15 of 2 February 1754 (CE 1/1) describing the arrangements for bringing the coins to the museum from the bank.

11. BM, Central Archives, GM, vol. I, fol. 186 of 12 July 1757 (CE 1/1) notes 'As the medals of Sir Hans Sloane's collection are now actually in the museum' (i.e. since the previous meeting of the Trustees on 17 June).

12. BM, Central Archives, GM, vol. I, fol. 195 of 12 November 1757 (CE 1/1).

13. BM, Central Archives, OP, vol. I, fol. 44 of 27 August 1756 (CE 4/1).

14. No order from the Trustees specifically to this effect survives, but it was, and is, normal museum practice. A report to the Trustees dealing with sorting of the coins and medals of 11 February 1768 says that the remaining (Sloane) coins and the Cotton collection will be 'put into their proper places, in the several series'. (BM, Central Archives, OP, vol. I, fol. 221) (CE 4/1). Later, on 24 February 1780, Matthew Duane reporting about the coins given by Lord Maynard, mentions 'a few gold and silver that have been put away in the different serieses [sic]' (BM, Central Archives, OP, vol. I, fol. 360) (CE 4/1).

15. BM, Central Archives, OP, vol. I, fol. 55 (CE 4/1).

16. BM, Central Archives, Trustees Standing Committee minutes, vol. V, C.1308 (CE 3/5). The correspondent was Hans Stanley, Sloane's grandson by his daughter Sarah (see Chapter 2).

17. BM, Central Archives, Trustees Standing Committee minutes, vol. V, C.1289 of 15 March 1771 (CE 3/5).

18. BM, Central Archives, OP, vol. I, fol. 257–8 of 23 July 1771 (CE 4/1). Matthew Duane (1707–85) was a lawyer and coin collector; Dr Andrew Gifford (1700–84) was a Baptist minister and the first Assistant Librarian at the British Museum to curate the coin collection; Thomas Snelling (1712–73) was a coin dealer and numismatic writer.

19. Langfords, 7–8 March 1774.

20. Sloane acquired some Spanish-American pieces-of-eight while he was in Jamaica, 1687–9 (see Chapter 1). The gift of Evelyn's Numismata at New Year 1698 (ibid.) might suggest that Sloane already had some coins, but it may merely have been Evelyn returning a compliment. Among Sloane's papers is a printed notice about a theft of coins at Oxford on 22 September 1691 (BL, Sloane MS 118, fol. 321). This may have been sent to Sloane because it was thought that he was an interested collector who might be offered some of the coins, but it is perhaps more likely that it was sent to Courten to be inherited later by Sloane along with his friend's coins and other papers.

21. See above, Chapter 1.

22. Reports by Evelyn and Thoresby, see Chapter 1.

23. BM, Central Archives, OP, vol. I, fol. 45 (CE 4/1). James Empson's paper of 27 August 1756 on the arrangement of Sloane's collections in the British Museum notes that 'the greatest part of the coins and medals concern foreign countries, and in particular that a great number of them are German'. BM, Central Archives, OP, vol. I, fol. 221 of 11 February 1768 (CE 4/1) although dealing with the collection of coins in general, most of which were Sloane's, gives an idea of the range. The following are noted: English, French, Spanish, Hungarian, Dutch, Danish, Swedish, Polish, Russian, 'Eastern', Italian, Scottish, Irish, Greek kings, states and cities, Roman Republican and Imperial denarii, Roman bronze coins and Greek Imperial coins. Of medals there are listed specifically Papal, Imperial and Electoral (German, probably including the large medallic silver talers).

24. BL, Sloane MS 3961, fols. 66–8.

25. BL, Sloane MS 3961, fol. 27. The following is typical of a series of notes by Courten on his purchases each over a period of a few months: May – July 1689: 'of Mr Wright 30 coins; of Mr Partridge 9 coins; of the barber at ye Hermitage 1 King James Scotch money; of Mr Partridge 3 silver and one brass Imperial'.

26. BL, Sloane MS 3407, fols. 116–52, a record by Sloane of his Roman Republican coins.

27. BL, Sloane MSS 3961, fol. 2 and 3407, fol. 112.

28. See below.

29. See Chapter 1.

30. BL, Harley MS 6466, fols. 39–52.

31. See Chapter 12. The loss of the provenances of Conyers' London finds is particularly serious as the location of coins is of great importance in establishing the history of the city in Anglo-Saxon times, especially the dating of the re-occupation of the walled area in the ninth century.

32. See Chapter 10.

33. See Chapter 12.

34. Ibid.

35. See note 18.

36. See Chapter 12.

37. See below.

38. See J.D.A. Thompson, Inventory of British Coin Hoards AD 600–1500. Royal Numismatic Society, SP 1 (London, 1956); D.M. Metcalf, 'Find-records of medieval coins from Gough's Camden's Britannia', Numismatic Chronicle (1957), pp. 181–207; and idem., 'Eighteenth-century finds of medieval coins from the Society of Antiquaries', Numismatic Chronicle (1958), pp. 73–96.

39. See Chapter 1. The collection was worth £7,000 in bullion terms alone: see BL, Additional MS 4241, fol. 25; Thomas Birch, 'Memoir of Sir H. Sloane'.

40. The General Contents of the British Museum (London, 1761), p. 15, speaks of 'upwards of twenty thousand coins'.

41. See Chapter 1.

42. Ibid.

43. BM, Central Archives, GM, vol. I, fol. 12 (CE 1/1).

44. See note 26, above.

45. See Chapter 1.

46. See Chapters 1 and 12.

47. Eight coins in the British Museum, possibly derive from the Hundon, Suffolk, hoard found in 1687. It was published by Sir Philip Skippon in the Philosophical Transactions 16 no. 189 (1687), pp. 356–60 and 17 no. 203 (1693), p. 874. (See also British Numismatic Journal 28 (1955–7), pp. 180–2 and Numismatic Chronicle (1957), pp. 194–5.) The museum coins were acquired before 1838 and their source is unknown. Although the coins did not belong to Sloane when the papers were published, had he acquired any of them later? For seventeenth- and eighteenth-century medieval coin-hoards generally see Thompson, op. cit. (note 38), and Metcalf, op. cit. (note 38).

48. Taylor Combe, Veterum populorum et regum numi qui in Museo Britannico adservantur (London, 1814). This book included the derivative series of Celtic coins.

49. N.F. Haym, Del Tesoro Britannico 2 vols (London, 1719–20). Sloane was a subscriber. After completing the work on this, the present author discovered that her former colleague Dr Ian Carradice had already prepared a manuscript listing of Sloane's coins from Haym for departmental use.

50. For example the coins on p. 49, IX.

51. BMC followed by a number in the following discussion of all series of coins denotes that number in the appropriate volumes of British Museum catalogues.

52. BL, Sloane MS 3407, fol. 113.

53. BL, Sloane MS 3407, fols. 105–6; Laurentius Beger, Thesaurus ex thesauro Palatino selecta (Heidelberg, 1685).

54. BL, Sloane MS 3407, fols. 116–52. Vaillant went through many editions. That used by Sloane was probably J. Vaillant, *Nummi antiqui familiarum romanum* (Amsterdam, 1703).

55. BL, Sloane MS 3407, fol. 120. He describes this coin as showing a head of Roma/Jupiter in a quadriga. No coin of this type is known.

56. BL, Sloane MS 3407, fol. 118.

57. BL, Sloane MS 3961, fol. 26.

58. Lady Grace Granville, daughter of the 1st Earl of Bath, and heiress to the Bath estates was the wife of the 1st Baron Carteret who died in 1695. She died in 1744. Sloane later acquired antiquarian material from her husband's collection with the Kemp collection. These coins had possibly been his also, although she might have had a personal interest in them.

59. BL, Sloane MS 3407, fols. 112–4.

60. BL, Sloane MS 3407, fols. 92–104.

61. BL, Sloane MS 3961, fols. 12–13 and 16–17.

62. BM, Central Archives, OP, vol. I, fol. 257–8 of 23 July 1771. (CE 4/1).

63. Ibid.

64. See note 48.

65. D.F. Allen, 'William Stukeley as a numismatist', *Numismatic Chronicle* (1970), pp. 117–32. Allen discusses at p. 119 the Society of Antiquaries' projected *Metallographia Britannica* first mooted on 3 January 1722, when the minutes record that it was to 'attempt a compleat description and history of all coyns relating to Great Britain from the earliest times to our own. Wm. Stukeley undertook the British coyns in Sir Hans Sloan's [sic] cabinet or elsewhere'. Stukeley's notebook in the Bodleian Library, Oxford, includes many careful annotated drawings of Sloane's coins which should allow some of them to be identified in the British Museum collection. His noting of provenances is particularly valuable. Allen makes no attribution to Sloane's collection in the early draft manuscript of a projected catalogue of the British Museum collection of Ancient British coins which was not completed before his death, so this detailed work remains to be done, but is likely to be most productive.

66. Richard Gough, *A Catalogue of Coins of Canute* (London, 1777), p. 3.

67. BL, Sloane MS 3961, fols. 28 and 39 respectively.

68. BL, Sloane MS 3961, fol. 102.

69. G.C. Brooke, *A Catalogue of English Coins in the British Museum. The Norman Kings* (London, 1916).

70. BL, Sloane MS 3961, fol. 84.

71. BL, Sloane MS 3961, fol. 31.

72. See note 18. Gunmoney was the coinage in base metal issued instead of silver denominations by James II to pay his troops when he was campaigning in Ireland in 1688–9, trying to recover his throne. The idea was that the coins should be redeemed when he had been restored but, as he never was, the gunmoney (so called because some of the metal had come from old guns) became worthless as currency.

73. See Chapter 1. Described as 'coins of a king of England crown'd in Paris'.

74. BL, Sloane MS 889, fol. 308.

75. BL, Sloane MS 3988, fol. 17. This coin is not in the British Museum.

76. See Chapter 1.

77. BL, Sloane MS 3961, fols. 66–8.

78. BL, Sloane MS 3961, fol. 19. As there is no description, these may be not medals, but coins.

79. BL, Sloane MS 3961, fol. 39.

80. George Vertue, *Medals, Coins, Great-Seals, Impressions, from the elaborate work of Thomas Simon* (London, 1753), p. 49.

81. See Chapter 1.

82. See note 18 and note 78.

83. Drawings of small round objects in the Sloane's Oriental Catalogue are of seals not coins. (I owe this identification to my colleague Venetia Porter.) The early British Museum catalogues of Oriental coins do not cite provenances; a Sloane provenance is written on some tickets but cannot now be checked. Eight Sloane coins are included in the British Museum *Catalogue of the Arab-Byzantine and Post-Reform Umaiyad Coins*, by J. Walker (London, 1956) (nos. 439, 557, 563, 747, 843, 845, 957 and 959).

84. See note 18.

85. The Devonshire collection although formed by William, 2nd Duke of Devonshire (1672–1729) was not sold until 1844: 'Very important collection', Christie and Manson sale 18 March 1844 (7 days) and 26 March 1844 (5 days).

86. BL, Sloane MS 3407, fols. 59–60.

10 Classical Antiquities
Sloane's 'Repository of Time'

Ian Jenkins

* In all the great mass of Hans Sloane's manuscripts in the British Library there is nothing to indicate that in collecting antiquities he had any incentive beyond the fashionable desire among men of his profession to assemble a cabinet.[1] He seems to have conducted no correspondence on antiquities outside his function as editor of the *Philosophical Transactions* of the Royal Society.[2] The submissions he received from prospective contributors form no comparison for the lively antiquarian discourse colouring the exchange of letters between those two great worthies of seventeenth-century antiquarianism, Nicholas-Claude Fabri de Peiresc and Cassiano dal Pozzo.[3] Sloane, it must be said, appears to have had no more interest in antiquities, his own included, than he did in an account in his possession of maggots taken out of a man's ear on 27 August 1702 by J. Hare, Vicar of Cardington, Bedford;[4] or in the verses by John Suckling, 'being a censure on a fart that was let in Parliament House by Mr H. Ludlow'.[5] In his 'Arsenal of Secrets' all matters are reduced to the same peculiarity as specimens artificial or natural.[6]

Only in the field of numismatics does Sloane appear to have cultivated a degree of interest, making notes from learned publications and pursuing particular pieces to fill gaps in his collection (see Chapter 9).[7] Coins and medals, reflecting the historical sequence of their issue offered a ready opportunity for an amateur to arrange a collection according to a system.[8] With a knowledge of the classics he could decipher the legends and with practice distinguish each tell-tale image.[9] Roman Imperial coinage particularly lent itself to this sort of treatment. Joseph Addison gives a résumé of the various ways in which medals, by which was usually meant coins, supplied a 'body of history', complementing and even rivalling the authority of written texts.[10] In a series arranged chronologically, the life of an emperor is 'coined out', to use Addison's own remarkable jargon. In quoting a coin as a source, the scholar does not appeal 'to a Suetonius or a Lampridius, but to the Emperor himself, or to the whole body of a Roman Senate'. More than just the lives of rulers are recorded, however, for in coins we find a 'collection of pictures in miniature; a kind of Printing before the art was invented'. One topic of antiquarian pursuit after another is listed: portrait types of historical rulers and legendary heroes; representations of the famous women of antiquity; of the ancient gods; personifications of human virtues such as Hope, Constancy, Fidelity etc., and of nations, provinces and cities; portraits of poets and Olympic victors. In addition to faces are shown the sartorial habits of the age; the furniture; the instruments of music, mathematics and mechanics; ancient customs; 'sacrifices, triumphs, congiaries, allocutions, decursions, lectisterniums, and a thousand other antiquated names and ceremonies that we should not have had so just a notion

of were they not still preserved by coins'. They illustrate the history of architecture by recording harbourworks, triumphal arches, and temples. Then there are the famous sculptures of antiquity including the Hercules Farnese, the Venus de Medici, the Apollo Belvedere, and the equestrian Marcus Aurelius, all of which are portrayed on coins. Finally, there is the matter of civil law, geography and, the particular interest of Addison himself, ancient poetry.

Coins neatly laid up in cabinets were a portable index of knowledge about the ancient world, comparable in this respect with the 'Paper Museum' compiled by Cassiano dal Pozzo in the first half of the seventeenth century. Plans to engrave this were never realized, and it failed to achieve the impact it might otherwise have had.[11] Accordingly, the first such compendium to be published was Bernard de Montfaucon's *L'Antiquité expliquée*, brought out in fifteen volumes between 1722 and 1724. With its stated aim of bringing together all antiquity arranged by subject, and its erudite commentary heavy with citation of the classical authors, Montfaucon's work was the natural companion for a collection of antiquities.

To speak of Sloane as a collector of antiquities is, perhaps, to give him more than his due: his was a half-hearted interest and his assemblage an unremarkable affair. Not surprising, perhaps, when we consider that as a physician his scholarly interests were in natural history: 'Rare monkish manuscripts for Hearne alone', quipped Pope, 'And books for Mead and butterflies for Sloane'.[12] Even in Dr Richard Mead's 'Temple of Nature and Repository of Time', however, there were plenty of fine antiquities, while Sloane's cabinet had no major piece apart, perhaps, from one or two bronze lamps and the gems.[13] It was, moreover, relatively small until the 1730s, when he trebled its size by bulk-buying the dross of Cardinal Gualtieri's collection from Rome and added to it a mass of material from a Roman dealer by the name of Sterbini.[14]

In December 1712 an anonymous visitor to Sloane's museum commemorated the occasion of his visit in doggerel.[15] Praising the proprietor's industry in compiling this microcosm of the universe he first calls to mind the specimens of natural history, whereby all the living world seemed to be represented:

If there's a Paradise on Earth tis here
No more the traveller from pole to pole
Shall search the seas . . .

And then he goes on to describe the artificial rarities:

Insatiable hand with nature not content
A second world thy paintings represent . . .
Nor Nature's works have filled thy draughts alone
The Arts and customs of the world are shown . . .

So fine art and ethnography are dealt with; when at last we come to antiquities, the bard's enthusiasm began to flag:

The Muse omitts the cabinet with dread
Where all antiquities in coyns are layd
And wondering venerates the awful dead.

Not to describe in detail the coins and medals is understandable. At this date they were largely those inherited from William Courten, who bequeathed his collection to Sloane in 1702.[16] Lovingly classified by subject and laid up in drawers they were, as the verse implies, a collection in their own right.[17] But what of other antiquities? Sloane, as we shall see, inherited a few from Courten but these were not very numerous. Even in 1725, while Sloane's collection of coins and medals stood at some 20,228, he possessed only 302 antiquities. By the date of his death in 1753 these last had grown to 1,125.[18]

The explanation for this increase is simple. The Register of the Department of Greek and Roman Antiquities of the British Museum begins with a transcript of Sloane's own inventory.[19] Scattered through this list are the names of some of the persons and places whence Sloane acquired his collection. Many entries, however, have only a suffixed abbreviation; at first glance this appears to be *Jd*, but is in fact *Id*, 'the same'. This observation, hitherto overlooked in catalogues of the Department's collections, throws light on the provenance of the major portion of Sloane's antiquities. Throughout one large section of the inventory (451–1120) just two names recur, either written in full or indicated by the abbreviation. Thus two thirds of the collection may be ascribed to two Italian sources, namely Cardinal Gaultieri and the Abbé Sterbini.

Cardinal Filippo Antonio Gualtieri (died 1728) is best known for his collection of vases, the earliest of its kind. Many were bought from a Neapolitan, Joseph Valetta and came from tombs in Chiusi.[20] These were kept in his palazzo on the Strada Ferrantina in Rome together with his considerable library and cabinet of engraved gems, coins and other antiquities, many of which he acquired from Francesco Antonio Rensi.[21] The best of the vases passed into the papal collection of Clement XII (1730–40) and were displayed in the new wing of the Vatican library, placed like finials along the tops of the bookcases.[22]

The list of objects acquired from Gualtieri begins at 528 in the inventory and runs through to 735. At 1097 ff. further items are given as being 'From Cardinal Gaultieri's collection by the Abbé Sterbini'. The lists largely consist of Roman glass and numerous Roman terracotta lamps. There are besides a few carved gemstones, including a reclining dog in chalcedony forming the handle of a knife,[23] and a sard bust of Zeus. The head of this last is restored and set into a modern draped bust wrought in gold (Fig. 50).[24]

28b/665
28b/667

Sloane's manuscripts do not refer to his acquisitions from Gualtieri, nor do they mention the other major source. A Sterbini sale-catalogue survives in the British Library and lists antiquities, paintings and other objects, 'lately brought

Fig. 50 Sard bust of Zeus; Roman, second century AD. The head (restored) is ancient; the shoulders and drapery in gold are modern. Height 2.9 cm. BM, gems and cameos, 3938. Reproduced by courtesy of the Trustees of the British Museum.

from Rome' and put up for sale at Cock's, Covent Garden, on 13 March 1733.[25] It is unlikely, however, that this is the source of Sloane's acquisitions, since they are both too numerous to be compared with the sale catalogue and not always of the right sort. There is, for example, no obvious candidate in the catalogue for the marble statuette of Asclepius acquired from Sterbini and featuring in the oil portrait of Sloane reproduced as Plate 1 of this volume.[26] Here, standing in a niche, the figure bears a head, probably restored, which has since been removed and is now lost. Further research in Rome might throw more light upon the process through which Sloane acquired so many objects from Sterbini. What little can be gleaned from contemporary English sources suggests he was known among the cognoscenti as something of a shark.[27] It was no doubt in the spirit of a business transaction, rather than out of selfless interest in the Republic of Letters, that he acted as the agent for transmission to England of at least some of Sloane's acquisitions from Gualtieri.

28b/451

The pieces Sloane acquired from Sterbini include bronzes,[28] south Italian figured vases[29] and numerous pieces of south Italian black-glaze, Italic and Roman plain wares. There are besides quantities of terracottas, both Greek made in Italy and native Italic,[30] and the inevitable profusion of terracotta lamps, mostly Roman made in Italy.[31] Two of

28b/451–512, 806–1129

28b/955, 960 the Sterbini terracotta figurines are engraved in Montfaucon, where they are said to belong to Gualtieri.[32] The likely explanation of this apparent contradiction is that more of the Gaultieri collection came to Sloane by way of Sterbini than is suggested by the inventory.

Turning now to that part of the collection assembled from other sources, we find this in the first part of Sloane's *28b/1–448* inventory. A number are unprovenanced and they probably include antiquities acquired through Courten's legacy. Courten's papers among the Sloane manuscripts contain records spanning the years 1666 to 1701 listing his purchases, mainly of coins, medals, prints and natural history specimens, but also of a few antiquities.[33] Courten acquired several pieces from two individuals to whom he refers by means of his cipher as *iagfvp)* and *cv-yops:* these decode as Bagford and Conyers. The find-spot of some of these pieces is given as St. Paul's, that is to say the excavations conducted under the old cathedral destroyed in the Great Fire of London. Thus we find: 'I goose *Rv-a-, Gv, fv\-).,* at Paul's'.[34] The cipher translates as 'Roman Go (Goose) *28b/36* found'. In Sloane's inventory, accordingly, we find: 'A goose in brass', unprovenanced but surely to be identified with Courten's.

In discussing the finds from Old St. Paul's I have strayed into the territory of a separate contribution to this volume (see Chapter 12). The division of spoils is problematic, however, since a number of these objects are probably today incorporated in the collections of the Department of Greek and Roman Antiquities and not, as perhaps they should be,

in those of the Department of Prehistoric and Romano-British Antiquities. There is, for example, in the Greek and Roman Department a bronze lamp-lid in the form of a goose which may well be the 'brass goose' of Sloane's inventory (Fig. 51).[35]

Among other names of those who supplied Sloane's collection, we find that of John Kemp. A manuscript note of Sloane's biographer Thomas Birch inserted into a copy of *Museum Kempianum* in the British Library gives valuable information about this famous antiquary, who died on 19 September 1717 around the age of fifty-two.[36] Upon Kemp's death his collection was sold in March 1721 for £1,090. 8s. 6d.

Kemp's cabinet became one of the curiosities of London with a number of small-scale statues, twenty busts, sixteen reliefs, a quantity of small bronzes and several lapidary inscriptions.[37] Sloane acquired five of these last; all came *28b/195–199* originally from Rome, and four were once in the Villa Mattei.[38] He also acquired from Kemp a fine Roman bronze *28b/229* lamp supporting a statuesque Cybele flanked by recumbent lions.[39] This had already acquired a certain fame, being engraved for La Chausse's *Romanum Museum* (Fig. 52).[40]

Moving now to other contributors to the Sloane collection, a letter dated 24 March 1730 was addressed to Sloane by one Jean Nadler of Saxe Meiningen.[41] It begins by lamenting the death of 'jeune Mon. Scheuchzer' (on whom see Chapter 1) and continues in bad French to offer for £30 sterling some vases Nadler had bought for £40 from a Venetian named Soranzo.[42] It seems the younger Scheuchzer's premature death had interrupted a negotiation for the vases, which Nadler now wished to sell to Sloane. The Soranzos were an old Venetian family living near the church of S. Massimo.[43] They undertook diplomatic missions in the eastern Meditteranean and acquired fragments of antique columns, altars and inscriptions.[44] Sloane bought some of the Soranzo vases, listed as numbers 416 to 431 in his inventory.[45]

These are the principal sources for Sloane's Greek and Roman antiquities. There are besides a few names mentioned in the inventory from whom he acquired the odd piece. Some, like the Earl of Arundel and Lord Pembroke,[46] *28b/222–3;* are well known, while others, including Dupuy, Oldsworth *409–411* and Brown are not.[47] The manuscripts hold a clue to the *28b/134;* identity of some of the more obscure names.[48] Among them *160–5* is that of John Purnell who contributed two Roman bronze *28b/132,* lamps, one in the dramatic form of a boy riding a Dolphin *138–148* (Fig. 53), the other in the form of a crab.[49] The inventory *28b/382* records that they were taken out of a tomb at Smyrna. *28b/383* Sadly, Sloane's manuscripts throw no further light upon this source, but Purnell did write several letters between 1730 and 1735 trying to persuade Sloane to purchase a collection of coins.[50] These had been put together during his sojourn at Smyrna, Aleppo and Antioch. Purnell was at Smyrna until May 1706 when he left for England, travelling back through Italy and Germany in the company of one Dr Picinini. The latter had studied medicine at Padua, and we catch a glimpse

Fig. 51 Roman bronze lamp-lid in the form of a goose, probably found during the excavation of Old St. Paul's Cathedral; second century AD. Height 3 cm. BM, bronzes, 1889. Reproduced by courtesy of the Trustees of the British Museum.

Fig. 52 Engraving from La Chausse's *Romanum Museum* (1707), showing a bronze lamp with two lions and a handle ornament in the form of the goddess Cybele standing in a shrine. Roman, third century AD. Height of lamp, 15 cm. BM, lamps, 39. Reproduced by courtesy of the Trustees of the British Museum.

Fig. 53 Bronze lamp in the form of Eros riding on a dolphin. Roman, first century AD. Length 24 cm. BM, lamps, 29. Reproduced by courtesy of the Trustees of the British Museum.

of the social world of antiquarian-minded physicians as we learn of their gatherings at Battoni's coffee-house in London, where Picinini was introduced into the circle of a more famous graduate of Padua university, Dr Mead.[51] In compiling a summary list of his coins Purnell had consulted his friend Edmund Chishull and, at the suggestion of Sloane, Robert Ainsworth.[52]

Medical men dominated the age of curiosity that flowered in England during the seventeenth and early eighteenth centuries. The passion for collecting is rarely passed on to a second generation and most cabinets were sold up and dispersed upon the compiler's death. Sloane's was the exception in becoming part of the founding collection of the British Museum. Even this did not save it from obscurity, however, and after some two hundred years it is now impossible to identify in the Museum's collections many of the objects listed in Sloane's inventory, where minor bronzes, coarse pottery, terracotta lamps and plain glass abound. Since they were not marked with Museum inventory numbers from the start, many have become confused with the general collections, and Sloane's classical antiquities are scattered through at least three departments.

Sloane's curiosity for antiquities, like that of many of his contemporaries, was of the blinder sort; nor was he alone in surrounding himself with objects about whose meaning he felt no obligation to expound. It would be unjust, however, to say that he was simply a magpie, content with the mere act of gathering and possessing *things*. As we have seen, two thirds of his antiquities were bulk-bought, and he was perhaps less concerned in every case with the *parts* of his collection, than with the *whole*. His principal motive, in common with other compilers of cabinets, seems to have been to assemble a microcosm of the world; to display all nature and art together in one museum.[53] Krzysztof Pomian has sought to define the status of objects in such collections by the term *semiophore*: objects so classified, whether they be minerals forged by nature or implements fashioned by man, change their function; they cease to be *useful* and become *meaningful*. In so doing, they render the invisible *visible* by representing Time's remote past and the secrets of Nature.[54] Of coins alone one of the interlocutors in Addison's *Dialogues* has this to say in praise of his companion's numismatic eloquence, 'You have shown us all conditions sexes and ages, emperors and empresses, men and children, gods and wrestlers. Nay you have conjured up persons that exist nowhere else but on old coins, and have made our Passions and Virtues and Vices visible':[55]

The medal, faithful to its charge of fame,
Through climes and ages bears each form and name:
In one short view, subjected to our eye,
Gods, emperors, heroes, sages, beauties lie.

Alexander Pope on reading Addison's *Dialogues* was inspired to pen an epitome of them.[56]

This idea of a microcosm, already rather old-fashioned in Sloane's day, suggests the key to understanding his antiquities; or, at least, such a broad definition is as far as we are able to go in extracting any sort of meaning from Sloane's antiquarian activities. In so doing, it is important to remember that the world and its history, as it appeared to the early eighteenth century, was not as it is conceived today. 'It is worthwhile to recall', writes Paolo Rossi, 'that for many, many, centuries the history of man was conceived as coextensive with the history of the earth'. Thus fossils and coins, vases and shells exhumed from the earth were analogous as representing creation and Man's part in shaping it.[57]

'Classification', observes Arnaldo Momigliano, 'can dispense with chronology':[58] we know very little about the physical arrangement of Sloane's collection, but what little indication there is suggests no attempt at chronological sequence but rather a grouping by type: drinking vessels together, so-called sacrificial instruments, Egyptian gods and so on.[59] In this Sloane will have been guided by Montfaucon's publication with its heavy bias towards subject-category suggested by close reading of the ancient authors. In the preface to the first volume of Montfaucon's great work we read: 'Il s'agit ici de toute l'antiquité . . . Quand les figures manquent sur certains sujets, je ne laisse pas d'expliquer ces sujets.'[60]

The desire for totality impels Montfaucon to include every subject thrown up by ancient literature, and testifies to the continuing supremacy of literary over non-literary evidence. The seventeenth century had witnessed a phenomenal increase in the authority of archaeological documents, notably in the fields of numismatics and epigraphy.[61] We have already seen how Addison considered coins preferable in some circumstances to the written word. This preference was selective, however, and competence in the understanding of painted vases, bronzes, decorative sculpture and engraved gems lagged behind the advances that had been made in the study of coins and inscriptions.[62] Addison, for all his secret desires, is in no doubt as to the dangers of declaring the independence of objects from texts:

I have sometimes fancied it would be an impertinent design to make a kind of an old Roman wardrobe, where you would see *togas* and *tunicas*, the *chlamys* and *trabea* and in short all the different vests and ornaments that are mentioned in the Greek and Roman authors. By this means a man would comprehend better and remember much longer the shape of an ancient garment, than he possibly can from the help of tedious quotations and descriptions . . . To enlarge the design, I would have another room for the old Roman instruments of war, where you might see the *Pilum* and the shield, the eagles, ensigns, helmets, battering rams and trophies, in a word, all the ancient military furniture in the same manner as it might have been in an Arsenal of old Rome. A third apartment should be a kind of Sacrifice for altars, idols, sacrificing instruments, and other religious utensils. Not to be tedious one might make a magazine for all sorts of antiquities, that would show a man in an afternoon more than he could learn out of books in a twelvemonth.

An interlocutor in the *Dialogue* points out the hazards of such an adventure, warning him of the likely response from men of letters:

They will tell you that things of importance must not be taken on trust; you ought to learn them among the Classic Authors and at the fountain-head. Pray consider what a figure a man would make in the republick of letters, should he appeal to your University-wardrobe, when they expect a sentence out of the *Re Vestaria*?[63]

The intimidating presence of classical learning made it difficult for the classification of objects to establish itself as an independent discipline. Since Sloane's day the great advances in iconography and archaeological typology, in areas where literature can throw no light, have given the science of objects its emancipation from texts. This process received its greatest impetus in the Enlightenment of the later eighteenth century.[64]

Thirty years after the publication of Montfaucon's encyclopaedia of antiquity Anne-Claude-Philippe de Tubières-Grimoard de Pestel de Levis, Comte de Caylus (1692–1765) published his *Receuil d'antiquités* in which he expounded a new understanding of ancient art, contrasting it with the historical or textual approach.[65] In the preface to the *Receuil* he made his intention plain:

I am restricted to publishing in this collection only those monuments that belong to me or were once owned by me. I have had them drawn with the greatest accuracy . . . Objects can explain particular practices, they clarify customs that are obscure or badly described by the authors, they bring the progress of the arts to our attention and serve as models for those who cultivate them. But antiquaries have seldom seen them thus; they have regarded them only as the supplement to and the proof of history, or as isolated texts requiring elaborate commentary.[66]

Caylus went on to make the case for a system of classifying antiquity that cut across subject categories and would, moreover, take account of the aesthetic virtue of ancient art and of its progress in a chain, whose links led from Egypt through the Etruscans to the Greeks, whom the Romans in their turn both plundered and imitated. The idea of tracing the rise of the arts had been adopted by both Pliny and Vasari and was not new;[67] in the mid-eighteenth century, however, it acquired new immediacy as antiquarian scholars sought a system analogous with that represented by the 'chain of being', a familiar metaphor used to describe the taxonomic hierarchy of the natural species.[68] The evolution of the 'chain of art' could be traced most readily in the glyptic arts of sculpture and gem-carving. Winckelmann's *History of Ancient Art* (1764) with its avowed intention of tracing the progress of art among the ancients did so by close analysis of sculptural style and provided the model for all subsequent connoisseurship.[69]

In the light of such developments in the critical study of art history, Sloane's collection, with its emphasis on small objects of little aesthetic value, soon seemed inadequate as the basis of the national collection of antiquities. The acquisition in 1772 of Sir William Hamilton's first vase collection, awarded sculpturesque grandeur by D'Hancarville's extraordinary publication, went some way towards raising the status of the British Museum's antiquities. Only with the arrival of the first Egyptian sculptures, however, with the purchase of Charles Townley's sculptures and with the advent of the Bassae frieze and the Elgin Marbles from Greece, did the Museum achieve real distinction. In minor antiquities also, the name of Sloane was eclipsed by Townley, Cracherode and Payne Knight, whose vases, bronzes, terracottas and gems far surpassed those of the founding collection.[70]

Sloane is not one of the great classical antiquaries; his principal claim to fame is that of having helped to found the British Museum. His archaeological limitations should be assessed, however, within the context of an age when art and science were not separated as they are today, but seen as complementary, or even as parts of the same discipline of *history* in the ancient Greek sense of the word meaning simply 'enquiry'. Sloane's antiquities, although not particularly interesting in themselves, gain in stature when seen as emblematic of an insatiable curiosity in what the greatest poet of the age described as:

The glory, jest, and riddle of the world.[71]

Notes and References

1. For a list of Sloane's manuscripts see M.A.E. Nickson, *The British Library: Guide to the catalogues and indexes of the Department of Manuscripts* 2nd edn. (London, 1982), p. 5. A useful but by no means comprehensive tool is the index compiled by E.J.L. Scott (1904). The nineteen unpublished volumes of the catalogue listed by Nickson at 4 and 5 should also be consulted.

2. See, for example BL, Sloane MS 4025, fol. 289: 'A letter from Mr. Ralph Thoresby FRS to the publisher concerning the vestigia of a Roman town lately discovered near Leeds in Yorkshire'. This is a very interesting account of Romano-British antiquities dated 23 November 1702. See also fol. 265.

3. J.F. Lhote and D. Joyal (eds.), *Nicholas-Claude Fabri des Peiresc: Lettres a Cassiano dal Pozzo (1627–1637)* (Clermont Ferrand, 1989), with the review by David Jaffé in *Journal of the History of Collections* 3 no. 1 (1991), pp. 100–104 alluding to the more important work of F. Solinas and A. Nicolo (forthcoming).

4. BL, Sloane MS 4134, fol. 13.

5. BL, Sloane MS 2024, fol. 59.

6. For this metaphor see BL, Sloane MS 1512, a document of the seventeenth century in the handwriting of Theodore Turquet de Mayerne.

7. See the lists and quotations from ancient authors, biographies of Roman emperors etc. gathered into BL, Sloane MS 3407, eg. fol. 59, 'Description of the pillars of Trajan and Adrian whereof I have coins' and fols. 92–104, 'The number and values of my great brass coins contained in eleven drawers of my best cabinet, 25 July 1709 – and also my middle brass coins'. See also Chapter 9

8. Sloane's collection of coins and medals was largely inherited from William Courten as was his manner of arranging them. Courten was a scholar and collector of considerable energy, whose papers in his distinctive hand are preserved in the Sloane manuscripts: see, for example, BL, Sloane MSS 3961 and 3962.

9. On early coin-collecting, see the chapter 'Medals/shells = erudition/philosophy', in Krzysztof Pomian, *Collectors and Curiosities* (English translation, Cambridge, 1990) especially pp. 128, 130.

10. Joseph Addison, *Dialogues upon the Usefulness of Ancient Medals especially in Relation to the Greek and Latin Poets* (London, 1746 edition).

11. Compare the system of ordering Cassiano dal Pozzo's 'Paper Museum', Ian Jenkins 'Pars pro toto: a Muse from the Paper Museum', in I. Jenkins and J. Montagu (eds.), *Cassiano dal*

Pozzo's Paper Museum, Quaderni Puteani 2 (Milan, 1991) pp. 49–65.

12. Alexander Pope, *Moral Essays: Epistle IV to Richard Boyle, Earl of Burlington*, 10.

13. *Musei Meadiani: Pars Altera* (London, 1755). Annotated copy with engravings – BL, C.28.g.15. Sloane made separate lists of his intaglios and cameos, but as with the other antiquities only some can be identified; see p. 291, no. 2b–c.

14. For Gualtieri and Sterbini see below.

15. BL, Sloane MS 1968, fol. 192.

16. For the Courten bequest see E. Edwards, *Lives of the Founders of the British Museum* (London, 1870), p. 273.

17. See note 8, above.

18. Edwards, op. cit. (note 16), p. 303

19. See p. 291, no. 4a, and p. 294, no. 28b.

20. O. Jahn, *Beschreibung der Vasensammlung König Ludwigs in der Pinakothek zu München* (Munich, 1854), p. ix.

21. F. Deseine, *Rome moderne, première ville de l'Europe* (Leiden, 1713), vol. I, pp. 42–3.

22. G. Morello, 'Il Museo Cristiano di Benedetto XIV', *Bollettino Monumenti Musei e Gallerie Pontificie* 2 (1981), pp. 60–1; C. Pietrangeli, *I Musei Vaticani, cinque secoli di storia* (Rome, 1985), p. 30.

23. BM, GR, 1756. 1–1. 665. BM Catalogue of Gems 3967.

24. BM, GR, 1756. 1–1. 667. BM Catalogue of Gems 3938.

25. *A Catalogue of Signor Sterbini's Curious Collection lately brought from Rome*, Mr Cock's Covent Garden, 13 March and two following days, 1733.

26. BM, GR 1756. 1–1. 451. BM Catalogue of Sculptures 1695.

27. Described by Roger Gale in a letter to William Stukeley, dated 26 December 1740, as 'a true trading italian': *The Family Memoirs of the Rev. William Stukeley, M.D.* vol. I, (Publications of the Surtees Society 73) (London, 1880), p. 470.

28. E.g. Priapus: BM, GR, 1756. 1–1. 478; BM Catalogue of Bronzes 1511.

29. E.g. BM, GR, 1756. 1–1. 485. BM Catalogue of Vases F326.

30. BM, GR, 1756. 1–1. 955, 954, 956, 951, 952. BM Catalogue of Terracottas D242–46.

31. A great number of these have been identified and catalogued by D.M. Bailey.

32. Bernard de Montfaucon, *Supplément au livre de l'Antiquité expliquée*, tom. I (Paris 1724), pl. LXXXV illustrating BM Cat. D242 and D252. For a recent discussion of these see L. Bonfante in J. Swaddling (ed.), *Italian Iron Age Artefacts in the British Museum* (London, 1986), pp. 202–3.

33. BL, Sloane MSS 3988 and 3961.

34. BL, Sloane MS 3961 fol. 52, April 1693: 'An Account of things then bought of Mrs. Conyers and Mr. Bagford for which paid £5. 8. 0d'. The goose was one of the purchases from Bagford.

35. BM, GR, 1975. 5–1. 8. BM Catalogue of Bronzes 1889.

36. *Monumenta Vetustatis Kempiana in Duas Partes Divisa* (London, 1720). BL, 811.g.28.

37. Adolf Michaelis, *Ancient Marbles in Great Britain* (Cambridge, 1882), pp. 47–9.

38. BM, GR, 1756. 1–1. 195; Kemp (op. cit., note 36) 11 *CIL* VI 8207, ex Villa Mattei; 196/15/18718; 197/16/173; 198/14/15112; 199/28/8962, once L. Agostino.

39. Kemp, op. cit. (note 36), p. 129. 1. BM Catalogue of Lamps 39; Bronzes 2521.

40. M.A. de La Chausse, *Romanum Museum* (Rome, 1707), p. 92. 7.

41. BL, Sloane MS 4050, fol. 296.

42. Johann Jakob Scheuchzer, father of Johann Caspar, was Professor of Natural History at Zurich and an acquaintance of Sloane, with whom he corresponded. The Scheuchzers had sent Sloane '4 Tesserae Badenses found in the fields at Zurich and Baden of several magnitudes . . . with his dissertation about them': BL, Sloane MS 1968, fol. 184.

43. S. Savini Branca, *Il Collezionismo Veneziano nel '600* (Padua, 1964), pp. 279–80; M. Zorzi and I. Favaretto, *Collezioni di Antichità a Venezia* (Rome, 1988), p. 117. See also Soranzo in Scott's index to the Sloane manuscripts, (op. cit., note 1); and see BL, MS Reg.14 A xiii, fols. 1–43 dated 1582, being a [?] seventeenth-century copy of Jacopo Soranzo, *Memoria di un Viaggio a Constantinopoli*.

44. I. Favaretto, *Arte Antica e Cultura Antiquaria nelle Collezioni Venete al Tempo della Serenissima* (Rome, 1990), p. 169. It was perhaps Giacomo who provided the Sloane vases (*ibid.*, p. 162).

45. Sloane's summary descriptions are insufficient to identify actual pieces.

46. 410 = BM Catalogue of Bronzes 1093.

47. Oldsworth is perhaps Austin Oldsworth, draper, see BL, Sloane MS 4055, fol. 186.

48. Dupuy: probably the correspondent of BL, Sloane MS 4058, fol. 280, rather than C. Dupuys who is also found in Scott's index (op. cit., note 1).

49. BM, GR, 1756. 1–1. 382 and 383, BM Catalogue of Bronzes 1924 and Lamps 29 (dolphin); Bronzes 1919 (crab).

50. BL, Sloane MS 4054, fols. 70 and 82.

51. Note 13, above.

52. Edmund Chishull (1671–1733) had been chaplain at Smyrna, 1698–1702; Robert Ainsworth (1660–1743), lexicographer and collector of coins.

53. Antoine Schnapper, *Le Géant, la licorne, la tulipe. Collections et collectionneurs dans la France du XVIIIᵉ siècle* I *Histoire et histoire naturelle* (Paris, 1988), p. 9.

54. Pomian, op. cit. (note 9), p. 32; Schnapper, op. cit. (note 53), p. 7.

55. Addison, op. cit. (note 10), p. 16.

56. Preface to Addison, op. cit. (note 10).

57. P. Rossi, *The Dark Abyss of Time: the history of the Earth and the history of nations from Hooke to Vico* (English translation, Chicago and London, 1984), p. 120.

58. A. Momigliano, 'Ancient history and the antiquarian', *Journal of the Warburg and Courtauld Institutes* 13 (1950), p. 311.

59. See Chapter 11.

60. Montfaucon, op. cit. (note 32), preface p. 1.

61. Momigliano, op. cit. (note 58), pp. 295–302.

62. *Ibid.*, p. 304.

63. Addison, op. cit. (note 10), pp. 17–19.

64. Pomian, op. cit. (note 9), pp. 129–31, 175.

65. Le Comte de Caylus, *Recueil d'antiquités* (Paris, 1761–7). For Caylus and a number of other persons and themes touched upon in the second part of this essay see F. Haskell, *History and its Images. Art and the interpretation of the past* (New Haven and London, 1993).

66. Caylus, op. cit. (note 65), preface pp. 1–2.

67. See the essay, 'The Museum: past, present and future', in E.H. Gombrich, *Ideals and Idols. Essays on values in history and in art* (Oxford, 1979), p. 194.

68. A.O. Lovejoy, *The Great Chain of Being* (Cambridge, Mass. and London, 1936).

69. E.H. Gombrich, *The Ideas of Progress and their Impact on Art* (New York, 1971), ch. 1.

70. Edwards, op. cit. (note 16), pp. 369–80 (Townley); 417–21 (Cracherode); 401–12 (Payne Knight).

71. A. Pope, *An Essay on Man*, Epistle II.1.

11 Egyptian Antiquities

Arthur MacGregor

* The Egyptian antiquities acquired by Sir Hans Sloane were few in number and unremarkable in nature. At this early stage in the development of European interest in Egyptology, things could hardly have turned out otherwise: Egypt was still perceived (with some justification) as fairly hostile territory and access to its archaeological riches remained restricted. None the less, Sloane was not unusual in owning such pieces, though like most of his contemporaries his interest in them remained general rather than particular. As in certain other areas, his principal merit from our point of view lies in his role as an accumulator and preserver of material that otherwise proved all too ephemeral in the market in antiquities that developed among the virtuosi of the age. That so little of his legacy survives today is no fault of his.

Egyptology in Sloane's Era

The time at which Sloane built up his Egyptian collections has been characterized as lying at the end of a period when the European scholarly world began to encounter in particular the civilization of Lower Egypt and at the dawn of a new era of more purposeful exploration, beginning with the journeys in 1737–8 of Richard Pococke and of Frederik Norden, and culminating in the first systematic survey under Napoleon of all the visible monuments as far south as Nubia.[1] In the century and a half before Sloane's death, some bolder spirits had penetrated to the Egyptian interior, subsequently publishing accounts of their observations and carrying home the more portable forms of archaeological souvenirs. As a result, Egyptian antiquities (mostly from the region around Cairo) already formed common though numerically restricted elements in European princely cabinets of curiosities and in early museums of antiquarian character. Among the first pieces to find their way on to public display were those originating in a visit to Egypt by David le Leu de Wilhem (1588–1658) in 1619 and donated to the cabinet of curiosities in the Anatomy Theatre of the University of Leiden in the following year; these items, including shabits, a canopic jar, mummy-cases and a mummy, were joined by others over the following decade.[2] Around 1630 the French antiquary Nicolas-Claude Fabri de Peiresc had dispatched an agent on a collecting expedition from which he was to return with two mummies for Peiresc's famed museum at Aix-en-Provence. The cabinet founded in the library of the abbey of Sainte-Geneviève in Paris by Père Claude Du Molinet (d. 1687) and which later inherited elements of Peiresc's collection included a number of figurines, shabtis, amulets, vases and a sistrum, as well as a number of partial and complete mummies.[3] Perhaps the most ambitious Egyptological collection

to be found in Europe in Sloane's day was that established in the College of the Society of Jesus in Rome by Father Athanasius Kircher (1602–80), a polymath who numbered the study of hieroglyphics among his many interests.[4] More modest accumulations were to be found in most European countries.

In several of these collections, notably those of Peiresc and Kircher, a specific interest in manuscript material (including Coptic and Arabic texts) may have played an important role in introducing the scholars in question to Egypt, and this particular dimension remained an important element in the interests of this first generation of collectors. Needless to say, since no success was achieved with the decipherment of hieroglyphics until 1822, the value of this historical evidence for the Dynastic period remained entirely unrealized during Sloane's lifetime.

As for the artistic skills of the Egyptians, they were as yet held in scant regard by a society for which the classical ideal, as embodied particularly in Roman architecture and sculpture, reigned supreme. Contemporary Anglo-Saxon attitudes were summed up in a wholly deprecatory article by Sloane's (admittedly highly opinionated) contemporary John Woodward (see Chapter 1), prepared some time before his death in 1728 but published only in 1786.[5] Woodward found, for example, that '. . . little can be collected in favour of the Egyptian skill in architecture': of the pyramids – the only Egyptian structures, most probably, of which he had the least knowledge, and that entirely at second hand – he concluded that '. . . when these works come to be scanned and considered by a nation that were judges . . . they should pronounce these piles *barbarous* and uncouth, and think the mon[e]y expended in the raising of them very *idly* and *indiscreetly* employed'.[6] He is equally dismissive of Egyptian skill in modelling and carving, for of all the pieces he has seen in the cabinets of the curious (including some from his own collection) or published by authors such as Kircher, he claims:

. . . there never appears one single figure that shews any thing of art or good work. Their limbs are stiff, and ill-proportioned; their bodies awkward, shapeless, and far inferior to the life . . . They really aimed at something that was hideous, deformed, and monstrous; a beast, or a fowl, with the head and face of a man; the head of a dog, or some other brute, of an hawk, or the like, upon an human figure . . . They seem to have affected what was ugly and irregular, as much as the Greeks, the Romans, and others, who had something of spirit and a genteel fancy, did what was handsome, well-proportioned, beautiful, and like nature.[7]

In the same dismissive sweep he denigrates 'their historical or hieroglyphic gravings' in which 'everything is flat, stiff, and ill finished'; their painting, of which he concedes he

 * Marginal numerals in this chapter refer to Sloane catalogues listed on pp. 291–4

has little knowledge but concludes that amongst those who were such 'very poor masters in the art of design, or drawing ... it is most certain that such could never be good painters'; their costume, which is contrasted with the 'noble and graceful dresses of the Greeks and Romans'; and their vanity and misguidedness in mummyfying their corpses.[8]

Woodward's attitudes, although no doubt extreme in nature, reveal the hostility of the climate of opinion in which Egyptian antiquities competed for attention in early eighteenth-century England. It should come as no surprise to find, therefore, that their impact on Sloane's collection, as on others of the day, remained slight.

Sloane's Egyptological Specimens: Character, Origins and Associations

Despite its modesty of character, Sloane's collection presents a number of interesting features,[9] not the least being the historical associations recorded for some of the items listed in the catalogues. Most surprising of these is a link with George Sandys (1578–1644), the earliest Englishman to leave an account of an antiquarian expedition to Egypt. Sandys visited the Sphinx and the pyramids at Giza in 1611; his intentions to investigate also the 'sepulchres of the mummies' towards Memphis were frustrated, but he left a description of them in which rumours and hearsay are interwoven with observations he made on mummies from elsewhere. He describes them as lying:

... in long vaults (belonging, as should seeme, to particular families) hewne out of the rocke, with pillars of the same. Betweene euery arch the corses lie ranckt one by another, shrouded in a number of folds of linnen, swathed with bands of the same: the brests of divers being stained with Hieroglyphical characters. Within their bellies are painted papers, and their Gods inclosed in little models of stone or metall: some of the shape of men, in coate-armours, with the heads of sheepe, haulkes, dogs, &c. others of cats, beetles monkies, and such like. Of these I brought away diuers with me ...[10]

Some of these items he later donated to the museum established by John Tradescant at Lambeth.[11] Sandys died sixteen years before Sloane was born, yet it seems to be ultimately to him that 'A small Ægyptian earthen idole of a blew colour from Egypt by Sandys' noted by Sloane in his catalogue must be ascribed, although the intermediaries through whom it necessarily passed are unrecorded.[12] Also recorded in Sloane's catalogue of 'Humana' is 'The head of an Egyptian mummy dried in the sands brought from Egypt by Mr Sandys'.

Another piece in the Sloane collection, described as 'An Ægyptian idol of blew earth taken out of a mummie by D*r Huntington*',[13] is associated with another important figure in the early history of British Egyptology. After graduating from Merton College, Oxford, and holding a fellowship there for a time, Robert Huntington (1637–1701) was appointed chaplain to the Levant Company in Aleppo in 1670 and travelled widely in the Near East during the fol-

lowing ten years, visiting Egypt at least twice. He collected a range of natural (botanical) rarities as well as antiquities and manuscripts (nearly 700 of which were eventually given to or bought by the Bodleian Library).[14] He also donated to the Ashmolean Museum two sculptural fragments and a wooden coffin lid inscribed with hieroglyphics.[15] Huntington appears to have stood unsuccessfully for election to the Royal Society in 1699, proposed by Sloane,[16] so that a clear line of communication can in this case be established between donor and recipient.

The former presence in the collection of a dozen further shabti figurines is recorded in the catalogues, all identified as of clay but no doubt made of faience.[17] One of these is referenced to a series of illustrations of inscribed shabti figures, as published by Giovanni Nardi in 1647: 'A very large *Ægyptian idol* in blew clay. Figlina idola variae magnitudinis reperta in mummiarum ventre consuta Io. Nard. in Lucret. p. 654'.[18] Sloane also possessed 'An Ægyptian wooden idole taken from the pyramids'.

Figurines of Egyptian gods and goddesses account for a second numerous category. 'Mr Brigstock'[19] is recorded as the source of 'An Egyptian earthen *idole* w*t Hieroglyphicks upon it', identified as Isis and compared with one published by Montfaucon.[20] Further representations of the same deity include 'An Egyptian *Isis* in blew earth w*t Hieroglyphics', and a smaller version of the same 'w*tout Hieroglyphics', both given by 'Monsieur Dupuy', and 'An Ægyptian figure of a *woman* in a very heavy metall having on her left arm a basket in her hand laid on her breast a ... in the right hand stretching out for something wanting w*t many ornaments and some hieroglyphicall characters on her back'.[21] 'Isis & Orus' occur together elsewhere.[22]

'*Osyris*? Taken up from the ditch in repairing the fortifications at Port Mahon in Minorca given to me by Lord *Cadogan*. [Osyris standing w*t two litui in his hands w*t a three cornered cape]',[23] and 'Isis and Orus',[24] are both ascribed to the same donor, presumably the second Lord Cadogan, Sloane's son-in-law (see Chapter 1).[25] A third representation of Osiris, formerly in the Gualtieri collection, was catalogued by Sloane as 'An Etruscan Figure', but was reclassified as Egyptian in an eighteenth-century British Museum manuscript list, where it was said to have on its head '... a Cap with a Round Discus upon it, and a stick with a double Hook in both Hands', and was taken to represent 'either Osiris or one of the priests'.[26]

Among Sloane's collection of scarabs is another item to which a curious provenance is ascribed: 'A large Ægyptian *beetle* or *scarabeus* w*t Hieroglyphics upon it. From the East Indies from D*r Waldo*', again referenced to Montfaucon.[27] Sloane received other material of undoubted 'East Indian' provenance from Waldo, who visited India on his own account (see Chapter 15); no doubt the scarab was acquired by Waldo on his homeward journey via the Gulf of Suez and the Nile delta. Of the remainder, one or two heart-

28b/135

21f/93

28b/21

28b/273–85

28b/273

28b/84

28b/107

28b/258*

28b/259*

28b/782

28b/356

28b/244*

28b/245*

28b/537

28b/180

Fig. 54 J. & A. Van Rymsdyk, *Museum Britannicum* (1778), tab. xxix, 4: '*An Ibis*, preserved by the Egyptians in an Earthen Red Cylindrical Pott, or Urn, sealed up with a White Cement . . . given to Sir H. Sloane, by my Lord Sandwich, who brought it from the Pyramids of Egypt.' No longer identifiable.

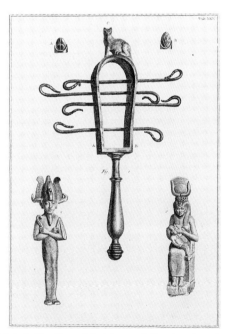

Fig. 55 J. & A. Van Rymsdyk, *Museum Britannicum* (1778), tab. xxix, 1: 'A *Sistrum* from *Cardinal Gualtieri's* Collection, it's an Ancient Musical Instrument or Rattle, in form of a Racket, traversed by four moveable bars, the ends of which are like Serpents Tails.' The Van Rymsdyks erroneously attribute its presence in the British Museum to the gift of Colonel Lethieullier; in fact it belonged to Sir Hans Sloane. BM, GR, 1756.1–1.541.

scarabs triggered a response from Sloane the naturalist, including 'An Ægyptian large *beetle* wᵗ the wings striated lengthways in touchstone. From Mr Kennedy';[28] 'An *Ægyptian scarab* wᵗ the elytra sulcated lengthways &c';[29] and a lesser variety 'not sulcated wᵗ Hieroglyphics'. He also possessed 'An Ægyptian *scarab* in *Lapis Lazuli*'. [28b/254 28b/801 28b/802 28b/296]

Sloane was not one of the company that met on 11 December 1741 at the Lebeck's Head tavern to form the short-lived Egyptian Society,[30] although by this time he was of course eighty-one years old and living in the comparative remoteness of Chelsea. The Earl of Sandwich, a founder member of the new society, which sought to further 'the promoting and preserving Egyptian and other ancient learning', was the donor of one item in Sloane's collection: 'An ibis preserved by the Ægyptians in an earthen red cylindrical pott sealed up wᵗ white cement. In these are contained sometimes hawks. Given me by my Lord Sandwich who brought if from the Pyramids of Egypt'. The vessel, which is likely to have originated at Saqqara, was later described and illustrated by the Van Rymsdyks (see Fig. 54); today it is no longer identifiable. [28b/1119]

William Stukeley, who attended the inaugural meeting of the Egyptian Society, records that a debate ensued (to which he contributed at some length) on the origins of the sistrum, which instrument the President had laid before him as an emblem of office and as a means of calling silence.[31] Sloane too owned such an instrument; this is to be identified with that described and illustrated in the Van Rymsdyks' guide to the British Museum (Fig. 55), where it is erroneously attributed to the benefaction of Colonel William Lethieullier and is said to have been formerly in the Gualtieri collection.[32] [28b/541]

Woodward reserved particular scorn for the sistrum: so far were the Egyptians from appreciating the excellency of music, he commented, that this, 'their most celebrated instrument, was much more likely to fright or offend a man of sense, than please or gratify him . . .' Several examples were preserved 'in the cabinets of men of learning and curiosity', he continues, but the construction of the instrument is such '. . . that it is not possible to play anything like a tune upon it . . . the noise of it is so hideously jarring, so harsh, and untuneable, that I have not heard of any thing so rude among any the most savage and uncivilized people in being'.[33]

One canopic jar is registered in the catalogue: '*Vas Ægyptium uti videtur ultimum* Dʳ *Woodward* Mus. p. 259 [a canopus of white alabaster wᵗ Osiris head or that of a hawk wᵗ four hieroglyphicks]'.[34] It was illustrated by Gordon and by the Van Rymsdyks (see Fig. 56), and survives today in the British Museum, now attributed to one Horudja.[35] [28b/406]

Sloane also owned at least one mummy – the highest form of currency among collectors of Egyptian antiquities.[36] This may have been acquired – with much else amongst the Egyptological specimens – as part of the collection of

Fig. 56 J. & A. Van Rymsdyk, *Museum Britannicum* (1778), tab. xiii, fig. 2: '*Vas Ægyptium*, a Canopus, with Osiris'-Head, or that of a Hawk . . . The *Hieroglyphics* are painted black, on this beautiful formed Vase, and the Substance is White Alabaster.'

John Kemp (see Chapter 1), described by a contemporary as follows:

This collection chiefly relates to the Antiquities of the Ancient *Ægyptians, Greeks* and *Romans*. He hath several ancient *Ægyptian* Gods in Metal, divers Sorts of Stones and Artificial Earth, two ancient Mummies in their Wooden Coffins, the Heads of a Man and a Woman carved on the Outside of the Coffins. You may discern the folds of the Linnen, their painted Hieroglyphicks, and several of their Seals several Thousand Years Old.[37]

The Royal Society's Committee for the Repository, on its visit to Sloane's museum (see Chapter 1), evidently was impressed by the way in which the mummy was displayed and resolved to commission a cabinet similar to Sloane's for the Society's own specimen, 'only without casters'.[38] The Duchess of Portland proclaimed herself less impressed in 1742, following a visit to Mead's cabinet: there the Duchess had been

. . .extremely well entertained the other day with seeing Dr. Mead's curiosities. They are much finer than Sir Hans Sloane's. In particular he has a mummy much finer preserved. . .[39]

No record has been found to confirm that Sloane's mummy ever reached the British Museum.[40]

Amongst other items which did reach the British Museum at its inception but which have failed to survive were 'an Egyptian god in shape of a bull; amulets worn as charms against bad fortune; the head of Cynocephalus, a dog worshipped by the Egyptians; figures of a cat, a monkey, &c.'. Such 'superstitious toys' were to be found in great numbers in cabinets all over Europe, according to Woodward, but to judge from the response of the irascible though ever-rational doctor, they inspired little more than a thrill of horror, conveying '. . . more of the air of dreams, or the rhapsodies of men under a frenzy or distraction, than of sense or reality'.[41]

The Sloane catalogues mention a number of 'Periapta   28b/286 figlina colorata vitro obducta quæ post mortem etiam curato cadaveri appendebant Ægyptii', referenced to 'Io. Nard in Lucret. p. 652 Tab. 6'.[42] These are perhaps to be equated with the '*Periapta* . . . small oblong pieces of enamelled earth, notched to mark the rising and falling of the Nile', called 'by the best authors' *nilometri* or *niloscopia*, as recorded in *The General Contents of the British Museum*;[43] today they are no longer recognizable among the collections, but objects of this type are now identified as amulets and go by the name of Djed-pillars.[44]

One further piece in the British Museum has long been associated with the Sloane collection – a monument of Nekau and others.[45] This piece cannot be identified with certainty in the catalogues, although the suggestion has been made that it may correspond to 'Some Ægyptian   28b/737 figures in a basaltes'.[46]

As with other elements of Sloane's collection, we can detect here the presence of a considerable proportion of material acquired in bulk from earlier 'ready-made' collections. Of particular importance in the case of Egyptian antiquities was material derived from the museum of Cardinal Filippo Antonio Gualtieri, quantities of which reached Sloane via the Abbé Sterbini following Gualtieri's death in 1728 (see Chapter 10). Of around 160 items identified as Egyptian in an early British Museum manuscript list of Sloane antiquities, over one third appear to be derived from   1a the Gualtieri collection.[47] This marked degree of bulk-buying seems accurately to reflect the unfocused and undiscriminating character of Sloane's Egyptology interests, suggesting little more than a conscious attempt to boost an underdeveloped facet of an otherwise well-rounded collection. Only the two items he may be presumed to have sought out at Woodward's sale hint at more purposeful buying, while a significant proportion of what remains can be identified as gifts from ever-solicitous friends. It is, perhaps, characteristic of Sloane that he has earned his place in the history of Egyptology not by innovation but by his sheer assiduousness as a collector.

Acknowledgements

It is a pleasure to acknowledge the patient counsel of my colleague Dr Helen White-house in the compilation of this brief account, and the generosity of Dr Morris Bierbrier in giving me free access in advance of publication of the results of his own researches on the Sloane collection. I am also grateful to the Society of Antiquaries and to the President and Council of the Royal Society for allowing me to quote from their respective manuscript collections.

Notes and References

1. For this comment I am indebted to Dr Helen Whitehouse: see her recent paper, 'Towards a kind of Egyptology: the graphic documentation of ancient Egypt, 1587–1666', in *Documentary Culture: Florence and Rome from Grand Duke Ferdinand I to Pope Alexander VII* (Villa Spelman Colloquia 3) (Bologna, 1992), pp. 63–79.

2. Rijksmuseum Amsterdam, *Leidse Universiteit 400. Stichting en erste bloei 1575 – ca.1650* (Amsterdam, 1975), pp. 114–20.

3. Claude du Molinet, *Le cabinet de la Bibliothèque de Sainte-Geneviève* (Paris, 1692), pp. 7–16; Sloane evidently owned a copy of this work and cited it in relation to prehistoric and Roman antiquities (see Chapter 12). The most impressive of the mummies entered the collection after Du Molinet's death: see Françoise Zehnacker and Nicolas Petit, *Le cabinet de curiosités de la Bibliothèque Sainte-Geneviève des origines à nos jours* (Paris, 1989), pp. 33–5.

4. See, in particular, V. Rivosecchi, *Esotismo in Roma Barocca. Studi sul Padre Kircher* (Biblioteca di Storia dell'Arte 12) (Rome, 1982).

5. John Woodward, 'Of the wisdom of the ancient Egyptians', *Archaeologia* 4 (1786), pp. 212–310.

6. Ibid., p. 229.

7. Ibid., pp. 231–2.

8. Ibid., pp. 233–5.

9. I have not attempted here to list exhaustively the Egyptian items in the Sloane collection. This task has recently been undertaken by Dr Morris Bierbrier of the Department of Egyptian Antiquities, British Museum, who kindly provided me with a copy of his work in advance of publication: see M.L. Bierbrier, 'The Sloane collection of Egyptian antiquities', in *Aegyptus Museis Rediviva. Miscellanea in honorem Hermanni de Meulenaere*, ed. L. Limme and J. Strybol (Brussels, 1993), pp. 15–33.

10. George Sandys, *A Relation of a Journey begun An. Dom. 1610* (London, 1615), p. 133; the text is accompanied by an illustration of seven of the figurines brought back by Sandys. For references to other early accounts of these tombs and of the material which they yielded to early travellers, see Helen Whitehouse, 'Egyptology and forgery in the seventeenth century: the case of the Bodleian shabti', *Journal of the History of Collections* 1 no. 2 (1989), pp. 187–95.

11. In the printed catalogue of the Tradescant collection, Sandys is credited as donor of 'The Idol *Osiris*. *Anubis*, the Sheep, the Beetle, the Dog, which the Ægyptians worshipped' (John Tradescant, *Musæum Tradescantianum* (London,

1656), p. 42). A visitor to the Tradescant museum in 1638 recorded seeing there 'the hand of a mummy', but its source is unrecorded: see Arthur MacGregor (ed.), *Tradescant's Rarities* (Oxford, 1983), p. 21.

12. The following two entries [4a/136–7] simply read 'Another', but whether these too came from Sandys is unclear.

13. Bierbrier, op. cit. (note 9), p. 28, proposes a tentative equation of this figure with a surviving shabti of Ptahhotep born of Tasheritkeri (BM, EA, 9101), although the evidence is equivocal. See also J. and A. Van Rymsdyk, *Museum Britannicum* (London, 1778), p. 78.

14. Later Huntington was appointed Provost of Trinity College, Dublin, and Bishop of Raphoe in Donegal. From Dublin he contributed a paper on granite obelisks in Egypt to the *Philosophical Transactions* in 1693, during Sloane's secretary-ship: see R. Huntington, 'A letter from Dublin to the publisher of these tracts, concerning the porphyry pillars in Egypt', *Philosophical Transactions* 14 no. 161 (1684), pp. 624–9. For an account of Huntington's career see Thomas Smith, 'The life and travels of the Right Rev. and learned Dr. Robert Huntington', *Gentleman's Magazine* 95 pt. 1 (1825), pp. 11–15, 115–19, 218–21.

15. See Jaromir Málek, 'The largest piece of Egyptian writing in Europe', *The Ashmolean* no. 4 (1983), pp. 12–13.

16. Michael Hunter, *The Royal Society and its Fellows 1660–1700. The morphology of an early scientific institution* (BSHS Monograph 4) (Chalfont St. Giles, 1982), p. 58.

17. A number of these are identified in Bierbrier, op. cit. (note 9), p. 29, fig. 4.

18. See Ioannis Nardii, *Titi Lvcretii Cari, De Rervm Natvra libri sex* (Florence, 1647), p. 654, tab. vii: 'Non tam expono, & publici facio iuris figlina Idola variæ magnitudinis, reperta dudum Mummiarum in vētre consuta, quàm curiosa prouoco ingenia, vt vernaculos olim Egyptijs expiscentur characteres, seriemq; Elementorum hinc admoniti, nec non ex superioribus Tabb. seduli venentur, quibus, nempe, gens illa vtebatur Pharaonibus imperantibus, non Ptolomeis . . . Asseruantur & haec apud nos.'

19. Owen Brigstock, FRS, FSA. A letter from Brigstock to Sloane, dated 12 October 1731, states that it was from him that the Royal Society had purchased their premises in Crane Court, following which transaction he '. . . made them a present not only of Dr Brown's Book cases &c. but of all his Presses wherein were contain'd all the Curiosities which for Scores of years he had been collecting' (Royal Society, Miscellaneous MSS, vol. IV, nos. 49–50).

20. Bernard de Montfaucon, *L'Antiquité expliquée et representée* 2nd edn. (Paris, 1722–4), vol. II supp., p. 280, pl. 20, cxi. Bierbrier, op. cit. (note 9), p. 28, equates this item in the Sloane catalogue with a surviving shabti of Pipu (BM, EA, 9138).

21. Equated with a surviving bronze Isis, BM, EA, 60284: see Bierbrier, op. cit. (note 9), p. 31.

22. BM, EA, 60755; identified as such by Bierbrier, op. cit. (note 9), p. 29.

23. The provenance is not impossible: occasional discoveries of Egyptian items are made around much of the Mediterranean littoral (though not necessarily from ancient contexts); I am grateful to my colleague Dr Helen Whitehouse for this information. An eighteenth-century catalogue in the British Museum [1a] adds the information that the figure was '... in Brass upon a Pedestal'. Bierbrier, op. cit. (note 9), p. 28, fig. 2, identifies this figure with BM, EA 60602 and with that published in Alexander Gordon, *An Essay towards Explaining the Ancient Hieroglyphical Figures, on the Egyptian Mummy, in the Museum of Doctor Mead* (London, 1737), pl. xxi, 11.

24. Bierbrier, op. cit. (note 9), p. 29. fig. 2, identifies this figure as BM, EA, 60758, published by Gordon, op. cit. (note 23), pl. xxi, 3.

25. Minorca was taken by a British force under General James Stanhope in 1708: see J.S. Corbett, *England in the Mediterranean ... 1603–1713* (London, 1904), vol. II, pp. 299–308.

26. BM, EA, 36063; see Bierbrier op. cit. (note 9), p. 30, fig. 3, where it is identified as the figure published in Gordon, op. cit. (note 23), pl. vii, 3.

27. Montfaucon, op. cit. (note 20), vol. II suppl., pl. cxxxv. Bierbrier, op. cit. (note 9), p. 28, fig. 1, identifies this item as a surviving heart scarab of Teti (BM, EA, 7877).

28. This is perhaps to be identified with 'A Scarabeus in Ægyptian Marble taken out of a tomb at Alexandria. With hieroglyphical writing at Bottom. In poss[ess]ion of Dʳ Kennedy', recorded and illustrated by William Stukeley in the Commonplace Book of the Society of Antiquaries (MS 265), p. 62.

29. Bierbrier, op. cit. (note 9), p. 31, tentatively identifies this with a surviving heart scarab of Djedkhonsiufankh (BM, EA, 791121), and equates it with a scarab published by Gordon, op. cit. (note 23), pl. xxii, 6.

30. The Society was dissolved in 1743: see Warren R. Dawson, 'The first Egyptian Society', *Journal of Egyptian Archaeology* 23 (1937), pp. 259–60.

31. *The Family Memoirs of the Rev. William Stukeley, MD* (Publications of the Surtees Society) (1882–7), vol. I, p. 326.

32. Van Rymsdyk, op. cit. (note 13), tab. xxix, fig. 1. The statement (p. 73) that this sistrum had come from Cardinal Gualtieri's collection points

up the Van Rymsdyks' error: Sloane acquired a great deal of material from this source via the Abbé Sterbini (see Chapter 10), whereas no sistrum is recorded amongst the items bequeathed to the British Museum by Lethieullier. The instrument still survives (BM, GR, 1756.1–1). Sloane's catalogue entry for this item states that it was 'graved in Benedict Bach de sistris ... no. xx', a reference to Benedetto Bacchini, *De Sistris ... ad illustrissimum D. Leonem Strozza dissertatio* (Trajecti ad Rhenum, 1696), frontispiece, no. xx; here it is said to have been '... repertum Via Aurelia, in Suburbana Villa Ill.ᵐⁱ Laurentij de Corsinis, et ab eodem dono datum D. Leoni Strozza, cuius in Museo hodie asseruntur'.

33. Woodward, op. cit. (note 5), p. 236.

34. See C. Bateman and J. Cooper (eds.), *A Catalogue of the Library, Antiquities &c. of the Late Learned Dr. Woodward* (London, 1728), p. 259: 'Aliud [vas] non dissimile nisi quod pro operculo habeat solem Ιερανσκέφαλσμ seu Osirim'.

35. BM, EA, 37937; Gordon, op. cit. (note 23), pl. xviii, 3; Van Rymsdyk, op. cit. (note 13), p. 33, tab. xiii, 2; Bierbrier op. cit. (note 9), p. 29.

36. Almost inevitably, Sloane's pharmaceutical cabinet would have contained a quantity of 'mummia', a bituminous residue resulting from the mummification process which found its way into European medicine with the popularization of works by Arab writers such as Avicenna (980–1037), who declared it efficaceous for a wide range of maladies. Its presence here would have carried no antiquarian connotations. For an account of the trade in mummia see Karl H. Dannenfeldt, 'Egypt and Egyptian antiquities in the Renaissance', *Studies in the Renaissance* 6 (1959), pp. 16–22.

37. 'A description of the Musæum of Mr. J. Kemp near the Hay-Market', *Monthly Miscellany, or Memoirs for the Curious* 2 (1707–8), p. 259.

38. 'Mʳ Jackson should be sent to, & desired to repair & put the Mummy belonging to yᵉ R.S. into yᵉ same sort of Case as the Mummy at yᵉ President's, only without casters' (Royal Society, MS 490 CMB.63, minutes of 11 May 1732.

39. Quoted from E.J. Climenson, *Elizabeth Montagu ... her Correspondence from 1720 to 1761* (London, 1906), vol. I, p. 128.

40. Sloane would have been unlucky if his mummy had simply disintegrated in the course of the intervening ten years, but Woodward (op. cit. (note 5), p. 235) reminds us of their potential instability: 'I myself saw here a mummy, brought formerly out of Egypt, that, after it had been for some time in our more humid air, began to corrupt and grow mouldy, emitted a foetid and cadaverous scent, and in conclusion putrified and fell to pieces.'

41. Ibid., p. 256.

42. Sloane's wording is taken directly from Nardi, op. cit. (note 18), p. 652.

43. *The General Contents of the British Museum* 2nd edn. (London, 1762), p. 42.

44. I am grateful to Dr Morris Bierbrier for elucidating this problem.

45. BM, EA 511. This piece was illustrated (in a plate inscribed 'Viro Illustrissimo bonis literis et humanitate excultissimo Dⁿᵒ H. Sloane Barn.ᵗᵗᵒ et Med. Regio Tabulam hanc DDD'), by Alexander Gordon, op. cit. (note 23).

46. Bierbrier, op. cit. (note 9), p. 31.

47. Reproduced in ibid, pp. 17–24. It may be noted that J.M. Sweet ('Sir Hans Sloane: life and mineral collection', *Natural History Magazine* 5 (1935), pp. 106, 112) is in error in identifying the source of Sloane's specimens as Niccolo Gualtieri (1688–1744), professor of medicine at the University of Pisa and physician to the Medici family.

12 Prehistoric and Romano-British Antiquities

Arthur MacGregor

* I am very sensible of your great Treasure, & if I should come to London (where I never was yet), I would endeavour to make myself better acquainted with it, especially since there is so much in it about Antiquity . . .[1]

So wrote the influential Oxford antiquary Thomas Hearne to Sir Hans Sloane on 1 January 1722. Notwithstanding this encomium from a seemingly impeccable authority, it is clear that Sloane's unquestioned importance in other areas of collecting was not matched to the same degree by his concern for antiquities. Even in this marginal area of interest, however, he acquired material with a degree of consistency uncharacteristic of his age, to the extent that he accumulated what was in its day one of the most extensive antiquarian collections in England.[2]

There can be little doubt that Sloane's involvement with the Royal Society conditioned his approach to this as to other activities, for his election coincided with a fundamental change of attitude in the learned community to the role that antiquities might play in understanding the past. It is now well established that although the seeds of this reappraisal had been sown by earlier antiquaries, the circle of scholars in the Royal Society around the turn of the seventeenth century provided it with both focus and impetus. Although the membership was never overwhelmingly inclined to antiquarian matters, the Royal Society was important in establishing a context in which the *disiecta membra* of earlier peoples, formerly treated with indifference, could now be prized and studied for their own sake, in just the way that obscure and hitherto disregarded areas of the natural world now became proper subjects for scrutiny.[3] It is noteworthy that the numbers of papers in the *Philosophical Transactions* dedicated to antiquarian subjects reached a peak during the period of Sloane's editorship[4] and that by 1739 half the council of the Royal Society were non-scientists (three of them belonging to the Society of Antiquaries).[5] A reaction later set in and the presidency of Martin Folkes, who succeeded Sloane, attracted criticism for its antiquarian bias.[6]

Similarly, although the Society's Repository had never been designed to harbour antiquities, by the turn of the century it had come to include alongside its more scientific collections, in Ned Ward's words, quantities of '*Ægyptian Mummies*, Old *Musty Skeletons*, and other *Antiquated Trumpery*'.[7]

That there was already among the wider public a growing taste for collections of antiquities is confirmed by the accounts of collections built up by Sloane's contemporaries, as mentioned elsewhere (Chapter 1), and by the appearance of dealers catering to these nascent antiquarian appetites. One such, named Campe, possessed near Charing Cross

'an extremely elegant cabinet' containing 'as many as two hundred or two hundred and fifty of all kinds of statuettes, idols, "utensilibus" and other such things', some of doubtful authenticity but all for sale at 'monstrous' prices.[8] On the whole, however, Sloane's brand of connoisseurship held such materials in no special regard, displaying instead a taste for more prosaic artefacts of a rather more 'archaeological' nature.[9]

Given that antiquarian matters were not central to Sloane's interests, some explanation is needed for the rapidity with which his museum came to be held in such high regard in this as in other fields. The answer emerges from an analysis of the catalogues, where the comparatively few individual purchases and gifts are outweighed considerably by bulk acquisitions from other ready-made museums. William Courten's bequest undoubtedly provided the foundation for Sloane's antiquities collection; considerable quantities of material can also be traced back through the sale of John Woodward's antiquarian collections to the museums of James Petiver and John Kemp, and there are other concentrations which speak of similar judicious acquisitions (see Chapter 1 for these earlier collections).

Apart from a few citations of works alluding to actual specimens in the collection (the *Catalogue of the Library, Antiquities, &c. of the Late Learned Dr. Woodward* (1728), from which sale Sloane acquired a number of specimens, for example) or to the sites which produced them (John Morton's *Natural History of Northampton-shire* (1712) may be noted), there are few references in the catalogue entries to other authorities. Camden's *Britannia* and the works of Edward Lhwyd are mentioned occasionally, but Bernard de Montfaucon's *L'Antiquité expliquée* (1719–24) – an essential source for the eighteenth-century antiquary – is the only work cited with consistency.[10] While it may be unjust to compare Sloane's working catalogues to his published works, there is none the less a striking contrast here with the attention he pays to numerous other authors in, for example, his *Catalogus plantarum* or indeed in the manuscript catalogues of natural specimens (see, for example, the vertebrate catalogues quoted extensively in Chapter 4).

Prehistoric European Antiquities

Although a substantial number of prehistoric antiquities can be identified in the Sloane catalogues, and a few survive to the present day, they constituted in his day a class of material that was as yet little understood, due largely to the absence of any developed concept of a time span – let alone a chronology – for pre-Roman Europe. Archbishop Ussher's calculation of 4004BC for the date of the Creation

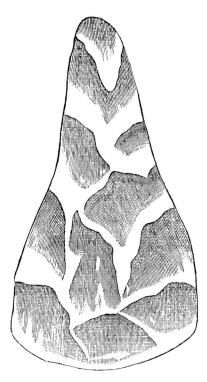 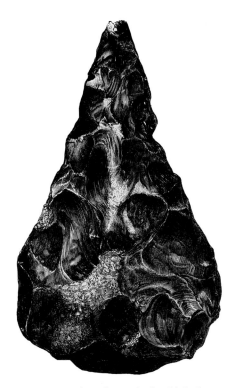

Fig. 57 Two views of Sir Hans Sloane's Upper Palaeolithic handaxe from Gray's Inn Lane. *1*: after John Bagford, published in Thomas Hearne's edition of Leland's *Collectanea* (1771), vol. I, p. lxv; *2*: from John Evans's *Ancient Stone Implements* (2nd edn., 1897), fig. 451. BM, PRB, Sl.246.

achieved the status almost of holy writ when printed in the margin of the Authorized Version of the Bible in 1701, but no-one at that time was so rash as to place any British antiquities at such a remote date. The earliest biblical event for which testimony might be expected in these islands was the Flood, from the seventeenth century generally assigned to the period *c.*2500–2000BC. Sloane's contemporary and sometime protagonist John Woodward explained the presence in rocks of fossil plants and other organisms in terms of the universal deluge but, needless to say, he neither sought nor found evidence of accompanying human activity.

The prevailing inability to distinguish early from late and the tendency to ascribe all British material to the eve of the Roman conquest is encapsulated in contemporary perceptions of the most ancient artefact in Sloane's possession, an Acheulian handaxe which he catalogued in the following terms:

28b/246   A British *weapon* found w^t Elephants tooth opposite to black Marys near Grayes inn lane. *Conyers.* It is a large black *flint* shaped into the figure of a *Spears* point. K[emp].

The celebrated discovery of this handaxe (Fig. 57), found along with the remains of a mammoth in 1679, forms a dramatic curtain-raiser in the annals of British Palaeolithic

archaeology. Conyers' own observations[11] (which include all the details reproduced by Sloane) reveal that the find was made during gravel digging; he concluded that the remains were those of an elephant which had been killed by this 'British' weapon, and that they had lain there together 'as long as Claudius Caesars time'. This telescoping of time, with the native British who opposed the Roman incursion assigned to (in our terms) the Stone Age rather than the Late Iron Age, was typical of the period.[12] The flint evidently passed from Conyers to Arthur Charlett, Master of University College, Oxford; Hearne saw it there in 1707 before it entered Kemp's museum (where John Bagford made a drawing of it (Fig. 57a) which he communicated to Hearne) and ultimately was acquired by Sloane.[13]

Sloane included an account of the structure of one of the Gray's Inn tusks[14] in a paper delivered to the Royal Society, but without mentioning the handaxe. Such finds (including, by implication, that from Gray's Inn) he attributed to the consequences of the Flood rather than the Romans, by implication severing any connection between the axe and the tusk.[15]

It is noteworthy that Sloane (like Conyers) confidently identified the Gray's Inn handaxe as a weapon, just as he did several flint arrowheads in his collection, but the very recent establishment of the true nature of these items should

28a/651,695, 1470–1; 28b/34,64

not be forgotten. When Nehemiah Grew published his catalogue of the Royal Society's Repository in 1681, for example, he still assigned the flint arrowheads in that collection to the category of 'regular stones', where they rubbed shoulders with natural crystals and the like.[16] Their true nature seems first to have been recognized in Italy;[17] in England Sir William Dugdale was precocious in identifying in 1656 a number of stone axes from Warwickshire as 'made by the native Britans . . . for weapons, inasmuch as they had not then attained to the knowledge of working iron or brass to such uses',[18] while Robert Plot, acknowledging on the authority of Julius Caesar that the coastal Britons made use of iron, none the less concluded in 1686 that 'for the most part at le[a]st they sharpen'd their *warlike instruments* rather with *stones* than *metall* . . .'[19]

28a/234
The comparative novelty of the acceptance of these items as man-made artefacts is underlined by another of Sloane's entries: 'An *arrow* head of white flint used in former times in Scotland & there called now Elfs arrows said to be shott into cattle by witches or elves'.[20] Here he records a popular piece of mythology that yet retained some currency among the credulous. Sloane's knowledge of such things no doubt derived largely from Edward Lhwyd's researches in the Scottish highlands in 1699–1700, as reported by Sloane in the *Philosophical Transactions* after Lhwyd's death.[21] Among the superstitions surrounding them was the belief that they were 'certainly known to fall from the aire';[22] such a view had been widely held on the Continent in the sixteenth and seventeenth centuries and may have been transferred to the British Isles only at this time.[23] It surfaces elsewhere in the Sloane catalogues:

28a/1907
'An ancient gray stone *hatchet* w^t notches to be fixed to its handle called by some *thunder stones*' seems to show Sloane confident of his identification but characteristically assiduous in recording the superstitions surrounding these objects,[24] while in 'An Irish *hatchet* made of green spleen

28a/779
stone found after a shoure & thunder by a [hedger, deleted] ditcher who thought it hott . . .' there is perhaps a hint of credulity and an equally characteristic carefulness in preserving all the attendant information, just in case.

Also to be included among the prehistoric lithic material

28b/100*
are some 'Fragments of the devills *arrows* at Burrowbridge sent me by Dr *Richardson*'.[25] The remainder of this famous group of millstone grit standing stones (the tallest 7m high) survives today beside the Great North Road at Boroughbridge in Yorkshire, despite depredations by generations of curiosity collectors: as early as the 1720s, William Stukeley deplored the fact that 'silly people have knocked off the edges'.[26]

Bronze Age weapons form the most significant category of prehistoric material in the catalogue. Here again, contemporary understanding of their status and origins was very murky indeed: not only was there considerable confusion as to the function of particular types but, more significantly, there was as yet disagreement as to whether bronze artefacts should be assigned to the Romans or to

the 'Britons'. Plot expressed the prevailing opinion with his assertion that they were Roman, identifying axe-heads, for example, as the heads of *catapulta* bolts and assigning equally fanciful identities to other objects.[27] An earlier assertion by Camden[28] that such items might be British was ignored in the seventeenth century until Lhwyd declared his support for it, admitting that he too had for a long time subscribed to the opinion that they were 'too artificial to have been made by the Britains before the Romans civiliz'd them'.[29] Hearne contributed a lengthy paper on the subject to the *Philosophical Transactions*, in which he restated the Roman case in wholly misconceived terms, further support for it coming from Sir Robert Sibbald in 1710 and from Alexander Gordon as late as 1726.[30]

The prevailing confusion obscured the significance of even the largest and most important group of material acquired by Sloane:

A large brasse instrument called a *Celta* by some or wedge by others found in the Isle of Wight by Mr Cook who gave it to me . . . [illeg.].   28b/743

[illeg.]   28b/744

A very large brasse *Spear point* found at the same place w^t a hole at base.   28b/745

The *same* a little different.   28b/746

The *same* smaller.   28b/747

Another yet smaller. They were all found together.   28b/748

Considerable information survives concerning the discovery of this important Bronze Age hoard (Plate 16) and the transfer of part of it to Sloane. It was first brought to public notice when a number of pieces (seemingly those listed above) were exhibited to the Society of Antiquaries in London on 11 December 1735 by Benjamin Cooke of Newport, Isle of Wight, having been discovered 'shortly before' that date. Additional items were exhibited by Peter Collinson at the Antiquaries on 17 March 1737, accompanied by a letter from Cooke (Collinson's cousin) giving details of the circumstances of the discovery.[31] Shortly afterwards Collinson wrote to Sloane as follows:[32]

Lond^n April 20 1737

Sr Hans,

My Cousen Mr Ben^n Cook In the Ile of Wight desired Mee where I had Duplicates of the Ancient Weapons that He sent Mee that was found in that Island, that I would present them to you In His Name, Inclosed Is his acc^t of them.

I am Truly y^rs

P. Collinson

Contemporary opinion, predictably, was that they were Gaulish, '& belonged to ye Roman auxiliarys'.[33] A century after their discovery, when first published in an adequate manner, A.W. Franks discounted the possibility of their belonging to such a late era but was unable to consign them to a more precise period than 'that vast and obscure portion of our history unrelieved by any written records'.[34] In the course of the twentieth century, their proper place in the Early Bronze Age (*c*.1500BC) came to be recognized, the hoard providing the type specimens for the 'Arreton Tradition' of metalworking.[35]

Several further items in the collection can now be identified as Bronze Age axes, but the range of terminology used by Sloane in his descriptions again reflects the uncertainty that in his day surrounded not only their age but also their function:

28b/30   An ancient brasse *hatchet head* found in Essex near Brentwood in a gravell pitt. (Plate 17, no. 6).

28b/101   The head of a Roman *wedge* or *catapulta* of brasse from Kent. (Plate 17, no. 4)

28b/249*   A wedge or what is called a *Celta* w^t^out any ear hole at the top or ring. from Yorkshire by my Lord *Burlington*. (Plate 17, no. 1).

An interesting series of Bronze Age (and later) pieces from Windsor (not all, apparently, forming a related group) can be reconstructed from the records:

28b/247   A *brasse vessell* or part of a vessel of an hemisphericall figure like a hatt w^t^ an apex . . . [illeg.] having a hole struck in it by a spade in digging found w^t^ Roman things in Windsor forrest.

28b/251   The head of a *spear* in *brasse*. It is 4 cornered tapering & hollow. taken up near Windsor. (Plate 17, no. 9).

28b/300   A *wedge* w^t^ a loop, of brasse taken up within a mile & an halfe of Windsor in a common five foot deep where was a melting house formerly & where are dug up many potts of an unusual figure. (Plate 17, no. 2).

28b/372   A *celta*, or wedge w^t^ a hollow on each side for a handle found near Windsor in the forrest in an antient fortification. (Plate 17, no. 3).

28b/373   *Another* with a loop to it. Id.

A letter from the Hon. Benedict Calvert to Hearne[36] provides some background information here, although clearly it also includes references to later material discussed elsewhere (Chapter 13):

Yesterday I accidentally went into Tooke, ye Bookseller's Shop, when a Countryman loaded with ancientry, was exposing them to the view of the family. There was a spur of an extraordinary bigness, ye rowell or pointed part was broader than ones hand. a broad iron sword 3 foot att length. A brass head of a battle Ax. A strange odd form'd iron lamp. a brazen trumpet with severall fair . . . Roman Coyns & Medalls . . . These with many others he lately dug up in a place call'd St Leonard's Hill in Windsor forest. Sr Hans Sloane has offered him 10 Guineas. I would have purchas'd the Coyns of him, judging them to be the most Valuable part of his new Acquisition. But he would not part with them without the whole.

Some of these items came to be exhibited at the Society of Antiquaries, where illustrations of them were inserted by William Stukeley in the 'Commonplace Book'.[37]

A group of Late Bronze Age socketed axes is linked by an implied origin in Kemp's collection, but the evidence is, as we shall see, contradictory in at least one case and whether any of them had any earlier relationship is now unclear:

28b/237   A *celt* or *wedge* in *brasse* w^t^ a loop & hole for the haft. K[emp].[38] (Plate 17, no. 8).

The *same* broader & shorter from Kiddall in Yorkshire neer Leeds,   28b/238 found in the grounds of Wm *Ellis* Esq & given me by Dr Richardson. Mr *Gale* showed me one in the mould from Yorkshire. Id. (Plate 17, no. 7)

The *same* without a loop. broad. Id.   28b/239
The *same* narrow. Id.   28b/240

The second item in this list is one of a group of axes found in April 1709 that gave rise to a flurry of correspondence between several antiquaries of the day and to several publications,[39] the most influential of them by Thomas Hearne, in which he sought to explain the significance of these contentious artefacts.[40] Hearne begins with an account of their discovery communicated to him by Thoresby and dated 19 November 1709, opening as follows: 'As the Servants of Mr. *Ellis* of *Kiddall* . . . were plowing at a place called *Osmondthwick*, near the noted *Bramham-moor*, they discover'd 5 or 6 brass Instruments . . . somewhat in the form of a wedge . . .' The ensuing description and an accompanying 'rude Draught' make it clear that all were socketed axes, though Thoresby inclined to the view that they were 'the heads of Spears or Walking Staves of the civilized *Britains*'. Hearne ventured that he had formerly thought them 'a sort of *Axes* which the *Romans* made use of in their *Sacrifices*', but now held that they were '*Roman Chisels*, and that they were us'd to cut the *Stones*, and other *Materials* . . . for building the *Camps*'. The sockets, he suggested, were clearly 'to fasten *Handles* to them for more *convenience* in driving them in', while the loops may have been for securing the handle 'or perhaps they were design'd for ease of the *Souldiers*, who in their *Journeys* might by this means fasten them to their *Girdles*'.

Hearne's opinions commanded widespread attention, but they failed to impress Richard Richardson: sending Hearne his opinion about these 'Old Instruments',[41] Richardson included many pertinent observations concerning the method of manufacture of these axes and the unsuitability of their material for the purposes conjectured by Hearne. He further included a drawing showing how this type of axe 'might have been fixed to a crooked Handle . . . the Loop on the Side serving to make the Instrument more firm by putting a Wire through it; and tying it to the Shaft' — exactly the form of hafting that finds favour with present-day archaeological opinion.

Independent evidence exists to confirm that Richardson acquired one of the Osmondthick axes and gave it to Sloane in 1721, and further that it was indeed Sloane and not Kemp who was shown (in 1719) the axe from Yorkshire still in its mould as mentioned in the catalogue entry.[42] There can be no possibility, therefore, that the information given is quoted from Kemp's catalogue nor that the axe itself came from Kemp (who died in 1719); hence the contraction 'Id.', implying that like the entry before it this item had come from Kemp's collection, is erroneous. The hoard as a whole has been officially listed as lost,[43] but Sloane's axe, at least, survives today.

28b/315   Also surviving (Plate 17, no. 5) is 'One of the largest *Celta* taken up 2 yards deep out of a vaulted place covered w^t a glasse cover made w^t lead. There were 9 such together. From Sr Griffith W^m.' Clearly this formed part of another hoard, but nothing further is known of it.

  Further evidence of an interest that transcended mere curiosity is provided by the fact that Sloane possessed repli-

28b/1125   cas of similar pieces: in particular, 'The model of a Brass Celta w^t a loop found in a Tuft Bogg or Marsh within two Miles of Macclesfield sent to me by Mr Ashwort' would have been meaningless in a dilettante collection and speaks of a degree of serious antiquarian interest. The formal and typological variety of these axes would have held an understandable appeal to one drawn as Sloane was to the processes of classifying and ordering.

28b/347   In the case of one entry, 'A pair of *celta* taken up [at Reculver]' the provenance might suggest a Roman rather than a Bronze Age date, but a letter from Sloane to Hearne in which he discusses the axes from Bramham Moor mentions that he has 'several of the Roman brass instruments, but without the loop; the last from Kent, supposed to be used by the Romans in their *catapultae*'.[44] Clearly they belong with the other Bronze Age examples.

28b/316   Neither the 'brasse *tuba* or ancient *trumpett* taken up in

28b/317   a field near Manooth in Ireland . . .' nor the 'Part of *another* taken up w^t it' survives today, but a letter and a drawing

among the Sloane manuscripts allow these finds to be restored to the prominence they deserve.[45]

Griffinrath, near Manooth Oc^br ye 29th 1726

Sir,

Tho' I have not ye Honour of being acquainted wth you, I am no stranger to your Character. Therefore, w^thout any farther Preface give me leave to tell you, that on ye 15th of Feb^ry last, as my men were making of a Ditch in a meadow near my house, about 8 inches from the Surface of ye Earth, they met with ye Lituus used by ye Romans, a Draught of wch I sent to ye Bp of Worcester. It has pretty well escaped ye Injurys of Time. There was an other Instrument lying by ye Lituus wch I take to be ye Tuba, but it is in so many pieces, y^t I dont well know what to make of it. I have enclosed 'em in a Box, and directed it to Sr Hans Slone Baronet at his house at ye upper end of Southampton Square, London. Since they were found in your own Country, I flatter my self, that you will receive 'em into your Noble Repository of Raritys, wch will be a great pleasure to

    S^r

  y^r constant admirer & faithfull hum^ble Ser^t

  Sankey Winter

The accompanying drawing (Fig. 58) leaves no doubt that the 'Lituus' was in fact an end-blown copper-alloy horn of Late Bronze Age or Early Iron Age date. The serpentine profile, the zones of ribbed decoration along its length, the ring of spikes or domes indicated by a series of circles

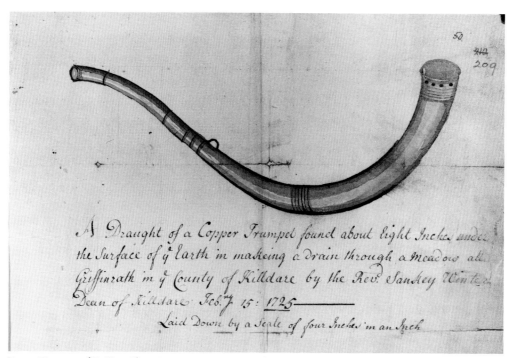

Fig. 58 Drawing of Sir Hans Sloane's Bronze Age trumpet, found at Griffinrath, near Maynooth, 1725. The trumpet no longer survives. BL, Sloane MS 4048, fol. 209. Reproduced by courtesy of the Trustees of the British Library.

around the mouth, the cast suspension loop – all are typical features of a well-defined group of such instruments whose distribution is concentrated in north-eastern Ireland.[46] These are regularly provided with tubular flanged mouth-pieces, which may be either cast-on or inserted: the open terminal on the Maynooth horn suggests that it belonged to the latter group and that its mouthpiece had already been lost. Current opinion dates the appearance of these instruments to c.750 BC and suggests a survival as late as the second century BC. Very often these horns have been found as pairs of unmatched instruments. Such would seem to have been the case at Maynooth, since Winter interpreted the more damaged piece as a tuba rather than a trumpet.[47]

An account of a gold sleeve-fastener, originally published in the Society of Antiquaries' *Archaeologia* for 1773, is accompanied in the second edition of the relevant volume (issued in 1809) by a note to the effect that 'such an one was shewn from Sir Hans Sloane's collection 1740'.[48] The minutes of the Antiquaries' meeting in question show, however, that what was exhibited was a lead-alloy copy of the original, and the catalogues reveal that he possessed two such replicas – 'Models in lead of 2 Antique gold Rings found in Ireland. Sent to me by Dean Copping' – further evidence, it might be suggested, of a degree of seriousness of purpose on Sloane's part in antiquarian matters.[49]

28b/1123

Further material of Bronze Age date occurs in the collection. Of these items there survives: 'A piece of an ancient *brasse sword*' – in fact a short, two-edged stabbing weapon of the type generally (albeit inaccurately) termed a dirk, now lacking its riveted hilt (Fig. 59, no. 2);[50] and 'The head of a *spear* from Scotland, by Dr Rosse, found at Bannockburn upon the field of battle between the Scots & English in Robert Bruces reign & that of Ed. 2 of England.' Although acquired, no doubt, for its supposed historical associations (see Chapter 13), the latter item (Fig. 59, no. 1) is a typical leaf-shaped spearhead of Late Bronze Age type.[51] Also to be included here is one item listed in the catalogue of 'Humana': 'Part of the occipital bone of a man taken from the tumuli Sepulchrales near Amesbury on Salisbury plain in Wiltshire.'

28b/89

28b/447

21f/23

Prehistoric pottery vessels are rare in the catalogue, as might be expected. An appearance is made by 'A Brittish *urn* dugg up in a barrow near Castell Danis in Lugwall parish in Cornwall anno D[ni] 1730', a gift from William Stukeley. Sloane and Stukeley were well acquainted, the latter having trained as a physician (under Richard Mead) before taking holy orders at the age of forty-two and having sought Sloane's influence on more than one occasion in furthering his career.[52] The fortified summit of Castle-an-Dinas lies at the landward end of the parish of Ludgvan, which was for fifty years from 1722 under the care of the Revd William Borlase, author of *The Antiquities of Cornwall* (1769). Borlase included in this survey a brief account of the Iron Age fortifications, and in a letter of 1728 recorded the recovery of an urn from the pillaged remains of a barrow 'about a

28b/443

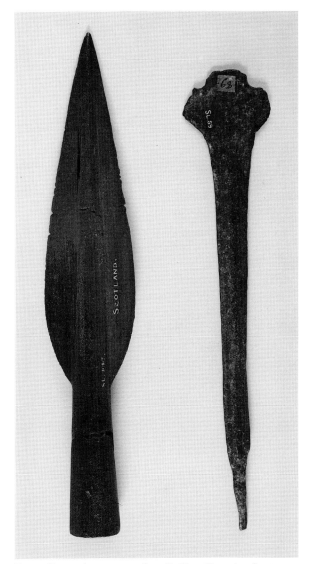

Fig. 59 Bronze Age weapons from Sir Hans Sloane's collection. *1*: spearhead from Bannockburn [BM, PRB, Sl.447]; *2*: dirk, unprovenanced [Sl.89]. Reproduced by courtesy of the Trustees of the British Museum.

furlong to the north-west of Castle-an-Danis': whether this is the same urn and if so how it came into the possession of Stukeley are matters which remain unresolved.[53]

Among other items perceived by Sloane as of 'British' origin must be placed his 'Druid beads' or 'adder beads'. Four pieces were classified as such:

A blue or green glasse *bead* or Druids *amulet* found near Rowel in Northamptonshire.[54]   28b/168

Glain Naidr [Gleineu Nadroedh] snake stones or *adder beads* of Lhuid add. Cambd. p. 683. This the whorle or verticillum of a spindle.

[Ditto] Smaller found at Dingly.[55]   28b/169

Earthen druid *bead* or *amulet*. the same w[t] 168 only of stone.[56]   28b/175

The *same* of lead. M[orton].   28b/176

Although Sloane apparently recognized the true nature of these items, he demurred to Lhwyd, whose Celtic expertise made him an unchallenged authority on these matters. While conceding in his amendment to Camden's *Britannia* (as cited by Sloane)[57] that 'The smallest of them might be supposed to have been glass beads worn by the Romans', Lhwyd wrote uncompromisingly concerning them to Thoresby on 20 May 1702:

I am fully satisfied that they were amulets of the Druids, as were also some other such like trinkets still retained by the Highlanders of Scotland ... and see not much reason to doubt but that they themselves made them with snakes, for the better imposing on the vulgar.[58]

From the variety of beads illustrated by Lhwyd[59] as belonging to this class it is clear that they included some of Roman date and others from as late as the sixteenth or seventeenth century, so that little can be said concerning those collected by Sloane since none can now be recognized.

Roman Britain

In character Sloane's collection of Romano-British antiquities is almost modern in its somewhat prosaic range of artefacts of everyday nature. Ease of access ensured that specimens from London formed a significant element of the collection. Domestic pottery made up the bulk of it, again mostly from London.

Amongst the items recovered from the capital, John Conyers, part of whose collection Sloane acquired, is identified as the principal source. Conyers occupies a significant position in the development of archaeology in England, for he 'made it his chief Business to make curious Observations, and to collect such Antiquities as were daily found in and about London',[60] notably those exposed during rebuilding operations following the Great Fire of 1666. Perhaps his most valuable observations were made along the course of the Fleet Ditch[61] and among the foundations for the new cathedral of St. Paul's.[62] Some account of his discoveries was later published by Woodward, Conyers himself having 'had not encouragement to set forth some relation of them' and lacking also the financial means of achieving such an aim, 'he having only the Returns of his Profession to depend upon'.[63] Woodward eventually bought part of the Conyers collection and is acknowledged as the immediate source of most of the items which entered Sloane's museum.

Even allowing for the inflated claims he made for himself, it must be conceded that Woodward's appreciation of the potential of archaeological evidence was more highly developed than Sloane's. His museum, though largely of geological interest in its surviving state,[64] was described by a contemporary as 'a Treasury of all sorts of Commodities and Utensils, sacred and profane, of ancient Heathen *Rome*', The author of this opinion, John Strype, goes on to give some account of Woodward's collecting philosophy:[65]

One great Intention of this learned Gentleman (as he hath assured me) in amassing together in so great Number of these Things ... was in order to clear and give Light to those ancient Writers who mention and treat of them, *viz.* the *Greeks* and *Romans*; which he hath read and studies with great exactness. Another of his Ends herein was, to illustrate the History and Antiquities of this great and noble City; out of ruins of which these things were retreived, upon the Occasion of that great digging ... that was made in all Parts, after the late great Fire ... And farther, from the various Places in which the Urns were found reposited (which, according to the Laws of the Twelve Tables, were to be buried without the Walls) he is able to ascertain the ancient Bounds of this City, whilst *Roman*.

These theories, which are imaginative and purposeful for their time in a way that cannot be matched in Sloane's case, were applied by Woodward to the funerary remains found at Bishopsgate, within the ultimate limit of the Roman defences. From the location of these burials, he deduced that an earlier and more restricted phase of settlement had preceded that represented by the surviving walls.[66]

Most frequently mentioned in the catalogues are items recovered during excavations for the foundations of Sir Christopher Wren's new cathedral of St. Paul's. These diggings seem to have provided Londoners with one of the earliest-recorded and most thought-provoking glimpses of the archaeological deposits beneath the City. Strype records that there was discovered there:

... great Variety of *Roman* sacrificing Vessels, whereof a great Quantity of the Fragments were digged up. They were made of curious red Earth; the Glazing of them still remains, which is curious. They are of divers Shapes and Sizes, as Occasion should require them to be made Use of in their Sacrifices. And in many the Potter's Name was stamped at the bottom.[67]

Nearby, at the south-west corner of the cathedral, one of a series of pottery kilns was uncovered, where, it was conjectured, 'the abovesaid sacrificing Vessels probably were made'.[68] As well as drawing this kiln, Conyers sketched a number of the associated vessels and noted the stamps on their bases.[69]

Several items from Conyers' diggings reached Sloane (via Kemp and Woodward) along with the records pertaining to them. In addition to items from St. Paul's, these include Roman material (mostly pottery vessels) from the Fleet Ditch,[70] Spitalfields, from a cemetery at Goodman's Fields near Aldgate,[71] Bishopsgate,[72] The Tower, and St. Mary Woolnoth.[73]

Further afield the most significant concentrations come from Kent, most notably from the Saxon Shore forts of Reculver and Richborough, with some lesser contributions from Chatham, Canterbury and the Isle of Sheppey. A note in the catalogue under 'Severall pieces of broken *Paterae* & urns some of Red earth & some of Black earth wch have been washt by the Sea', picked up under the sandy cliff at Reculver by Cromwell Mortimer in 1730, records the circumstances leading to the recovery of so much material around that time: 28b/435

... the cliff was at that time considerably washed away within yᵉ memory of some old people who remember'd it 40 or 50 feet farther into yᵉ Sea, they had now staked & hurdled the beach for a quarter of a mile or more, wᶜʰ prevents ones finding coins or such small things as can fall thro' yᵉ faggots . . .[74]

A second small concentration can be recognized from the Midlands, notably material from the Roman forts of Wroxeter in Shropshire and Castor (Durobrivae), Northamptonshire. John Morton (the source of at least some of Sloane's acquisitions from this area) records that 'At Castor, in digging a little way beneath the Surface, they frequently meet with small square Bricks or Tiles, such as the *Romans* were wont to make their Chequer'd Pavements of'.[75] Other Northamptonshire material comes form Rowel [Rothwell] and Cottestock near Oundle, and from Weekley ('A piece *28b/171* of a *patera* . . . of a [bright] red' and 'A piece of a Roman *28b/172* white *urne*').[76] Chance finds or small groups of objects come *28b/188* from Bourne, Sussex ('A piece of a white tesselated . . . pave- *28b/184* ment'), and Wisbech, Cambridgeshire ('A piece of an *urne* . . .'), while Woodchester, Gloucestershire, and Caerleon, Monmouthshire, are the other principal Roman sites contributing Roman material. Another Welsh find (if Roman) is of some interest:

28a/2046 A Shovell head of oak found 40 Foot down in the Mine called Trelogan (an old Roman worke) in Flintshire: the Miner happen'd to break it with his Pick, wᶜʰ occasion'd its being mended wᵗ Tin. It had a long shaft or handle that was join'd to it going into a hole & fastened at its short & broad end.[77]

Pottery vessels account for the most numerous class of items among Sloane's Roman collections. None can now be identified and his descriptions rarely allow for much comment. 'Urns' comprise the largest category, in which the nature and the quality of the information varies markedly. At the least informative end of the spectrum is to be found *28b/798* an entry for 'Severall pieces of *urns*'; even here, however, it is of no small interest that Sloane concerned himself with collecting sherds (which would certainly have been eschewed by the dilettante collectors of his age). In some *28b/2* instances no more than the colour is given: 'A Roman *urn* *28b/242* of red earth'; 'One [very small] yellowish wᵗ brown lines *28b/9* on it'; 'A very small *urn* of gray earth', which cost 10s.; *28b/172* 'A piece of a Roman white *urne* from Weekly field in North- *28b/327* amptonshire'.[78] In others the form is indicated: 'A narrow *28b/393* mouthd high urn' from Woodward's collection; 'A wide *28b/394* mouthd small gray *urne*', and 'One higher & narrower'. Some *28b/3, 80* came with (or were represented only by) their lids: 'The *28b/387* *cover* of an *urn* of gray earth'; 'The cover of a large Roman *urne* of a pale red colour from Reculver'. In a few cases *28b/395* decorative schemes are alluded to: '[A wide mouthd small *28b/261* gray urne] with lines lozenge ways on the Outside'; 'One ovall [urn] wᵗ lines of ornament points on the outside'; and two more elaborate which were probably of Castor ware – *28b/7* 'A small *urn* with 2 greyhounds following a hare of gray *28b/113* earth', and 'Part of a gray earthen *urn* wᵗ an animals head on its outside perhaps a hunters', given by Oldsworth.[79]

A few urns are ascribed provenances, the majority of them coming from London or from Roman sites in Kent. London provenances include Goodman's Field ('*Urna* fic- *28b/233* tilis'); Bishopsgate ('dug up . . . 1707', from Woodward's *28b/259* collection); St. Mary Woolnoth ('Pieces of *urns*'); and one *28b/187* bearing an inscription in Conyers' hand to the effect that it had been 'Effossum ex agris juxta turrim Lond.' Those *28b/258* with Kentish origins include 'A large gray *urn* found at *28b/323* blackstakes below Chatham upon the ebbing of the tide'; 'A small *urn* taken up near Richborough . . . of gray earth *28b/318* wrought on the edge'; two entries for Reculver – 'A pale *28b/392* red narrow mouthd Roman *urne*' and 'Severall pieces of *28b/435* broken *Paterae* & urns some of Red earth & some of Black earth wᶜʰ have been washt by the sea'; and from Canterbury 'a peice of a black *Urn* found . . . lying in yᵉ street near *28b/436* yᵉ corner of yᵉ garden wall of yᵉ Friars' (the latter two entries in Cromwell Mortimer's hand).

Occasional mention is made of the contents of Sloane's urns. One had contained a coin hoard: 'A piece of an *urne* *28b/184* in which there was found near halfe a bushell of coins of Tetricus & Victorinus near Wisbech', given by Dr Massy. From Kemp's museum came 'One *hemisphericall* [urn] of a *28b/243* reddish clay wᵗ mud in it'. Others evidently were cinerary urns, including 'A very large gray *urn* from Spittalfields? *28b/257* from Mr *Conyers* collection by Dʳ *Woodward* . . . It hath burnt bones in it';[80] and 'A smaller *urn* intire wᵗ bones in *28b/260* it', also from Woodward. One further example can be traced to Warwickshire through its donor: 'An *urn* said to be taken *28b/108* up wᵗ its mouth inclining towards the East from amongst others wᶜʰ had crosses upon them. from Mr Morton. I doubt it . . .'[81]

A second numerous group is that designated *paterae*. These were generally all-purpose skillets, but the temptation to ascribe ritual functions to them was never far away:[82] the only instance in which Sloane hazards a guess as to function is 'A small deep *patera* for sacrificing . . .' *28b/766* Several are described only according to colour – black, grey, red – while three are said to be 'glazed': Sloane applies *28b/190, 244,* this term to the glossy slip coating of terra sigillata, as *305* in 'A small Roman *patera* of red clay glazed with letters *28b/244* in the bottom of it', from Kemp's collection. Others are dec- orated in various ways: '. . . flourish'd abᵗ the edges with *28b/16* leaves &c'; '. . . with a fox? on it'; '. . . wᵗ figures on its *28b/17, 57* outside'; '. . . wᵗ bas reliefs', and one '. . . whereon are the *28b/134;* remains of a dragon embossed'. Occasionally details are *28a/1355* given of the form: one 'with the lips doubld over on wᶜʰ *28b/762* are made flat fishes?'; 'A large ash coloured *patera* wᵗ a spout *28b/446* to it to power any liquid from'. The most frequently noted feature, however, is the presence of a name stamped into the clay of the base, accurately '. . . supposed to be that *28b/134* of the Workman' – or more properly the proprietor of the factory, since these are all products of highly industrialized Gaulish terra sigillata production centres. A number of names are recorded, and a few can be equated with known potters:[83]

[28*b*/11, 389] ROMA; [28*b*/12] DOMUNG; [28*b*/13] SULPICI (?Sulpi); [2*b*/53] L SATR; [28*b*/134] CRAUAH (Carcuna?); [28*b*/325] PRIMANI (Primantius?); [28*b*/388] PENSIAS; [28*b*/739] CRISPVS (Crispus, 1st century); [28*b*/759] INSALNIO; [28*b*/760] ANSI; [28*b*/761] ALBUCINI (Albucius?); [28*b*/766] MATERNI (Maternus, 2nd century); [28*b*/768] EXTIMUS; [28*b*/773–4] QVINTVSM (Quintus, Lezoux or Quintus, La Graufesenque); [28*b*/784)] SATURNIN; [28*b*/785] CRISPIN [28*b*/800] L . . . LVSM.

28*b*/325   One of the above may be compared with a vessel illustrated by the Van Rymsdyks (see Fig. 60): clearly it is what would be termed today a straight-sided bowl and not a patera in the conventional sense. Along with other items, this corresponds with vessels noted by Conyers from the St. Paul's excavations, suggesting a source for some of Sloane's specimens:[84]

. . . Redd earthen Pottsheards the Potts as redd & firme as sealing wax & upon som[e] of the Pott or Cupp bottoms inscriptions som[e] upon Cupps to drinke others upon dishes like sallett dishes but cuningly devised & wrought the inscriptions on som[e] de Primani: other de Parici: other Quintimania others Victor: other Janus & Reciniox: all w[h]ich appeares to bee of the old Romans use in Britannia.

28*a*/1355; 28*b*/171,186, 435,305   Otherwise, the sources are much the same as those for urns, including Weekley, St. Mary Woolnoth, Reculver and Richborough, the latter 'A very large *patera* or dish of red glazed earth found . . . under the banks faln into the sea from the Roman ruins of that ancient place'. A fine example in terra

28*b*/437   sigillata, 'beautifully adorned with flourishes & Ivy-leaves' was given by a Canterbury physician, Dr Gray, to Cromwell Mortimer, who contributed it to Sloane's museum.

28*b*/729   Another, 'covered w[t] small vermiculae or tubuli marini & some rock oysters',[85] was said to have been 'Taken up from the sea by a rock between the end of the Island [of] Sheppey & the main continent': allowing a little latitude, this may have been one of the eponymous vessels from Pudding Pan Rock, the site of a Roman shipwreck; the author of a brief account of the site published in 1782 mentioned that he had in his possession pieces which had been dredged up fifty years previously,[86] so that the opportunity certainly existed for Sloane to have acquired some specimens at an

28*b*/440   equally early date. Another marine find came from 'S[t] Peters sand at y[e] mouth of y[e] River Blackwater w[ch] runs by Maldon . . . upon y[e] sea wall stands an old Roman building now a barn, but commonly called S[t] Peters chapple; this seems to have been y[e] place where stood the Othona of y[e] Romans or Ithanchester of y[e] Saxons.'[87]

Other forms are represented infrequently. Three 'bottles'

28*b*/4   or flagons are listed: one, 'taken up by M[r] *Conyers* in Goodman's fields amongst urns anno 1680' is designated 'Praefericulum' and cross-referenced to Montfaucon;[88] it is

28*b*/5   followed by 'Another *bottle* of the same', priced at 2*s. 6d.*

28*b*/789–92 28*b*/324   A second group of four bottles is listed more cursorily. 'A large *plate* of red Earthenware' came from Blackstakes near Chatham, having been found with the urn mentioned

Fig. 60 J. & A. Van Rymsdyk, *Museum Britannicum* (1778), tab. xxvi, fig. 1: 'A Shallow Red Roman Patera, Pocullum, or little Cup. . .' The Van Rymsdyks equate this piece with one [28*b*/325] found at 'Black Stakes, below Chatham', but alternatively it might be one of the 'Cupps to drinke' found at St. Paul's by Conyers, amongst which a 'Primani' inscription was recorded.

above. From amongst the pots with marine encrustations from Sheppey came 'A vessel w[t] 2 ears in the form of a   28*b*/734 *crucible* of red earth' – perhaps a hemispherical bowl. While most of the 'lachrymatories' so described are of glass, one example, described as a 'Phiala *lachrymatoria* fictilis', came   28*b*/236 from John Kemp's collection.[89]

Some vessels are ascribed more arcane titles. 'A small   28*b*/235 black earthen *urceus*' originated in Kemp's collection: the term was applied to almost any form of one-handled jug for general purposes such as holding water or oil or for ritual use in pouring sacrificial wine. Other entries seem a little eccentric in the terminology they adopt. For example, the catalogue entry for 'A gray *Simpulum* without a handle',   28*b*/114 from Oldsworth's collection, is illustrated by a drawing (seemingly inserted by A.W. Franks) of a vessel with a small foot, a swelling belly surrounded by a band of criss-cross ornament, and a flaring mouth; an accompanying note (also by Franks) describes it as of 'pale ware with brown painted ornament. H[eight] 4 3/4'. Another entry for 'A gray long   28*b*/167 *urne* or *Sympulum*?', is accompanied by an original note that it was acquired from Lord Peterborough and was priced at 2*s. 6d.* How these urns came to be identified with the *simpulum*, which was essentially an earthenware ladle that came in the later Roman period to be used almost exclusively during sacrificial rituals, is unclear.

Glass accounts for the second major category of Roman vessels in the collection. Several of these again came from Conyers, who had been told by the workmen at the Fleet Ditch of what were identified as glass furnaces.[90] Again the vessels provided Sloane with a source of scientific speculation in the form of the irridescent or metallic-looking surfaces which commonly form on Roman glass due to oxidation.[91] Half a dozen entries in the antiquities

28b/29
28b/31,93

catalogues allude to this feature, generally by the name of *electrum Britannicum* or *armatura*, quoting in one instance Conyers and elsewhere Camden as authority.[92] Sloane

28b/29
28b/86

offers explanations of his own for this phenomenon, referring to it as a 'sulphurous or pyriticall substance' or supposing that it might originate in lime. That it was the result of long-term degradation is recognized in his account of a

28b/450

'piece of *glasse* from the window of a chaple in Sussex whereon are sev[ll] pieces of . . . electrum', for here Sloane mentions that he had been told 'that some of the same glasse window had holes eaten thro' it by time'.

28b/25

Three unguent vases are identified in the catalogue, the type being characterized as 'A *glasse vessell* for holding the ointments w[ch] were putt near the dead by the Romans'.

28b/121

Another funerary type is represented by 'A Roman *Lachrymatory* of *glasse* wide in the midle & tapering towards the lower end' from Oldsworth's collection, followed in the

28b/122
28b/23–4,120

catalogue by 'A *glasse ampulla* bigger than a *lachrymatory*' from the same source. Three other lachrymatories are not identified in the catalogue as to material, but on the basis

28b/23

of one surviving example (Fig. 61), 'found at the making of Fleet ditch near a wooden coffin, by M[r] Conyers', are likely all to have been of glass. Although he had no complete glass urn to match the example given by Wren to the Repository of the Royal Society,[93] Sloane had a number

28b/28, 52
28b/59

of urn fragments, including an 'ear' or handle, a piece with an irridescent surface and one 'w[t] the mark of the iron' or pontil on it.

Finally among this funerary material might be included

28b/234

an '*Ossarium* plumbeum' acquired from Kemp's collection,[94] and (less likely to be Roman but evidently perceived as

28b/48

such) 'A piece of a *coffin* of oak turn'd blackish taken up out of the earth when fleet ditch was dugg . . . where were likewise lachrymatories'.

28b/1

Sloane's 'Roman *stone weight* w[t] 4 points on its top, for the marks of its weight' can be confirmed as Roman from the accompanying cross-reference to Montfaucon.[95] Such stone weights — usually of black basalt, spherical in outline with a flat facet at the bottom and another at the top on which the weight is indicated — are common types throughout much of the Roman period; the four dots mentioned by Sloane indicate that this weight (no longer identifiable among the collections) was a *triens* — one third of a pound.[96]

Mosaic pavements formed one of the most easily recognizable indicators of Roman structures and their presence was seized upon and reported by many assiduous antiquaries in the late seventeenth and eighteenth centuries. Sloane acquired fragments from several examples. Some of his specimens were no more than individual tesserae in a

28b/60,321

variety of materials: 'A blew *glasse* for Mosaic work'; 'Some of the *tessellae* from a Mosaic pavem[t] these made of red

28b/246*

earth bak'd'; 'Tesselae of sev[ll] colours taken up from a Roman mosaic work pavement at Woodchester near

28b/755

Minchinghampton in Glocestershire &c.'; 'Some *tessellae* taken from a Roman pavement 20 foot sq[r] of sev[ll] colours

Fig. 61 Glass phial or lachrymatory from the Fleet Ditch, acquired by Sir Hans Sloane from John Conyers' collection. BM, PRB, Sl.23. Reproduced by courtesy of the Trustees of the British Museum.

found in Cotterstock field near Oundle in Northamptonshire', from Charles de la Fontaine. Others were evidently more substantial pieces of patterned work, recovered intact: 'A piece of an ancient *floor or pavem[t]*' from 'Mr Lloyd' — perhaps Edward Lhwyd; 'A peice of a *Mosaic Pavement*, red & white, y[e] tesserae, or dice, of w[ch] it is composed are about ½ inch square'. Occasionally the source is given: '*Pietra comesse* or *Mosaic work* found under Pauls'; '*Tessellae* us'd in the Roman pavement at Castor (Durobrivae) in Northamptonshire';[97] 'A piece of a white tesselated or *Mosaic work pavement* found near Bourne in Sussex', given by Dr Brooks. A somewhat lengthier account, in Cromwell Mortimer's hand, of the original context accompanies the entry (dated September 1730) for some tesserae which formed part of an extensive mosaic found in the 'Hall yard' next to West Mersea parish church in Essex.[98]

More surprising is the inclusion of other elements from Roman buildings of less immediate appeal to the collector. These include complete and fragmentary bricks and tiles, most of which, such as 'A *tile* w[t] raised edges taken out of Reculver ruins' with oyster shells on it and others 'w[t] their mortar', must have had a very restricted antiquarian

28b/149
28b/381
28b/85
28b/151,170
28b/188
28b/441

28b/63,193,
439
28b/346

28b/118   interest. Of wider appeal was one with '*Leg. II Aug.* wrote
28b/133   on it', from Oldsworth; one 'with lines upon the sides of
28b/123–31 it'; and pieces of '*tile* or Vessell of pale red earth w^t Roman
letters on it in 2 lines'. An extensive entry in Cromwell
Mortimer's hand accompanies one brick fragment:

28b/438   Part of a Roman *brick*, with furrows on one side of it, of this sort
are all ye Key bricks of ye arches over ye loop-holes of ye Roman
pharos in Dover castle: this seems to have been a singular contrivance to let in ye sand & stones mixt with ye mortar while liquid,
wch would insinuate itself, & ye stones would lodge in those furrows & keep ye bricks at a proper distance spreading at top to
form an arch.

There follows an allusion to the 'Great dispute among Antiquarians whether this, or some Stones called by ye Natives
ye Devills bit upon an hill South West of the castle on y^e
other side of ye town was ye Roman Watch tower'. Sloane
28b/448   also had from 'Mr le Neve' some 'Small bored hollow
earthen *pipes* for conveying water',[99] and from 'Mr Nash'
– presumably Richard 'Beau' Nash (1674–1762), who
presided over the fashionable rise of the spa at Bath – what
28a/1683 may have been a more substantial piece: 'part of a white
marble bason which was to receive the Bath water under
the pump, which being by accident broken was found by
the heat or virtue of the waters made very friable . . .' It
is unclear whether or not Sloane considered the latter piece
to be Roman in origin, but (whatever its origins) most prob-

ably it formed part of the bathing apparatus of the late
seventeenth or early eighteenth century.[100]

An interesting (though sadly lost) model of an archaeological field monument owned by Sloane may be be noted
here: '*Amphitheatri* Romani Durnovaria icon or model in   28b/301
plaister of Paris of the Roman amphitheatre desined by Dr
Stukely given to me by him'. Presumably it was following
a visit to Dorchester (Roman Durnovaria) in Dorset that
Stukeley recorded in his diary on 6 December 1720: 'I cast
the Amphitheater in plaist. of paris'.[101] Following a return
visit in 1723, he published an account of the amphitheatre
together with a number of views of the site (Fig. 62) which
must give a close impression of the appearance of the
model.[102]

Little in the way of original Antique sculpture penetrated
the collection. The catalogues do, however, record 'A *head*   28b/47
of the Emperor *Verus*? in white marble belonged to Sr Peter
lely bought of his son' for £6. 9s. The Sloane manuscripts
record the approach made by Lely's son John in 1703, when
he offered 'an antick buste in marble of M. Aurelius, which
is an incomparable piece of antiquity and worthy to be
placed in the museum of any potentate in Europe'; he asked
£10 for it, saying it would be worth £40 but for a broken
nose, although this had been 'well mended'. Lely suggested
that the advice of Grinling Gibbons should be sought on
the matter, and protested when Sloane took other counsel

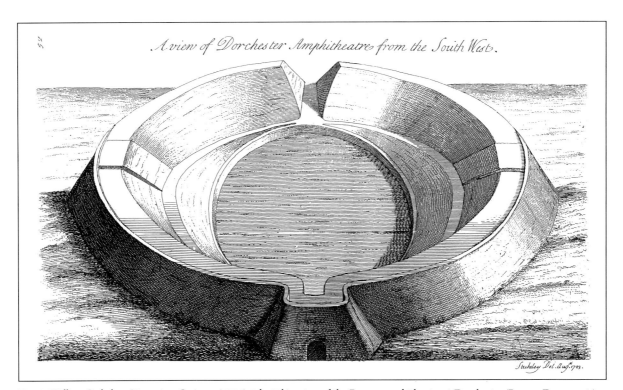

Fig. 62 William Stukeley, *Itinerarium Curiosum* (1724), tab. 51*bis*: view of the Roman amphitheatre at Dorchester (Roman Durnovaria),
Dorset. Sloane received from Stukeley an 'icon or model in plaister of Paris' of the amphitheatre [28b/301].

and made a lesser offer, but in the end agreement evidently was reached.

28b/405 A 'cast of an ancient *head* in plaister of Paris from Dr Woodwards collection'[103] is less remarkable than the casts of artefacts mentioned earlier, since such sculptural copies formed a normal part of the eighteenth-century antiquarian collection.

An alternative preoccupation, with inscribed monuments, also had a venerable ancestry in England stretching back to Sir Robert Cotton. Sloane possessed a single monu-

28b/412 ment of this type: 'An *inscription* found a[t] Caerleon in Wales & brought thence by Mr *George*'. The discovery of this piece was communicated in a letter dated 21 March 1717 to the readership of the *Philosophical Transactions*:[104]

A Person last Week being at Plow in a Close near the Bank of the River Usk . . . came thwart a Stone, and finding Letters thereon, took it up whole . . . There was underneath it some seeming Oblong Square Sepulcher of Stones, rude in order . . .

The most recent reading of the inscription is as follows 'D(IS) M(ANIBUS)/G(AIUS) VALERIUS G(AI) F(ILIUS)/GALERIA VICTOR/ LVGDVNI SIG(NIFER) LEG(IONIS) II AVG(USTAE)/STIP(ENDIORUM) XVII ANNOR(UM) XLV CV/RA(M) AGENT(E) ANNIO PERPETVO H(EREDE)': 'The spirits of the departed; Gaius Valerius Victor, son of Gaius, of the Galerian voting-tribe, from Lugdunum [Lyons], standard-bearer of the Second Legion Augusta, of 17 years' service, aged 45; set up under the charge of Annius Perpetuus, his heir'.[105] Caerleon (Roman Isca) was garrisoned by the Second Legion from the last quarter of the first century to the end of the third century. In recent years the slab has been returned to Caerleon, on loan to the site museum from the British Museum.

28b/218 'A *vase* of red & Gray *marble* w^t green veins w^t a cover from the Earl of *Arundels* collection' evidently had a distin-
28b/219 guished pedigree, as had 'An oval vase of the same', but the means by which they came into Sloane's possession are not recorded.

Some small bronzes are more characteristic of the material sought after by the eighteenth-century collector.
28b/36 These include: 'A *goose* in brasse' (see also Chapter 10, Fig. 51)
28b/37, 288, and 'A *mouse* in the same'; two figures identified as
292 Harpocrates; 'The *figure* of a *boy sitting* holding up his hands'
28b/380 from Reculver (Fig. 63, no. 8), which is not certainly Roman;
28b/1455 'An ancient brasse head from Reculver' (Fig. 63, no. 1), which is, in fact, an anthropomorphic escutcheon from a vessel, incorporating a handle-loop on top; some figures
28b/409–11 of Venus and Cupid, one given by Lord Pembroke; and
28b/92, 164, a number of priapic figurines and amulets. Of the latter,
292 one, 'A *priapus* in brasse w^t the penis at one end & a mans
28b/249 head on the other', an antiquity from the collection of James Petiver (see Chapter 1), which otherwise was dominated by natural history specimens. 'A Roman *souldjer* from M^r
28b/256 *Kemps* collection & Mr *Warners*' may also belong with these figurines.

The fragmentary nature of other metal figures in the collection (probably all small in scale) would not have

recommended them to collectors of more dilettante persua-
sion. Such were 'The brasse *foot* of a Roman idol or votive 28b/33 taken up at Uriconium or Wroxeter in Shropshire', given by Dr Harwood; this piece (Fig. 63, no. 6) may perhaps be interpreted more convincingly as a furniture mount. 'The 28b/138 *hand* of a brasse statue of *Jupiter* holding a thunderbolt', given by Dr Brown, has now disappeared, as has a 'foot 28b/185 of a *statue* or votive . . . cast in lead' given by Hadrian Bever- 28b/524 land; 'The head of Apollo in brasse', from Cirencester, still survives (Fig. 63, no. 2).

A variety of small objects completes the list of Romano-
British artefacts. These comprise keys in iron and bronze, 28b/348,32,359 including a group of four from Reculver (Fig. 63, no. 3); 28b/374–7 a bronze bell; part of a bronze mirror; and a number of 28b/298,81 bronze styli. Amongst personal ornaments, pins form the 28a/1362–3 most numerous category (though their dates must remain 28b/40,355 conjectural): they include 'Large & small *pins of bone* & 28b/41–4 *brasse*'; 'A *pin of Jett*'?; 'A silver *bodkin*' from Reculver or 28b/141,343 Canterbury; and one entry for 'A great number of brasse 28b/399 *pinns*, pieces of fibulae &c'. Other items designated fibulae include 'A Roman *fibula* found in Hampshire given me by 28b/302 Mr Stanley'[106] – presumably one of Sloane's sons-in-law; three from Reculver, of which one survives (Fig. 63, no. 12), 28b/299, a 'Backworth' type of trumpet brooch of Collingwood type 331,341 Rii;[107] and others complete or fragmentary, of which little 28b/62,330, can be said. A second group designated by Sloane 'armillae' 354,399 comprises bracelets or arm-rings: 'an *armilla*? of Jett or 28b/35 Kennell coal'; 'Ancient *armillae* in pieces of *jett*?'. Other 28b/141 more fragmentary pieces evidently presented difficulties of interpretation, however, so that we find 'Severall pieces of 28b/38–9 severall sorts of *armillae* or *fibulae*', with references to brace-lets and brooches in Montfaucon.[108] Other pieces referred to in the catalogue include: 'Broken *armillas* found among 28b/248 urnes in the field Northwest of the tower of London together w^t the silver & beads' from Conyers' collection via Kemp; 'An entire *armilla*' found near Windsor; and 28b/252 'Pieces of *armillae*, rings &c from Reculver'. Three copper- 28b/788 alloy finger rings of Roman date survive in the Sloane col-lection in the British Museum: one (Fig. 63, no. 9), a second-century type, was found in one of the Anglo-Saxon cinerary urns acquired by Sloane from Sir Thomas Browne (see Chapter 13); a faceted ring (Fig. 63, no. 10) is now wrongly numbered Sloane 94 but is accepted as from the collection; and a fourth-century example similarly misnumbered Sloane 86 (Fig. 63, no. 11) is also accepted as from the Museum's foundation collection. There also survives a loop 28b/522 and pin from a copper-alloy buckle of late fourth- or early fifth-century type, with opposed dolphins at the corners (Fig. 63, no. 5); the Van Rymsdyks, who mistake the dol-phins for lobster claws, identify it as from Cirencester, though it is presently recorded as unprovenanced.[109]

Together with these personal ornaments might be included a number of beads listed in the catalogues, includ-ing 'Small green *glasse beads* found with armillas &c'; 'A 28b/46,344 black & white glasse large *bead*' from Reculver or Canter-bury; and what was evidently a large example described

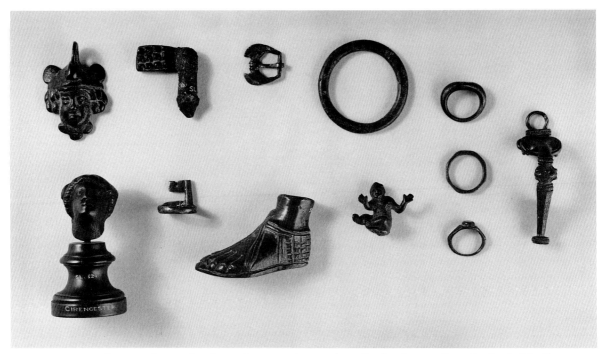

Fig. 63 Romano-British copper alloy metalwork. *1*, anthropomorphic escutcheon, Reculver [BM, PRB, Sl.1455]; *2*, head of Apollo, Cirencester [Sl.524]; *3*, key, Reculver [Sl.375]; *4*, ring-key, Verulamium [Sl.513]; *5*, buckle loop, unprovenanced [Sl.522]; *6*, terminal in the form of a foot, Wroxeter [Sl.33]; *7*, ring, unprovenanced [Sl.331[?]]; *8*, figurine of a boy (not certainly Roman), Reculver [Sl.380]; *9*, finger ring, unprovenanced [Sl.115]; *10*, finger ring, unprovenanced [Sl.94[?]]; *11*, finger ring, unprovenanced [Sl.86[?]]; *12*, trumpet brooch, Reculver [?] [Sl. 299]. Reproduced by courtesy of the Trustees of the British Museum.

as 'A glass *bead* or *verticillum*' (i.e. a spindle whorl) from Richborough (see above).

The minutiae of Sloane's antiquarian collections exert an appeal complementary to that of the more spectacular pieces. They generate an encouraging sense of familiarity, suggesting that here were at least the rudiments of a useful and usable study collection. If Sloane himself made no attempt at synthetic analysis of the artefacts which he accumulated and constructed no hypothesis concerning the societies that produced them, in his careful tending of the material and his assiduous recording of provenance and donor, he proved a model curator. Even today, when few of the items themselves can be identified, the quality of Sloane's documentary legacy is such that it can still form a viable basis for research unmatched by any of his contemporaries. Posterity could hardly have been better served by a collector for whom antiquity was of no more than minor and peripheral interest.

Acknowledgements

Notes and References

I am glad to record my debt to the staff of the Department of Prehistoric and Romano-British Antiquities of the British Museum for assistance in identifying the surviving specimens: my particular thanks are due to Dr Ralph Jackson, Dr Catherine Johns, Dr Ian Longworth, and Dr Stuart Needham. I am also grateful to the Society of Antiquaries of London for allowing me to consult and quote from the early Minute Books of the Society.

1. *Remarks and Collections of Thomas Hearne* (Oxford Historical Society) (Oxford, 1885–1921), vol. VII, p. 310.

2. At the Ashmolean Museum, the only public museum in England at this period, some moves towards the establishment of a systematic antiquarian collection might have been expected from Edward Lhwyd (keeper 1690–1709) when, having completed his fundamental survey of British fossils with publication of the *Lithophylacii britannici ichnographia* in 1699 and laid the foundations of the Ashmolean's palaeontological collections in the process, he anticipated turning his attentions in his proposed multivolume *Archaeologia Britannica* to archaeological artefacts: one volume (subtitled *Glossography*), concerning itself purely with language, was published in 1707, while vols. 3 and 4 were to deal with Roman and British monuments and antiquities in Wales. However, Lhwyd's death in 1709 put paid to the idea, and his successors harboured no such ambitions.

3. See M.C.W. Hunter, 'The Royal Society and the origins of British archaeology', *Antiquity* 45 (1971), pp. 113–21, 187–92. As an example of the incredulity of the world at large at the recondite activities of the new naturalists, we may cite the case of one 'Lady Glanvil' (on whom see p. 116), an early amateur lepidopterist: E. St. J. Brooks (*Sir Hans Sloane. The Great Collector and his Circle* (London, 1954), p. 126) recounts how some relations, dissatisfied with the terms of her will, attempted to have it set aside under the Acts of Lunacy since 'none but those who were deprived of their senses would go in pursuit of butterflies'. Sloane and John Ray were subpoenaed to appear in support of her character, though only the latter is recorded as having appeared on her behalf, at Exeter.

4. See Hunter (op. cit. (note 3), p. 115) for the relevant figures. Sloane's successor as president of the Royal Society, Martin Folkes, was a vice-president of the Society of Antiquaries; the treasurer, James West, was also a Fellow (and from 1749 a vice-president) of the Antiquaries (Joan Evans, *A History of the Society of Antiquaries* (Oxford, 1956), p. 95).

5. Ibid., p. 94. The same author notes (p. 83) that when the Antiquaries were in reduced circumstances in 1729 an attempt was made to unite them with the Royal Society, but nothing came of it. Sloane himself never stood for the Antiquaries, although so many of his friends were Fellows that election would have been a mere formality, had he wished it: that he did not seems to confirm his lack of serious commitment to antiquarian studies. He did, however, join (but made no recorded impact on) the Gentlemen's Society at Spalding, a body with declared wide interests in 'the Liberal Sciences and Polite Learning' but with a marked antiquarian bias: see 'An account of the Gentlemen's Society at

Spalding', in J. Nichols (ed.), *Bibliotheca Topographica Britannica* vol. III: *Antiquities in Lincolnshire* (London, 1790), appendix p. [xxvii].

6. For the anti-antiquarian reaction and for the general decline in scholarship under Folkes see C.R. Weld, *A History of the Royal Society* (London, 1848), vol. I, pp. 482–5. The sentiment also pervades the chapter entitled 'Of antiquities commemorated in the Transactions of the Royal Society', in Sir John Hill, *A Review of the Works of the Royal Society* (London, 1780), p. 47.

7. [Edward Ward], *The London Spy Compleat* 3rd edn. (London, 1706), p. 60. When published in 1681, the section of the Repository's catalogue dedicated to 'Matters relating to Antiquity' took up less than a page and a half: see Nehemiah Grew, *Musaeum Regalis Societatis, or a Catalogue and Description of the Natural and Artificial Rarities belonging to the Royal Society* (London, 1681), pp. 380–1.

8. Z.C. von Uffenbach, *Merkwürdige Reisen durch Niedersachsen, Holland und Engelland* (Ulm, 1753–4), vol. II, pp. 464–6; passage reproduced in W.H. Quarrell and M. Mare, *London in 1710 from the Travels of Zacharias Conrad von Uffenbach* (London, 1934), pp. 36, 185.

9. Evidently, however, Sloane was acquainted with this particular dealer, for it was Campe who arranged von Uffenbach's introduction to Sloane: see Chapter 1, Appendix 2.

10. Unfortunately Sloane's references to Montfaucon are frequently disappointing in the search for identities of lost antiquities, since they generally allude to pages and plates in which Montfaucon has combined material of such disparate dates and kinds as to be of little value in our task. Père Claude Du Molinet's catalogue of the *Cabinet de la Bibliothèque de Sainte-Geneviève* (Paris, 1692) is also mentioned once [28*b*/237].

11. 'Mr Conyers Observations' are to be found among the papers of John Bagford (BL, Harley MS 5953, part I, fols. 112–13, reproduced in J. Burnby, 'John Conyers, London's first archaeologist', *Transactions of the London and Middlesex Archaeological Society* 35 (1984), pp. 78–9: here the 'Brittish weapon made of flint dexterously shaped', is said to have been found 'by one of yᵉ Teeth'. For Bagford see W.Y. Fletcher, 'John Bagford and his collections', *Transactions of the Bibliographical Society* 4 (1896–8), pp. 185–201; M. Nickson, 'Bagford and Sloane', *British Library Journal* 9 (1983), pp. 51–5.

12. Bagford's account of this implement, communicated in 1715 to Hearne and reproduced in the latter's edition of Leland's *Collectanea* 2nd edn. (London, 1770), vol. I, pt. 1, p. lxiv, states that such weapons were 'very common amongst the Ancient Britains . . . they having not at that time the use of Iron or Brass, as the Romans had'. He further describes it as 'a Flint Lance like unto

the **Head** of a Spear, fastened into a Shaft of a **good Length**', but Conyers makes no mention of such a haft and current identification of this type of implement as a hand-held axe would make the presence of one extremely unlikely.

13. Hearne, op. cit. (note 1), vol. II, p. 59, mentions on 7 October 1707 that 'Ab¹ fourteen years since on yᵉ North-West of London was found large Elephants Bones, amongst yᵐ Teeth, & near to them a flint like our Scotch Elf Arrows.' Further, he records, 'some Curious Persons' were of the opinion that this flint 'was yᵗ with whᶜʰ yᵉ Elephant was kill'd', a perceptive conclusion which Sloane seems to have overlooked (or disregarded) in a paper he published on the tusks (see below, note 15) where the death of this and other 'elephants' was attributed to the Flood.

14. As well as the tooth found with the handaxe, Conyers had recovered on 11 December 1673 'an Elephants Tooth and part of yᵉ blades bone' from a site adjacent to that in Gray's Inn Lane. In Sloane's catalogues the tusk that accompanied the Gray's Inn handaxe was catalogued quite separately from it, with the zoological specimens (see Chapter 4).

15. Hans Sloane, 'An account of elephants teeth and bones found under ground', *Philosophical Transactions* 35 (1727–8), p. 458; he includes here an account of mammoth remains found in Siberia, but no connection is made between these and the London finds (see also the observations in note 13, above). A version of this paper was also published in the *Histoire et Mémoires de l'Académie Royale des Sciences* (1727), pp. 1–4. Jacquot's observation on this essay might be applied to a great deal of Sloane's works: 'On the whole Sloane had no original theory to propose. His strong point was the combination of extensive reading with a systematic method of collecting and classifying specimens. The wide range of his curiosity, and the amplitude of his means as a collector, enabled him to bring together many facts which, by their mere juxtaposition, gave rise to new problems which in their turn required new interpretation' (Jean Jacquot, 'Sir Hans Sloane and French men of science', *Notes and Records* 10 (1953), pp. 93–4). Sloane's common-sense pragmatism also played a part in his dismissal of a Roman origin, as illustrated in a report by Stukeley of a debate on the subject at the Royal Society, when 'Sir Hans observed against that opinion that no one would be so ridiculous as to bury their ivory teeth, which are of high price with all nations, and ever were' (*The Family Memoirs of the Rev. William Stukeley, M.D.* (Publications of the Surtees Society) (London, 1882–7), vol. III, p. 2).

16. Grew, op. cit. (note 7), pp. 303–4. Under the title of 'The Flat Bolthead. *Anchorites*', Grew describes one arrowhead as 'pointed like a *speer*. Having at the other end . . . a short handle. 'Tis likewise toothed on the edges, and the sides as it were wrought with a kind of undulated sculpture . . .'; another, he notes, has a '. . . deeper Indenture, but not handle. Both of them strike fire like other *Flints*.' The descriptions are accompanied by the statement that 'Not only *Moscardo*, but others reckon them amongst the *Ceraunia* or *Thunder-bolts*' (cf. *Note overo Memorie*

del Museo di Lodovico Moscardo (Padua, 1656), pp. 148–9.

17. Michele Mercati (1541–93), keeper of the botanic garden at the Vatican, professed the opinion that these 'cerauniae' were man-made artefacts, the first recorded instance in which the true nature of flint implements was recognized; since the crucial text (in his *Metallotheca* (Rome, 1719), p. 243) remained unpublished for over a century, however, it had little influence on contemporary opinion.

18. Sir William Dugdale, *The Antiquities of Warwickshire* (London, 1656), p. 778. Dugdale's son-in-law, Elias Ashmole, inherited at least one of these flints and preserved it in his collection until, in 1679, 'that Chesill or Axe found at Oldbury' was destroyed along with other antiquities in a fire at his chambers: see C.H. Josten, *Elias Ashmole, 1617–1692* (Oxford, 1966), vol. IV, pp. 1643–4.

19. Robert Plot, *The Natural History of Staffordshire* (Oxford, 1686), p. 396. Plot drew on ethnographic parallels to elaborate on his conclusions relating to axes, commenting that 'how they may be fastened to a *helve*, may be seen in the *Musaeum Ashmoleanum* where are several *Indian* ones of the like kind' (ibid., p. 397). Sloane too had a 'West Indian axe, similar to those that were used in former times before they discovered iron', complete with its wooden haft: see Chapter 1, Appendix 3.

20. Four other flint arrowheads are recorded among Sloane's 'Miscellanies': [28a/649] 'A large head of an *arrow* of yellow flint, from Scotland? Al. Br.'; [28a/650] 'A lesser one of the *same*'; [28a/651] 'A lesser one of the same arrow-heads made of a semi diaphonous flint of a paler colour. from the same'; and [28a/695] 'The head of an *arrow* shap'd like a lozenge of redish flint from Scotland. Dr. Cheyne'.

21. 'Extracts of several letters from Mr. Edward Lhwyd . . . containing observations . . . made on his travels thro' Wales and Scotland . . .', *Philosophical Transactions* 28 no. 337 (1713), pp. 99–100. See also a letter from Lhwyd to Ralph Thoresby of 4 May 1703 (*Letters of Eminent Men addressed to Ralph Thoresby, FRS* (London, 1832), vol. II, p. 2). A useful survey of the folklore surrounding elf arrows is given by Thomas Davidson, 'Elf-shot cattle', *Antiquity* 30 (1956), pp. 149–55. Elsewhere, in another entry for 'Elfs arrows from Scotland' [28a/1896] Sloane gives a reference to Olaus Worm's *Museum Wormianum* (Leiden, 1654), p. 85.

22. Reply from the Revd John Fraser to Lhwyd's questionnaire, reproduced in J.L. Campbell and Derick Thomson, *Edward Lhuyd in the Scottish Highlands 1699–1700* (Oxford, 1963), p. 33. Elf arrows were thought to bring death or illness to cattle and other beasts but could also be converted into amulets in order to avert these dangers.

23. In support of this suggestion, the opinion held by Lhwyd (op. cit. (note 21), p. 99) that 'these elf arrow-heads have not been used as amulets above thirty or forty years' seems per-

suasive. Lhwyd himself was in no doubt as to the true nature of these and other flints, calling on ethnographical evidence to demonstrate that 'they are just the same chip'd Flints the Natives of *New England* head their Arrows with at this Day; and there are also several Stone Hatchets found in this Kingdom, not unlike those of the *Americans*' (ibid.).

24. Compare another entry for [28a/1544] 'A *Thunder bolt* from Bohemia. A wedge or antient weapon of granite stone . . .'

25. This was Dr Richard Richardson, one of Sloane's closest friends and most assiduous correspondents (see Chapter 1).

26. William Stukeley, *Itinerarium Curiosum: or an account of the antiquities and remarkable curiosities in nature or art observed in travels through Great Britain* 2nd edn. (London, 1776), centuria II, p. 74.

27. Plot, op. cit. (note 19), pp. 403–4.

28. *Camden's Britannia, newly translated into English: with large additions and improvements*, ed. Edmund Gibson (London, 1695), p. 6. Discussing some 'spear-heads, axes, and swords, all wrap'd in Linnen', found by St. Michael's Mount in Cornwall, Camden observes that 'it is plain from the Monuments of Antiquity, that the Greeks, Cimbrians, and Britains, made use of brass-weapons'.

29. Ibid., p. 672.

30. For a discussion of the general debate see Stuart Piggott, *Ancient Britons and the Antiquarian Imagination* (London, 1989), pp. 95–9, and idem., 'Bronze, Britons and Romans', in R. Miket and C. Burgess (eds.), *Between and Beyond the Walls: Essays . . . in honour of George Jobey* (Edinburgh, 1984), pp. 117–25.

31. A total of sixteen bronzes from the site were exhibited on these occasions; those shown at the second meeting were ordered to be drawn for the Society's records (Society of Antiquaries of London, Minute Books, vol. II (1732–7), pp. 128–9; the letter from Cooke to Collinson, dated 1 January 1737, is on p. 285).

The bronzes had been found by a farmer during the widening of a marl-pit, on a ridge named Arreton Down on the Isle of Wight; they were 'ranged in a regular order, the axes laid on the spear-heads'. Apart from the six items from the Sloane collection, the British Museum now possesses seven other original pieces of the Arreton Down hoard, acquired at various times between 1856 and 1988; the most recently-discovered piece, a flanged axe, was formerly in the McAlpine Collection (see Arthur MacGregor (ed.), *Antiquities from Europe and the Near East in the Collection of the Lord McAlpine of West Green* (Oxford, 1987), p. 101, no. 11.1) and was presented to the Museum by Lord McAlpine in 1988. The Manchester University Museum also has a spearhead bought in 1953. For details of these see Stuart Needham, 'Towards the reconstitution of the Arreton Down hoard: a case of faked provenances', *Antiquaries Journal* 66 (1986), pp. 9–28; idem., 'The decorated flanged axe from the Arreton Down hoard, Isle of Wight', *Antiquaries Journal* 69 (1989), p. 315.

32. BL, Sloane MS 4055, fol. 98.

33. Letter from Cooke to Sloane, 1 January 1737, Society of Antiquaries of London, Minute Books, vol. II, pp. 285–6.

34. Augustus W. Franks, 'Notes on bronze weapons found on Arreton Down, Isle of Wight', *Archaeologia* 36 (1855), p. 331.

35. Dennis Britton, 'Traditions of metal-working in the later Neolithic and Early Bronze Age of Britain: part 1', *Proceedings of the Prehistoric Society* new ser. 29 (1963), pp. 284–97.

36. Bodleian Library, Oxford, MS Rawl. Lett. 4, fol. 350.

37. Society of Antiquaries of London, MS 265, pp. 11–12. These drawings were later engraved and published by Stukeley in his *Itinerarium Curiosum*, op. cit. (note 26), centuria II, pl. 96.

38. Sloane includes a reference here to 'Du Molinet pag 19 hache antique': in this publication (Du Molinet, op. cit. (note 10), p. 19) the Bronze Age axe in question is described imaginatively as '. . . une hache dont les Prêtres se servoient pour immoler les victimes en leur fendant la tête'.

39. A very full survey of the history of the discovery and of the discourses to which it gave rise is given in Stephen Briggs, 'Thomas Hearne, Richard Richardson, and the Osmondthick hoard', *Antiquaries Journal* 58 (1978), pp. 247–59.

40. Thomas Hearne, 'A discourse concerning some antiquities lately found in York-shire, in a letter to Mr. Thoresby of Leeds', in *The Itinerary of John Leland the Antiquary* vol. I, ed. T. Hearne (Oxford, 1710), pp. 97–114. Earlier Hearne had published 'A letter from Mr. Tho. Hearne . . . to Mr. Ralph Thoresby, FRS, occasion'd by some antiquities lately discover'd near Bramham-Moore in Yorkshire', *Philosophical Transactions* 26 no. 322 (1709), pp. 395–412. Elsewhere Thoresby mentions to Hearne that he had written both to Sloane and to Woodward concerning these axes and that 'they each strive for yᵉ honour to introduce it at Gresham Col.' (Hearne, op. cit. (note 1), vol. II, p. 343.

41. Richardson's letter is reproduced along with the illustration mentioned below in Briggs, op. cit. (note 39), p. 250, pl. liiib. Briggs (p. 254) comments that 'Richardson's observations upon the axes, their possible use, method of hafting and casting put him at the forefront of contemporary learning, or at least should have done. His was, in fact, one of the first reasoned accounts of prehistoric artifacts based upon first-hand observation.'

42. No doubt the same mould that was exhibited at the Society of Antiquaries in January 1720 and drawn by Stukeley in the 'Commonplace Book' (Society of Antiquaries of London, MS 265, p. 60; discussed and reproduced in Stephen

Briggs, Kevin Leahy and Stuart Needham, 'The Late Bronze Age hoard from Brough-on-Humber: a re-assessment', *Antiquaries Journal* 67 (1987), pp. 11–28, fig. 1.

43. Briggs, op. cit. (note 39), p. 252; P.K. Schmidt and C.B. Burgess, *The Axes of Scotland and Northern England* (Prähistorische Bronzefunde Abt. IX Bd. 7) (Munich, 1981), p. 259.

44. Hearne, op. cit. (note 1), vol. II, p. 334.

45. BL, Sloane MS 4048, fols. 208 (letter) and 209 (drawing). I am grateful to Professor George Eogan for drawing to my attention two earlier notices concerning this instrument: Michael Herity, 'Early finds of Irish antiquities from the minute-books of the Society of Antiquaries of London', *Antiquaries Journal* 49 (1969), pp. 3–4; C.S. Briggs and R.G. Haworth, 'Dean Sankey Winter and the Bronze Age trumpet from "Manooth"', *Journal of the Royal Society of Antiquaries of Ireland* 108 (1978), pp. 111–15.

46. See J.M. Coles, 'Irish Bronze Age horns and their relations with Northern Europe', *Proceedings of the Prehistoric Society* 29 (1963), pp. 326–56, with further bibliography. The Maynooth horn belongs to Coles's Class 1, whose distribution is given in his fig. 3: it is not the only outlier from the north-easterly distribution, for a hoard at Dowris, Co. Offaly, included no fewer than twenty-eight horns.

47. E. MacWhite, 'Irish Bronze Age trumpets', *Journal of the Royal Society of Antiquaries of Ireland* 75 (1945), p. 98; the author notes that the broadly contemporary Continental *Lürer* were similarly played (and deposited) in pairs, Briggs and Haworth (op. cit. (note 45), p. 114) seem disinclined to believe that there were two horns in this deposit, but the reason for their doubt is not made plain.

48. R. Pococke, 'An account of some antiquities found in Ireland', *Archaeologia* 2 (2nd edn., 1809), p. 40, note o.

49. Society of Antiquaries of London, Minute Books, vol. VI (1740–44), p. 4: 'Dr Mortimer brought from Sʳ Hans Sloan a model in pewter of some Curiositys lately found in Ireland . . . [a drawing of the sleeve-fastener is given here]. The Doctor was pleased to promise a sight of yᵉ letter to Sʳ Hans relating to these curiositys.' The fastener along with two horns from Dungannon is published with details in 'An account of some ancient trumpets, and other pieces of antiquity, found in the County of Tyrone in Ireland. In a letter from Francis Nevill, Esq., to the Right Reverend the Lord Bishop of Clogher, FRS', *Philosophical Transactions* 28 no. 337 (1713), pp. 270–3. The letter itself, dated 1713, is preserved in BL, Sloane MS 4065, fol. 138. In 'A letter . . . to . . . the Earl of Cromertie', *Philosophical Transactions* 27 no. 330 (1711), p. 305, Sloane mentions the finding of gold chains and pieces of money in the Irish bogs.

50. C.B. Burgess and S. Gerloff, *The Dirks and Rapiers of Great Britain and Ireland* (Prähistorische Bronzefund Abt. IV Bd. 7) (Munich, 1981), pp. 11–12 no. 50, where it is conjecturally provenanced to Ireland.

51. John M. Coles, 'Scottish Late Bronze Age metalwork: typology, distributions and chronology', *Proceedings of the Society of Antiquaries of Scotland* 93 (1959–60), p. 81.

52. See Stukeley, op. cit. (note 15), vol. II, pp. 259, 265; see also Stuart Piggott, *William Stukeley, an Eighteenth-Century Antiquary* revised edn. (London, 1985). Stukeley took part with Sloane in the dissection of an elephant at Sloane's house in Chelsea in 1720 and later published an account of his observations: see William Stukeley, *Essay towards the Anatomy of the Elephant* (London, 1723).

53. Although Borlase later struck up an acquaintance with Stukeley, this seems to have dated only from 1749: see P.A.S. Pool, *William Borlase* (Truro, 1986), pp. 73–5, 125–6.

54. A reference here reading 'Mort N.H.N. p. 499 tab. 14, fig 1' is to John Morton's *Natural History of Northampton-shire* (London, 1712), where this bead is described and illustrated.

55. There is a note here to ibid., tab. 14. fig. 2.

56. There is a note here to ibid., p. 499.

57. Gibson, op. cit. (note 28), p. 683.

58. Lhwyd, in Gibson, op. cit. (note 28), p. 683. Here Lhwyd gives an account of the supposed manner in which a number of snakes 'joyning heads together and hissing, a kind of Bubble is form'd like a ring, about the head of one of them, which the rest by continual hissing blow on till it comes off at the tail, and then it immediately hardens and resembles a glass ring'. See also Thoresby, op. cit. (note 21), vol. I, pp. 413–14.

59. Reproduced in R.T. Gunther, *Life and Letters of Edward Lhwyd* (Early Science in Oxford 14) (Oxford, 1945), p. 247. Elsewhere (p. 419) Lhwyd mentions that 'they are all made of glasse, but sometimes plain & sometimes variegated: Amongst these I saw one with 9 snakes painted on it, some with three, & several with one.'

60. John Bagford, quoted in 'A letter to the Publisher, written by the ingenious Mr John Bagford', in *Leland's Collectanea*, ed. T. Hearne, 2nd edn. (London, 1770), vol. I, part i, p. lxiii.

61. Conyers occupied premises close by the Fleet, for a time near Peterborough Court on the north side of Fleet Street and later around the corner in Shoe Lane. John Aubrey (*Monumenta Britannica*, ed. John Fowles (Sherborne, 1980), p. 511) mentions that 'Mr Conyers (Apothecary) at the White Lion in Fleet Street, hath preserved a world of antique curiosities found in digging of the ruins of London, principally Fleet Ditch . . .'

62. BL, Sloane MS 958. The text is reproduced in Burnby, op. cit. (note 11), appendix 1.

63. John Woodward, *An Account of some Roman Urns and other Antiquities lately Digg'd up near Bishops-Gate* (London, 1713), p. 6. Woodward expresses regret that there were at that time 'so

very few that were forward to contribute any Thing to the Support of such Studies, however curious and useful', and mentions that he had purchased 'the Remains' of Conyers' collection.

64. See D. Price, 'John Woodward and a surviving British geological collection from the early eighteenth century', *Journal of the History of Collections* 1 no. 1 (1989), pp. 79–95, where a few surviving antiquities are mentioned.

65. John Stowe, *A Survey of the Cities of London and Westminster*, ed. J. Strype (London, 1720), vol. II, appendix p. 22.

66. While Woodward's observations remain correct in principle, evidence of an earlier and more restricted circuit of the Roman civil defences has not been forthcoming and the status of the Bishopsgate cemetery remains equivocal: see Royal Commission on Historical Monuments (England), *Inventory of the Historical Monuments in London* vol. III: *Roman London* (London, 1928), p. 153.

67. Strype, op. cit. (note 65), vol. II, appendix p. 23. John Bagford, 'a Citizen of *London*, studious of Antiquities', recovered some of these 'with his own hands' (ibid.); nearby were found 'several Scalps of Oxen, and a large Quantity of Boars Tusks', which were widely interpreted as the remains of sacrificial animals. Sloane was similarly attracted by the idea of sacrifices: in addition to [25e/222] 'The bone in an oxes legg taken up at Pauls & supposed to be of those sacrificed in time of the Romans when it was an heathen temple', his collection included [28b/332] 'A *bone* taken up at [Reculver] from among those of sacrificed beasts'.

68. Conyers recorded that 'The kiln was full of the coarser sort of pots, so that few were saved whole, viz., lamps, bottles, urns and dishes' (BL, Sloane MS 958, fol. 105). From the drawings made by Conyers of some of these vessels, the kiln has been estimated to have belonged to the first century AD (Royal Commission on Historical Monuments, op. cit. (note 66), p. 140; see also *vCH London*, vol. I (1909), pp. 124–5. Contemporary opinion was that the kiln was situated 'near to the temple where *Diana* was worshipped, for the more Convenience of the People that came thither to Sacrifice' (Strype, op. cit. (note 55), p. 23). The preoccupation with sacrifices was typical of the period, as was the tendency to identify almost any domestic vessel recovered from Roman levels with sacrificial rites.

69. Moulds were also said to have been found in the vicinity and to have been acquired by Woodward for his collection (Strype, op. cit. (note 65), p. 23). If this testimony is to be trusted, these would undoubtedly be of great archaeological interest today, other such moulds being unknown from London.

70. Conyers recorded watching the labourers there digging to a depth of fifteen feet or more between the Fleet gate and Holborn bridge and finding there large quantities of 'red earthen ware cupps' (BL, Sloane MS 958, fol. 105ᵛ).

71. Strype (op. cit. (note 65), p. 23) mentions

that 'since the Buildings there, about 1678, have been found there (in digging the Foundations) vast Quantities of Urns, and other *Roman* Utensils, as Knives, Combs, &c, which are likewise in the Possession of Dr *Woodward*. Some of these Urns had Ashes of Bones of the Dead in them, and Brass and Silver Money . . .'

72. Woodward (op. cit. (note 63), pp. 7–9) gives an account of the material 'lately Digg'd up' at Bishopsgate, some of which he acquired via Conyers. This included a number of urns, '. . . the largest capable of holding full three Gallons, the least somewhat above a Quart', containing 'Ashes, and Cinders of burn'd Bones'. The area was believed to have been of particular importance to the Romans: Bagford records the accepted view that it had been '. . . their Field of Mars, in which place the Romans train'd up and exercised their Young Soldiers . . . in the skill and Exercise of Arms' (Hearne, op. cit. (note 60), vol. I part I, p. lxi).

73. Strype (op. cit. (note 65), p. 24) records that on this site in 1716 '. . . were found *Roman* Vessels, both for sacred and domestic Uses, of all Sorts, and in great Abundance, but all broken: And with all were taken up Tusks and Bones, of Boars and Goats. As also many Meddals, and Pieces of Metals; some tesselated Works, a Piece of an Aqueduct; and at the very Bottom a Well filled up with Mire and Dirt . . . These Sheards were in such vast Quantities, that many Cart Loads were carried away with the Rubbish, and the Roads about St. *George's Fields* in *Southwark* mended with them.' See also *vCH London*, vol. I (1909), p. 123.

74. Aubrey, op. cit. (note 61), p. 1016, records that 'Mr Archdeacon Betteley of Canterbury gave me a dozen little copper Roman coins no bigger than half-pence, found at Reculver in Kent. He has an ounce or more of them. I gave mine to the Museum at Oxford'.

75. Morton, op. cit. (note 54), p. 509.

76. The Weekely material is provided with a reference to Morton (op. cit. (note 54), pp. 529–30), who gives the following: 'In Weekly Field, not far from *Hall-wood* . . . I observed also Fragments of *Urns*, or of Vessels very like to 'em: as also several other antique Earthen Vessels of different Figures and Colours; some of 'em a lively red Colour, and made of very fine Earth. These last seem to have been Pieces of a shallow Vessel, perhaps of one of the *Plates* or *Patellae* wherein *Libamina* were put.'

77. A duplicate entry for this item [28a/1783] mentions that it came from a lead mine and that the donor was a Mr Mason.

78. There is a reference here to Morton, op. cit. (note 54), p. 529.

79. Cf. Conyers on certain vessels from St. Paul's: 'Now these pottsherds . . . were curiously layed one the outside wth like Thorne pricks of rosetrees & in the manner of raised work this upon potts of Murry collour & here & there greyhounds & staggs & hares all in rais'd worke other of these were Cinamon Collour urne

fashion & were as guilded wth Gould . . .' From the Fleet Ditch too came '. . . Potts of curious thinn sydes as thinn as Glass wth inbossed or outward Raised worke & these as of a silverd or bellmettle colloured glaseing the Imagry hounds hares staggs thornes trees & branching flourishings all Raised workes' (Burnby, op. cit. (note 11), p. 75).

80. A reference follows to *A Catalogue of the Library, Antiquities, &c. of the Late Learned Dr Woodward* (London, 1728), p. 267 no. 9: 'Tres Urnae, quarum una tantum integra, effossae *Spittle-fields*' (which sold for 7s. 6d.).

81. Morton (op. cit. (note 54), p. 530) mentions this urn as being in his possession, having been 'lately digg'd up' at Monks Kirby in Warwickshire. There, he reports, a number of such urns '. . . were reposited upon a Causey of broad Pebbles running East and West. One of the largest of them had a Christ's *Cross* coarsely painted on the outside of it. They were each of them placed with their Mouths dipping to the East: and cover'd with a piece of Slate. Within were Ashes, and calcin'd Bones, with a Mixture of Earth. These by their being set inclining to the *East*, and by the *Cross* upon one of them, seem to have been the *Urns* of Christians: and are then a Proof that the *Roman* Converts to Christianity did not so immediately upon that change of Religion, lay aside their ancient Custom of burning their Dead, as Antiquaries have generally thought they did.' The Roman origin of these urns is likely enough (see *vCH Warwickshire*, vol. I, p. 238), but the Christian connotations are unsupportable. Sloane's entry continues: 'Part of the upper chap of a man. Some monkeys bones from the *same*'; there seems to be no suggestion, however, that these came with the urn.

82. Montfaucon, on whose opinion Sloane relied heavily in antiquarian matters, places paterae among the 'instrumens de sacrifice' (Bernard de Montfaucon, *L'Antiquité expliquée et représentée* 2nd edn. (Paris, 1722–4), vol. II, pp. 62–7.

83. See Felix Oswald and T. Davies Pryce, *An Introduction to the Study of Terra Sigillata* (London, 1920), *passim*.

84. Burnby, op. cit. (note 11), pp. 73–5.

85. Descriptions of this sort hint at Sloane's comparative lack of interest in pottery for its own sake, revealing a tendency to be seduced by characteristics of physical or biological (rather than purely archaeological) significance. Further evidence of this tendency can be seen in catalogue entries such as [28a/734] 'A vessell wt 2 ears in the form of a *crucible* of red earth on wᶜʰ grows vesicaria marina & a small balani', or for another [28a/758] 'covered on the inside & outside wt . . .? of sea oysters, abies marina &c'.

86. Edward Jacob, 'Observations on the Roman earthen ware taken from the Pan-Pudding Rock', *Archaeologia* 6 (1782), pp. 121–3.

87. There follows a refence to Gibson's edition of Camden's *Britannia* (op. cit. (note 28), p. 344). The site, at Bradwell-on-Sea, is now recognized as that of a Saxon Shore fort – the only one in

Essex. The chapel, identified here as Roman, is now equated with those which, according to Bede, were built among the East Saxons by St. Cedd *c*.653: see *vch Essex*, vol. III (1963), pp. 52–3.

88. Montfaucon, op. cit (note 82), suppl. vol. II, pl. xvi. Elsewhere (vol. II, pp. 140–1) Montfaucon provides a discussion of the *praefericulum* (a handled jug) and its role in sacrificing: this no doubt formed the basis of Sloane's understanding of the type.

89. Cf. Robert Ainsworth, *Monumenta Vetustatis Kempiana* (London, 1720), p. 179.

90. Conyers records that in these kilns were found '. . . broken Crucibells or Vesls for melteing of glasses together wth boltered glasse such as is to be seen remaining at glass housen amongst the broken Glass wch was glasses spoyled in the makeing' (BL, Sloane MS 958, fol. 106^r). Burnby (op. cit. (note 11), p. 68) observes that Conyers would have had the opportunity of becoming familiar with glass house technology at the Savoy glass works close by his premises.

91. Strictly the phenomenon of irridescence is caused by the diffraction of light from a sequence of layers separated by air spaces, a product of weathering of the surface.

92. Cf. BL, Sloane MS 958, fol 106^r (reproduced in Burnby, op. cit. (note 11), p. 75), where Conyers alludes to 'a Gilded sort of Earthen Ware wch might possibly be of the Electrum of the Brittans as Cambden mencioned'.

93. Aubrey, op. cit. (note 61), p. 511, mentions that in 1678 'was digged up in Spitalfields a fair urn of glass, (and that as fine as our looking glasses now) . . . with the ashes of the dead. Sir Christopher Wren has it, and intends to present it to the Royal Society'. Grew (op. cit. (note 7), p. 380) later records there 'A Roman Urne, of Glass, with a Handle . . . Almost like a Bottle containing a Gallon and 1/2, but with a very short Neck and wide Mouth, and of whiter Metal. Encompassed girth-wise, with five parallel Circles. Found in *Spital-fields*.'

94. See Ainsworth, op. cit. (note 89), p. 178 no. 7: 'Ossarium plumbeum, cum operculo marræ petitionibus fracto, cui ossa sua insunt: *alit. plusquam* dodrantali.'

95. Montfaucon, op. cit. (note 82), vol. III, p. 168, pl. xciii.

96. See, for example, Bruno Kisch, *Scales and Weights. A historical outline* (New Haven and London, 1965), pp. 150–1; F.G. Skinner, *Weights and Measures: their ancient origins and their development in Great Britain up to AD 1855* (London, 1967), pp. 64–6, pl. ix.

97. Given by John Morton and mentioned in his *Natural History of Northampton-shire* (op. cit. (note 54), p. 509): 'At *Castor*, in digging . . . they frequently meet with some small square Bricks or Tiles, such as the *Romans* were wont to make their chequer'd Pavements of'.

98. '[It] is but a foot under ground, I traced it to ye Church yard pailes & had an hole dug in ye Church yard about 4 feet deep at about 10 feet distance from ye stile & there found a continuation of ye same pavement, ye course of ye tessulae being paralell to those in ye Hall yard & on ye same levell; they lay 20 degrees to ye Eastward of ye North. The Minister & Sexton told me y^t the whole church yard was paved at ye same depth & y^t most of ye coffins stand on these pavements wch are East; & SE of ye church large tyles 19 inches square, in ye Chancell red tessulae 1½ square & West of ye church small tyles 2 or 3 inches square & y^t once two Brass coins were found here, but I could not learn whose they were, they being lost again, y^t the tessulae in the Chancell seem to form ye rays of some large stars. The Mosaick work in ye Hall yard forms only Squares, Wreaths & a border of Ivy leaves: ye colours are white, Black, blew, red & yellow, disposed in shades being white outermost, then blew & terminating in black & in other parts of white outermost then yellow & ending in Red.' For further references to this mosaic, and an illustration of it prepared in 1956, see *vch Essex* vol. III (1963), p. 158.

99. Referenced to Montfaucon, op. cit. (note 82), vol. III, p. 208, pl. cxxv.

100. Only at this time was the pump introduced into the bathing procedure, allowing water to be directed under pressure on to the affected parts of the bather. 'The pump' was housed in a small chamber off the main bath. I am grateful to Mr Peter Davenport of Bath Archaeological Trust for these details.

101. Stukeley, op. cit. (note 15), vol. I, p. 72.

102. Ibid., p. 72; Stukeley, op. cit. (note 26), centuria I, pp. 161–75. An earlier verbatim publication, *Of the Roman Amphitheatre at Dorchester*, is generally listed as published in 1723, but (apparently) three years earlier Stukeley recorded in his diary (26 December 1720) 'My Ldy Hartford present^d my book of the Amphitheat. of Dorchest. to the Princess'. There are, however, later interpolations in the text as published and it seems likely that this entry too is a later insertion: see Stukeley, op. cit. (note 15), vol. I, p. 76.

103. A reference is given to Woodward, op. cit. (note 80), p. 257 no. 6: 'Ectypum Capitae virilis in terra Cotta', which sold for 2*s*. 6*d*.

104. 'Extract of a letter of the Reverend Mr William Rice, rector of Caerleon upon Usk . . . giving an account of an ancient Roman inscription lately found there. With some conjectures thereon by the Reverend Dr John Harris, STP and RSS', *Philosophical Transactions* 30 no. 359 (1719), pp. 945–6.

105. R.G. Collingwood and R.P. Wright, *The Roman Inscriptions of Britain* vol. I: *Inscriptions on Stone* (Oxford, 1965), p. 124, no. 365.

106. Referenced to Montfaucon, op. cit. (note 82), vol. III, p. 40, pl. xxvii.

107. I am grateful to Dr Catherine Johns for drawing this brooch to my attention. It was published by John and Andrew van Rymsdyk (*Museum Britannicum* (London, 1778), p. 27, no. 7 and tab. x, 7) with an erroneous provenance to Windsor, and then for years was misattributed to the collection of Sir William Hamilton, until recognized by Dr Johns. It now bears the number P.1974.11–1.1.

108. Montfaucon, op. cit. (note 82), vol. III, pp. 48, 50, pls. xxvii, xxxi.

109. Van Rymsdyk, op. cit. (note 106), p. 27, tab. x, fig. 5.

13 Medieval and Later Antiquities

Sir Hans Sloane and the Collecting of History

John Cherry

The collections of Sir Hans Sloane which have survived in the Department of Medieval and Later Antiquities in the British Museum may be most appropriately described as a miscellany. Part was indeed catalogued by Sloane as 'Miscellanies or Miscellaneous Things'. The very idea of a miscellany belongs to the late sixteenth or seventeenth century.[1]

'The Miscellanies' is the title and first section of the catalogue now housed in the Department of Ethnography of the British Museum.[2] There are 2,111 entries in this first section, and so it is larger than the more closely defined sections which follow. These are 'Antiquities', 1,129 entries; 'Impressions of seals, etc.', 268 entries; 'Pictures', 471 entries; 'Mathematicall Instruments etc.', 57 entries; 'Agate handles, etc.', 239 entries; and 'Agate cups botles spoons etc.', 303 entries. The other catalogue that contains relevant material is housed in the British Museum Department of Medieval and Later Antiquities. This contains lists of gems, 232 entries; cameos etc., 290 entries; and annuli or rings, 115 entries. The date of compilation of this latter catalogue is uncertain, but the former must have been completed by c.1740 when Thomas Stack, Sloane's librarian, completed the indexes which are partly bound up with it ('Seals' and 'Mathematicall instruments' and the rest in a separate volume). No indexes exist for the gems, cameos, and rings. The precise number of objects does not relate to the number of entries since, particularly in the 'Miscellany', some objects were entered at least twice. One entry states: 'The preceding numbers from 1991 inclusive are probably already entered in the catalogue: but their numbers of entry being lost they are entered anew'. This might suggest that the objects were unmarked. However, rectangular paper labels with numbers written in ink in an early eighteenth-century hand have been stuck on some objects amongst the seals, miscellanies, antiquities and pictures. There is no way of telling from the label to which series a particular number belonged. This may suggest that the series were kept separate; it has certainly led to a great deal of confusion in the past 200 years. It is not within our scope to untangle here all the problems caused by the failure to differentiate after 1753 the different series. Today some of the collection is referred to under its original Sloane numbers, but other parts of it have been re-registered under other numbers or is most easily referred to under later catalogue numbers. The continuing survival of the objects today will be referred to in the notes: if no reference is given in the notes then the object cannot now be identified. The following is by no means a comprehensive survey: a great deal of work

remains to be done on the analysis and occasionally the identification of items from the Sloane collection.

If one looks at the overall numerical development of the collections by comparing the numbers of specimens in 1725 with those in 1753, it is clear that mathematical instruments hardly increased at all (from 54 to 55), while pictures and drawings actually decreased (from 319 to 310). Most of the other categories show a two- to four-fold increase between those years.[3] The reasons for Sloane's interest in medicine, botany, natural history and zoology are clear, but there seems less evidence as to why or at what stage in his life he developed his interest in such categories as seals, antiquities or curiosities. It is likely that the crucial stage in Sloane's collecting in this area was the acquisition of the collection of William Courten or Charleton (1642–1702) who left his collection to Sloane as residuary legatee and sole executor (see Chapter 1). Courten's collection was kept at the Temple and Thoresby described it when he visited it in May 1695 as:

[the] most noble collection of natural and artificial curiosities, of ancient and modern coins and medals, that any private person in the world enjoys . . . He also has a costly collection of medals of eminent persons in Church and State, and of domestic and foreign Reformers.[4]

There are four items in the Miscellany that either came from Courten or belonged to him. Another collector whose material came to Sloane was the physician Sir Thomas Browne (1605–82), who possessed in Norwich a house and garden which John Evelyn described as a 'Paradise and Cabinet of rarities'. Sloane acquired not only books from his sale but also manuscripts belonging to Browne and the four urns recovered from the Anglo-Saxon cemetery at Walsingham, Norfolk that formed the inspiration for his *Hydriotaphia, or Urne-Buriall*, and are commemorated on its frontispiece.[5]

How far were other collections in the late seventeenth century concerned with history? One of the earliest collections to be involved with the bringing together of the relics of history was that of Sir James Balfour (1600–57) who, having compiled a library of some distinction and antiquarian flavour, and appreciating 'that things and events involved in obscurity are often illustrated by ancient coins, rings, seals, and other remains of a former age', carefully collected this precious antiquarian material and arranged it in cabinets to supplement his library.[6] Coins and medals were regarded by John Evelyn as a 'necessary adjunct' to a Library, being an extension of the portraits deemed essen-

* Marginal numerals in this chapter refer to Sloane catalogues listed on pp. 291–4

tial for a library of any pretensions.[7] The ornamentation of libraries with representations of poets and philosophers has classical antecedents, and the development of the decoration of libraries to provide a pictorial statement of the contents has been studied by André Masson.[8] The combination of manuscripts and books together with coins, medals and antiquities has been one of the great strengths of the British Museum from its foundation in 1753 to the present decade. That achievement was due to the nature of Sloane's collections.

Some parts of Sloane's miscellaneous collections will be discussed as categories on their own, notably the collections of rings, of agates, and of mathematical instruments, but the main theme of this chapter will be to consider how far Sloane's collections illustrate history and how far his collections can be considered to have formed a base for the British Museum as a show-case of English history. This aspect of his collections was particularly noted in Sloane's own lifetime, as is shown by the account of the museum on the occasion of the visit by the Prince and Princess of Wales in 1748 (see Chapter 1, Appendix 4). This notes how ancient and modern coins and medals in gold and silver are 'the lasting monuments of historical facts'. The way in which this description is turned from classical figures such as Prusias, Alexander, Caesar and Titus to the more modern figures of Pope Gregory XIII, Charles IX, to 'the happy deliverance of *Britain* by the arrival of King *William*; the glorious exploits of a Duke of *Marlborough*, and the happy arrival of the present illustrious *royal family* amongst us' sounds very much like a précis of the speech that Dr Mortimer, acting as the guide to the Prince and Princess, thought appropriate to the occasion.

The development of the study of the historical past in the period 1660 to 1730 has been outlined by David Douglas.[9] In that period a long succession of highly distinguished Englishmen brought to its proper culmination the best sustained and the most prolific movement of historical scholarship which this country has ever seen. The controversies of the late seventeenth and early eighteenth centuries were often conducted with reference to historical examples. For instance, the autocracy of James II was both attacked and defended by reference to the reign of William the Conqueror and ejected ministers who refused to take the oath to William III – the non-jurors – cited the example of earlier non-compliers. Douglas comments that it would not be difficult to defend the opinion that Anglo-Saxon studies have never progressed with greater rapidity than in the period which elapsed between the publication of William Somner's *Dictionary* in 1659 and the death of Humfrey Wanley in 1726. Wanley worked briefly as Sloane's librarian in the early 1700s,[10] and also wrote the second volume, the great catalogue of Anglo-Saxon manuscripts *Catalogus Librorum Veterum Septentrionalium*, to the incomparable *Thesaurus Linquarum Veterum Septentrionalium* of George Hickes. The late seventeenth century saw the

discovery of notable Anglo-Saxon antiquities such as the Alfred Jewel found at Newton Park near Athelney, Somerset in 1693 and the Sutton (Isle of Ely, Cambridgeshire) brooch found in 1694.[11]

One of the clearest illustrations of the connection between scholarship and objects is the Late Saxon gold ring in Sloane's collection with an inscription reserved in the metal against a background of niello. Described in the catalogue as 'An ancient broad gold ring wrote upon in runic, *2e/64* Roman, and Saxon characters', it is inscribed AETHRED MEC AN EANRED MEC AGROF (Aethred owns me, Eanred wrought me). This inscription attracted the attention of Hickes, who included a reference and an illustration in his *Thesaurus* or 'Treasury of the Northern Tongues', whose publication in 1705 marked an epoch in linguistic and historical Anglo-Saxon scholarship.[12] Another example of an Anglo-Saxon antiquity in the collection is the 'glasse boll ribb'd of a *4a/304* greenish glasse found in a stone coffin about 20 foot deep under the old Portico of St. Martin's church, given me by Sir John Colbatch'. This must have been found during the excavations in 1722 for the building of the new portico of St. Martin-in-the-Fields, designed by James Gibbs.[13] The most important Anglo-Saxon antiquities that relate to the scholarly revival of interest in the past are the four urns *4a/109–12* which were dug up in a field at Old Walsingham, supposed to have been Roman by Sir Thomas Browne who used them as the starting point for his discussion of *Hydriotaphia*.[14] They all contained cremations and one of these produced a ring (see Chapter 12). Sloane had other Anglo-Saxon urns, *2e/115* notably one found at North Elmham in Norfolk in 1711, *4a/384* given him by Dr Wood, and another with protuberances *4a/385* on it (Fig. 64).[15] A bronze pin set with an amethyst, found *4a/523* at Cirencester, Gloucestershire, has since been identified as Anglo-Saxon.[16] Sloane's collection of Anglo-Saxon coins is discussed elsewhere (see Chapter 9). The last Anglo-Saxon King of England is represented in the collection by a lead impression of the seal of King Edward the Confessor.[17] *4d/56*

The section of the catalogues devoted to seals was compiled between 31 August and 12 September 1738. It is composed of impressions of seals sometimes in wax but also in other materials. There are a large number of lead casts. Inter-mixed with the seals there are medals, bale seals, plaquettes, Papal bulls, some perpetual calendars, book stamps,[18] seal rings, and seal matrices. Some were single, others were mounted on card and one such card, no. 17, contained twenty-four casts of chasings of medals, on pew- *4d/231–46* ter silvered, mostly indecent.[19] Whether Sloane's collecting of seals and impressions was related to his collecting of manuscripts is a question yet to be explored. It is interesting to note the range of materials used for impressions in the Sloane collection: lead was the most common but wax, plaster, and sulphur were also used. In his collection of miscellanies there was a sample of 'an amalgam of tin and mercury *4c/1272* for taking off the impressions of seals from Mr. Courten'. Stranger materials were also used, notably a form of wax

Fig. 64 Urn from an Anglo-Saxon cremation cemetery [4a/385].
BM, MLA, Sl.385. Reproduced by courtesy of the Trustees of the British Museum.

of seals and medals of 'the late Sir Hans Sloane' is mentioned twice in that book as including a gold memorial medal of Cromwell,[26] and a gold medal of Thomas, Earl of Southampton.[27] Sloane seems to have been particularly keen on Simon's works. A paper with wax impressions of seals had an impression of the seal of Sir Edward Nicolas, [4d/264 [8]] Secretary of State to Charles II, and the catalogue entry is annotated 'Simons fecit'.[28] Finally Sloane had sixteen wax portraits on darkened glass by Abraham Simon (c.1622– [4f/289–92] c.1692), the elder brother of Thomas, including a self portrait.[29]

Sloane possessed a wax death-mask of Oliver Cromwell [4c/2010 or] (Fig. 65). David Piper believed it to be an authentic wax [4d/160] death-mask of the period, though not of Cromwell, but the traditional attribution is more probable.[30] A reference to Cromwell in the catalogue of seals stems from the fact that in August 1738, there was struck at the Tower a copper bust of Cromwell from a dye lately discovered in Holland. The impression was given by Mr van der Elst.[31] A more [4d/189] dramatic relic of the Civil War was 'one of the sluggs used [4d/654] by the 6th [sic] Monarchy men' presumably referring to a musket ball of the Fifth Monarchy men.

[4d/103,9** or 170,171] known as Rye paste, clay, and 'stampt on leather'. Finding themes to thread a way through this miscellany of seals is not easy.

The catalogue of Sloane's collection of seals commences with an impression of the seal of Oliver Cromwell as Protector, 1653 to 1658, engraved by Simon and taken off in lead. [4d/1] This was the Great Seal of Scotland.[20] Joan Evans notes that in the 1720s there was a general interest in Cromwell among the Antiquaries, since a number of portraits of him were noted.[21] Sloane had casts of a medal of Cromwell in [4d/9,9*,9**] different materials such as lead, red wax, and clay: 'Oli. Cromwel. Milit. parl. dux Gen. his busto taken off in lead.'[22] [4d/99] He also had a 'red wax in a box' impression of the small seal of Parliament made by Simon whose legend is described as '1st yeare of Freedom by God's blessing'.[23] There [4d/157] was in addition a sulphur cast of the seal of the Parliament of the Commonwealth of England.[24] Simon was also responsible for the engraving of the Great Seal of Cromwell [4d/100] as Lord Protector and there was a lead impression of the reverse of this seal.[25] Thomas Simon (1623?–1665) was the foremost medallist and engraver of dies during the Civil War, and has been described as the finest medallist who ever worked in England. Sloane was clearly interested in his work, although it may be that the occurrence of these impressions in the collection was due to the study of these seals by George Vertue, published in 1753. The collection

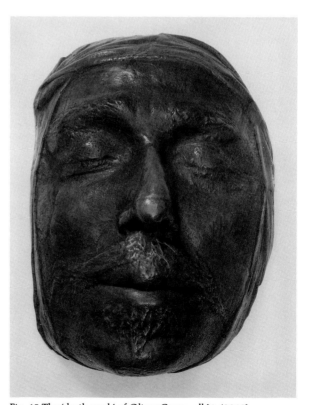

Fig. 65 The 'death mask' of Oliver Cromwell [4c/2010].
Reproduced by courtesy of the Trustees of the British Museum.

Plate 29 Attributed to Jan van Huijsum: *Cabbage Rose*. BM, PD, 5283, N.5–147. Reproduced by courtesy of the Trustees of the British Museum.

Plate 30 Copy after John White: *English sailors in a skirmish with Eskimo.* BM, PD, 5270, fol. 12ᵛ. Reproduced by courtesy of the Trustees of the British Museum.

Plate 31 Albrecht Dürer: *Study of water, sky and pine trees.* BM, PD, 5218–167. Reproduced by courtesy of the Trustees of the British Museum.

Plate 32 Hams Baldung Grien: *Old man with a heavy beard.* BM, PD, 5218–26. Reproduced by courtesy of the Trustees of the British Museum.

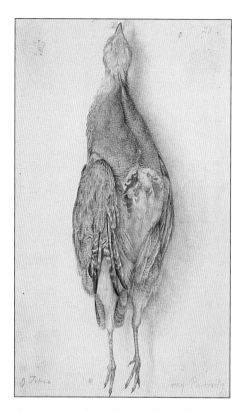

Plate 33 Jacopo de' Barbari: *Dead partridge.* BM,
PD, 5264–23 (1928–3–10–103). Reproduced by
courtesy of the Trustees of the British Museum.

Plate 34 Maria Sybilla Merian: *Spiders, ants, and two large spiders in
a Guajava tree.* BM, PD, Sloane 5275, N.1–18. Reproduced by courtesy
of the Trustees of the British Museum.

Plate 35 Verso of a mid sixteenth-century blockbook calendar, with the printer's name and signs of the months. BL, C. 36. aa.4.
Reproduced by courtesy of the Trustees of the British Library.

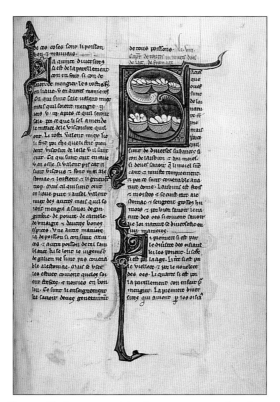

Plate 36 The beginning of the chapter on eggs, milk and
cheese from Aldobrandino's 'Livro dou santé', late
thirteenth-century. BL, Sloane MS 2435, fol. 68ʳ.
Reproduced by courtesy of the Trustees of the
British Library.

Plate 37 Venus, with the zodiacal signs Libra and Taurus, from the 'Introductio in astrologicam' of Albumasar, mid fourteenth-century. BL, Sloane MS 3983, fol. 43ᵛ. Reproduced by courtesy of the Trustees of the British Library.

Plate 38 The retinue of the Dutch annual tribute mission from its Deshima factory to the Shogunate court at Edo (present-day Tokyo). Sketched by Engelbert Kaempfer, 1691. No. 15 is Kaempfer himself accompanied by his Japanese groom and servant. BL, Sloane MS 3060, fol. 501. Reproduced by courtesy of the Trustees of the British Library.

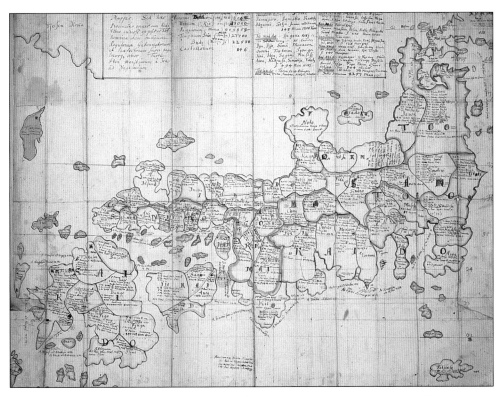

Plate 39 Map of Japan drawn by Engelbert Kaempfer, based on a Japanese original, 1690–2. BL, Sloane MS 3060, fol. 450. Reproduced by courtesy of the Trustees of the British Library.

Plate 40 Shijō Kawara. A painting showing theatre and other entertainment by the Kamo river in the Shijō district of Kyoto. From an album of celebrated sights of Japan, *c.*1670. BL, Additional MS 5252, fol. 37. Reproduced by courtesy of the Trustees of the British Library.

On the other side of the Civil War, Sloane had royal
4d/34–6 impressions, notably three (two lead and one tin) of the
4d/91 head of King Charles I, as well as a yellow wax impression
of the Great Seal of Charles I in a box, with the usual
5a/352 inscription. In addition there was 'a busto of King Charles
the first done upon leather by Mr. A. Sadler, at Norwich'.
The commander of the royal forces in Ireland during the
Civil War, James Butler, 1st Duke of Ormond, was represented
4d/55 by his seal impression. Sloane had an impression of the
4d/107 Great Seal of James I, and the arms of James I 'stampt on
4d/171 leather'. There was also a piece of 'the covering of King
4a/49 James's coffin' presumably part of the pall cloth used in
1625.[32] James's daughter Elizabeth, the Winter Queen,
2b/189 appeared on an onyx cameo.[33] For the Tudors he had an
4d/105 impression of the Great Seal of Elizabeth, but his finest piece
4c/1778, of Elizabethan jewellery was the Phoenix Jewel of Elizabeth
2014 I, made about 1570–80[34] (Plate 18). The inconsequential
jumble of the arrangement of the catalogues is well illustrated by this spendid item which finds itself between an
East Indian God made of gold and some shoes made and
worn by the Indians at Campeche from a Mr Laurie. The
defeat of the Spanish Armada was commemorated in the
4c/580 collections by a shield described as 'a piece of a dish or
target covered with gilt leather taken up out of the Spanish
galleon that was shipwrecked in 1588 on the coast of
Scotland'.[35]

For the earlier Tudors there were wax impressions of
4d/103–4 Henry VIII's broad (Great) seal and a smaller seal possibly
4d/220 of the Augmentations Office. He also had 'a busto of K.
Henry VIII relief on silver gilt, round' that seems to have
been the cover of a box[36] (Fig. 66). The sense of history
went even further back. There was a copy of a picture of
5a/387 Frank of Borsalia, Earl of Ostrevant (Fig. 67), who died in
4a/447 1470.[37] English medieval kings were represented by the seal
of Edward the Confessor (see above) and the victory of
the English over the Scots in 1314 was marked by 'the head
of a *spear* from Scotland by Dr. Rosse, found at Bannockburn
upon the field of battle between the Scots & English in
Robert Bruces reign & that of Ed. 2 of England' (for which
see further Chapter 12, Fig. 59, 1). Sloane also possessed
a lead badge of the Black Prince which is interestingly
4d/126 misdescribed in the Catalogue as 'A [raised] Impression in
Lead of the Institution of the Order of the Garter Edward
3rd kneeling before a crucifix and encircled by the Garter
with the motto Hony soyt ke mal y pense' (Fig. 68). The
spelling of the inscription makes it clear that this is the lead
badge showing the Black Prince, son of Edward III, kneeling
before the Trinity.[38]

The Order of the Garter occurs on a number of objects.
The Order attracted general antiquarian attention at this
time illustrated by the publication by Elias Ashmole
(d. 1692) of his most famous work, *The Institution, Laws and
Ceremonies of the Most Noble Order of the Garter* in 1672.
4d/3 The seal of the Garter appears immediately after those of
Cromwell.[39] There is an ivory plaque of Burnet as Chancel-

Fig. 66 The silver cover of a box with the bust of Henry VIII
[4d/220]. Reproduced by courtesy of the Trustees of the British
Museum.

Fig. 67 Copy of the painting by Frank of Borsalia, Earl of
Ostrevant (died 1470) [5a/387]. Reproduced by courtesy of the
Trustees of the British Museum.

Fig. 68 Lead badge showing the Black Prince kneeling before the Trinity [4d/126]. Reproduced by courtesy of the Trustees of the British Museum.

Fig. 69 Stirrup with the Garter and motto on the side [4c/1451]. BM, MLA, Sl.1451. Reproduced by courtesy of the Trustees of the British Museum.

lor of the Order (see below). Sloane possessed a very fine gilded stirrup of the period of Henry VIII which has the Garter and Motto on the side, probably originally surrounding an enamelled coat of arms (Fig. 69).[40] In his manuscripts there is a warrant for a new seal of the Order of the Garter in 1704.[41] His interest in the Garter may have been related to his interest in finds from Windsor and his position as royal physician (see Chapter 1).   4c/1451

Although contemporary history is illustrated in the collection, there is nothing that marks the Restoration of 1660. There were no impressions of the Great Seals of Charles II although there was one in red wax of Catherine of Braganza, the Queen of Charles II.[42] The Great Fire of London in 1666 is marked by the very first entry in the 'Miscellanies', 'A parcell of knives with bone hafts burnt in the fire of London'. The was a 'busto' of Charles II with an oval wreath of flowers and fruit in lead. He also had a mask of Charles II's face from Mr Killigrew and there is a death-mask of Charles II with the legend around 'CHARLES II POST MORTEM'.[43] There was 'A lead plaque with the Pope blessing one strangling Sir Ed Bury Godfrey', recording the murder of Sir Edmund Berry Godfrey in 1678. It was supposed that the Catholics were determined to murder Godfrey in order to destroy the evidence that Titus Oates had confided to him.[44] A lead medal is described as showing James, Duke of York, as a naval commander: 'A fleet of ships with an Admiral [James, Duke of York] standing in a commanding posture, at bottom is this motto "pro talibus ausio".' The standing figure is misidentified and was in fact Charles II since this is the naval reward medal of that King.[45] The 'relickes that the Duke of Monmouth carried about him and had in his pocket when he was captured' were given to Sloane by Thomas Tennison, Archbishop of Canterbury (1695–1715) and kept in the collection though, alas, they are not described. This refers to the capture of Monmouth after the defeat of Sedgemoor in 1685. Sloane also had an ivory plaque ('busto') depicting Gilbert Burnet, Bishop of Salisbury (1643–1715), shown as Chancellor of the Order of the Garter. He was a firm opponent of James II and played a large part in his replacement on the throne by William and Mary (Fig. 70).[46] The death of James II in 1701 was marked by 'a fine busto impress'd on lead'. The early eighteenth-century Wars of the Spanish Succession were represented by 'a brasse head three barrels of which were left by the French when they retired from Brussels under the Elector of Bavaria shott by them from their great gunnes'. It was given to Sloane by Lord Halifax who had it from the Duke of Marlborough. The political consequences of the Hanoverian settlement were recorded in the collection in two ways. Firstly, the trial or impeachment of Robert Harley, Earl of Oxford, in 1715 was commemorated by part of the broken staff of Lord William Cowper who was created Lord High Steward for the trial.[47] Secondly the invasion of 1715 was curiously marked by 'two rams horns covered with leather and tied together with

4d/72

4c/1

5a/395

4c/2009

4c/1987

4d/33

4d/175

4c/821

5a/360

5a/396

4c/499

4c/897

4c/736

Fig. 70 Ivory plaque showing Gilbert Burnet, Bishop of Salisbury (1643–1715) as Chancellor of the Order of the Garter [5a/360]. Reproduced by courtesy of the Trustees of the British Museum.

it in which was a paper with cyphers taken on board a French privateer about the time of the Pretenders invasion.' Inevitably there were walnut shells carved with the busts 4c/1183,1184 of William III and George I.[48] Finally in this section he had 4d/267 Sir Robert Walpole's portrait bust in plaster of Paris made by Natter.[49] Sir Robert Walpole was Prime Minister in 1738 and his inclusion shows how the collection was kept up to date.

Contemporary events abroad do appear in the collection. The campaigns against the Turks in Greece under the leadership of the Venetian general Morosini is commmem- 4d/176 orated by a lead medal with the date 12 August 1690.[50] 4d/247 There are medals of the Duke of Bavaria, the victory 4d/248 of 1697, and casts of the Corporation medal of Frederick 4d/249–50 III King of Prussia in 1701, and the late Emperor Joseph 4d/251 when King of the Romans with his queen Wilhelmina. Joseph I (1676–1711) was Emperor of Germany from 1705 until his death in 1711. An earlier monarch represented was 4d/129 Eric XIV of Sweden, whose bronze seal Sloane possessed. The son of Gustavus Vasa, he succeeded to the throne in 1561 and reigned until 1568; he died in 1577.[51]

A further category of seals is represented by those of learned societies and institutions of learning. This would come quite naturally to one who was Secretary (1693–1712) and then President (1727–1741) of the Royal Society and also President of the Royal College of Physicians

(1719–1735) (see Chapter 1). Of the major learned societies he owned a lead impression of the seal of the President, 4d/7 Council and Fellows of the Royal Society, which was also a work of Thomas Simon.[52] Sloane also had a red wax impression in a box of the seal of the Royal College of 4d/101 Physicians, made in 1737,[53] and a wax impression of the 4d/167 seal of the Society of Antiquaries of London: this was not the current seal, which was not engraved until 1770, but either the stamp for books or the steel seal-manual for sealing the letters of the Society which was acquired in February 1738.[54] His wax impression had a lighted lamp with a label underneath with the motto 'NON EXTINGUETUR 1717' and round the border 'SOC. ANTIQ. LOND.' He had a wax impression of the seal of Göttingen University which was founded 4d/168 by George II in 1737 and a plaster impression of the seal of the University of Leiden ('MAJUS ACADEMIAE LUGDUNENSIS 4d/53 apud batavos'). The only college seal in the collection was a cast in lead of Queen's College, Cambridge.[55] 4d/10

His collection of seals may be compared with other late seventeenth- and eighteenth-century collections. John Conyers, who died on 8 April 1694, had a collection of rarities that in 1691 included seals; much of Conyers' collection passed to Dr John Woodward and thence to Sloane (see Chapter 1). Richard Rawlinson, the antiquary and non-juror, was a major collector of religious seals. He began his collection in the first half of the eighteenth century and commented in 1742: 'I believe I have the largest collection in Europe, at least in England'. Rawlinson was also interested in Italian seals and he bought the collection, created in the seventeenth century, of Signore Giovanni Andrea Lorenzani in Rome in 1721. Rawlinson was a considerable collector of impressions and the climax of his many successful bids at auction was his purchase of nearly 2,000 impressions at Mrs Kennon's sale in February 1755.[56] In contrast, the interest of Sloane's collection lies in its wide variety, particularly the collection of small seal matrices and foreign matrices.

The most important medieval religious seal that Sloane possessed was the Romanesque ivory matrix of the Benedictine Abbey of St. Albans, described as being 'defaced 4d/110 by the Destroyers of the Monastery'[57] (Fig. 71). Other important religious seals include the wax impression of the 4d/109 seal of William Courtenay, Archbishop of Canterbury (1381–96). This fine red impression enclosed in a thick mass of bronze-green wax must have been taken from a charter.[58] It seems surprising that there are so many foreign religious seals. There was a series of six Papal bulls from Alexander 4d/64–70 III to Eugenius IV arranged almost correctly in date order, the seal of Antonio de Dominis, Bishop of Zeugg and 4d/15 Modorus in Dalmatia from 1593–6,[59] and the seal of Vincentio Agnelli Soardi, Bishop of Mantua from 1620 to 4d/128 1645.[60] Sloane possessed an example of a group of Roman hospital seals that aroused a considerable amount of interest in the eighteenth century: this was the bronze matrix of 4d/111 the Fraternity of the Hospital of St. Thomas the Martyr in Rome.[61] Some six seal matrices of this Fraternity are now

English Prime Minister, so also he had a wax protrait of 4c/2102 the current Pope, Clement XII (1730–40).[68]

Some rings, particularly the signet rings, are catalogued under seals, while others are included under 'Annuli'. Sloane collected a wide range of rings with that universality of approach that characterizes his collecting, yet it is clear that he was particularly interested in rings for their medical, or their magical and amuletic purposes. His collection does not include very fine signet rings or rings of important people: his signets are curiosities. The nine signets are characterized by enigmatic letters or devices engraved on their bezels. Two have merchant's marks: Sloane uses this term to des- 2e/80; 4d/95 cribe the mark on the former.[69] Perhaps the most enigmatic is the fifteenth-century silver ring with an octagonal bezel 4d/124 with the letters 'ION' crowned, and on one shoulder the letters 'RRD' with a leaf and on the other 'BCD'.[70] The reli- gious rings have inscriptions such as 'AVE MARIA', or 'IHESUS 2e/89 NAZARENUS REX IUDEORUM', both amuletic inscriptions, or 'ANNA MARIA' or religious scenes such as the Virgin and 2e/78,77 Child.[71] Sloane had two memento mori rings – 'old burying 2e/68–9 rings' – both found at Canterbury and both dating to the seventeenth century. The shoulders are decorated with enamel and in the centre of the bezel there is a skull in white and black enamel and the legend 'MEMENTO MORI', the inscription from which this group of rings takes its name.[72] He also had a small group of the enamelled decora- tions – 'deaths heads and skeletons' – used by goldsmiths 4c/1931 for the production of these rings.

Sloane as a physician was presumably interested in attitudes to death since he also had a very fine French fifteenth-century ivory memento mori displaying a human 4a/804 head on one side eaten by worms and a skull on the other, in the mouth of which a toad is visible; on the forehead is inscribed 'A LA SAINT NAVOT' and on the frontal bone of the skull 'POINT DE DEVANT A LA MORT' (Fig. 72).[73] One of the most interesting rings from a medical point of view was the 'ancient broad' gold ring engraved with the figures 2e/65 of St. John the Baptist and St. Anthony with a tau cross between them: the inscription 'A.A. C.O.M.F.O.R.T.' refers to the hope that St. Anthony, whose emblem was a tau cross, would preserve or comfort the wearer against the disease of erysipelas or St. Anthony's fire.[74] Since most of the liter- ature on this is nineteenth-century, and since the description of the ring is 'graved upon the outside with a scallop 2 erect figures, (St. Anthony and St. John Bapt.) with glories and on the inside with letters (A COMFORT)', it is doubtful whether Sloane realized the significance of the tau cross. It is however interesting to note that the portrait of Frank of Borsalia (see Fig. 67) shows him wearing a tau cross and bell.

Another area in which the collection of an object can be ascribed to Sloane's medical interests is:

An impression struck in brass (in ye manner of a medal) of the 4d/120 seal of the hospital of the Quinze vingts at Paris having on one side a King of France in his regalia standing and stretching out

Fig. 71 Ivory seal die of the Abbey of St. Albans, Hertfordshire (English, c.1100–1120) [4d/110]. Reproduced by courtesy of the Trustees of the British Museum.

known, dating from the fifteenth century. In the early eighteenth century only three were known, two in Gale's collection (probably that of Thomas Gale, Dean of York)[62] in addition to this example.

What was Sloane's attitude to religion? For a Protestant and a Whig he included in his collection religious objects such as Popish relics, two Malines alabasters (one a rather

4a/215 routine late Gothic Entombment and the other a Baptism, of mid sixteenth-century date, showing more Italian influ-

4c/231 ence).[63] The collections also include a white wax agnus dei

4c/1271 issued by Pope Innocent XI in 1700,[64] an agnus dei and cros- ses worn by Roman Catholics from Dr Covell,[65] several

4c/637 Popish trinkets, crucifixes and beads in a musk-rat's skin

4c/638 made into a pouch, and a 'Popish trinket made up like a watch of brasse with a crucifix and several earths from Jerusalem'. Both of these came from Alexander Brown. Sloane also had two examples of the intarsia models of the churches in the Holy Land that were widely prized by col- lectors in the seventeenth century: one was of the Church

4c/151 of the Nativity at Bethlehem, and the other a model

4c/150 of 'the Temple of the Sepulchre of our Lord Jesus Christ of Mount Calvary in Jerusalem with an explanation of the same, beads, measures etc.'[66] In addition there were pieces

4a/51 of 'the mosaic work of the Temple or the great Church at Bethlehem which is admirable and was built by St. Helena'.[67] Finally, just as he had a representation of the

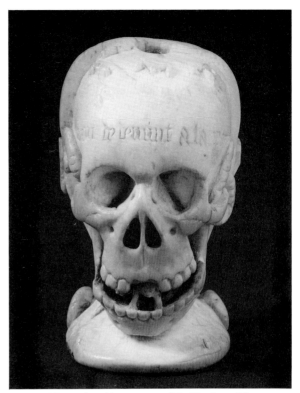

Fig. 72 Two views of an ivory *memento mori* (French, fifteenth-century) [4a/804]. Reproduced by courtesy of the Trustees of the British Museum.

his right hand to three figures kneeling in a suppliant posture; at his left hand a house; with this inscription Sigilu Domus Pauperum Cecorum Parisien. On the Reverse a Kings Bust with this Inscriptⁿ S. Domus Cecorum Paris.

This was the hospital for the three hundred blind men founded by Louis IX in 1270.[75] Sloane was particularly interested in sight since he wrote an account of 'a most efficacious medicine for soreness, weakness and several other distempers of the eyes' which was published in 1745 (see Chapter 3). There are a number of other medicinal entries scattered about in the 'Miscellany', most notably 'a powder used in Hampshire for the piles'.

4c/457

From the earliest times rings have been thought to have magical or amuletic effect. Sloane had two amuletic rings. One is set with a conical piece of horn, 'a dogg fish tooth ... For the Cramp?'.[76] Claws, teeth and horns set in rings were thought to be efficacious against the falling sickness or cramp. The *Pharmacopoeia Londinensis* of 1661 states that 'Elks' claws or hoofs are a sovereign remedy for the falling sickness, though it be but worn in a ring ...' and the *Musaeum Regalis Societatis* of Nehemiah Grew, published in 1681 records in a description of the river horse or hippopotamus that rings made of his teeth are believed to be very effectual against the cramp.[77] The other ring has a large circular applied bezel with astrological characters. In

2e/22

2e/83

the interior are engraved the names of three angels SADAYEL + RAPHAEL + TIRIEL 'with some other magicall characters said to cause the person wearing it never to want money. This belonged to the Lord Weymouth'.[78] Another magical object that may have belonged to Sloane was the crystal 'shew stone' of the Elizabethan magician Dr John Dee.[79] Sloane does not appear to have had any rings associated with the royal touching for scrofula or the cramp. The last monarch in England to touch was Queen Anne. Touching was practised by the Stuarts but not by William III or the Hanoverians. Sloane did however have lozenges or pastilles 'perfumed and burnt at the K. of Eng. touching for the evil to prevent infection'. This must refer to Charles II or James II.[80]

4c/613

Despite Sloane's close association with the Royal Society, no part of his collection was specifically concerned with scientific instruments. He did have a collection designated as 'mathematicall instruments', and various other items such as microscopes and thermometers are included amongst the miscellanies. The collection of mathematical instruments is concerned with measurement of distance. It begins with protractors, squares and compasses, including a 'way wiser to be fastened to the britches and knee to measure the distance any person walks'; this would now be called a pedometer.[81] The list continues with rules

5b/8

213

5b/10 for fortification including a set of instruments for fortification made by Mr Butterfield.[82] At least two instruments belonged to the Duke of Albemarle, whom Sloane served as physician in Jamaica from 1687 to 1689 (see Chapter 5b/24 1). These included an 'opticall tube bought of Wynne'[83] 5b/34 and a Newhouse quadrant.[84] He had two tubes (telescopes), 5b/20 one of which was 12 ft. long, made by Eustachio Divini,[85] together with several glasses belonging to the larger. 4c/185 Another Italian piece was the 'small perspective glass made by Campani at Rome given me by Mr Lenoy'.[86] Two other 5b/9,43 instruments, a universal dial and a silver horizontal dial for the pocket were made by the famous instrument maker Michel Butterfield (died 1724) at Paris. Other makers of instruments are mentioned, notably Mr Marshall, who 4c/176 made 'Mr. Beddeioles standing microscope for observing 4c/179,192, the circulation of the blood',[87] Mr Wilson, Mr Mellin, 653; 4c/180 whose 'sett of microscopes cost 5.7.6.'[88] and Stephen Gray 4c/194 of Canterbury who 'invented and made a brasse microscope for seeing objects in a drop of water'.[89] One of the micro- 4c/910 scopes in Sloane's collection came from James Petiver, whose botanical collection came to Sloane in 1718 (see Chapter 1). Foreign contacts reflect his friendship with foreign scientists. René Réaumur (1683–1757) gave Sloane 4c/1785 a thermometer of a new invention and 'Mr. Birley, opposite

to St. Martin's church', made 'a mercuriall thermometer in 4c/1938 imitation of Mr. Reaumurs'. Thermometers were attracting greater interest in scientific work and the problem of calibration interested scientists of the period, notably Robert Hooke, and later Réaumur.[90] The contacts of Sloane with the Continent are reflected by a 'sett of microscopes made 4c/181 by Mr. Musschenbroock of Holland sent me from the Prince of Orange by Mr. Desmarets and brought by Mr. Bentinck when sent over to complem't Kg James on his coming to the crown'.[91] Another Continental import was a hygrometer, a new invention from Germany, given to 4c/2092 Sloane by 'Mr. Wildy at the corner of Pauls churchyard'.[92]

There were at least three astrolabes. Sloane possessed the finest English medieval astrolabe; this, described as 'a 5b/54 brasse astrolabe made at London for the latitudes of Rome, London with a perpetuall alma[na]k upon it' has attracted much attention, and has been widely illustrated (Fig. 73).[93] He also had an early eighteenth-century Iranian astrolabe 5b/55 made by the Persian astrolabist Abd-al-Ali in 1712 (see Chapter 14, Plate 23). Inscribed with the name of the Safavid ruler of Persia, Shah Sultan Husain (1694–1722), a contemporary of Sloane, it probably found its way to Europe after the sacking of the Safavid palace in 1736.[94]

There is one instrument closely related to contemporary

Fig. 73 *a–b* The Sloane astrolabe (English, late thirteenth-century), obverse and reverse [5*b*/54]. Reproduced by courtesy of the Trustees of the British Museum.

4c/182   scientific enquiry and this is 'a ballance for weighing the specific gravities of bodies in air and water which was made by Mr. Handesbee [sic] ye elder'. This was presumably Francis Haukesbee the elder who died in 1713.[95]

4c/1984–5   Of his great scientific contemporaries, Sloane had at least four representations of Sir Isaac Newton, two in plaster and
4c/161–2   two in wax, one of which was from a cornelian of the Earl of Abercorn cut by Claus.[96] Next to these two waxes in
4d/163   the list of seals is an impression from a seal of Martin Folkes, who succeeded Sloane as President of the Royal Society in 1741. Folkes intensified the literary and antiquarian interests of the society, continuing the older and more comprehensive tradition of curiosity that Sloane represented, in contrast to Newton who confined the field of interest of the Society to the experimental sciences.[97]

Mining and the engineering problems associated with it attracted attention in the early eighteenth century, and so it is not surprising that Sloane had objects relating to
4c/1783   mining. One was 'a shovell head of oak found 36 feet deep in an old Roman lead mine in Wales. It had a long haft or handle that is joined to it by going into a hole and fastened at its short and broad end from Mr Mason.' This
4c/2046   entry is later repeated in the 'Miscellany' where the mine
5a/368   is identified as Trelogan in Flintshire.[98] He also had 'A drawing of workers working in a mine etc. from Lord Yarmouth',
5a/349   as well as 'A print of the multiplying wheel bucket engine',
5a/378   and 'A perspective of Mr. Churchman's engine for raising water'.

Sloane was an enthusiastic collector of stones, and examples of worked stone. The mineralogical aspect of the collections has already been dealt with (see Chapter 7). His agates were catalogued in two sections dealing respectively
5c/1–239   with agate handles and agate cups and saucers although
5d/1–303   there are one or two relevant objects elsewhere. His agates were mainly collected for the fascination of their changing and contrasting colour and for the opportunity for the imagination to perceive trees, landscapes, faces and clouds in the translucent stones. This aspect of his collecting has been discussed by Jessie Sweet, who drew attention to the fact that Sloane's own snuff-box is made of panels of agate (Fig. 74).[99] The importance of Sloane for the collection of agates is that he appears to have been the first collector of such a large number of specimens. They were certainly collected earlier: there are two examples in the Cheapside hoard, which shows that agate might form the stock of a seventeenth-century jeweller, while agate vessels are shown in a painting by Johann Georg Haintz of 1666.[100] The catalogues mention only very occasionally the people from whom Sloane acquired agates and often it is not clear whether they sold or gave them to him. Suppliers are Dr Stuart, the Bishop of Carlisle (William Nicolson (1655–1727)), Dr Waldo, Mr van Lulfe, Mr Marlow, Mrs Hayes, Mr Pinfold, Mr van Mildert, Mr Dupuys, Mr Bell, Mr Ranby, Mrs Shepherd, and Madam Montmorency. The
5c/164   geographical source is occasionally given: 'a haft for a knife

Fig. 74 Sir Hans Sloane's snuffbox, made of panels of agate [NHM, BM 60924]. Reproduced by courtesy of the Trustees of The Natural History Museum.

of a green and white marble or jasper in the fissures of which lies the lapis amiantus' comes from the Isle of Anglesea in Wales, which is also the source for another, 'a knife haft
5c/186   made of the asbestus or stone in which it lyes, being a marble or sort of serpentine of a dark green or yellow colour'. There are some agates from the East Indies, and from Germany and Bohemia. The mention of Germany may refer to Idar Oberstein on the Nahe in Germany where agate has been worked from the fifteenth century to the present day. Sloane also had examples of Florence stone, stone cut
5a/330   into particular shapes: one had 'a boy and an hare in Mosaich work'. Florence stone is specifically mentioned in Morand's description of Sloane's collections in 1729 (see Chapter 1, Appendix 2).[101] He also had vessels of serpentine, white alabaster and 'the red earth of Madera or Portugall', as well as vessels of crystal which are included in the section of the catalogues on agate cups. There was a
5d/83   'chrystall cup on a pedestall sett in silver gilt and Queen
5c/86   Elizabeth's picture in it' as well as 'a crystall flagon sett in silver'.

The engraved gems, either cameo or intaglio, belonging to Sloane have been fairly described as 'with a few remarkable exceptions, of indifferent quality'.[102] Many of the multitudinous and ill-cut stones were of the type used to embellish objects of use on the table such as cups, spoons or furniture. Among the more remarkable gems are the
2b/189   onyx cameo of Elizabeth of Bohemia, daughter of James I
2b/176   (see above) or the Italian fifteenth-century onyx cameo of

Fig. 75 Ivory plaque of our Saviour (seventeenth-century) [4f/277]. Reproduced by courtesy of the Trustees of the British Museum.

a King who may be Scanderberg.[103] Sloane also had collec-
4a/1120 tions of impressions of gems. In particular there was a 'black
ebony cabinet wherein are contained the impressions of
many seals or intaglios of the Earl of Arundel taken off
by Mr. Fuller the painter in sulphur bought by me from
Mr. Benjamin Mott painter to the parish clerks of London'.
4f/200 He had a painting of Arundel, 'Lord Arundell's picture on
board' as well as other objects from his collection, the most
4f/277 notable of which were, 'the bustos of our Saviour and Mary
Magdalen cutt in basso relievo in ivory. From the
Arundelian collection' which may be identified with two
ivories published by Dalton in 1909 (Fig. 75).[104] At least
one of the gems came from Arundel's collection: this was
2b/233 a cameo sardonyx with a female bust.

The materials from which objects were made was of
interest to Sloane. One of the most curious items of his
4c/1205 collection was 'a purse made of the stone asbestos . . . from
Mr. Franklin from New England' (see Chapter 7, Fig. 31).
The raw materials of ceramics also interested him. He had
4c/1246 'cinders from the iron furnace at Sussex by Mr Fuller' beside
which there is the note 'glasse bottles are made from it at
4c/2036 Bristoll'. Sloane also had some of the 'Delf potters glaze
being a mixture of tin, sand and kelp melted together.
[Query] whether this body is not like China ware from Mr.
Paine.' He had seven pieces of Italian maiolica. The first
5a/361–2; two were from the collection of Cardinal Gualtieri, and the
4c/1689–93 last five from the Abbé Sterbini (see Chapter 10). Two were
thought to have been painted by Raphael, but both are now

thought to be from the Marches and to date from the mid
to late sixteenth century. One of his most interesting pieces
is a large wine cooler, described as a 'cistern of earthenware   4c/1689
painted in Italy with several figures by Puenas 1554'. This
is now thought to have come from the workshop of Gia-
cinto Grassi in Urbino; the original date on the base, 1654,
must have been fraudulently altered by the time of the writing of Sloane's catalogue.[105]

As for the subject of medieval antiquities and archaeology, Sloane had medieval tiles in his collection although
it has been widely assumed that the collecting of these
started only in the second half of the eighteenth century.
He had 'a small red tile with white inlaid figures on it, taken   4a/525–7
up four feet under the pavement of a chappell at Coudray
the Lord Montacutes in Sussex, where there was a floor
covered with such tiles of various figures'. He also had
'Flanders tiles wᵗ wᶜʰ they floor stables', from Dr Brown.   4c/670

The collection of costume was a feature of ethnographical collecting (see Chapter 15) but Sloane also collected costume, and weapons particularly from Scotland. Among the
weapons there was 'a dagger of the Duke of Argyles fol-   4c/1506
lowers in Scotland' reflecting the abortive rising in Scotland
in 1685 led by the Archibald Campbell, 9th Duke of Argyll.
There was also a two-handed sword from the Isles of Scot-   4c/14
land and 'a Highland Scotch sken or dagger with a wooden   4c/40
haft' followed by the same longer with a wooden haft.[106]   4c/41
He had examples of Highlander's dress, notably the 'blew   4c/623
pinked doublet of a scotch Highlander wth pockets in his
short skirts wᵗ slittes in the back and sleeves', and 'britches   4c/624
and stockins made of yellow and red pladd of the same
Highlanders'; also in the collection were 'Highlander's   4c/625–9
garters', 'brooch', 'durk and knife', 'powder horn' and 'pistoll
(which was all of iron)'.[107]

The human curiosity that inspired Sloane is reflected in
one of the pictures in his collection, painted by Woolaston,   5a/470
of Mr Thomas Briton who was a 'small coal man who went
about the streets of London with a bag of them on his back
but in his leisure hours studied Chymistry, Antiquities,
Books of which he had a considerable collection, musick
of which he had a consort once a week resorted to by some
people of good fashion.' The combination of curiosity and
collecting that led to the growth of scholarship is reflected
in a number of antiquities from Windsor. Some such as the
two-handed sword or the iron mace may have come from   4a/364, 365
the castle since Sloane had advised Queen Anne on her
health and was appointed first physician to George II in
1727. Others were found in the locality, such as the head
of a spear, a bronze plate embossed with the face of a lion,   4a/251, 265
a very large iron spur found enclosed in a chimney,[108] an   4a/371
enamelled box, brass large spurs found at Windsor, a brasse   4a/379
George from Windsor, or the sixteenth-century Limoges   4c/1591
4c/1626
painted enamel, 'an enamelled picture of St. Jerome kneeling   4a/303
with a boy's head by his knees', found in the earth by Windsor Forest.[109]

The find that caused the greatest interest in the early

Fig. 76 The fourteenth-century bronze lamp found on St. Leonard's Hill, Windsor [4a/367]. Given to the Society of Antiquaries by Sir Hans Sloane in 1738 and exhibited at every meeting of the Society. Reproduced by courtesy of the Society of Antiquaries of London.

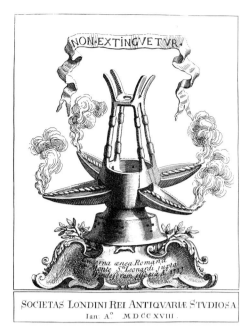

Fig. 77 Print of the lamp found on St. Leonard's Hill, Windsor, drawn and engraved by John Talman, 1718. Reproduced by courtesy of the Society of Antiquaries of London.

4a/367 eighteenth century was the bronze lamp found on St. Leonard's Hill, Windsor in 1717 (Fig. 76). It was drawn and engraved by John Talman, and the plate was presented to the Society of Antiquaries in 1718 (Fig. 77). Ever since then it has served as the device of the Society. On the print it is described as 'Lucerna ænea Romana ex Monte Sancti Leonardi iuxta Windsoram effossa Anno 1717', but a study by Professor Ian Richmond has shown that it probably dates from the fourteenth century. Sloane presented it to the Society of Antiquaries on 28 July 1738.[110] In Talman's design the lamp was shown with burning wicks and above on a scroll was the inscription 'NON EXTINGVETVR'. The idea that ever-burning lamps survived in ancient tombs was revived in the mid sixteenth century when the tomb of Cicero's daughter Tullia was said to have been discovered on the Appian Way, containing a still-burning light. Actual lamps, said to have been still alight in ancient tombs, were preserved in collections such as that of Aldrovandi in Bologna or in the museum formed in 1589 in the Anatomy School in Leiden.[111] The interest in the ever-burning lamp with the possibility that its secret might provide the formula for the construction of an inextinguishable light for miners was at its height in the late seventeenth century. In 1684 Dr Robert Plot read a paper to the Royal Society on 'the

Sepulchral Lamps of the Ancients, shewing the possibility of their being made divers waies.'[112] The inscription used as the motto of the Antiquaries must originally have been intended to mean that the light of learning is inextinguishable, in exactly the same way that a sepulchral lamp was inextinguishable. The preservation of this part of Sloane's collection as the emblem of the Society of Antiquaries and as an object which is still exhibited at every meeting of the Society provides a link between the collecting of antiquities in the late seventeenth and early eighteenth centuries and their continuing study at the end of the twentieth century.

Notes and References

1. In the *Oxford English Dictionary* the first use of the term miscellanea as a collection of diverse literary compositions is in the title of a book written by William Alley, *The poore mans librarie to which is enjoined certaine . . . annotations which may be properly called Miscellanea* (London, 1571), frontispiece. A clear use of the term miscellany in Sloane's sense occurs in Henry Maundrell, *A Journey from Aleppo to Jerusalem at Easter* (Oxford, 1721), p. 40, where he describes a 'confused miscellany of trees'.

2. The catalogues are discussed further in P. Murray Jones, 'A preliminary check-list of Sir Hans Sloane's catalogues', *British Library Journal* 14 (1988), pp. 38–51.

3. E. Edwards, *Lives of the Founders of the British Museum* (London, 1870), p. 303.

4. *The Diary of Ralph Thoresby, F.R.S.*, ed. J. Hunter (London, 1830), vol. I, p. 299 (24 May 1695). See also A. MacGregor, 'The cabinet of curiosities in seventeenth-century Britain', in O. Impey and A. MacGregor (eds.), *The Origins of Museums* (Oxford, 1985), pp. 157–8. See also BL, Sloane MS 3987, 'Notes on the productions and antiquities of England by W Courten 1663', and Sloane MS 3988 which records some of the curiosities that came into Courten's collection in 1666 and 1667. Not all of the objects came directly from Courten to Sloane. There was [4f/6] 'a bird upon a pear tree branch in mosaic or inlaid work – bought of Mr. Pinfold. He formerly had it of Mr. Courten at 1.5.0. I paid him 1.10.0'.

5. The libraries of Sir Thomas and Dr Edward Browne were sold on 8 January 1711. Dr. Browne provided 4c/670–85.

6. MacGregor, op. cit. (note 4), p. 154.

7. See Evelyn to Pepys, 1689 (printed in Evelyn's *Memoirs*, ed. W. Bray (London, 1827), vol. IV, pp. 296–323.

8. A. Masson, *The Pictorial Catalogue. Mural decoration in libraries* (Oxford, 1981). I am grateful to Dr Nigel Ramsay for this reference.

9. D.C. Douglas, *English Scholars 1660–1730* (London, 1951).

10. M.A.E. Nickson, 'Hans Sloane, book collector and cataloguer, 1682–1698', *British Library Journal* 14 (1988), p. 53.

11. The Alfred Jewel was first published by Dr William Musgrave, a London physician, who was an active member of the Royal Society, in *Philosophical Transactions* 20 no. 247 (1698), p. 441. For the current opinion on it see D. A. Hinton, *A Catalogue of the Anglo-Saxon Ornamental Metalwork 700–1100 in the . . . Ashmolean Museum* (Oxford, 1974), pp. 29–48. The Sutton,

Isle of Ely, brooch was first published by George Hickes, *Linguarum Veterum Septentrionalium* (London, 1705), vol. III, pp. 187–8. For a modern account see D.M. Wilson, *Anglo-Saxon Ornamental Metalwork 700–1100 in the British Museum* (London, 1964), pp. 174–7.

12. O.M. Dalton, *Catalogue of Finger Rings in the British Museum* (London, 1912), no. 181. The discovery of the ring some years earlier was recorded by Charles Leigh, *Natural History of Lancashire, Cheshire, and the Peak* (Oxford, 1700), appendix, unpaginated: it was discovered 'by a countryman by plowing in a Watling Street or Roman Way, adjacent to a Roman fortification near Manchester.' For Hickes see Douglas, op. cit. (note 9), pp. 77–97.

13. BM, MLA, OA 240. For a recent discussion of its significance see A. Vince, *Saxon London, An archaeological investigation* (London, 1990), p. 14 and fig. 6.

14. These four urns cannot now be identified in the British Museum collections. The suggestion by E.T. Leeds, *Archaeology of the Anglo-Saxon Settlements* (Oxford, 1913), p. 38 that some of the urns described in *Hydriotaphia* are in the Ashmolean is clearly wrong: see P.D.C. Brown in A. MacGregor (ed.), *Tradescant's Rarities* (Oxford, 1983), p. 274. Other objects in Sloane's collection came from Browne, notably 4a/123,139–43,146,148.

15. Although 384 cannot be identified, 385 still exists. Sloane had a series of pictures, 'done on paper by Sir Thomas Brown' [*sic*], mainly of birds, [4f/201–5] '3 green plovers?, two cuckows?, a curlieu?, and a sea pye?' given to Sloane by Mr Bustock. These are followed by 'Two urnes from the same' [4f/206], and it is not improbable that this was a drawing of two of the urns from Browne's collection.

16. BM, MLA, Sloane 523: 'A pin with a large round head of glasse from Cirencester'.

17. BL, MSS Seals XXXIV.3. W. de G. Birch, *Catalogue of Seals in the British Museum* (London, 1887), vol. I, p. 2 no. 9.

18. BM, MLA, Sl. 119. Book stamp with the symbol of St. Mark.

19. Only sixteen are listed. Most, apparently, had the engraver's mark 'MB'. All had inscriptions in Latin, with the exception of two in German. As a medical man, Sloane may have been amused by [4d/234] 'A woman sitting on a bed, Cupid shooting an arrow at her, a doctor feeling her pulse with one hand, and in the other holding an urinal at which he looks with this motto: Vulva dolet, urina docet.'

20. A.J. Nathanson, *Thomas Simon, 1618–65* (London, 1975), p. 45, dated to 1656. See also

G. Vertue, *Medals, Coins, Great Seals and other works of Thomas Simon* (London, 1780), pl. xix. Sloane's impression also appears in Pictures and Drawings [4f/65].

21. Joan Evans, *History of the Society of Antiquaries* (Oxford, 1956), p. 66.

22. E. Hawkins, *Medallic Illustrations of British History* (London, 1885), MI 388/7. No. 9 survives as a lead cast (BM, CM, M7325) in the Department of Coins and Medals. The clay impression [9**] also survives in that Department. This medal is the oval example described by Vertue as 'with his head in front, boldly projected'. See Vertue, op. cit. (note 20), pl.xii.B, and p. 14. I am grateful to Mark Jones and Luke Syson for help with the medals.

23. The exact identification of this is not clear. Neither of the two seals of Parliament have this inscription: see Vertue, op. cit. (note 20), pl. v. This is most likely to have been the reverse of the seal for the Court of Common Bench or the reverse of the seal for the Common Pleas of the County Palatine of Lancaster: see Vertue, op. cit. (note 20), pls. iii and iv.

24. Vertue, op. cit. (note 20), pl. v. Curiously the matrix of this seal was given to the British Museum in 1963 (BM, MLA, 1963,4–3,2).

25. Birch, op. cit. (note 17), vol. I, no. 603, p. 65. See also Nathanson, op. cit. (note 20), pl. 19, and Vertue, op. cit. (note 20), pl. xviii.

26. In the Department of Coins and Medals there is a gold example of the round that might have been Sloane's (Hawkins, op. cit. (note 22), 434/84) (BM, CM, M7401).

27. In the Department of Coins and Medals there are two gold examples of this medal either of which could have belonged to Sloane: Hawkins, op. cit. (note 22), 502/137 or 138.

28. Nathanson, op. cit. (note 20), p. 46. See also Vertue, op. cit. (note 20), pl. xxxi. It is worth noting that among the Sloane manuscripts there are two warrants addressed to Thomas Simon. One (BL, Sloane MS 856, fol. 4b plus 9) for engraving new seals for the Duchy of Lancaster, the Privy seal for England, the Great Seal and the seals for the three Courts of Justice for Ireland, and the other to prepare stamps or dies for coining gold and silver moneys in 1661.

29. BM, MLA, Sl. 289–92. E.J. Pyke, *Biographical Dictionary of Wax Modellers* (London, 1973), p. 136.

30. The two entries which could apply to this death mask are [4c/2010] 'A mask of Oliver Cromwell from Mr. Killigrew' or [4d/160] 'an impression in red wax of Oliver Cromwell's head from Mr. Ranby's seal cast by Claus ?'. The

first is the more probable, since the neighbouring entries to 160 refer to small red wax impressions, and Cromwell's mask is preceded by 'a mask of Charles 2nd face from Mr. Killigrew'; Killigrew remains obscure. For Piper's reservations see D. Piper, 'The contemporary portraits of Oliver Cromwell', *Walpole Society* 34 (1952–4), p. 41. Given the reference in the miscellany, Sloane's appreciation of the work of Thomas and Abraham Simon, and since a 'Mr Symons' modelled the wax funeral effigy of Cromwell in 1658 (Piper, p. 41), it is likely that the traditional attribution is correct.

31. This may be the same as the medal of Cromwell as Lord General, 1650, where the die is said to have been carried over to Holland about 1720 after which impressions in copper were struck, see Hawkins, op. cit. (note 22), p. 388. This impression still exists: BM, CM, M7324.

32. In the Sloane Manuscripts there is a notice of the death and funeral of James I with the Proclamation of Charles I in London in 1625 (BL, Sloane MS 826, fol. 22).

33. O.M. Dalton, *Catalogue of the Engraved Gems of the Post-Classical Periods in the British Museum* (London, 1915), no. 387.

34. *Princely Magnificence, Court Jewels of the Renaissance, 1500–1600*, exhibition catalogue, Victoria and Albert Museum (London, 1980), p. 59, no. 35, and *Jewellery through 7000 Years*, exhibition catalogue, British Museum (London, 1976), no. 194, p. 178. There was also the Phoenix Badge, 1574; see Hawkins, op. cit. (note 22), p. 125 and no. 71.

35. It is interesting to notice that there are two other references to finds from ships which suggests an early interest in nautical archaeology. They were [4c/1279] 'the piece of a barrell of a gun or fusee which was in an East India ship cast away on the north of Scotland. She was sent from Holland about 1712 and there sticks to the barrel a gold ducat and many pebbles, sand etc.'. There was also [4c/1286] 'a lump of pebbles and sand and sticking to and cemented with a ducaton in the middle of it. I saw another piece with the year 1711 on it. They were taken up in the year 1725 and lay in 13 fathoms of water. I had them from the diver who brought them up.' E. St. John Brooks, *Sir Hans Sloane* (London, 1954), p. 181 notes the friendship between Sloane and Admiral Sir Charles Wager who was first Lord of the Admiralty from 1733 to 1742 and thus in a position to encourage naval commanders to look out for curiosities that Sloane was amassing; see also Chapter 1.

36. This still exists. There were also versions in both wax and chalk [4d/221–2], which no longer exist, and [4f/282] 'the busto of Henry the eight in brasse. From Mr. Warner.'

37. This copy, which still survives, is derived from a lost original. Another copy is in the Rijksmuseum Amsterdam: see Y.D. Ovink, *Catalogue of Paintings, Rijksmuseum Amsterdam* (Amsterdam, 1960), p. 9, no. 131. The exact relationship between the Sloane and the other copies has not been elucidated. Frank of Borsalia's main claim to fame was that he married Jacqueline of

Bavaria who previously had been married to Humphrey, Duke of Gloucester: for her marriage, see K.H. Vickers, *Humphrey Duke of Gloucester* (London, 1907), p. 128. Sloane also had a piece of Humphrey's coffin, presumably from St. Albans Abbey, where he was buried. This is recorded under Vegetables [7/32]; see *The Sloane Herbarium*, ed. J.E. Dandy (London, 1958), p. 17.

38. BM, MLA, OA 100. See *The Age of Chivalry*, exhibition catalogue, Royal Academy (London, 1987), no. 68, p. 222.

39. BL, MS Sloane charters xxxiv.36. The Great Seal for the Order of the Garter was another work of Thomas Simon. See Vertue, op. cit. (note 20), pl. xxxv and Nathanson, op. cit. (note 20), pl. 47.

40. 'A very large stirrup used in the tilts or tournaments by some of the Knights of the Garter.' This still exists in BM, MLA, Sl. 1451. The most recent publication of this stirrup is in *Henry VIII, A European court in England*, exhibition catalogue, National Maritime Museum, ed. D. Starkey (London, 1991), p. 99.

41. BL, Sloane MS 3958, fol. 14.

42. This does not appear to survive amongst the BL manuscripts. For Catherine of Braganza's seals see Birch, op. cit. (note 17), vol. I, nos. 813–5. Sloane also possessed a drawing for the Great Seal of Queen Catherine with an order of the King to Thomas Simon to engrave it [5a/357]. For this seal see Nathanson op. cit. (note 20), pl. 48 and Vertue, op. cit. (note 20), pl. xxxiii.

43. BM, MLA, Sl. 1987.

44. Could this be the same as Hawkins, op. cit. (note 22), vol. I, p. 573–5?

45. A uniface lead cast of the reverse, which presumably belonged to Sloane, survives in the Department of Coins and Medals; Hawkins, op. cit. (note 22), MI 503/139.

46. O.M. Dalton, *Catalogue of the Ivory Carvings in the British Museum* (London, 1909), p. 146, no. 425. There is an impression of William and Mary's seal (GB 776, BL Sloane charters xxxii. 55) not in Dalton's catalogue.

47. *DNB*, s.v. Harley, Robert.

48. BM, MLA, Sl. 1183 (William III) and Sl. 1184 (George I). Both still exist.

49. Johann Lorenz Natter (1705–63) of Biberach in Swabia. For Natter see T.V. Buttrey, 'Natter on gem collecting. Thomas Hollis, and some problems in the *Museum Britannicum*', *Journal of the History of Collections* 2 no. 2 (1990), pp. 219–26, and Julia Kagan and Oleg Neverov, 'Lorenz Natter's *Museum Britannicum*: gem collecting in mid 18th-century England', *Apollo* 120 (1984), pp. 114–21 and 162–9.

50. In 1690 Morosini captured Monemvasia in Greece. There are a number of Venetian objects notably a lead impression of Marcius Contareno,

Doge of Venice [4d/63], and a series of drawings of Venice by Hofsted van Essen including St. Mark's Square 'with the masques at the time of the Carneval', the Rialto and St. George's [4f/213–18]. On the Turkish side Sloane had a picture of the Grand Visier done at Constantinople in 1702 from Lord Paget [4f/243]. This picture still hangs in the Department of Medieval and Later Antiquities. None of the medals mentioned in this paragraph survives in the Department of Coins and Medals.

51. Birch, op. cit. (note 17), vol. VI, p. 675, no. 23,146. The matrix still exists in the Department of Medieval and Later Antiquities.

52. Vertue, op. cit. (note 20), p. xxxi.

53. BL, MS Sloane xxxiv. 39. Birch, op. cit. (note 17), vol. II, p. 115, no. 5104.

54. Evans, op. cit. (note 21), p. 86.

55. BL, MS Sloane xxxiv. 70. Birch, op. cit. (note 17), no. 4761.

56. The best account of Rawlinson as a seal collector is in the unpublished thesis of B.J. Enright submitted in 1956, 'Richard Rawlinson, collector, antiquary, and topographer' (Bodleian Library, Oxford, MS D. Phil. d. 1786), p. 304.

57. A.B. Tonnochy, *Catalogue of British Seal-Dies in the British Museum* (London, 1952), no. 852.

58. BL, MS Sloane Charters xxxiv, 66. Birch, op. cit. (note 17), no. 1230.

59. BM, MLA, 38,12–32,4.

60. Birch, op. cit. (note 17), no. 22,333. The Italian ecclesiastical seal matrices may have come from Gualtieri or Sterbini.

61. Tonnochy, op. cit. (note 57), no. 885. There is no evidence to suggest that Sloane ever had two seals of this Fraternity and Tonnochy is mistaken in assigning his no. 886 to Sloane.

62. The best discussion of these matrices is by Albert Way, 'Notice of a formula of a Papal Indulgence, printed by Pynson, and of some other documents of a like character', *Archaeological Journal* 17 (1860), pp. 250–6. Gale is probably Thomas Gale, Dean of York, or his son Roger Gale. The seal of the Hospital, now in the Fitzwilliam Museum, Cambridge, probably came from this source.

63. Malines alabasters were also collected by Tradescant see C.H. Lloyd, in MacGregor, op. cit. (note 14), pp. 276–7, nos. 218–21. No. 221 is a very comparable panel representing the Entombment. The Baptism in the Sloane collection is probably from the circle of the Malines sculptor Willem van den Broecke (1530–80).

64. British Museum, *A Guide to the Medieval Antiquities* (London, 1924), p. 1.

65. Dr Covell (1638–1722) was Master of Christ's College, Cambridge.

66. Two models survive of the Holy Sepulchre (BM, MLA, OA 10338–9). It is not possible to say which of these is Sloane 150.

67. A. MacGregor, 'The King's Disport. Sports, games and pastimes of the Early Stuarts', in *The Late King's Goods*, ed. A. MacGregor (London, 1989), p. 416.

68. BM, MLA, Sl. 2102.

69. The two rings are Dalton, op. cit. (note 12), nos. 584 and 631.

70. Ibid., no. 429.

71. Ibid., nos. 702, 695 and 776.

72. Ibid., nos. 816–17.

73. Dalton, op. cit. (note 46), no. 441.

74. Dalton, op. cit. (note 12), no. 721. See also J. Cherry, in the *Proceedings* of the British Archaeological Association Conference at Hereford in 1989, in press.

75. For details of this Hospital see *La France de Saint Louis*, exhibition catalogue, Salle des Gens d'Armes du Palais (Paris, 1970–1), no. 140, and also L. Le Grand, 'Les Quinze vingts depuis leur fondation jusqu'à leur translation au Faubourg Saint Antoine', *Mémoires de la Société de l'Histoire de Paris* 13 (1886), pp. 107–260. It is interesting to note that John Thomas de Woolhouse, who was physician to the Hospital for the Blind at Paris in the early eighteenth century, corresponded with Sloane between 1722 and 1730. He was also the author of the epigram on Queen Caroline's visit to Sloane's Museum (see BL, Sloane MS 3516, fols. 4, 79). He may have been the source for this impression or medal which does not survive in the Department of Coins and Medals.

76. Dalton, op. cit. (note 12), no. 906. Sir Thomas Browne was interested in the medical use of amulets and discussed their use in *Pseudoxia Epidemica* (London, 1650), book ii, ch. 5, p. 65.

77. *Pharmacopoeia Londinensis* (London, 1661), p. 20. Nehemiah Grew, *Musaeum Regalis Societatis* (London, 1681), p. 15. Sloane's vertebrate collections included [25e/1311] 'Sea horse beard bristles to make a ring for the cramp' (see Chapter 4).

78. Dalton, op. cit. (note 12), no. 894.

79. It has so far escaped identification in the Sloane catalogues. It still exists (BM, MLA, Sl. 232), but there is no evidence for that number relating to the object in the Sloane catalogues. It may have come from the Cotton collection. See *Proceedings of the Society of Antiquaries* 21 (1907), p. 380.

80. For an account of the decline and death of the royal touch see Marc Bloch, *The Royal Touch. Sacred monarchy and scrofula in England and France* (London, 1973), pp. 219–23. He attributes the decline to the political changes of English monarchy in the late seventeenth century and early eighteenth century.

81. I am grateful to John Leopold for many helpful comments on this section. For a similar example see Anthony Turner, *Early Scientific Instruments, Europe 1400–1800* (London, 1987), pl. 66.

82. For Butterfield see F.A.B. Ward, *A Catalogue of European Scientific Instruments in the British Museum* (London, 1981), p. 145 and also M. Daumas, *Les instruments scientifiques aux XVII et XVIII siècles* (Paris, 1953). A pocket case of drawing instruments signed 'Butterfield à Paris' is illustrated in Turner, op. cit. (note 81), pl. 144.

83. Henry Wynne (free of the Clockmakers Company 1662, died 1709), maker of various instruments (E.G.R. Taylor, *The Mathematical Practitioners of Tudor and Stuart England* (Cambridge, 1954), pp. 242–3; B. Loomes, *The Early Clockmakers of Great Britain* (London, 1981), pp. 597–8).

84. The instrument referred to was presumably Daniel Newhouse's sinical quadrant, described in his book, *The Whole Art of Navigation* (London, 1685); see also Taylor op. cit. (note 83), p. 400.

85. For Eustachio Divini, an important maker of optical instruments in Rome, see R.S. Clay and T.H. Court, *History of the Microscope* (London, 1932), p. 78. The great tube still survives in the British Museum, see Ward, op. cit. (note 82), no. 446. Ward misquotes the Sloane number since the tube is 5b/21 while the glasses (which do not survive) are 5b/20. Sloane also had another optical tube bought at Rome [5b/23].

86. Apparently Giuseppe Campani in Rome (c.1620–c.1695), the most renowned maker of optical instruments of his time: see Daumas, op. cit. (note 82), p. 87.

87. John Marshall (1663–1725), optical instrument maker (Taylor, op. cit. (note 83), p. 280). See also Turner op. cit. (note 81), pl. xix, and Clay and Court, op. cit. (note 85), p. 249. He was visited by the von Uffenbach brothers in 1710: they found his work 'only tolerable; one might almost say bad'.

88. John Melling (fl.1672–1704), optical instrument maker: Taylor, op. cit. (note 83), p. 265. A set of lenses made by Melling was accepted by the Royal Society.

89. Stephen Gray (fl.1694–1701), amateur instrument maker in Canterbury: Taylor, op. cit. (note 83), p. 290. See also Clay and Court, op. cit. (note 85), p. 245.

90. For thermometers see Turner, op. cit. (note 81), pp. 130–1. It is also interesting to note that among the Sloane manuscripts there is a seventeenth-century account of experiments with the thermometer (BL, Sloane MS 2880, fol. 224), and an account of a 'Thermometer [sic] fondé sur le nouveau Barometre double de M. Hugens' (BL, Sloane MS 1775, fols. 156b–161).

91. Johann van Musschenbroek of Leiden (1660–1707), member of a distinguished family of instrument makers and himself chiefly famed for his microscopes (see M. Rooseboom, *Bijdrage*

tot de geschiedenis der instrumentmakerskunst in der Noordelijke Nederlanden tot omstreeks 1840 (Rijksmuseum voor de Geschiedenis der Natuurwetenschappen te Leiden, Mededeling 74) (Leiden, 1950), pp. 105–6, with portrait.

92. George Willdey (fl.1695–1733), optical instrument maker (Taylor, op. cit. (note 83), p. 292). Hygrometers (instruments for measuring the amount of humidity in the air) have been made since the seventeenth century. The Accademia del Cimento and the Royal Society respectively experimented with them and Hooke made at least one.

93. Generally known as the Great Sloane Astrolabe: R.T. Gunther, *Astrolabes of the World* (Oxford, 1932), no. 290; Ward, op. cit. (note 82), no. 324. It is worth noting that Sloane had two copies of Chaucer's *Treatise on the Astrolabe* (BL, Sloane MSS 314, 446).

94. Gunther, op. cit. (note 93), vol. I, p. 147 and no. 33; D. Barrett, *Islamic Metalwork in the British Museum* (London, 1949), p. xx and pl. 40.

95. Francis Haukesbee the elder (worked c.1700, died 1713), maker of various instruments; Taylor, op. cit. (note 83), pp. 296–7.

96. There were also two wooden medallions among the four turned on an engine invented by John Jackson in 1749 [4c/2101].

97. For a discussion of the effect of the presidencies of Sloane and Folkes see Evans, op. cit. (note 21), pp. 94–5.

98. See F.J. North, *Mining for Metals in Wales* (Cardiff, 1962), p. 78.

99. Jessie M. Sweet, 'Sir Hans Sloane: life and mineral collection, part II: mineral collection', *Natural History Magazine* 5 (1935), pp. 97–116.

100. The numbers of the agates in the Cheapside hoard are A 14084 and A 14206. Johann Georg Haintz's painting of a cabinet is illustrated in L. Hansmann and L. Kriss-Rettenbeck, *Amulet und Talismann* (Munich, 1977), no. 299.

101. For Florence stone see *Splendori di pietre dure. L'arte di corte nella Firenze dei Granduchi*, ed. Annamaria Giusti (Florence, 1988).

102. O.M. Dalton, *Catalogue of the Engraved Gems of the Post-Classical Periods* (London, 1915), p. xiv. Sloane's gems and intaglios are catalogued in two series, *A* and *B*. The distinction between the two series is not clear: *A* appears to contain intaglios only, while *B* is mainly cameos but also includes intaglios.

103. Ibid., no. 373.

104. Dalton, op. cit. (note 46), nos. 447–8. Here they are catalogued as French, seventeenth-century, but there seems to be no reason why they should not be Italian. No. 447 is registered as BM, MLA, OA 1339. No. 448 is not available. Sloane also had 'a vase of red and grey marble with green veins wt a cover' and an oval vase of the same [4a/218] from Lord Arundel's collection.

105. T. Wilson, *Ceramic Art of the Italian Renaissance* (London, 1987), p. 155, no. 245. I am grateful to Dr Dora Thornton for help with the maiolica.

106. 4*c*/14 may be BM, MLA, OA 3189.

107. For Scottish costume of the period see S. Maxwell and R. Hutchinson, *Scottish Costume 1550–1850* (London, 1958). Sloane also had a Scotch quaich [4*c*/661].

108. There is a drawing of this spur by William Stukeley in Society of Antiquaries, MS 265, fol. 37.

109. BM, MLA, Sl. 303.

110. Evans, op. cit. (note 21), p. 62.

111. See S. Piggott, *Ruins in a Landscape* (Edinburgh, 1976), pp. 87–9.

112. Robert Plot, 'A discourse concerning the sepulchral lamps of the ancients, shewing the possibility of their being made divers waies' *Philosophical Transactions* 14 no. 166 (1684), p. 806.

14 Oriental Antiquities

Oliver Impey

Sir Hans Sloane assembled a small collection of Eastern works of art, mostly of applied art, almost by accident. Those pieces that would come under this category today, would then have been perceived as curiosities or would have been acquired for their significance in some other field. Thus, for instance, the Chinese prints of flowers and insects were of interest to Sloane for their subject matter; today they are prized for their rarity and their interest as examples of fine Suzhou woodblock printing of the seventeenth century. The oriental things most readily available during Sloane's lifetime – the export porcelains and lacquers of China and Japan – he more or less ignored. These he could have bought easily in London had he chosen to do so. Those few pieces that he did acquire seem to have been significant either on account of their purpose (e.g. the 'white china earthen ware *ink pott* white painted wᵗ brown', and its pair which are in fact Japanese incense burners, though doubtless Sloane bought them for their presumed connection with the process of writing in which he was interested) or for the subjects portrayed in models, as in most examples of the *blanc-de-Chine*. This is supported by the fact that he acquired so many soapstone carvings of various deities (see below). It must be admitted, however, that we have no way of identifying any of the porcelain described as blue-and-white.

28a/1056–7

Of those oriental objects that survive in the collection, the Persian paintings, most of the Chinese prints and a considerable proportion of the Japanese items, including many of the most interesting, were acquired by purchase from the nephew of Engelbert Kaempfer, who had been surgeon at the Dutch East India Company's trading station in Japan, Deshima, until 1695.[1] The books from this purchase are discussed in Chapter 18. Many of the Chinese objects were acquired directly from persons who had worked in China, such as Father Fontenay and Captain James Cunningham (or Cunninghame), and who were in correspondence with Sloane. Many of these items are now classified as ethnographic and are discussed in Chapter 15. The distinction here drawn between art and ethnography is far from precise.

Oriental objects can be found in most of the catalogues drawn up by Sloane; 'Miscellanies' contains the majority, but items can also be found in 'Paintings', 'Antiquities', 'Agate handles &c' and others. A separate list of the objects acquired from Kaempfer survives in the British Library.[2]

In the 'Miscellanies' catalogue, the objects possibly ascribable to China represent the largest contribution of any geographical area; this cannot be quantified as so many of such articles are possibly Japanese. Japan provides the second largest contribution, bearing the same proviso in mind, that the identification may be incorrect.

In fact, Sloane's identification of the origins of most of the oriental objects is remarkably accurate. He did, of course, obtain many things from correspondents who had actually collected the items and therefore could be relied upon. In some cases he has led us into the trap of thinking that a description means a site. He frequently, for instance, followed contemporary nomenclature over porcelain and lacquer. There was a tendency in the eighteenth century to call all porcelain Chinese (china) and all lacquer Japanese (japan[n]). Thus 'A blew and white China *saucer*' is as likely Japanese as Chinese, and the same is true of much of the rest of the porcelain. Similarly, in 'A case made of *Bambo* lacquer'd in Japan wherein are five Chinese *instruments* of feather ear pickers &c. for tickling the ears', the word Japan might describe either the country or the material – indeed the word Chinese might here mean simply oriental.

28a/69

28a/272

A large number of items are thus insecurely ascribable to China or Japan, though one can with some confidence assume that they may derive from the one or the other. Sloane himself was often unsure rather than simply ambiguous; 'A Chinese or Japanese *comb* made of *Bamboo*, the teeth being severall single join'd at the middle & ends by broad pieces of the same lacquerd over', or 'A very long and strong Japan'd *bow*. From Japan?' or 'A Chinese or Japanese *seal*, letter mark or word cutt upon *chrystall* which is an inch square made cubicall & on which is carved a lyon'.

28a/465

28a/892

28a/898

Ceramics

Sloane must have been well aware of both Chinese and Japanese porcelain, specifically made for export to the West, which was flooding into Britain and into the rest of Europe in huge quantities. This was readily available in London from the travelling 'China-men' or 'India merchants' as well as from shops in Leadenhall Street or direct from the East India Company's headquarters in the same street. Doubtless it was precisely for this reason that he did not buy much of it.

He had several pieces of unidentifiable blue-and-white porcelain, including basins, saucers and coffee cups. The 'China saucer, blew and red', the 'China whitish tea dish wt. the gold fish painted on it from Dr Mortimer' and the 'china plate whereon are enameld four sorts of the China fish kept in Jarrs by the Chinese for their diversion' were presumably enamelled *famille verte* or *famille rose*, unless they were Japanese Imari or its Chinese imitation. The 'red China earthen *dish*' was presumably Yixing, a polished red stoneware.

28a/72–4, 84, 88
28a/91, 89–90,92 etc.
28a/71,1851
28a/1989

28a/137

The 'ink potts' described above are still preserved and are a rare form of Japanese Imari with no underglaze blue, and enamelled in red and silver, now oxidized. The 'Nests of China earthen ware *boxes* blew & white 3 boxes in each', of which two remain (one incomplete) are decorated in underglaze blue, and overglaze red, gold and silver. These are also Japanese Imari of the third quarter of the seven-

28a/1056–7

28a/1058–60

teenth century and are identical to a pair at Burghley House which were bequeathed to Elizabeth, Countess of Exeter by her mother, the Countess of Devonshire, in 1690.[3]

Much of the porcelain is, or was, *blanc-de-Chine*. This is a porcelain with an unusually white- or cream-coloured body, lacking the blue tinge of most eastern porcelain. It was made in or around Tehua in the southern province of Fujian. This town was the centre of the ivory trade and it has been plausibly suggested that much of the porcelain was made as a cheap imitation of ivory; this would be especially true of the figurines, of which Sloane had several, two of which can be identified today. These figures were a considerable feature of Chinese export porcelain; the Earl of Arundel had three at Tart Hall in 1651,[4] and by the beginning of the eighteenth century they were a common feature in great houses all over Europe. The Countess of Exeter inherited several in 1690 (see above)[5] and some were inventoried in the Danish Royal Collection in the same year.[6] The Sloane examples known today can be identified with the Taoist Goddess of prosperity and long-life, Tou-Mu;[7] this may be 'A *Chinese* Goddesse sitting on the water lilly w^t persons one on each side adoring her'. The Bodhisattva Ta Mo is probably 'A *Chinese Idoll* w^t a [pott, deleted] shoe' (see also a soapstone example in the Sloane collection). Another *blanc-de-Chine* piece still extant is 'A white china *cup* w^t a crab in the bottom', where the crab is modelled in full relief. The 'China earthen ware *figure* of a *woman* sitting w^t a scroll in her hand white & not glazed' and 'The *same* w^t a pott in her hand' survive, as biscuit figures.[8]

Sloane apparently did not possess any of the *blanc-de-Chine* cups or saucers or teapots with sprigged decoration in relief on the outside; he did possess some Meissen imitations or pastiches of these along with some other Meissen imitations of Chinese porcelain. 'A white [*China*, deleted] *Porcelain* bason, made at [Berlin, deleted] *Dresden* in imitation of *China* w^h blew characters at bottom', 'Another. Both given me by Lady *Darlington*', and 'A white tea dish w^h a handle made of a vine branch w^h its leaves towards the bottom in strong gold colour from the *same*'.

Sloane lists five pieces of 'redish earth glaz'd over w^t green' that must be celadon. 'A rib'd two eard *China bottle* very ponderous made of redish earth glaz'd over w^t green said to be 1000 years old from Dr *Waldo*' was probably fifteenth-century Zhejiang celadon, which had been imported into the Near East in great quantities; it was rarely transported after 1600 and is thus not so well known in Europe as the blue-and-white. An early dated example of this ware is the Warham Bowl, given to New College, Oxford, probably in 1532.[9] Other pieces from the same source (Dr Waldo) were a large dish, a beaker (and two broken pieces) and 'A *jarr* and cover of the *same*, flowerd'. In view of the fact that 'A plate of the same sort of *China* ware w^t 1481' and its pair are pale crackled Kuan-type dishes, it is possible, but very unlikely, that all the pieces here identified as celadon were Kuan.[10]

It might be conjectured that the 'ancient very heavy

(margin references, left column)
28a/1179
28a/289
29a/930
28a/107
28a/1054
28a/1055
28a/1195
28a/1196
28a/1197
28a/1478
28a/1479
28a/1481
28a/1480
28a/1492–3
28a/1705

earthen *China jarr* covered w^t green varnish' was indeed ancient, possibly a Han dynasty (206BC–AD220) lead-glazed vessel.

The 'Four China *basons* of a dark brown colour waved w^t white lines' can be identified from the three that survive (Plate 19) as Japanese, from Utsusugawa (near Nagasaki). It would be interesting to know what were the 'very large Japan earthen *bason* w^t yellow & blew marks & figures. very ancient' and the 'black earthen old Japan *saucer* enameld w^t figures and birds. given me by Mr *Ranby*. old' and its pair. This latter might have been Chinese *famille noire*, though that was hardly 'old' at the time. 'A Chinese blew watering *pott*' survives as a peach-shaped wine ewer with a turquoise glaze; the '*cock in China*' is a polychrome biscuit figure of a phoenix on a rock surrounded by peonies in high relief.[11]

In view of Sloane's scientific concerns, it might surprise one that he did not experiment with the age-old fiction embodied in the entry 'A sort of *China ware* which is said to admit of no poyson but immediately breaks'. (He did try out a poisoned arrow; 'One of the poyson'd *arrows* [from Borneo] wch being try'd had no effect on a wounded pigeon'.)

Soapstone and other Carvings

Soapstone, or steatite, was unfamiliar in Europe in the late seventeenth century and not well known in the eighteenth. In the Danish Royal Collection there are several soapstone figures described as *udskaaren af Een grønagtig steen som een jaspis* ('carved out of a greenish stone like a jasper') in the 1690 inventory.[12] For much of the eighteenth century this was called in Danish *Fedtsteen* ('figure-stone'). In the 1740 inventory of the Duc de Condé it is called *pierre du lard*.[13] Sloane was not sure if it was a modelling agent or if it was carved; he used the terms 'grey soft stone or past', 'reddish alabaster or marble', 'past', 'stone or rice past', 'past or a sort of alabaster', or 'past or alabaster'. Dated examples of this material are useful as the styles of carving have changed little in three hundred years. There are some precisely dated examples in Denmark, imported on the ship the *Kronprins Christian* in 1732 from Canton, and others inventoried in 1737.[14] In 1777, the examples in the collection of Queen Ulrika Eleonora of Sweden were described as of alabaster.[15] Fourteen examples survive in the Sloane collection, some as cups, others as seals or perfume burners. Others are figurines, reinforcing the suggestion that Sloane was interested in the depiction of figures of alien deities etc.; some can be identified as gods or goddesses; Kuanyin, Guanti (Plate 20) or Shoulao; others as philosophers, Laozi, or as monks.[16]

The '*China rock* in which are cutt A ship at bottom, a pagoda at top & 2 sumer houses one of each side with staires' may have been made from a boulder of jade.

The wood-carvings, like much of the soapstone and *blanc-de-Chine*, are mostly figurines, carved in the round, of gods or goddesses or of *sennin* (Immortals), not always

(margin references, right column)
28a/1698
28a/1704
28a/1716–17
28a/149
28a/922
28a/422
28a/325
28a/184,418
28a/562,929
28a/1174, 1176
28a/184, 418,562
28a/1174, 1181
28a/1175–6, 1178
28a/1180
28a/923

28a/20,144
28a/1172, 1182

28a/1008, 1173,1754,
28a/1078
28a/1837

28a/1185–91
28a/1499
28a/1192–4
28a/1493–4
28a/1939

28a/1710

28a/143,158, 172,631,1142, 1713–15
28a/1142

28a/1120
28a/1512

e.g. 28a/1004
28a/1761

easily identifiable; Liu Hai, Li Tu Guai and two others.[17] These, like the soapstone, would be undateable without this evidence. Sloane had at least three other wooden Chinese figures, now untraceable. He also had (the first from Kaempfer) two miniature shrines, 'The Goddesse *Quonem* [Kuanyin] worship't by the Japanese. & esteemed their greatest God' and 'A Japan *pagode* w^t. the *Idol* standing over a flower &c'.[18]

Bronze or brass figures pose the same problems; at least seven figures from Sloane's collection survive today, of men and boys, and a kylin's head, 'The figure of a *Lyons mouth* w^t a horn on its forehead'. Three kylins and two large cranes are among the figures that cannot be found today. The *'cray-fish*. lizard & fly in metall made for ornaments in China?' may have been simple or articulated figures; if the latter then they were probably Japanese.

A particularly intriguing entry is 'A *Chinese* figure recumbent of Mr *Gilbert* done from the life in China earth'. This, now lost, is likely to have been a modelled portrait of a ship's Captain or Supercargo such as those in the Danish Royal Collection;[19] there there are four miniature figures seated on wooden Chinese chairs of the Captain and of three supercargoes of the ship the *Kronprins Christian,* which returned from Canton in 1732, and one life-sized bust portrait of Captain Allewelt of the *Kongen af Danmark* of 1738. The first of these, of Captain Michael Tonder, is described in the 1737 inventory as *meget proper og med særdeles Fliid af fiin Indianisk Jord eller Ler posseret af en Chinesisk Kunstner i Canton* ('very skillfully made of fine Indian earth or clay and passemented by a Chinese artist in Canton'). Similar standing figures are known from, e.g. the Victoria and Albert Museum and the Amsterdam Historical Museum; recumbent figures appear to be otherwise unrecorded. Nobody of the name of Gilbert who could be the sitter is recorded in Sloane's correspondence.[20]

There were eight or more cups carved in rhinoceros horn correctly identified though one is ascribed to Japan on account of its provenance from Kaempfer 'A *cup* of rhinoceros horn carvd & gilded from Japan from Dr. *Kempfer*'. Kaempfer was able to acquire a considerable number of Chinese things in Nagasaki; this must have been most misleading in Europe.

In ivory, Sloane had 'An *ivory head*', a large and fine Ming carving and 'An ivory cylindrical *ring* to hinder the hurting of the finger in drawing the bows in China carv'd & painted w^t a Landskip. From Mr. *Maidston*.' He had at least two figure carvings and a pagoda 'The *modell* of the *porcellan* and brick *towers* in China carvd in *ivory* there w^t in each floor of wch are the figures of the Goddesse Sloath carved. It is adorned with chains bells & other ornaments cutt in ivory out of whole pieces. They serve for beacons being built to give alarms of danger in times of danger from Mr. *Hodgson*.' Such models, often nearly a metre tall, are not uncommon; there are two fine examples at Burghley House and two lesser quality pagodas were imported into Denmark in 1732.[21] In Denmark there are also

similar models in pearlshell.

Lacquer

28a/78,94,138
28a/139
28a/2082

28a/1149

28a/1077
28a/1104
28a/1070
28a/115

28a/170

It is difficult to know how to read such descriptions as 'A Japan *bottle*' or 'A Japann'd *bottle*'; 'A Wooden *saucer* counterfeit'? Japan'd' may have been a European imitation. 'A coffee *cup* of wood Japan'd on ye outside & inlaid w^t mother of pearl' and 'A Japan'd Trunk inlaid w^t Mother of Pearl &c.' may have been either Chinese or Japanese *lac burgauté*, though the latter might just possibly have been Japanese *namban*. There is an identification[22] of a round monogrammed lacquer box with the Kaempfer purchase, 'A Japan cylindricall box lackerd black w^t gold flowers'. In the list of Kaempfer purchases in the British Library[23] there is an entry that may correspond to this box: 'A round Box japanned half an ell in diameter with golden sprigs'. This would be far too big for the only box surviving with sprigs or flowers. It seems implausible that the large monogram on the lid of this export lacquer box would not have been mentioned, when the inconspicuous flowers on the sides were. A considerable number of other lacquer boxes are mentioned, some from Kaempfer, mostly interesting on account of their contents rather than as examples of lacquer; one of these, a container for acupuncture needles is illustrated in a drawing by Scheuchzer for Kaempfer's *History of Japan*.[24] There was also a Japanese spear, 'A Chinese lance or spear lacquered. From Mr Dupuys.' It is possible that 'A Japonese box for physick for powders and pills, with gold and silver labels and two silver bodkins' from Kaempfer was an *inro*, which were at that time used for medicine. The 'Chinese *pillow* in wch are *pencills* paper ink &c. brought of Mr Lapthorn' may have been similar to the Japanese lacquer pillow with a drawer inventoried in the Danish Royal Collection in 1690.[25] Another lacquer, the 'Japan ewer of red lacquer'd upon wood' may have been *negoro*, a black and red type of Japanese lacquer.

Chinese Prints

Among the most interesting things acquired by Sloane from Kaempfer's nephew were some series of Chinese woodblock colour prints of the late Ming and early Qing periods. Kaempfer had acquired them in Nagasaki which was then the entrepôt in Japan for the trade with both the Dutch and the Chinese; Chinese goods would have been easily available to the Dutch.

Colour printing had begun in China in the early seventeenth century and by the mid-century, when most of the Kaempfer/Sloane prints were produced, had become extremely sophisticated using such techniques as gauffrage and the wiping of the pigment on the blocks to produce gradations of colour. Sloane could not have failed to have been impressed by this skill, but he may well have been more interested in the prints more for their content – flowers, birds and insects – than for their artistic merit. So good are these prints that it is more than likely that Sloane thought that they were watercolours, hence their cataloguing as manuscripts.

Sloane bought from the Kaempfer collection twenty-nine large prints of flowers, some with birds or insects, produced by members of the Ding family of Suzhou (Plate 21).[26] These can be subdivided both by style and by quality into at least three groups; they were not, then, from a single publication. It is more likely that they were originally for sale individually or in groups of four and were used in China as a form of greeting card for the New Year. In Japan they would have been exemplars both of Chinese art and of woodblock printing technique – the ten-colour print was not achieved in Japan until 1765.

Of the other prints belonging to Sloane, twenty-eight may have been dismembered from more than one original book, while the books themselves may have been miscellanies. Thus there are figure prints as well as flower-and-bird prints. None of these are of the same standard of quality as the large series. Gray states:[27]

Among Kaempfer's papers were preserved until 1905 a series of Chinese woodcuts, mounted in an album in the Department of Manuscripts, numbered Additional 5052 [error for 5252], and lettered on the spine 'Japanese and Chinese pictures: e. mss. E. Kaempfer'. Inside is a notice, which the Department believes to be in the hand of James Em[p]son, who was employed in Sloane's library shortly before his death in 1753: 'Drawings of Japanese Temples: done by the Japanese themselves, all brought from there by Dr. Engelbert Kaempfer – Baskets of several fruits and flowers from China'.

The first part of these contents are referred to in the introduction to Kaempfer's *History of Japan* . . . as 'Views of the elaborate Temples, Castles and other Buildings of the Japanese, to the number of fifty, done by the Natives in watercolours', and since this album appears to have been bound in England between 1720 and 1730, there is a strong presumption that the whole of the contents were in fact from Kaempfer's collection. Apart from the woodcuts, these consist of appliqués, models of flowers, and figures in silk brocade and embroidery, some Chinese and some Japanese[28] . . . The woodcuts were taken out of this album and transferred to the Oriental Prints and Drawings in 1906, and [some] were duly included in the catalogue of Japanese and Chinese woodcuts in that Department, by Laurence Binyon, in 1916.

These would presumably include eight prints[29] also transferred in 1906, but not twenty-three prints[30] which are said by Gray to have come from Cunningham (who was in Canton in 1700), nor necessarily the book[31] which contains eight Chinese prints of which two are said to derive from Cunningham and nine Persian paintings which do come from Kaempfer. Both of these were accessioned in the Department of Oriental Antiquities in 1928.

Sloane also lists under 'Pictures &c.', 'A *Chinese print* on sattin' and 'Another' and 'A *Chinese* print of a *beggar*' and 'Another'. The 'East India *cow* given me by Mrs *Willoughby*' and the '*Chinese herb* etc' and '*Another*' might be prints or paintings.

28e/176–7
28e/181–2
28e/157
28e/174–5

Paintings
Japanese
The fifty 'Views of Temples, Castles and other Buildings'[32] mentioned above are a series of watercolours of famous places in Japan, about 30 by 40 cm in size, such as were bought as souvenirs by Japanese tourists. These mostly depicted well-known beauty spots many of which have been identified, including natural scenery (Amanohashidate, Mount Fuji), shrines (Miyajima, Kamojima) or temples (Sanjūsangendō, Ishiyamadera, Matsushima) and sometimes festivals (Gion festival in Kyoto). Many of these paintings were used as models for the engravings in Kaempfer's *History of Japan*. Kaempfer, like Sloane, had been buying information, not works of art.[33] The same will be seen to be true of all Sloane's oriental paintings.

Chinese
It appears that Sloane had only one album of Chinese paintings, eleven album leaves of fish painted by an artist called Yibu.[34] There is also in the Department a large bound album containing Chinese bazaar paintings with the manuscript title 'Chinese costume Trades and Flowers'. In fact it contains thirty-six paintings of trades, 110 paintings of plants or flowers and twelve paintings of boats (junks). It is labelled on the spine 'Landsdowne colln 1242 add 379' and bears the name 'Hans Sloane' written on an outer fly-leaf. I can find no evidence that it belonged to Sloane, it having been probably purchased at the Landsdowne sale in 1807.[35]

Turkish
Sloane had an album of Turkish bazaar paintings; 'A Book of 122 figures in Miniature representing the Habits of the Grand Signor's Court done on Persian paper'. These poor quality pictures must have been bought in sheet form and bound in Europe, as they bear Turkish inscriptions on the paper.[36]

Persian
Sloane bought two series of Isfahan bazaar paintings collected by Kaempfer, who had presumably acquired them there, in 1685. Nine figure paintings of poor quality make one series.[37] The other paintings are in an album in horizontal format made of European watermarked paper and comprise forty paintings of figure subjects and animals (Plate 22), as well as a world map, a map drawn by Kaempfer of 'Curdestan' and four architectural and topographical ink drawings by Kaempfer, one of which is on verso and recto.[38] It seems possible that the paintings were done in Isfahan to Kaempfer's order in a sketch-book that he had brought with him; the local format for paper would normally have been vertical.

Indian
The Sloane album of Indian (Deccani) paintings contains some fifty-four individual miniatures of portrait subjects

and ten of deities, all mounted on European paper.[39] Though hardly works of art, these are of better quality than are any of the other Near Eastern paintings — or any of the Far Eastern paintings for that matter.

Near Eastern Artefacts

28f/36 By far the most important Near Eastern artefact from the Sloane collection is a Persian brass astrolabe inlaid with silver (Plate 23).[40] This lovely instrument, dated AH1124 (AD1712) was made for Shah Husain (reigned 1694–1722), the last of the Safavid rulers. It was thus almost new when Sloane acquired it; how he obtained it is unkown. The astrolabe is signed as made by Abd-al-Ali, son of Muhammed Rafi al Juzil, and as engraved by his brother Muhammed Bakir.

28h/251 Other items included a number of Turkish engraved chalcedony pendants, a Turkish green nephrite plaque from a quiver, inlaid with gold and set with rubies and turquoise which Sloane presumably thought was Mughal, and a series of dagger or sword handles such as 'A scymiter haft of red *28h/185* *jasper* or *bloodstone* variegated with white blewish and trans- *28i/205* parent veins. From the East Indies' and a 'A Persian or Indian *dagger*, the *haft* of which is made of *lapis nephriticus* of a light colour adorned with small rubies. From Dr. *Waldo* from Suratte'.

From all the available evidence, it would seem that Sloane had very little interest in the artistic merits or demerits of the multifarious objects in his collection. He wanted information and he sought objects that could provide information on the lives or any aspect of the way of life of other peoples of the world, just as he sought specimens that would provide him with information on the natural history of the world.

Acknowledgements

I have relied on the help of many colleagues, in the British Museum, in the Museum of Mankind and elsewhere; I would like to thank in particular Yu-Ying Brown, Craig Clunas, Anne Farrer, Nick Irvine, Christiaan Jörg, Jonathan King, Hans-Dieter Olschleger, Venetia Porter and Rachel Ward.

Notes and References

1. Deutsches Institut für Japanstudien, *Doitsu-jin no mita Genroku jidai, Kaempfer-ten* (The Genroku period as seen by a German; the Kaempfer exhibition) (Tokyo, 1990).

2. BL Additional MS 4019, fols. 54–55ᵛ. This list of objects acquired from Kaempfer is entitled 'A list of several Indian and Japanese Curiosities'.

3. The Japan Society, *The Burghley Porcelains* (New York, 1986), no. 70.

4. Unpublished inventory of Tart Hall quoted by Peter Thornton, *Seventeenth-Century Interior Decoration in England, France and Holland* (New Haven and London, 1978), p. 249, note 22.

5. Japan Society, op. cit. (note 3), nos. 8, 10.

6. B. Dam-Mikkelsen and T. Lundbæk, *Ethnographical Objects in the Royal Danish Kunstkammer 1650–1800* (Copenhagen, 1980), nos. EDa38, EBa14, EBc203,4.

7. See P. Donnelly, *Blanc de Chine* (London, 1969), pp. 105, 159, 172–3; pls. 89c, 99a.

8. S. Jenyns, 'Oriental antiquities from the Sloane collection in the British Museum', *British Museum Quarterly* 18 (1953), pp. 18–20.

9. J. Ayers, 'The early China trade', in O. Impey and A. MacGregor (eds.), *The Origins of Museums* (Oxford, 1985), pp. 259–66.

10. See Jenyns, op. cit. (note 8).

11. Ibid.

12. Dam-Mikkelsen and Lundbæk, op. cit. (note 6), nos. EBa25–8, EBc193, EBc84 *et al.*

13. To be published by Christina Nelson in the *Journal of the History of Collections*.

14. Dam-Mikkelsen and Lundbæk, op. cit. (note 6), nos. EBc195,6 and, e.g. EBc197.

15. Å. Setterwall, S. Fogelmarck and B. Gyllensvärd, *The Chinese Pavilion at Drottningholm* (Malmö, 1972), p. 306.

16. The identifications followed here correspond to those of the Department of Oriental Antiquities as listed on a computer print-out dated 4 February 1991.

17. See note 16.

18. This is mentioned in BL, Sloane MS 4019, op. cit. (note 2), fol. 54ᵛ: 'a little black japanned Press with two doors, gilt within which contains the Chief Idol of the Japanese [skilfully, deleted] finely carved with a golden Shield'.

19. Dam-Mikkelsen and Lundbæk, op. cit. (note 6), nos. EBc255–8, and EBc259.

20. It is possible that this could have been the Captain T. Gilbert who commanded the *Duke of Dorset* in Canton in 1641. See H.B. Morse, *The Chronicles of the East Indian Company Trading to China 1635–1834* (Oxford, 1926–9), p. 277.

21. Dam-Mikkelsen and Lundbæk, op. cit. (note 6), nos. EBa8,9.

22. Deutsches Institut für Japanstudien, op. cit. (note 1).

23. BL, Sloane MS 4019, op. cit. (note 2).

24. BL, Sloane MS 5232, fol. 169.

25. Dam Mikkelsen and Lundbæk, op. cit. (note 6), no. EAc10.

26. See J. Fribourg, 'Wood engraving' in W. Speiser, R. Goepper and J. Fribourg, *Chinese Art* (London, 1964), pp. 318–20, pls. 151–2, 154–60. BM, OA, Additional MS 5252. The prints are now BM, OA, 1906.112.0.3–31.

27. B. Gray, 'Sloane and the Kaempfer collection', *British Museum Quarterly* 18 (1953), pp. 20–3.

28. At least three of these are *oshi-e*, padded pictures (BL, Additional MS 5252, fols. 68–70). *Oshi-e* of this period are very rare in Japan.

29. BM, OA, Additional MS 5303 (4), now BM, OA, 1906.1128.0.32 a–h.

30. BM, OA, Additional MS 5293, now BM, OA, 1928.0232.0.18–42.

31. BM, OA, Additional MS 5292, now BM, OA, 1928.0323.0.1–17.

32. BL, Additional MS 5252. These are mentioned in BL, Additional MS 4019, op. cit. (note 2) as 'Fifty Pieces of Japonese Painting, representing the chief Places of the Country of Japan, of its Monasteries, their Habits and Dress, finely painted, as also their Houses and Buildings'.

33. For illustrations, Deutsches Institut für Japanstudien, op. cit. (note 1), no. 9.

34. BM, OA, Additional MS 5503.3, now BM, OA, 1928.0323.0.43, a–k.

35. BM, OA, 1928.0323.044.

36. BM, OA, Additional MS 5258, now BM, OA, 1928.0323.0.46.

37. BM, OA, Additional MS 5292, now BM, OA, 1928.0323.0.1–9. This is described in BL, Additional MS 4019 (op. cit. note 2) as 'A Persian Book in a green Binding with Pictures, viz: Persian Dresses, Animals and other things . . .'

38. BM, OA, Additional MS 2925, now BM, OA, 1974.01617.0.1 a–as.

39. BM, OA, Additional MS 5254, now BM, OA, 1974.0617.0.2 a–bo.

40. The only description of an astrolabe that could be identified as this remarkably ornate and beautiful instrument is the bald 'A brasse *astrolabe*' which is here accepted. Now BM, OA, 1753 OA + 369. See R.T. Gunther, *The Astrolabes of the World* (Oxford, 1932), pp. 147–8.

15 Ethnographic Collections
Collecting in the Context of Sloane's Catalogue of 'Miscellanies'

J. C. H. King

'A poem occasioned by the viewing Dr Sloans museum London Dec: 1712'[1]

Nor Natures works have filled thy draughts alone
The arts & customs of the world are shewn
Here full of lore ye Indian Heroine burns
and Ends in flames ye mutuall Flame she morns
There Persian Caravan a goodly train
A Dangerous War and hade at once maintain
That Europe may Superfluous trifles gain
The British Nymph bedeck'd in Asian Pride
Nere dreads the fate her Merchants have defyd . . .

* The importance of Sloane's ethnographic collection lies not only in the uniqueness of many of its constituent artefacts, nor in its extent. It is, instead, the scholarly manner in which it was assembled, and the scientific detail with which it was recorded, that sets it apart from other collections made before 1800. Sloane was a virtuoso collector rather than a princely one. His aim was to collect materials which, in themselves, and in his ordering of them, provided information and scientific understanding. There are no great groupings of sixteenth-century materials from Mexico, no superb Siberian or American costumes, and only a few Afro-Portuguese ivories made to European taste. Neither is there a great wealth of comparatively minor objects, such as have survived, for example, in the early collections of the National Museum of Denmark in Copenhagen. Instead there are a little more than 100 objects from an original collection of more than 2,000 'Miscellanies'.[2] While many of the individual artefacts are well known, having been first published at the beginning of this century, little primary use has been made of Sloane's manuscript catalogue and its associated correspondence. The intention here is to provide an initial analysis of the materials, particularly the ethnography, originally contained amongst the 'Miscellanies', and to place them in the context of contemporaneous collections.

The apparent modesty of Sloane's surviving collection belies an exceptional importance. This arises because of Sloane's self-education as a collector of natural history, in Europe as a student and then in Jamaica in 1687–9 (see Chapter 1). Intellectually, as one would expect of a seventeenth-century scientist, he was a follower of Thomas Hobbes (1588–1679) and John Locke (1634–1704). Science was, in the seventeenth century, God's own instrument for the revelation of truth. Man, as an object of nature, was to be explained by principles of natural science. This was to be achieved by formulation of laws based on materialistic and scientific explanation. But Sloane was not inspired by his appreciation of contemporary political philosophy to a study of human nature. His ideas did not contribute to the early history of anthropology, and he was not interested by the philosophy of the Enlightenment current at the end of his life after most of his collecting was finished. Instead it was his interest in taxonomy, perhaps particularly the botanical taxonomy of John Ray (1627–1705) and Joseph Pitton de Tournefort (1656–1708) which contributed most to his scientific methodology. It was from this methodology, practised in the mundane business of the recording of his collections, that his important ethnographic collection emerged.

He was, as mentioned above, one of the first urban, scientific collectors to construct an ethnographic cabinet having himself worked in the field. This experience underlay the exceptional care with which he asembled and documented ethnography, and retained the associated correspondence. As a scientist, and as President of the Royal Society,[3] he was constantly preoccupied with recording scientific opinions and with assessing the work sent to him by others for publication. It must have seemed entirely natural to him to compile records in a systematic manner. Many ethnographic collections from before 1750 are known from inventories, and publications, and occasionally from surviving artefacts. The publications may, rarely, be illustrated with woodcuts or copper-plates in the text, in the manner of an illuminated medieval manuscript. Alternatively, the illustrations may consist of engraved views of the cabinet showing, incidentally, the layout and ethnographic materials. Sloane's collection can, rather unusually, only be assessed from a manuscript – his catalogue – and from his letters. Few early manuscript catalogues of collections of ethnography have been published,[4] and, indeed, surviving evidence is such that rather few attempts have been made to compare formally early printed catalogues with the surviving collections. Publications about early cabinets have, in general, concentrated on the intellectual context of such collections, rather than attempting to construct practical models to illustrate the methodology of a particular collector.

The Chronology of the 'Miscellanies' Catalogue

The first work on Sloane's ethnography, and on his mansucript catalogue, was carried out by A.W. Franks (1826–97).[5] It is generally accepted that Sloane's catalogues date to between *c*.1685 and the 1740s.[6] The importance of 'Miscellanies' lies, in part, in that it is, like Sloane's other catalogues, a document arranged in some chronological sequence. Single artefacts and collections in 'Miscellanies' can be given specific dates from manuscript sources. This enables, in a complex process only now beginning, otherwise undocumented material to be dated. The most important date in the sequence is that of 1725, at which stage we know that 1,169 artefacts had been accessioned and listed.[7] Earlier information is provided by the approximate date of contacts between Sloane and the earlier collectors of individual pieces recorded in the catalogue. After 1725, and particularly in the 1730s and 1740s, the specific dates of letters can sometimes be attached to the individual artefacts to which they refer.

In the early pages of the catalogue three easily datable collectors' names appear. One, James Cunningham (or Cuninghame), was a Scottish doctor working for the East India Company. Correspondence about his collecting survives for the period between 1700 and his death in 1709.[8] Of the five artefacts associated with his name, one, 28a/64 a Chinese compass, is referred to in a letter of 22 November 1701 from Chusan.[9] The previous year Cuningham had sent back miscellanies, so it may be that the first of his artefacts, 28a/9 'A *hatt* from Tunquin', was sent to England in 1700.[10] Other accessions before number 500 also suggest that this initial section of the catalogue refers to material catalogued, if not acquired, during the first decade of the eighteenth century. A French Jesuit missionary, Jan de Fontenay, whose correspondence dates to this period, provided five artefacts.[11] A German doctor, named Krieg, who corresponded with Sloane and Petiver between 1699 and 1708 was the source 28a/55 of another early accession, 'A livonia *Cittern*'.[12] Sloane may also, during this period, have obtained ethnographic items dating from the previous century.[13]

Artefacts after number 550 can generally be dated through the chronological structure provided by the circumstantial evidence of the few dated accessions. 28a/572–4 Numbers 572–4 are three North American Indian artefacts traditionally assumed to have been brought to London in 1710 by the Mohawk and Mahican who visited Queen Anne.[14] The bulk of the nearly 100 miscellanies acquired from Petiver's estate after his death in 1718 are numbered 28a/910*– between 910* and 1019.[15] The collection of Engelbert 1019 Kaempfer (1651–1716), numbering more than fifty artefacts, came to Sloane in 1723 and 1725[16] and is almost 28a/1062– completely numbered between 1062 and 1170. After 1725 170 letters begin regularly to associate artefacts with specific 28a/1205 dates: Benjamin Franklin's famous asbestos purse (see Chapter 7, Fig. 31) was offered to Sloane in a letter dated 2 June 1725;[17] the Arctic costume offered by a trader named 28a/1332 Henry Elking is associated with a letter of 5 October 1727;[18] the important Inuit collection acquired by Alexander Light in Canada comes with a letter from Moose Factory dated 25 August 1738;[19] Christopher Middleton's superb 28a/2065 nest of Cree birchbark baskets came with a letter dated 11 November 1742.[20] By the early 1740s Sloane, then in

his eighties, more or less stopped acquiring (or at least accessioning) new miscellanies. The suggestion here, then, is that the catalogue of 'Miscellanies' refers at its start to material in Sloane's hands at the beginning of the eighteenth century. We do not know, yet, whether or not the catalogue was itself begun in around 1700, and it may be that it was started five, ten or more years later and that the sequence was based on Sloane's knowledge of the chronology of acquisitions.

Catalogue Data

A second significant feature of the 'Miscellanies', as of other Sloane catalogues, lies in the kind of data it contains and the structure within which the information is provided. Each catalogue entry includes a brief description; the name for the artefact is normally underlined, as is the other keyword, the name of the source, where one is provided.[21] Some 300 people are named as donors or vendors in the catalogue providing origins for perhaps a half of the 2,000 'Miscellanies'. Often the geographical and ethnographical origin of the artefact is provided, although, for instance in the use of 'Indian' and other terms this now often seems rather confused. Figures, which may be prices, are provided for less than 10% (around 175 entries) of the accessions, mostly in the earlier sections of the catalogue. We do not know whether the omission of this information from later entries arose because Sloane had less need to buy, or value, material since, as he became more famous, artefacts were donated to him; alternatively the values or purchase prices may have been omitted for some other reason. Other significant features of the catalogue include the provision of references to published sources, for about fifty artefacts, particularly to provide ethnographic contexts. As well as bibliographic references Sloane also provided cross-referencing between artefacts in 'Miscellanies' and other sections of his collection.[22] Artefacts were also recatalogued and renumbered.[23] De-accessions, such as the fan handle said to have belonged 28a/791 to Queen Elizabeth which was given by Sloane to Queen Anne (?), are noted. While this is confusing in trying to assess the precise numerical contents of the collections, as discussed below, it does indicate how much importance Sloane placed on the mundane business of keeping track of his possessions. Less coherent was the manner in which he numbered objects: for instance, he was never sure as to whether or not pairs of shoes should be two separate objects.[24] Elsewhere he might have accessioned large groups of Saami (Lapp) or Inuit material under a single number.[25] There are instances where Sloane has used numbers twice, or more; these numbers are given one or more stars as appropriate. Nevertheless Sloane's scientific approach to museum methodology was almost literally centuries ahead of his time. At the British Museum, for instance, little systematic enthographical cataloguing was undertaken between the foundation of the Museum in 1753 and the commencement of the first register in 1861.

Structure and Content

Sloane's 'Miscellanies' are in many important respects mis-named. While the catalogue includes many miscellaneous types of artefact, they were often individually considered highly significant by Sloane, and so, in that sense, were not at all miscellaneous. Early estimates of the ethnography suggest that there were, perhaps, only 350 ethnographic artefacts, but we can now suggest that more than half of the collection strictly speaking falls into that category. Because of the often rather general descriptions of objects now missing, it is not possible to define the exact parameters of the ethnography. Many of the artefacts are insufficiently described to determine ethnic or geographic origins. Some understanding of the full context of the collection is, therefore, essential in order to understand the significance of the ethnographic materials.

Apart from ethnography, two other groups of artefacts can be discerned in the 'Miscellanies'. The first is that of medical and scientific materials, including raw materials and the results of experiments. The second consists of European natural and artificial curiosities, including, particularly objects of vertue, artefacts of exotic materials or exceptional skill, and historic and personal relics. Significant amongst the medical and scientific materials are artificial eyes and limbs, a surgeon's needle and a spoon for the use of someone left-handed.[26] While these were important objects in their own right, this was a minor aspect of Sloane's collecting, particularly in view of his own profession. The medicines include some materials which Sloane describes as non-efficacious and other things on which he does not pass judgement, so that we do not know why he included these materials in his cabinet. Nevertheless he preserved a selection of remedies for gout, heart-burn, fevers, snake poison and piles, as well as numerous examples of Newberry pastilles.[27] The medicines are complemented by a series of dried sediments from mineral waters, including Epsom salts,[28] and by numerous oils including petroleum, olive oil, and palm oil.[29] Related to his interest in oils was a small collection of candles and soaps from various parts of the world, some no doubt with ascribed medical properties.[30] The tools and instruments include numerous microscopes and thermometers as well as measuring equipment. These in a sense complement those included in Sloane's catalogue 28f 'Mathematicall instruments &c',[31] just as the salts and vegetable materials might have been located by Sloane elsewhere.

The explanation for the gathering of the European materials is, perhaps, more difficult to understand. They include, as mentioned, many standard categories of materials from cabinets. There are twenty-five items of whimsical figurative skills – pictures made of seeds, leaves, feathers, and shells, and miniature silver spoons.[32] There are a few models, some of wax. The others include one of Christ's burial place in Jerusalem,[33] and some of diamonds which could have as easily been placed in the collection of 'Pretious stones'.[34] The sixteen personal relics include

a piece of rope broken by a strong man, and a necklace beaded by a woman without hands.[35] They merge imperceptibly in their miscellaneous intentions with the relics of historic importance: materials from the Palace of Westminster, from the Fire of London, and the Armada, and from the Scottish rebellions. Other materials were kept, no doubt, for their royal associations.[36] The natural rarities consist of artificial curiosities altered by nature and artifices of chance. There was, for instance, a dragon made of ray's skin, part of a pair of britches singed by thunder, and a bullet which went by chance through a door and killed a man on the other side.[37] The nautical relics in many ways overlap with those from other sources, some being historic relics, and others, if from shipwrecks, being man-made objects affected by prolonged immersion in the sea. Others may have been acquired from pirates in the West Indies.[38]

28a/765,974
28a/806

28a/390,
2019
28a/547,
1918

The majority of European objects in Sloane's 'Miscellanies' were objects of vertue, that is artefacts of exotic materials wrought with high skill and artistry. The numerous artefacts include turned and carved items, ceramics, sculpture, beads and boxes. The materials include ivory, lignum vitae, amber, onyx, and agate.[39] Rather separate is the series of materials to do with glass, in which Sloane seems to have had a greater interest than, for instance, in ceramics or turned wood and ivory. His preoccupation with glass is related to a number of other subjects: beads and beadwork, in which Sloane seems to have had a significant ethnographic interest; and to sand and vitrification, particularly as a result of thunderbolts, the spontaneous firing of hayricks, and slag from kilns. The collection also included glass made in imitation of minerals, including cyrstals as well as onyx and agate – semi-precious stones in which Sloane had an obsessive interest.[40] Beyond the objects of vertue are three small groups of materials, which, while usually European, are distinct in nature. There is a small collection of equestrian items: a stirrup, snaffle bit, and some crystals for trappings.[41] There is a similarly small group of European arms and armour, including an Italian stilleto, Spanish axe, and Polish sword.[42] More significant are the Christian, particularly Roman Catholic, materials, which include a number of crucifixes, rosaries and relics, and ten habits from religious orders in Flanders.[43] This interest in Catholicism may be related to the prejudices and interests of his time, and to his own origin as an Ulster Protestant, but it also clearly parallels his interest in amulets and other features of non-European systems of belief. In addition among the European materials is a loosely-defined group of coins, medals and seals, which Sloane might have included in his other catalogues. These encompass personal seals and materials, such as wax for taking impressions, and extend to Asian seals and coinage.[44] A final group of anomalous inclusions are the European antiquities mentioned amongst the 'Miscellanies'.[45]

The catalogue of 'Miscellanies' does indicate quite clearly the material in which Sloane was not interested. Clothing, and textile manufacture, were, it seems not of interest, although Sloane obtained many specimens from employees of the East India and Hudson's Bay Companies which traded textiles. While he acquired Kongo raffia textiles, and bark textiles, these were an aspect of his major interest in botany. Sloane was not concerned with mechanical devices that did not directly relate to his scientific interests in medicine, mineralogy and botany: there is little or no clockwork in the collection. Similarly he was not interested in transportation, as evidenced by the limited amounts of materials relating to horses, or indeed camels, and to vehicles of any kind including boats, and the whole technical apparatus of sailing – apart that is from compasses. The catalogue of 'Miscellanies' can therefore be used to define the outer limits of Sloane's scientific concerns since it draws together, more or less, the curiosities which could not be fitted elsewhere into his scheme of cataloguing. 'Miscellanies' also indicates that Sloane's concerns were scientific: the absence of important sculpture, of impressive Italian cabinets,[46] and of plate, suggest that he had a clearly defined idea of what a scientist should and should not acquire and document.

Classification

One frequent comment on Sloane's ethnography concerns the absence of any system of classification. His 'Miscellanies' were clearly, almost all artificial curiosities, but there were no divisions within this catalogue, and the only significant ordering principle was that of chronological accession. Earlier more modest collections such as those of the Tradescants,[47] the Royal Society[48] and Ralph Thoresby[49] define their material with simple schemes separating different types of relics – historic and personal, artificial and natural. Sloane on the other hand, while not publishing a guide or catalogue, left two implicit forms of classification: the physical arrangement of the material in his respective homes (adopted later in Montagu House), and the catalogues. For the ethnography, associated with other 'Miscellanies' there was no further division – into continents or by people, materials or artefact types – within the cataloguing system. The descriptions left by visitors of the collections as they were displayed in Sloane's lifetime are quite slight, and hardly mention ethnography at all.[50] On the other hand the arrangements of the collection at the British Museum from the 1750s onwards provide a useful idea as to how the material was organized and regarded immediately after Sloane's death, and so probably also during his lifetime.

Sloane's last curator, William Empson, organized the collection at the new museum and is believed to have followed Sloane's own ideas, though he gives virtually no explicit information as to why Sloane collected ethnography. However, the 1762 edition of the Museum guide states, unequivocally, of Sloane's manuscripts that 'The curious Reader may here find various and good Accounts of the Manners, Customs, Languages, Civil Government, Trade,

Diseases, natural productions, Antiquities, &c. &c. of many different Nations'.[51] Slightly later, in describing the 'Department of Natural and Artificial Productions', this theme is expanded upon: 'There is scarcely a Country, though ever so distant, that has not greatly contributed to enrich this Department. We may see here the Progress of Art in the different Ages the the World, exemplified in a Variety of Utensils each Nation in each Century has produced.'[52] So in this guide the function of the artefacts and manuscripts was said to be to provide material towards what even today would be an acceptable definition of ethnography. The artefacts themselves are also firmly anchored to those ideas of progress and evolutionary development that were to be so influential during the founding of archaeology and anthropology in the nineteenth century.[53]

The first museum guide was laid out to provide an explanation of as well as a guide to the collections. In the 'Department of Natural and Artificial Productions' two rooms seem to have been particularly designated for ethnography. The divisions between the categories of materials is rather unclear. The first room contained particularly materials to do with religion. 'American Idols' from Peru and Mexico were believed to be 'placed in High-ways, to be ready for the Adoration of Passengers'. Native Americans worshipped two gods, one 'the Author of all Good; the other of all Evil; The first they worshipped through Love, and thanked him for the Effects of his Goodness; the other through Fear, imploring him not to do them or their any Injury.' Another theme introduced here is the peopling of the Americas across the Atlantic from Europe. This was indicated by the supposed similarity of American and Egyptian figures.[54] Other religions are also introduced – for instance that of Japan where it is said that people keep pagodas, with figures – such as the one exhibited – in their homes to be worshipped like Roman household gods. Islam is represented by '*Turkish* Talismans, or Charms, with *Arabic* Inscriptions, being generally a sentence of the Alcoran. In these Superstitions among the *Mohametans* have great Faith . . .' Most significantly of all, as one would expect in a museum of the Enlightenment, Christianity is also included for comparison. 'Further on are some Talismans and Abraxas, a Kind of Spells or Charms with which some superstitious or artful People in the first Ages of Christianity pretended they could cure all diseases . . It was likewise imagined they were a Protection from Witchcraft and Enchantments.'[55] The importance of this display, which also included numerous ancient and modern tools, lies not in the information it contains, which is, though derived from received contemporary knowledge, often inaccurate. But it is highly significant that an attempt was made to convey ideas of religious differentiation through the comparative display of 'Idols'. It is important, for instance, that Christianity is included in this scheme, and that it is in part evolutionary. Even at an entirely basic level the use of words such as 'Arabic', 'Turkish' and 'Mohametan' together implies a differentiation of meaning designed to be imparted to the reader.

The other gallery of ethnography, the final room of the Department of Natural and Artificial Productions, was not explicitly organized so as to convey ideas to the visitor and reader.[56] Instead it contained groupings of artefact by material and continent termed 'Productions of Art'. These included a cabinet of glass and papier mâché articles, a group of the 'Utensils and Ornaments of the Indian Inhabitants of the great Continent of North America', a cabinet of 'European productions of Art. as some small Cabinets, Figures in Bronze . . .', Japanese and Chinese idols and gods, and numerous other things. Space is particularly devoted to the significance of wampum, the manner of preparing manioc in South America, and the utility of the kayak and birch bark canoe. Again it is quite extraordinary that ethnography should be grouped under the heading of 'art', something that was not to happen again until the middle of the present century, even though, of course, in this case the reference was not to aesthetics but to manufactured or 'artificial' productions. The guide to the Sloane collection in the British Museum indicates one further use for ethnography – the illustration of the native use of raw materials – particularly botanical materials such as maize, and various forms of bark and root. The guide explains that : 'The Indians in New England, and other Parts of North America, had no Vegetable but Maiz to make their Bread of; they call it Weachin; the Ear of Maiz yields more Grain than any of our Corn Ears.'[57] This maize may have included some of the following: 'Indian Corn, for Samp. Indian Meal, for hasty Puding. Indian Flower, for any sort of Puding. Cranberries for, Tarts or Sauce . . . [Sw]eet Corn dry'd in the Milk, that is when the Ears are very young, a dainty Dish with the Indians.'[58]

History of the Collection

The eighteenth-century display of Sloane's ethnography is likely to have remained more or less untouched for approximately twenty years. Apart from the guide to the Museum, the only publication to include material from 'Miscellanies' was the Van Rymsdyks' Museum Britannicum.[59] While this included such miscellanies as model diamonds and the alchemist's knife which survives in The Natural History Museum, it did not include ethnography. The advent of large collections on the return of the three voyages made by Captain James Cook stimulated the creation of a 'South Seas Room' which featured Pacific materials that included Hawaiian featherwork, a Tahitian mourner's costume, and collections from the Northwest Coast of America.[60] At the beginning of the nineteenth century Sloane's ethnography was displayed in a single room.[61] The ethnography, in general, was no doubt particularly prone to insect attack. Much was consigned to the basement. In two sales, in 1803 and 1816, large sections of the Sloane mineralogical collections were auctioned by the Museum. The first of these sales included numerous cabinets, which may have

belonged to Sloane, as well as a number of lots of ethnography – although the latter is likely mostly to have come from post-1753 Pacific voyages.[62] A further de-accessioning of Sloane's ethnography may have occurred in the 1820s when some materials in store in the basement of the British Museum were exchanged for 'fossil fruits from the Isle of Sheppey', received from a commercial museum owner in Margate called Francis Crow. Some of this collection later came, through Canterbury Museum, into the possession of the Horniman Museum. It includes a Bering Strait Eskimo bow drill (from Cook's Third Voyage) that was published in 1780 as being in the British Museum, and a North American Indian ball-headed club quite likely, on circumstantial evidence, to be from the Sloane collection.[63]

The first inventory of the Sloane collection was made by A.W. Franks from 1853 onwards. At this time artefacts were given new labels. Franks's initials and the date were entered alongside the appropriate entries in the manuscript catalogue, and a copy was made by Franks. At the same time he incorporated in a notebook a number of drawings of Sloane artefacts, particularly including an American antler comb, and antler arm-bands which may also have come from Sloane.[64] A systematic attempt to publish Sloane ethnography came at the turn of the century with an account by David Bushnell entitled 'The Sloane collection in the British Museum'; it is confined to North American ethnography excluding the Arctic and archaeological collections. He quotes thirty-four catalogue entries, and describes seventeen artefacts.[65] This was built on by Braunholtz for the bicentenial volume of the British Museum Quarterly: in this 1953 article it is suggested of the 2,111 items listed in the 'Miscellanies' that 'about 350 are ethnographic without counting the numerous objects of 'the higher oriental cultures'.[66] This is broken down with the majority of artefacts – some 139 – said to come from North America. No suggestion was made as to how many of these 350 items actually survived, and no breakdown was given of the ethnographic and other origins of further materials. These figures are exceptionally conservative; if all the Asian materials are included there were at least 1,200 ethnographic artefacts in 'Miscellanies'. A later edition of Braunholtz's paper includes at the end of the catalogue descriptions of surviving artefacts: four European, seven African, thirteen Asian and twenty-five American from 'Miscellanies'. An additional four American artefacts are included from Sloane's 'Antiquities' catalogue.[67] This group forms the basis of the surviving ethnography discussed below.

Sources of Ethnography

Sloane's excellence as a collector derives from his early experience in the field and as a scholar, combined with his later wealth and position which enabled him to expand his collection in a scientific fashion. It is not at all clear that any of his miscellanies include items collected by him in Jamaica during his visit in 1687–9.[68] However, we do know that he made collections of botanical materials, and it seems unlikely that he did not collect Jamaican materials along with other specimens.[69] Apart from his own work Sloane collected materials from a number of different categories of person. These include home-based collectors, overseas scientists, and provincial amateur collectors. Most important and most interesting are the collections made by overseas scientific correspondents. These were largely men employed by agencies such as the East India Company and the Hudson's Bay Company, or they were missionaries or professional scientists. In voluminous correspondence they exchanged materials around the world. For instance botanical specimens from Virginia might be sent to Russia by Sloane in exchange for Siberian specimens.[70] To these people ethnography was of very subsidiary importance. Reference has already been made to the Chinese compass sent to Sloane by James Cuningham, at the beginning of the century. This was included in the letter as an afterthought – 200 botanical specimens and a compass![71] This pattern, of the ethnography acting as a slight embellishment in transactions which were primarily to do with non-ethnographic scientific collecting, is frequently repeated.

Sloane's correspondence with Mark Catesby (1682–1749), the artist and naturalist working in Virginia and the Carolinas, concerns botanical and other specimens, and Catesby's drawings. Catesby's travels were sponsored, so that he was at pains to provide a sufficiency of sketches of birds and specimens to satisfy people who were, in effect, something close to being creditors. One aspect of Catesby's collecting was the acquisition of ethnographic items made of vegetable material which in turn could be used to illustrate botanical specimens. One item, now lost, mentioned 28a/1203 in a letter was the apron of beaten bark which features in 'Miscellanies'. Another category of artefact was basketry, which Catesby refers to as the only other exceptional art which he came across. The vicissitudes of collecting are also illustrated by the problems experienced by a collection dispatched by Catesby, captured by pirates and recaptured with resultant disarray to the specimens.[72] An example of the missionary-collector is provided by the French Jesuit Jan de Fontenay: his long correspondence (c.1704–8) with Sloane relates to the difficulties of obtaining passports and passages for missionaries to go to China during war with England. Again it is likely that the Chinese ethnography which he gave to Sloane was part of a complex set of transactions in which artificial curiosities were simply appendages to scientific materials.[73]

A related but slightly different sort of collector with access to the field is evidenced in Sloane's correspondence with Henry Elking, probably a trader in whale oil and other Arctic products during the 1730s. In this case Elking simply provided Sloane with materials that were brought back on the ships which he seems probably to have owned. They included as well as Greenlandic Inuit materials, a walrus head. Elking allowed a friend to show the head in a coffee house and then gave it to Sloane, subsequently regretting

that a tusk had been loosened while it was on display. That Sloane highly esteemed the contributions of people such as Elking, without much in the way of scientific training, is indicated by his gift to Elking of a copy of his *Natural History* of Jamaica.[74] A slightly different but nevertheless highly significant group of correspondents in Britain contributed to his collections. These were doctors who applied to Sloane for advice about the illnesses of their patients. In these transactions, as with the natural scientist correspondents overseaas, ethnography and antiquities were marginal units in an elaborate system of exchange of professional and private favours. The advice asked of Sloane by someone such as the Wisbech doctor, Richard Middleton Massey, c.1705–16, might include requests for information about saving the oil from a beached whale, of how to charge the appropriate authorities for medical services to shipwrecked sailors, about the values of books, and about assistance in labyrinthine struggles with intestinal and nasal worms; and in return artefacts, particularly local antiquities, would be sent on to Sloane in London. While ethnography, even Scottish ethnography, was of marginal significance in this system of exchange, it does indicate that Sloane sat at the centre of a highly elaborate network which stretched throughout Britain and Europe to Russia and China on the one hand, and to Hudson Bay, and the Americas on the other.

The documentation of Sloane's secondary acquisitions of other collections is more difficult to understand. These collectors often left little in the way of catalogues. The purchase of James Petiver's collection in 1718 illustrates this problem. It was in notoriously poor condition on Petiver's death; there was no manuscript catalogue, and few of these specimens are documented in any way. However, Petiver published a series of what we might call illustrated fascicles about his collection in the first decade of the century. These include artificial curiosities, particularly a Cherokee pipe and Asian items such as ink blocks. Beyond these engravings there is apparently no further information, although it is possible that details about Petiver's ethnography will be discovered in his correspondence.[75] On the other hand, Kaempfer's collection from Japan and the Far East, acquired in 1723 and 1725, was listed, but the listing in 'Miscellanies' and elsewhere has yet to be reconciled with the original manuscripts.[76] More modest, but perhaps more typical is the collection of a 'Mr Wilson': this was quite slight, listed on a scrap of paper. Sloane took the ethnography and, refining the descriptions, entered them almost entirely into his catalogue.[77]

African Ethnography

Some fifty items are listed in 'Miscellanies' as coming from Africa, the smallest number for any continent except, of course, for Australasia.[78] Four further African artefacts, including 'A Negros *wooden pillow*? . . . 0.2.6.' are recorded 28b/153 in 'Antiquities'.[79] It is also quite probable that some of the material listed below as unidentified ethnography was from

Africa. There is little apparent unity to the group, except that collections were made in coastal areas, particularly of West and South Africa, the Congo and Madagascar.[80] Significantly Sloane acquired a number of textiles, perhaps because of his interest in the ethnographic use of vegetable materials such as raffia. The seven surviving items recorded in 1970 include North African shoes, West African ivory bracelets, and Bakongo textiles. Since then a North African knife and sheath (Plate 24), and basketry cap from Nigeria (Plate 25) have been identified.[81] Most of the rest of this collection was of arms, tobacco pipes and ornaments. Also significant were the ivory artefacts (Plate 26), perhaps indicative of the early export trade in carved West African articles for the European market.[82]

28a/111, 424,588–9, 1260,1630, 1935,2105

American Ethnography
Three areas of the Americas can be separated from within the catalogue of 'Miscellanies': the Arctic, Eastern North America, and Latin America and the West Indies. There will however remain some overlap with other continental designations, particularly as a result of the general use of the word 'Indian' as a term for native Americans, and other non-European peoples.[83] Further confusion arises through the general use of the term 'West Indies' for much of the Americas including both Canada and South America.[84]

The American Arctic
During the fifteen or twenty years after 1725 Sloane acquired twenty-six items from the Arctic.[85] Artefacts from three catalogue entries survive: snow goggles, a line-attacher for a kayak, and, under the third designation a number of ivory tools and toggles. All of the Inuit material came from West Greenland and Eastern Canada. It included originally a very good cross-section of Inuit material culture. Amongst the artefacts now lost were: a snow knife, woman's knife *ulu*, darts and throwing boards, harpoon, fish harpoon and a model kayak.[86] The dozen or so small ivory artefacts surviving from the material collected in 1738 include three complete harpoon heads for hunting sea mammals, harpoon or sled line-swivels, gaming pieces, a socket for a harpoon foreshaft, a line-attacher for a kayak, a valve for blowing up a sealskin float, walrus teeth and a comb.[87] They survived probably because they are almost all of ivory, which being a semi-precious substance may have been accorded more respect than, for instance, the caribou, seal, gut and bird skin costumes and ornaments, all of which have disappeared. One of the most important Inuit artefacts, now lost, was a belt with ivory attachments decorated with engraved figurative designs.[88] In the Eastern Arctic engraved ivory ornaments are of exceptional rarity.[89]

8a/1333 or 1842 28a/1750 28a/1933

Eastern North America
Around 170 artefacts are designated as coming from North America between Hudson Bay and the Carolinas (Figs. 78–80).[90] The majority of these artefacts are Indian, from Cree

or other Algonquian-speaking peoples, or from the Iroquoian-speaking peoples: the Huron, Iroquois and Cherokee. Most of this material has been published; it includes three artefacts brought to London in 1710 by the Mohawk and Mahican visitors already mentioned and a unique Cherokee basket in double weave, sometimes credited with being the example which inspired the continued creation of such baskets.[91] In the 'Antiquities' catalogue are two further items of ethnography: 'A *garter* made of Bufalos hair & glasse beads. from Carolina. [*Mrs Dering*]', and 'A broad *belt* made by the Cherickee Indians of silk grasse? or Mulberry bark. *Id.*' To these are added a small number of things of Euro-American origin, most famous of which is the asbestos pouch sold by Benjamin Franklin to Sloane in 1725 (see Chapter 7, Fig. 31). Other Euro-American materials include soap, candles and a nut cracker.[92] More significant are materials collected from African slaves. Of these things only an Asante drum survives, said to have been collected in Virginia; however recent tests have suggested that the woods employed are West African, so that it may have been transported on a slave ship to Virginia.[93] A second Afro-American drum was also originally in the collection.[94] There is a small group of lithic material, probably constituting the earliest surviving archaeological collection from what is now the United States.[95] To this should be added 'One [*arrow-head*] of *Sparr* from Virginia' from the 'Antiquities' catalogue.

28b/402 28b/403 28a/1205 28b/65

Latin America and the West Indies
These collections, of rather less than 100 artefacts, are, as for North America, very general, with few apparent organizing principles.[96] A total of four artefacts may remain, with four additions from Sloane's catalogue of 'Antiquities'. These are a Mesoamerican painted gourd, a Central American axe (Fig. 81), a Mesoamerican pot and a penis sheath.[97] There is no significant grouping of material from any one people, although the sixteen items from Tierra del Fuego may have included a useful range of fishing implements, and ornaments. An additional Fuegian arrow head was recorded in the 'Antiquities' catalogue. One general interest of Sloane's was in hard green stone materials, which he terms nephrite and which relates to his more general acquisition of mineral artefacts with curative powers.[98] From the tropical forest peoples of Central and South America, come, as far as can be told from the descriptions, a relatively unremarkable series of bows and arrows, hardwood clubs, cassava squeezers, beaded aprons from Guyana, featherwork such as 'An Indian habit of feathers' and 'A West indian Kings crown made of the feathers of the maccaw'. The only gold artefact was 'A gold plate worn on the upper lip by the Indians of Darien going thro a hole in the partition of the nose'. The West Indian collection included material from African slaves, amongst which was 'A spoon used by the Indians & Negros of Jamaica' indicating, perhaps, the fusion of African and indigenous tradi-

28b/66 28a/43, 1038, 1826–7 28a/16–18 28a/21–2 28a/23, 990 28a/133, 1823 28a/518 28a/1945 28a/1277 28a/503

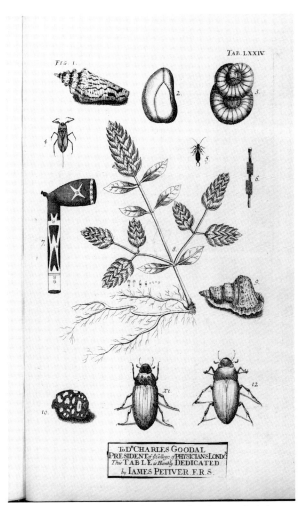

Fig. 78 James Petiver, *Gazophylacii* . . . (n.d.), pl. 74: included at fig. 7 is [28a/1452] 'A Tobacco pipe *used by the Kings of Carolina*'.

Fig. 80 Cherokee rattle, from the south-east United States. [28a/1237] 'A *Maracca* or *rattle* of a *gourd* made use of by the Indians of Carolina [as a rattle crossed out] in their triumphs . . .' Length 28 cm. BM, Ethno, Sl.1237. Reproduced by courtesy of the Trustees of the British Museum.

Fig. 79 Tobacco pipe bowl, sent from Pennsylvania by John Bartram to Sir Hans Sloane. [28a/1209] 'A large *Calumet* or *tobacco pipe* bole round made of black marble to which are fitted long pipes of reed or bored wood of sevll. figures . . .' Length 7.5 cm. BM, Ethno, Sl.1209. Reproduced by courtesy of the Trustees of the British Museum.

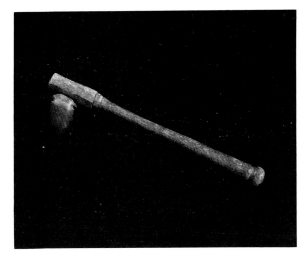

Fig. 81 Stone axe, Central America. [28a/43] 'An Indian *hatchett* sett in wood. It is a greenish stone or lapis nephriticus'. Length 46 cm. BM, Ethno, Sl.43. Reproduced by courtesy of the Trustees of the British Museum.

Fig. 82 Toltec [?] stone head, drilled as a pendant, from Mexico. [28*b*/518] 'An Egyptian *head* of the Sun in basaltes?'. Height 10 cm. BM, Ethno, Sl.518. Reproduced by courtesy of the Trustees of the British Museum.

Fig. 83 Chimu stirrup-spouted vessel, from Peru. [28*b*/726] 'An earthen *bottle* of gray earth coloured black in the form of a *porpesse* wᵗ. a handle from Peru by Dr. *Houston* said to be one of their Gods. (*Idol*)'. Height 17.5 cm. BM, Ethno, Sl.726. Reproduced by courtesy of the Trustees of the British Museum.

tions. Other materials included a strap for whipping slaves, a noose for catching and hanging slaves, as well as a bullet and clothing used by escaped slaves in Jamaica.[99] In the 'Antiquities' catalogue were three accessions of potsherds and bones recovered from a Jamaican cave.[100] Materials from Mesoamerica and the Andes were extremeley limited, no doubt in part because of the virtual impossibility of British travellers making authorized visits to those places. It seems quite likely that the materials collected in Campeche may have been acquired by a privateer,[101] as was perhaps what may have been a Mesoamerican mould-made pottery temple[102] in the 'Antiquities' catalogue. Also from the 'Antiquities' catalogue are the surviving Mesoamerican stone head (Fig. 82) and three surviving Peruvian pottery vessels (Fig. 83).[103]

Asian Ethnography

More than 600 artefacts, or about half the ethnographic collections, came from Asia. Of these artefacts more than 300 items come from China,[104] and nearly 100 from Japan.[105] In addition more than 200 artefacts were said to come from other parts of Asia: it is these last which are mentioned here.[106] As with the other ethnography, that from Asia is in no sense comprehensive. Most of the individual artefacts are highly portable. There are no groups of material which were capable of giving a general overview of a specific people. The largest groups of artefacts are those with the designations East Indies (about forty), or India (about sixty). However since these terms were employed to describe the countries of south and south-east Asia, attributions must remain vague. Other small groups of material are specifically said to come from places in India: Coromandel (Fig. 84), Fort St. George, Malabar and Surat (see also Plate 27). For south-east Asia the specific sources include Borneo, the Celebes, Java, Malacca, Malaya, Manilla and Sumatra. Much larger groups of artefacts are specifically assigned to Persia (fifteen) and Turkey (more than forty). A single weapon, in the 'Antiquities' catalogue, is said to come from Tartary. Much of the Asian collection appears, from the descriptions, to have been relatively slight.[107] Most would have been likely to have been the kinds of everyday materials which could be acquired in markets. Collections from remote peoples in areas away from the influence of the great literate religions seem to have been rather limited, and probably confined to arms. An exception to this is a costume from Kamchatka.[108] Numerous additional Asian artefacts are included in Sloane's other catalogues of mineral specimens. For instance in 'Agate cups bottles spoons &c' is a Mughal (?) bladed weapon from India 'A Persian or Indian *dagger* the *haft* of which is made of *lapis nephriticus* of a light colour adorned wth. small rubies. From Dr. *Waldo* from Suratte. 2.2.0.'

28*b*/157

28*g*/205

Fig. 84 One of a pair of lacquered shoes, from India. [28a/5] ['A *shoe* from Coromandel']. Length 24 cm. BM, Ethno, Sl.5. Reproduced by courtesy of the Trustees of the British Museum.

European Ethnography

About 100 artefacts can be designated as representing European ethnography.[109] There would, however, be considerable overlap with other categories of European materials, particularly objects of vertue. Of these perhaps four

28a/1417, survive: A Pyrennean shoe, a Scottish spoon, a Saami drum
401 (Plate 28) and a stone amulet (Fig. 85). The sources of
28a/1103, material, as provided in the 'Miscellanies' catalogue are not
755 surprising: England, France, Germany, Russia, and the other major countries. The English ethnography was limited and mundane. It included a whaling harpoon, and a broom from
28a/1494 Lancashire.[110] A broom of willow is one of the few objects obtained from Germany. The Irish material included 'a
28a/1413 pump or Irish brogue', a punch ladle and other minor arte-
28a/1847 facts. While there was nothing in the collection designated as Welsh, the sixteen Scottish items included interesting clothes of tartan. These have accession numbers relatively early in the chronology enabling the speculation to be made that they may have come from a soldier in the 1715 Jacobite rebellion.[111] The only comprehensive collection, from an ethnographic point of view, is that from Scandinavia. This included two Saami drums, costume, sled and other materials which would have provided a well-rounded collection. Also in the collection is a manuscript description of a Saami drum.[112]

Unidentified Materials, particularly from Asia and Europe

The imprecision of many of the descriptions in 'Miscellanies' means that many artefacts cannot be given definite ethnographic or geographic places of origin. Many of these

things, which number more than 200, are probably European objects of exotic materials. Many others are likely to be of Asian origin, and may fit into sequences of accessions as yet not fully understood.[113]

Conclusion

Perhaps the most significant feature of Sloane's ethnography is that it consisted largely of ephemeral artefacts. These were of two kinds. On the one hand are the artefacts of animal and vegetable materials that were designed by their makers to be used and discarded quite quickly: these would include Arctic skin clothing, and other American objects such as moccasins capable of, at most, only a few months' continual use. On the other hand are the materials, of ivory, ceramics and lacquer made for sale, either within local markets, or for export from West Africa or Asia. The collection includes many groups of highly important artefacts including some of the earliest textiles from Africa, the oldest Canadian Inuit collection, the only surviving eighteenth-century African artefact (the Asante drum) associated with slavery. Many of the apparently minor items are unique. Its importance, as a collection is, however, much more general than the rather limited survivals would suggest. This is because of the manner in which Sloane applied scholarly and scientific principles to the acquisition and recording of ethnography in a catalogue, accompanied by letters and other documents, whose chronological structure can be discerned. Situated as he was at the centre of a network of correspondents, Sloane was able, over a period of forty years, to gather ethnography in a uniquely scholarly

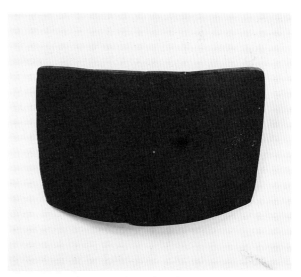

Fig. 85 A carved stone amulet [?] drilled for application, European [?]. [28a/755] 'A hollow'd oblong square piece of blackish *marble* with white spotts w^t. two holes in it to be fastened to the region of the spleen when that viseus is affected . . . (*amulet*)'. Length 25 cm. BM, Ethno, Sl.755. Reproduced by courtesy of the Trustees of the British Museum.

manner. This was accomplished not as an activity important in its own right, but as a minor adjunct to his other interests. As a scientist Sloane was primarily interested in medical materials, and in botany and mineralogy, particularly as they related to the natural sciences. The ethnography therefore contains African and Asian medicines and amulets, and their containers, used for a variety of purposes.[114] More generally, it contains numerous types of basketry and textile employing exotic materials: he acquired unusual artefacts made of bark, roots and grass, we may assume, because they illustrated the usefulness of the plants which he was recording by collection. Similarly he was interested in animal products: in garments of skin, gut and fur, which in turn related to his zoological interests. These included the keeping of an Arctic fox from Hudson Bay in London so as to observe seasonal fur colour changes (see Chapter 4). It is significant that most of the important costumes are of skins and furs from North America, Siberia and Scandinavia, of feathers from South America, and of bark, raffia and other botanical materials. It is extraordinary that, given the large collections from Asia, there is so little of silk, and virtually nothing of wool or cotton from anywhere.[115] This cannot have been because those materials were unavailable; instead it may have arisen because those more mundane materials did not serve to illuminate Sloane's scientific interests.

One of Sloane's strongest ethnographic-botanical interests was in tobacco. He collected dozens of pipe bowls, particularly from North America, and numerous water pipes from Asia. Perhaps more interesting than these were examples of cigars and cigarettes which he included in his cabinet.[116] Another obsession was in beads and beadwork: this seems to have been related to his mineralogical and conchological interests in the same way that tobacco related to botany. Sloane's beadwork included many glass beads, a subject, as mentioned above, of great importance to him. The dozens of examples of shell wampum (beads) from North America were carefully given values by Sloane, and reflects his general interests in numismatics. Moreover, beads, like coins, tobacco pipes and shoes, form a simple discrete category of object to collect and display in cabinets. Less easy to categorize is Sloane's interest in weapons and hunting gear. As mentioned above, he was only marginally interested in European weapons and armour; and yet he possessed hundreds of non-European weapons (almost all of which have disappeared), perhaps because of his interest not only in the woods and other botanical materials used, but also in the metals employed in their creation.

Collections often act as allegories for the real world. Through a process of acquisition, models of knowledge are created in which the assemblage of scientific series of specimens acts as a symbolic miniaturization of the wider world. Historically, collections of ethnography act in two directions: as mirrors for reflecting political and social realities in European society, and as tools for the comprehension of other societies. Sloane's ethnography was collected at the point in this dialectic at which the European treatment of non-European artefacts is of a scholarly quality that enables some contextualized comprehension of other peoples to be made. The end of Sloane's life coincided with a period of 'paradigmatic change in the collecting of non-European artifacts in Europe'. The development of new taxonomic systems of nature, and the voyages of exploration in the Age of Enlightenment resulted in a vastly increased interest in non-European peoples. For the first time there was a 'conscious effort to document . . . cultural context'.[117]

As a collector Sloane has been compared to Sir Ashton Lever and to William Bullock;[118] he was, however, more akin to Sir Joseph Banks. Lever, active twenty-five years after Sloane's death, was a non-traveller whose excessive (if commendable) collecting activities led to financial difficulties. He was in a sense a secondary figure, who, in neither creating nor supervising scientific expeditions acted as an opportunistic recipient of ethnography. Through his wealth and taste he was able to capitalize on the initiatives of others. Bullock, active fifty years after Sloane's death, was in a sense rather different: he was an impresario and entrepreneur who, like Lever, was (as far as science goes) interested in birds and natural history. But beyond that, as originally a travelling showman he was a speculator – in exhibition properties, Mexican silver mines and Kentucky land; he was a traveller in Europe and the Americas. Sloane was entirely different; like Banks he sat at the centre of an enormous network of professional and scientific colleagues. He was in constant contact with people in all his spheres of interest: he influenced what they did. In his collecting he was judicious, so that he did not over-stretch himself like Lever, nor concern himself with short-term speculations like Bullock. That he should have ensured that his collection was partly bequeathed and partly given to the nation must indicate that he, unlike Lever and Bullock, regarded the preservation of his collection as more important than its endless enlargement. Banks, in his wide role as a scientist, is analogous to Sloane. He was a scientist, traveller, and constant correspondent with people the world over. Unlike Sloane he was born to wealth, and was also a patron of the arts. But, for whatever reason, he did not record the ethnography that came into his personal possession and which he passed to the institution founded by his predecessor. In this business of collecting and recording ethnography, Sloane had no equal. It was only with the emergence of the formal discipline of anthropology in the second half of the nineteenth century that scientific collecting resumed within the British Museum.

Acknowledgements

Many people helped in the preparation of this paper. George R. Hamell and William C. Sturtevant made many suggestions about sources for Sloane's ethnography. John Mack, Elizabeth Carmichael and Rüdiger Joppien read through drafts of the paper and made helpful comments. Christian Feest, Christopher Spring, Uta Berger and Jim Hamill assisted in many important ways.

Notes and References

1. BL, Sloane MS 1968, fol. 192.22.

2. Most of the surviving ethnography is from China and Japan; see Chapter 14. This article primarily concerns the materials from the rest of Asia, the Americas, Africa and Europe.

3. It is interesting to note that Sir Joseph Banks, who was responsible for the accession of much ethnography to the British Museum between the 1770s and his death in 1820, did not, apparently, prepare a catalogue of ethnography, although accession lists occasionally accompanied incoming collections.

4. It is intended that the transcription of 'Miscellanies', on which this article is based, will be submitted, in edited form for publication.

5. For Franks see David M. Wilson, *The Forgotten Collector. Augustus Wollaston Franks of the British Museum* (London, 1984). Franks started identifying Sloane materials in the British Museum in 1853, having joined the museum two years earlier. At this time the ethnographic collections consisted of no more than a few thousand artefacts, so that it would have been a relatively easy task to identify Sloane's collection. In most cases Franks was accurate, but he did not identify all the items possessing Sloane labels, and it is likely that further Sloane artefacts will be identified. However the process of identifying Sloane artefacts today, in a collection now numbering 300,000 artefacts, is much more complex than it was in the middle of the nineteenth century. Franks continued to annotate his finds in the original catalogues until the 1880s. An accurate manuscript copy of 'Miscellanies' [p. 291, no. 4c] was made by Franks for internal use in the Museum.

6. See P.M. Jones, 'A preliminary check-list of Sir Hans Sloane's catalogues', *British Library Journal* 14 (1988), p. 40.

7. See H.J. Braunholtz, *Sir Hans Sloane and Ethnography* (London, 1970), p. 19 note 7.

8. See J.E. Dandy *The Sloane Herbarium* (London, 1958), pp. 117–22. Apart from two items discussed in the text, Cuningham also contributed: [28a/221] 'A *Baskett* or hatt made of cane split & palm boards ... from China'; [28a/273] 'A *paste* made of the flowrs of Quoi ... *used as a perfume* Ex quoi hoa sive floribus Quoi in pollinem redactis unde sit massa in hanc figuram impressa'; [28a/462] '*See-kin-ling*. fil ex Huinghoang mineral. Nien-hoang lap. & felio bov Tchu-sha mineral rubr. infar cinnabaris & shehiang moscho. *Cleyer.* med. sinic. No 266.'

9. BL, Sloane MS 4025, fol. 92.

10. BL, Sloane MS 4025, fol. 90. The first undated letter from Chusan is referred to in the second letter above as having been sent in December 1700.

11. See below.

12. Dandy, op. cit. (note 8), pp. 151–3.

13. See Braunholtz, op. cit. (note 7).

14. See Richmond P. Bond, *Queen Anne's American Kings* (Oxford, 1952), and John G. Garratt, *The Four Indian Kings* (Ottawa, 1985).

15. Five items were acquired before 910*, presumably acquisitions during Petiver's lifetime. Accessions from Petiver are often marked 'P', and continue until the 1730s, as though Sloane was continuing to find or re-catalogue Petiver's material. For Petiver see Chapter 1.

16. For Kaempfer see Chapter 18; and Deutsches Institut für Japanstudien, *Deutse-jin no mita Genroku-jidai, Kaempfer-ten* (The Genroku period as seen by a German, the Kaempfer exhibition) (Osaka, 1991).

17. BL, Sloane MS 4047, fol. 347. Published for instance in John Bigelow (ed.), *Autobiography of Benjamin Franklin* (Philadelphia, 1868), p. 143. See also C. Frondel, 'Benjamin Franklin's purse', *Archives of Natural History* 15 (1988), pp. 281–7.

18. See note 74 below for details of Elkings' letters to Sloane.

19. See note 87 below for Light's letter to Sloane.

20. Sloane's catalogue description is [28a/2065] 'A nest of Olagans or Thirty Basketts made w^t: Birch Bark & adorne'd w^t: Porcupines quils given me by Capt: Middleton who' brought them from Hudson bay. Different houragans, ou petits paniers faits d'ecorces d'arbres par les Sauvages du Canada. Biron p 281.' The letter of 22 November 1742 was written by Middleton to thank Sloane for the proposal to confer on him the Prize Medal at the next Royal Society meeting. At the end he says: 'I have sent by the Bearer hereof, a Nest of Olagans, which are the compleatest that I could get, and beg the favour of your acceptance, being with the greatest Respect ... Christopher Middleton' (BL, Sloane MS 4057, fol. 161). As elsewhere, Sloane's acquisition of the baskets was a minor element in a relationship between scientific colleagues that had little to do with ethnography.

21. In an entry in 'Miscellanies' such as [28a/1785] 'A *thermometer* of a new invention from Mr. *Reaumur*' the two significant words, the artefact type and source (i.e. Réaumur) are underlined for emphasis.

22. Twenty-three artefacts are cross-referenced to other collections. For instance: [28a/450] 'Yellow blew & red granulated *snuff* from Turkey? an the Dung of moths wch had eaten cloths of these colours? see no. 5162 Insect.' The

others are: [28a/] 12, 1133, 129, 187, 339, 427*, 656, 690, 704, 710, 742, 833, 1111, 1135, 1279, 1481, 1537, 1586, 1583, 1783, 1850, 2012, 2046.

23. So for instance a possibly Guyanese apron [28a/920] 'An *apron* made of beads . . .' becomes [28a/2015] 'An Indian apron formerly 920 made of bugles of diverse colours'.

24. Hence [28a/4] 'A shoe from Coromandel,' is followed by [28a/5] 'The same'. An example of a pair of shoes being given one number is provided by [28a/1398]: 'A pair of Muscovite womans *shoes*'.

25. The Saami accession is: [28a/1787] 'A *Lapland sledge* wᵗ. the bridle & trappings for the Rene deer: the habit of furrs viz. coat, stockings & shoes & gloves, wᵗ. the belt cap purse wherein is steel & flint wᵗ. some tobacco & a spoon, as also a knife hanging to it. vid. Le Bruns Muscovy. (from Mr *Grubb*, a Swede.' An Inuit accession [28a/1933] includes *c*.35 items; see note 87 below.

26. Examples are: [28a/196] 'An artificall *eye* made by *Verle*'; [28a/498] 'A silver *spoon* to teach left handed children to use only their right hand'; [28a/786] 'An artificall *glasse eye*'; [28a/877] 'A crooked surgeons *needle*. From Mr. *Cowper*'; [28a/1347] 'An artificall *ear* in *ivory* sent by Dr. *Hoffmann* to Dr. *Plumptree* & by him given to me'.

27. For example: [28a/491] 'A remedy for the *piles* from Hampshire used inwardly & outwardly?'; [28a/544] 'A *medicine* used for the cure of the *Kings evill*'; [28a/596] 'An *oyle* from Florence or Rome for bitings of vipers &c Dr. *Brown*'; [28a/784] 'A preparation of *arsenic* wᵗ. wᶜʰ. some French physicians – cure intermitting *fevers*. The dose is from 2 to 8 grains it vomits & purges but leaves behind hecticall heats [inflammations crossed out] in ye soles of the feet & palms of the hands wᵗ. a copper tast in the mouth taken off by lemons'; [28a/787] '*Lozenges* for the heart burn call'd Riders or Newberry lozenges said to be made of crabs or cray fish shells'; [28a/1256] 'A *vomit* of a vegetable juice perhaps asarabacc wᶜʰ. works quickly & easily'; [28a/1550] '*Drops* from Paris pretending to cure the gout from Mr. *Woolhouse*'; [28a/1769] 'One of *Wards* pills'. This last probably refers one of the quack doctor, Joshua Ward's pills, for which there is an analysis, dated 1737: BL, Sloane MS 4034, fol. 41.

28. A separate catalogue of more than 1,000 'Salts, Earths. clays &c' is in the Mineralogy Library, The Natural History Museum: see Jones op. cit. (note 6), p. 45. Those in 'Miscellanies' include for instance: [28a/1016] 'Talcum sal. *Epsom*'; [28a/1608] 'The *sediment* of Shuttlewood spaw Jus out of eight pints. Dr. *Short*'; [28a/1611] 'The *sediment* of five pints of Scarburgh water'; [28a/1612] 'The *sediment* of a pint & an halfe of Harrigate Sulphur well'; [28a/1615] 'The *sediment* of Buckley waters? Dr. *Short*'.

29. For instance: [28a/249] '*Oil of Scorpions* from Santa cruz'; [28a/393] '*phosphorus*, liquidus, or dissolv'd in oil of cloves'; [28a/399] '*Oil olive*?'; [28a/400] '*Oil* of vitriol?'; [28a/604] 'Oleum petrolei? Dr. *Brown*'.

30. For instance [28a/414] 'A *candle* an for processions?'; [28a/688] 'White *sope* made into an hexangular form with figures upon it'; [28a/1921] 'Jerusalem *sope* from Mr *Collier*'; [28a/1940] 'Hard *sope* from Smyrna?'.

31. In the Museum of Mankind. The instruments listed include: [28a/176] 'Mr *Bedderoles* standing *microscope* for observing the circulation of the blood made by Mr Marshall'; [28a/331] 'Mr *Boyles* lead glasse from Dr. *Hook*'; [28a/466] 'A piece of *watch work* belonged to Dr. *Hook*'; [28a/652] 'Two *glasses* for a *camera obscura* & painting *frame* from Mr. *Wilson* & Alexr. *Brown*'; [28a/874] 'A *Syringe* for injecting the vessels wᵗ. wax of severall colours? or [ ] from Dr. *Lavater*'; [28a/890] 'A water *clock* made by *Renard* le fils at Sens'; [28a/1595] 'One dozen of the small & fine *files* for watchmakers viz round, triangular, oblong &c from Sheffield by Dr. *Short* at 1sh. 6d.'; [28a/1785] 'A *thermometer* of a new invention from Mr. *Reaumar*'; [28a/2013] 'A new invented weather machine from Nurenberg'.

32. Numbers: 28a/283–5, 317, 329, 334, 366, 429, 1444–7, 1463, 1543, 1670, 1724, 1808, 1811, 1899, 2008, 2047, 2049, 2081, 2111. Others are included in the catalogue of 'Pictures'.

33. [28a/150]. Amongst the manuscripts is a seventeenth-century 'Description of the model of the sacred sepulchre' in Jerusalem (BL, Sloane MS 857, fol. 197). These models were standard features of cabinets, there being one in Copenhagen and another in Don Saltero's coffee house. See *Catalogue of the rarities to be seen at Don Saltero's coffee-house in Chelsea . . .* 39th edn, (London, n.d.), p. 1, and T. Lundbæk and B. Dam-Mikkelsen, *Etnografiske genstande i Det Kongelike danske Kunstkammer 1650–1800* (Copenhagen, 1980), pp. 90–1.

34. The other seven models are: 28a/151, 1336–8, 1433, 1546 and 1892.

35. The other items are: 28a/20, 791, 810–1, 821, 978, 1019, 1022, 1506, 1778, 1871, 1014, 2058.

36. Knives burnt in 1666 are in the first item in the catalogue [28a/1], while [28a/736] is a message written in code taken off a French vessel during the Old Pretender's attempt of 1715. The other items are: 28a/338, 475, 499, 580–1, 654, 736, 767, 897, 916**, 1102, 1554.

37. The others are: 28a/3, 367, 546, 888, 1026, 1035, 1283, 1388, 1674, 1683, 1731, 1834, 1906, 1910, 1942, 2019.

38. These are: 28a/3, 509–10, 515–6, 580–1, 888, 1026, 1167, 1279–80, 1586, 1834, 1900, 1922, 2098.

39. The general objects of vertue include: 28a/120, 168, 193, 195, 197, 287, 229, 313, 318–20, 368, 372–7, 387–9, 404, 430, 442–4, 528, 536, 561, 565, 634–5, 647, 655, 662, 677–8, 771, 782, 785, 788–9, 794–7, 803–5, 812–3, 815–20, 822, 825, 827, 833–4, 878, 881, 915, 972–3, 987, 1003–5, 1012–3, 1027, 1029, 1039–42, 1046–7, 1049–50, 1120, 1128–32, 1171, 1183–4, 1207–8, 1276, 1439–43, 1457, 1467–8, 1642, 1653, 1706, 1737, 1755, 1762, 1776, 1784,

1832, 1860–2, 1870, 1875, 1880, 1904–5, 1914, 1920, 1925, 1931, 1947, 1978, 1981, 1983–7, 2007, 2009–11, 2016, 2018, 2022, 2028, 2034, 2053, 2057, 2060–1, 2072, 2083–4, 2087, 2103. See also Chapter 13.

40. Glass items include: 28a/68, 74–6, 86–7, 93, 95, 106, 243, 264, 293–96, 298–310, 333, 335, 342–57, 359–63, 411, 413, 448, 478, 486–7, 508, 537, 560, 566, 674, 676, 718, 772, 774–5, 792, 823–4, 826, 829, 889, 909, 911, 977, 985, 1007, 1036, 1204, 1231, 1246, 1391, 1426–32, 1434–5, 1449, 1459–60, 1462, 1567–76, 1579–81, 1647, 1665–6, 1676–82, 1687, 1695–8, 1702, 1711, 1720, 1726, 1753, 1774, 1888, 1894, 1897, 1903, 1926, 1929, 2001, 2078, 2086.

41. Numbers: 28a/1448, 1587, 1667, 1912–3, 1924.

42. The numbers include: 28a/187–8, 188, 499, 513, 700, 1030, 1105, 1252, 1451, 1547–8, 1591, 1657, 1664, 1699, 1991–2, 2033, 2058.

43. Numbers: 28a/509–10, 521, 617, 637–8, 656, 798, 821, 833, 878, 1114–5, 1126–7, 1167, 1271, 1381–4, 1419, 1555, 1643, 1797, 1878–9, 1923, 2034, 2048, 2059, 2098, 2104.

44. Coins, seals and medals from all sources in 'Miscellanies' include: 28a/215, 418–20, 810–1, 835, 880, 898–9, 1272, 1279–80, 1509, 1529–30, 1671, 1709, 1778, 1859, 1900–1, 1984, 2006, 2014, 2062–4, 2071, 2074–5, 2101. Ethnographic currencies are additional.

45. The antiquities include: 28a/234, 403, 649–51, 695, 776, 779, 911*, 1355–67, 1455, 1470–1, 1544–5, 1683, 1688, 1783, 1831, 1896, 1907–8, 1911, 2046.

46. However there were in 'Miscellanies' some series of fittings for cabinets including: [28a/2072] 'Several pieces of carv'd Ivory likely taken from Amber Cabinets where they were for ornament'.

47. Tradescant's ethnography is divided into five sections: 'Mechanicks, choice pieces in Carvings, Turnings, Paintings', 'Other variety of Rarities', 'Warlike Instruments, European, Indian &c', 'Garments, Habits, Vests, Ornaments', 'Utensils, and Household stuffe.' See John Tradescant, *Musæum Tradescantianum* (London, 1656), pp. 36–55.

48. The ethnography in the Royal Society museum was classified under the rubric 'Of Artificial Matters', in sections 2 'Of things relating to Mathematicks; and some Mechanicks' and 3 'Chiefly of Mechanicks': see Nehemiah Grew, *Musaeum Regalis Societatis* (London, 1681), pp. 364–75.

49. Thoresby's ethnography appears under 'Plants', for vegetables, 'Artificial Curiosities. Things relating to war.' and 'Household-Stuffs, Habits, &c.' See Ralph Thoresby, *Ducatus Leodiensis* (London, 1715), pp. 448 *et seq*.

50. See Chapter 1, Appendices.

51. For Empson see Chapter 2. British Museum, *The General Contents of the British Museum*, 2nd edn. (London, 1762), p. 33. The manuscripts themselves include remarkable series of dictionaries and grammers, pictures, of accounts of voyages, travels and histories relating to the then known world, and of Arab manuscripts relating to science and medicine.

52. British Museum, op. cit. (note 51), pp. 34–5.

53. See Glyn Daniel, *A Hundred and Fifty Years of Archaeology* (London, 1975), for a discussion of evolution and archaeology in the early nineteenth century.

54. For the supposed Old World origin of native America, see Robert Silverburg, *Mound Builders of Ancient America. The Archaeology of a Myth* (Greenwich, Conn., 1968) and Robert Wauchope, *Lost Tribes and Sunken Continents* (Chicago, 1962).

55. British Museum, op. cit. (note 51), pp. 55–62.

56. Ibid., pp. 196–202.

57. Ibid., pp. 154–5.

58. These specimens are included in a list entitled '[T]o The Honourable Sr. Hans Sloane Baronet from Mr Winthrop.' (BL, Sloane MS 4063, fol. 30).

59. John and Andrew van Rymsdyk, *Museum Britannicum* (London, 1778). See John L. Thornton, *Jan van Rymsdyck Medical Artist of the Eighteenth Century* (Cambridge and New York, 1982), pp. 61–74.

60. The South Seas Room is best described by J.P. Malcolm, an American topographer working in London, in 1803. See J.C.H. King, *Artificial Curiosities from the Northwest Coast of America* (London, 1981), p. 97.

61. This was the 'Second Room': see King op. cit. (note 60), p. 98. A description of the gallery in 1805 can be used to associate many of the items with specific catetories of Sloane ethnography; for instance 'Opposite the windows – Musical instruments of various Nations. Swords, Daggers &c. of Do. Ancient Spurs. Glass and Crystal Vessels . . . On the left of the fire place & over it – Chinse figures in Brass, Stone and Wood. Chinese Scales, weights, compasses; and other Implements . . .'

62. See Leigh, Sotheby, and Son, *A Catalogue of a Collection of Minerals . . .* (London, 1803), p. 21. Lots 395–407* are cabinets. The evidence that they were Sloane's is circumstantial: see Jessie M. Sweet, 'Sir Hans Sloane: life and mineral collection', *Natural History Magazine* 5 (1935), pp. 98–100. Lots 408–17 are each lots described as 'Various Warlike Instruments, Paddles, &c. from Otaheite and other Islands in the South Sea'. These lots are likely to have contained materials mostly collected by Cook and Vancouver, and to have come from Pacific America as well as the Pacific Islands. But they may well have included Sloane ethnography, since the lotting of this material was so casual, although there is no evidence for this beyond the disappearance of such a large proportion of

'Miscellanies' before 1853 when Franks started work on the collection.

63. See M.J. Becker, 'A ball headed club from the Eastern Woodlands in the collections of the Horniman Museum, London', *Pennsylvania Archaeologist* 50 no. 1–2 (1980), pp. 1–8. Crowe's relations with the British Museum are described in King, op. cit. (note 60), pp. 39–40. The Keeper of the Department of Natural History, Charles König (in post 1813–51) reported of the 'objects of curiosity' desired by Crowe that: '. . . they may still be considered a nuisance, in as much as some of them harbour insects, and all take up much of the room which is wanted for other objects . . . Mr Konig cannot now specify the articles with any degree of exactness . . .' (ibid).

64. Franks's Sloane notebook is stored with registers in the British Museum, Department of Ethnography, at the Museum of Mankind.

65. David I. Bushnell jnr., 'The Sloane Collection in the British Museum', *American Anthropologist* new ser. 8 (1906), pp. 671–85.

66. H.J. Braunholtz, 'Ethnography in the Sloane Collection', *British Museum Quarterly*, 18(1), pp. 23–6, reprinted in Braunholtz, op. cit. (note 7) pp. 19–21.

67. Braunholtz op. cit. (note 7).

68. The artefacts from 'Miscellanies' which are most likely to have been collected by Sloane are [28a/56] 'Jamaica *strum strum* or musicall instrumt. made of an oblong – hollowed piece of wood with a crosse hole in the side, strings of a scandent herbs caulis [?]'; [28a/57] 'The *same* made of cucurbita lagenaria covered wt. skin – holed in the side'; [28a/58] 'One of another form wt. a bell in it'. These may be the instruments illustrated in Sloane's *Natural History*, (vol. I, pl. iii). Pl. ii includes two figures of Jamaican pottery, which may possibly be related to sherds in the 'Antiquities' catalogue listed in note 100 below.

69. The Jamaican ethnography is discussed below. See Dandy, op. cit. (note 8), pp. 204–8 for Sloane's Jamaican plants.

70. Sloane's correspondence with Johann Amman (1707–41), professor of botany in St. Petersburgh, includes a letter comparing native plant use in Canada and Siberia (Sloane to Amman, 17 December 1735; BL, Sloane MS 4068, fol. 281), another detailing Russian exploration towards Kamchatka and California (Amman to Sloane, 22 April 1738; BL, Sloane MS 4055, fol. 315), Saami and Tungus use of skin in shamanic and other clothing (Amman to Sloane, 20 January 1739; BL, Sloane MS 4056, fols. 28–9), letters from Amman (22 July 1739 and 22 April 1740) thanking Sloane for Virginia and Carolina seeds (BL, Sloane MS 4056, fol. 109; 5069, fol. 40). Among the few pieces of ethnography dispatched to Sloane was 'A Callmuck cheese. This is for ye most part ye provision of ye Callmuck in their journeys through ye Steps, or when they go to war. They dissolve it in mares milk, of wch. it is likewise & drink it like chocolate (BL, Sloane MS 4056, fol. 109).

71. Cuningham, in a letter from Chusan of December 1700, sent plants and 'a small box of Miscellanies' to Sloane (BL, Sloane MS 4025, fol. 9). The next letter, from Chusan 22 November 1701, encloses the 200 plants and 'small Chinese compass' (BL, Sloane MS 4025, fol. 92). See Dandy, op. cit. (note 8), pp. 117–22.

72. Catesby's letter apologizing for the collection which fell into the hands of pirates is dated 10 May 1723 (BL, Sloane MS 4047, fol. 90). He wrote from Charles Town on 12 March 1724 '. . . I am now Setting out for the Cherickees a Nation of Indians 300 miles from this place & who have lately declared War with another Nation which diverts them from injuring us and gives me an opertunity of going with more safety what particular commands you'l please to send me – shall be faithfully observed to ye best of my capacity . . .' (BL, Sloane MS 4047, fol. 90). The apron and observation about Cherokee basketry probably come from this trip: 'I now send ye capt. Easton in ye Neptune a Box of Dryed plants with an indian Apron made of the Bark of the wild Mulberry this kind of Cloath with a kind of Basket they make with Split cane are the only Mechanick Arts worth Notice' (letter dated 27 January 1724; BL, Sloane MS 4047, fol. 290). Sloane accurately included details of the apron and basketry in 'Miscellanies': [28a/1203]: 'An indian *Apron* from South Carolina made of the bark of ye wild mulberry tree, this kind of cloath wt. a kind of basket they make wt. splitt cane are the only mechanical arts worth notice. Mr Catesby.' The complaint about the extra work of copying drawings for all his subscribers is dated 15 August 1724 (BL, Sloane MS 4047, fol. 212). For his life see Dandy, op. cit. (note 8), pp. 110–13.

73. These were: [28a/7] 'A *sword* from China worn there by father *Fontanay* who gave it me. The Chinese wear swords with their hilts towards their backs'; [28a/119] 'A China *Chauffer mains* given by Father *Fontenay* being filld wt. ashes to warm the hands in cold'; [28a/269] 'A Chinese *horn* for gunpowder. given me by Fa. *Fontenay*; [28a/323] 'A Chinese *rule* given me by Fa. Fontaney, tis made of Bambo cane'; [28a/469] 'perfum'd *candles* from China given me by Father *Fontaney*'.

74. Elking's letter about the walrus head with a loose tusk is in BL, Sloane MS 4048, fol. 183: 'Sr: Hereby I send to you the head of a Wallross [or Morse, Sea Lyon, or Sea Cow because I don't know how to name it in English] it is brought over in Salt Pickle, and I would leave it so with the Flesh as it is, and not make it a skeleton by boiling of its Flesh here at the Train Cokesy thinking it more pleasing to See the shape of ye Same, I would have sent it to you last Wednesday but the Mr; of Elfford Coffe house desir'd me, to leave itt there for 2 days to shew itt to some of his and my friends, which I allowed him but I hear now that one of the Tusks is come lose by this my connivancy for wch: I am not well pleased, but hope you will accept of it as it is, and when ye 7 ships which we Expect stil from Greenland are arrived, I wil send you some birds and what else meight bring with them that is uncommon here. I am with due respect. Your most Humble & obedient servt. Sr. H:Elking.

South Sea Company Dock Saturday ye 6th Augt: 1726.' The ethnography is listed in a letter dated 5 October 1726[?]: 'From Davis's Straights, is, the Coat of a Woman made of seal skin, and a wooden ornament which they wear to keep the Sun out of their Eyes. A dart with the wood whereby they throw the same very dextrously to Birds and Fishes – By the small pin on the Wood, filled is the Socket of the dart, they govern the dart, and aim at a great distance, seldom or never missing to Strike or catch what they throw at. A pair of Children's Shoes. I have some mens Cloaths and other Voluminous things but they not being very clean, nor handsome think not worth your acceptance, though they are at your service, upon comand' (BL, Sloane MS 4049, fol. 44). The letter thanking Sloane for 'your Two Noble Volumes of the Naturall History of Jamaica' (BL, Sloane MS 4048, fol. 217) is dated 16 November 1726.

75. See James Petiver, *Gazophylacii Naturae & Artis Decas Septima & Octava* (London, n. d.), pl. 74, 'To Dr Charles Goodal President of ye College of Physicians London', caption on p. 8: fig. 6. '*A Pipe of small Eggs encompassing a* Pear-tree *Stalk*'; and fig. 7, 'A Tobacco pipe *used by the Kings of Carolina*, Cat 608.' This pipe was given the catalogue information: [28a/1452] '*The head of a tobacco pipe* graved by Mr. *Petiver* Gaz. Nat. belonged to the King of Carolina.' The other artifical curiosities in Petiver's publications are: at pl. 76 fig. 12, 'Petty. *A brass Coin current in* Batavia, Java &c.'; pl. 77 figs. 4–5, 'Two diferent Impressions of *China Inck Cakes*.'; pl. 79 fig. 2, 'A small *silver* Coin.'; pl. 79 figs. 7–8, 'A small Silver *Indian* Coin, with Characters on one side only.'

76. BL, Sloane MS 3061–2.

77. The following descriptions by Wilson (BL, Sloane MS 4019, fol. 68) can be compared to Sloane's: '2 pairs of Woman Muscovate Shoes' becomes [28a/1398] 'A pair of Muscovite womans *shoes*. From Mr. *Wilsons* collection'; '2 pair of Lanvance Matted Shoes' becomes [28a/1399] ' A pair of Lanvance matted *shoes*' and [28a/1401] '*Another* somewhat *diferent*'; '1 pair of Strange Matted Slippers' becomes [28a/1400] 'One pr. of strange matted *slippers*. from Japan'; '1 pair Turkey Slippers' becomes [28a/1402] 'One pr. of Turkey *slippers*'; '1 pair Seaneca Woman Slippers' turns into [28a/1403] 'One pr. of Senegal Womans *slippers*'; 'A Etiophisch Leather Shield' is rendered [28a/1404] 'An Aethiopish leather *shield*'; 'A Japans Sheath of Dog Skin Wherein are two knives of Cole black wood ye handels' is improved to [28a/1405] 'A Japan *sheath* of dogskin wherein are 2 *knives a fork* an ear instrument &c. a file, penknife & steel'; 'A Moscovate wth a Walrush knife & 2 With Wood handels' is refined to [28a/1407] 'A Muscovite *knife* wt. a Walrush or Morses tooth haft.' [28a/1408] 'The *same lesser*', and [28a/1409] 'A Muscovite knife wt. a wooden handle. Id.'

78. Africa: 28a/32, 54, 59, 109, 424, 723, 760, 763, 1257–60, 1422?, 1556, 1817?, 2039; Angola: 28a/1935; Capashear: 28a/1830; Congo: 28a/1425; Ethiopia: 28a/1404; Gambia: 28a/1763–6; Guinea: 28a/44, 111, 132, 543, 588–92, 876, 1027, 1031, 1624–7,

1630, 1816, 1830, 1833, 2021, 2051; Hottentot: 28a/246, 1915; Madagascar: 28a/1423–4, 2105, 2107; St. Thomas: 28a/1257–60; Senegal: 28a/1403.

79. The others are: [28b/335] 'A *bagg* made of an African grasse?'; [28b/400] 'A grasse *purse* of a yellow black & red colour from Guinea by Mrs. *Dering*'; [28b/401] 'A *belt* of the same. Id. the red dyed by mulberries'.

80. See E. Bassani and M. Mcleod, 'African material in early collections', in O. Impey and A. MacGregor (eds.), *The Origins of Museums. The Cabinet of curiosities in sixteenth- and seventeenth-century Europe* (Oxford, 1985), pp. 245–50.

81. These are 28a/1830, and 32. Additional surviving African ethnography included on the database on 6 February 1991 were: 28a/1268, 2024 (Guinea), 2105 (Madagascar). For the last see John Picton and John Mack, *African Textiles* (London, 1979), pp. 144–5. In the Department of Medieval and Later Antiquities is a sixteenth-century ivory horn from South-East Nigeria, with additional European carving. See note 82 (below) for the entry from 'Miscellanies' [28a/2021]; see also *Illustrated Archaeologist* 2 (1894), p. 31.

82. [28a/590]: 'An [Indian crossed out] *bracelet* wt. rattles to it cut out of the elephants tooth (*ivory*) worn upon the arms in Guinea.... 0.5.00 [marked C.H.R.]. [28a/591]: '*Another*.... 0.5.0. [28a/723]: 'An *ivory* hunting horn or *trumpet* such as Wormius's aureum cornu ... 0.10.00.' [28a/763]: 'An *ivory horn*'. [28a/1425]: 'A *Trumpett* usd in Congo in warr, ivory wt. the Lacerta Squamosa carved on it. vid Pigafetta p. 48. Marorla of Congo'. [28a/2021]: 'A trumpet in Guinea used by the Inhabitants of an elephants tooth on wch. are engraved the lacerta squaummosa an elephant, Hippopotamous Lion, goat & unicorn, a hats beaver duck a sword on a bores head, a dragon & some plants. This was afterwards turnd to a drinking cup with these lines drink you this & think no scorne though the cup be much like a horne 1559 fines from Ireland by Mr. Adams'; see above, note 81. For a survey of Afro-Portugese ivories see Center of African Art, *Africa and the Renaissance: art in ivory* (New York, 1988).

83. In the eighteenth century this use was extended to include the peoples of the Pacific, just as earlier the Spanish had employed it in the Philippines.

84. For instance in the entry: [28a/172] 'A West Indian *basket* made of birch bark from Canada'.

85. 28a/1329–30, 1332–5, 1385–6, 1617–21, 1750–2, 1838–42, 1844, 1909, 1933–4, 2044.

86. [28a/1335] 'A *dart* a. with the wood b. whereby they throw the same very dextrously at birds or fishes'; [28a/1617] 'The modell of a *boat* used in Davis's Straigts or *Groenland* by the natives'; [28a/1618] 'Their *coat* made of seals skins'; [28a/1619] 'Theyr *sword* made of bones'; [28a/1620] 'Their *knife* made wt. an iron semi-circular point the rest bone'; [28a/1751] 'An Indian *lance* made of fish *bones* headed wt. iron

to kill whales or large fish. The head of the lance is fastened to a long lance of whale Skin with which they are brought on shore'; [28a/1844] 'A *fish gigg* from *Hudsons* bay catch salmon made of two long bearded bones sett at the end a sharp woden pole fastened wt. fish gutts. from Mr. *Edwards*'.

87. See BL, Sloane MS 4055, fol. 370. 'Mooss River. James Bay North America August 25 1738. Sr: Hans In my Passages through Hudsons Straights In the Latitud 63°−00′ North and Longitud about 72.00 Wt. we mett with Severall Esquemos which Came along side our Ship In thayr Cannos and our Capt. Traded a small quantity of Wale Bone amongst the Natives I traded for sum Knives and Brass Butons Severall peices of Ivory 4 in of which I make bold to Troble your Honr. with the Names and Severall Uses by what I could Larn of them by Mottons ar as folows.

No. 1 as I observed is for thayr Lines to run out on and Each Canno hath one of them made fast to the Starboard side of the hole whar the man sits to paddle 2 ye same. 3. a harpoon 4 to Dress Skins with 5 is is mad fast to a harpoon flat 6 ye same 7 a Swivell for fishing Line 8 the same 9 an ornament hangin at thayr Brests 10 a Comb. 11 a pipe which theyr use in Skining the Seals 12 the but End of a harpoon Staff. 13 a sort of Buton on thayr Breast which the women have to Cary thayr Children on 14 made fast to the fishing Lines is a Harpoon Shathed with wood for fear of Cuting holes in thayr Cannos 16 an ornament for the Breasts 17 the same as 5 18 a harpoon 20 a tooth but of what Creature I know not. 21 Do 22 A contrivance belongin to a Drill. 25 is a faset to blow up Seal Skin Bage with 26 ye same as 20 28 an ornament for ye noose 29 an Ivory Idol 30 the same as 24 33 for Children to play with 35 the same as 29: 34 a Lance 32 In the paper is a Stone belonging to 3 27 an ornament hanging at a womans breast which I humbly refer to your Judgement Alexandr: Light

PS ... the Baskett which Contain this Ivory is of the Esquemos making ...'

88. [28a/1838] 'A *belt* made of unicorns *horn* on wch. are rudely engraved boats canoes &c.. wt. a [cord crossed out] fish skin. From *Hudsons Bay* by Mr. *Edwards*.'

89. The only other significant surviving pre-1750 collection of North American Arctic materials is that in Copenhagen. It is different in character, consisting mostly of Greenlandic harpoons, paddles and drums. There is little or no documentation for this collection See Dam-Mikkelsen and Lundbæk, op. cit. (note 33) pp. 3–16).

90. 28a/48, 110, 125–8, 162–4, 172–3, 201–204*, 218, 237, 260, 322, 369, 426, 446–7, 470–4, 572–5, 595, 648, 725, 734, 738, 752, 756–8, 776, 808, 885–7, 913, 1202–3, 1205–6, 1209–1228, 1250–1, 1254, 1278, 1368–73, 1387, 1411–2, 1452, 1458, 1485–6, 1525, 1532, 1534–6, 1622, 1628, 1655–6, 1727–33, 1735–6, 1738–47, 1782, 1819–21, 1835–6, 1843, 1845–6, 1884–7, 1930, 1998–2000, 2029–31, 2037–8, 2040–3, 2045, 2065, 2067–70, 2073, 2079–80, 2088–9, 2106.

91. See Bonita Freeman-Witthoft, 'Cherokee craftswomen and the economy and basketry', *Expedition* 19 no. 3 (1977), pp. 17–27.

92. [28a/218] 'A *candle* made of the berries of a tree from Carolina'; [28a/1278] 'A *nutt cracker* for walnutts made of cedar wood from Carolina'; [28a/1727] 'A *candle* & piece of soap made of the myrtle wax berries. from New England by Mr. *Wynthorp*.'

93. [28a/1368] 'An Indian *drum* made of a hollowed tree carv'd the top being brac'd w^t. peggs & thongs w^t. the bottom hollow from Virginia by Mr. *Clerk*'. The drum body seems now to be of *Cordia* sp., a genus of 250 species, some of which are native to West Africa (but not to the mid-Atlantic United States) and used for making drums; a drum peg has been identified as of *Baphia* sp., another African genus: letter form Paula Rudall, Royal Botanic Gardens, Kew, to Richard Burleigh, Research Laboratory, British Museum, 2 September 1986, ref. 169/958/PR/86. Bushnell originally identified the drum as being, in part, apparently of pine (or cedar), an opinion now unjustifiably strengthened by Braunholtz (Bushnell, op. cit. (note 65), p. 676; Braunholtz op. cit. (note 7), p. 20).

94. [28a/1458] 'A negro *drum* from S. Carolina by Mr. *Standish*.'

95. See J.C.H. King, 'North American ethnography in the collection of Sir Hans Sloane', in Impey and MacGregor, op. cit. (note 80), pp. 232–6.

96. (America): 28a/43, 247, 425, 464, 518–9, 525, 737, 914, 1397, 1454, 1473, 1491; Brazil: 28a/16–19, 21–2, 370–1, 838–41, 1248, 1812, 1945; (Central America): 28a/579, 1277, 1343; Columbia and the Guyanas: 28a/79, 133–4, 725, 1344, 1822–9, 2015; Mexico: 28a/540–2, 1108, 1590, 1779–81, 1852–3; Tierra del Fuego: 28a/225–6, 463, 507, 696, 704, 708–9, 742–8; West Indies: 28a/23, 45–6, 56–8, 402, 503–4, 719, 737, 891, 990, 1038, 1090, 1382, 1531, 1623, 1686, 1775, 1796, 1855, 1901, 1904, 1966–9, 2096, 2108.

97. The penis sheath [28a/579] has recently come to light. For the others see Braunholtz, op. cit. (note 7), p. 35.

98. In the catalogue of '*Agate cups bottles spoons &c.*' is a green stone ornament supposedly from South America, and now in the Department of Mineralogy: [28g/223] 'A pale *nephrite stone* from Guiana w^t. a hole in it. to hang it to the body by a string for the cure of diseases.' See Sweet, op. cit. (note 62), p. 159.

99. [28a/1090] 'A manati *strap* for whipping the Negro Slaves in the Hott W. India plantations From Dr *Covell*'. [28a/1623] 'A *noose* made of cane splitt for catching game or hanging runaway negros'; [28a/1796] 'A *bullet* used by the runaway Negros in Jamaica made of the pewter dishes & lead in a thimble. When there is too much tin they break in pieces on being shott. Mr. *Barham*'; [28a/1966] 'A coat of the runaway rebellious negros who lived in the woods of that Island made of the Maho[e?]t bark finer as the cap no [28a/1967]. Of the same fineness'; [28a/

1968] 'Britches of the same coarser as also his'; [28a/1969] 'His Knapsack to be carried over his shoulders all brought from Jamaica given me by Mr Millar.'

100. [28b/102] 'Part of an earthen *urn* found full of indians bones in a cave in Jamaica'; [28b/103] '*Another* piece of the same'; [28b/104] '*Another*.' These may have been collected by Sloane; see note 68 above.

101. This is suggested by the catalogue entry: [28a/540] 'A leather *purse* embroidered together with the figure of a hand in horn? fastened to it to be worn to prevent *thunder* in the mines of Sta. Maria near Campeche in New Spain taken [from the Indians crossed out] by the English of Jamaica from the Spanyards when they took those mines & given me by Coll. *Laws*.'

102. [28b/404] 'An Indian *Pagod* made of earthen ware of a whitish colour taken from the Spanish Indians by an Inhabitant of Carolina & brought thence by Mrs. *Standish* who gave it me.'

103. [28b/518] 'An Egyptian *head* of the Sun in basaltes?'; [28b/726] 'An earthen *bottle* of gray earth coloured black in the form of a *porpesse* w^t. a handle from Peru by Dr. *Houston* said to be of their Gods. (*Idol*)'; [28b/727] '*Another* two coloured of red earths in the form of a *busto* of a man Id. *fig.*'; [28b/728] '*Another* of 4 bottles of gray earth w^t. the statue of a man drinking. Id.'.

104. The Chinese artefacts are: [28a/7, 9, 13, 20, 24, 25, 33–5, 47, 60–4, 69–73, 77, 81, 83–5, 88–92, 107, 113, 115–7, 119, 129–30, 137, 143–9, 184, 191, 198–200, 212–3, 215, 219–221. 238–240, 242, 258, 267–273, 275–8, 287–9, 315–6, 323, 341–3, 384, 415–20, 422, 441, 462, 465, 469, 493–5, 501, 505–6, 529, 552, 553–8, 562–4, 576–8, 593–4, 616, 631–2, 644, 664, 697, 727, 764, 844, 869–70, 894, 898–899, 909*, 919*–20*, 921–39, 967–71, 989, 991, 997–8, 1008, 1018, 1037, 1044–5, 1051–60, 1074, 1080–1, 1088, 1104, 1120, 1134–7, 1166, 1172–82, 1185–94, 1241–43, 1247, 1262–4, 1270, 1273–4, 1281, 1339–42, 1352–4, 1374–80, 1437, 1453, 1472, 1478–82, 1492*, 1493, 1495–1500, 1504, 1509–10, 1512–24, 1526–30, 1533, 1542, 1616, 1631–4, 1650–2, 1671, 1673, 1694–8, 1700–1, 1703, 1705, 1710, 1718–9, 1723, 1734, 1754, 1758–61, 1772–3, 1794–5, 1802–5, 1810, 1813–15, 1837, 1851, 1854, 1863–6, 1881–3, 1916, 1927, 1937, 1939, 1976–7, 1989, 2002–5, 2023–5, 2050. In 'Antiquities' are a further four Chinese artefacts: 28b/155, 413–5. Of the Chinese artefacts the following are included in the database as of 7 November 1991 in the Department of Oriental Antiquities: 28a/20, 34, 62, 84, d 143, 144, 165, 172, 184, 212, 268, 288, 418, 562, 894, 1004, 1074, 1078, 1120, 1172, 1174, 1175, 1176, 1177, 1178, 1180, 1181, 1182, 1185, 1186, 1187, 1189, 1190, 1191, 1241, 1499, 1512, 1521, 1695, 1696, 1697, 1760, 1837, 1866, 2003. In the Department of Ethnography included in the database as of 6 February 1991: 28a/62, 113, 144, 145, 149, 184, 418, 552, 562, 576, 594, 632, 664, 898, 922, 1044, 1054, 1055, 1056, 1057, 1078, 1091, 1172, 1173, 1174, 1175, 1176, 1177, 1178, 1180, 1181, 1185, 1186, 1187, 1189, 1190, 1191, 1482, 1499, 1512, 1521, 1633,

1723, 1760, 1865, 1866, 2003. There are further Asian artefacts in the Department of Oriental Antiquities with a Sloane origin, ascribed by A.W. Franks but without Sloane numbers. See Chapter 14.

105. The Japanese, and 'Japanned' artefacts are: 28a/78, 94, 136, 138–40, 169–170, 272, 274, 465, 892–5, 898–9, 970, 1056, 1058–60, 1063–79, 1082, 1084, 1087, 1091, 1104, 1121, 1139–66, 1168, 1170, 1239, 1400–1, 1405, 1472, 1563, 1565, 1592–3, 1704, 1712, 1716–7, 1837, 1995, 2082. In 'Antiquities' is a single further Japanese item: 28b/154. Of these the following 'Miscellanies' items may survive in the Department of Japanese Antiquities as indicated by the database at 6 February 1991: 28a/1056, 1058, 1059–60, 1078, 1837; in the Department of Ethnography: 28a/970, 1074, 1143–44, 400–1. See Chapter 14.

106. Cultural and geographical designations for Asia are: Banians: 28a/244, 1484; Bengal: 28a/1508, 1654; Borneo: 28a/24–5, 324–5; Celebes: 28a/847–8; Coromandel: 28a/4–5; East India/Indian/Indies: 28a/114, 321, 407, 485, 502, 539, 568, 582–3, 673, 699, 702–3, 749, 800–2, 811, 1229, 1234, 1238, 1282, 1345, 1348, 1422, 1490, 1588, 1646, 1707, 1777, 1793, 1793*, 1799–1800, 1858, 1994, 2062–4; Fort St. George: 28a/1240, 1486, 1721; India/Indian: 28a/12, 27–8, 37–9, 213–4, 222–4, 257, 261, 279–83, 330, 493–5, 500, 520, 524, 526, 549, 551, 636, 673, 722, 741, 780, 843, 849–51, 873, 883–4, 896, 1010, 1255, 1483, 1502, 1542, 1563–4, 1713–5, 1944, 2012, 2110; Kamchatka: 28a/1768, 1770; Lanvance: 28a/1399; Malabar: 28a/222, 1663, 1757, 1818, 2076; Malaysia/Indonesia: 28a/517, 584, 1349–51, 1383, 1501, 1503, 1507, 1672, 1809, 1857, 1995; Manilla: 28a/1541; Mogul: 28a/1100, 1122; Persia: 8, 8*, 118, 522–3, 657–9, 663, 735, 1275, 1406, 2062–4; Siberia: 28a/1133; Surat: 28a/705–6, 845–6; Turkey: 28a/15, 26, 52, 108, 262, 423, 431–3, 450, 456, 570–1, 618, 630, 660, 707, 710–4, 777–8, 976, 1106–7, 1266–7, 1402, 1414–6, 1420, 1538–40, 1606, 1748, 2099–2100. Of these the database at 6 February 1991 suggests the following as surviving: in the Department of Oriental Antiquities: 28a/341–3, 1713; in the Department of Ethnography: India: 28a/4, 5, 1092, 1093, 1094, 1095, 1096, 1097, 1098, 1099, 1100, 1101, 1102, 1122; Indonesia: 28a/582; Turkey: 28a/1540.

107. For instance among the artefacts designated *Indian* are: [28a/222] 'Indian *writing* upon palm boards. Malabar?'; [28a/223] 'An Indian *purse* made of rushes dyed red & brownish?'; [28a/224] 'An Indian *baskett* & cover made of rushes, greenish black & red'; [28a/849] 'An Indian *hatt* of Cane split from Mr. *Heathcote*'; [28a/850] 'An Indian Damaskind *sword* wt. a carv'd wooden handle from the *same*'; [28a/851] 'A *daggar*. From the *same*.'

108. [28a/1768] 'The habit of the inhabitants of Kamkatchki of furrs & needlework from Mr. Captn. Jenkins from Petersburg. coat britches, shoes & stockings.'

109. England: 28a/254–6, 1626, 1993, 2056; France: 28a/759, 918–20, 1417–8; Germany:

28a/1195–1200, 1494, 1566, 1990; Low Countries: 28a/670, 2035; Hungary: 28a/67, 311; Ireland: 28a/1413, 1450, 1537, 1847–9, 2021; Italy: 28a/259, 286, 1709; Livonia: 28a/55; Portugal: 28a/159–61, 480, 751, 1466, 1807–8, 1812; Russia: 28a/756–7, 761, 1133, 1398, 1407–10, 1749, 1771, 1936; Scandinavia: 28a/1023–4, 1033–4, 1062, 1103, 1109, 1589, 1787–91, 1801, 2091; Spain: 28a/263, 434, 914*, 1261, 1421, 1902, 1943, 2039; Scotland: 28a/14, 40–1, 189, 381, 401, 623–9, 661, 1506.

110. [28a/1993]: 'An instrument or weapon? (an for ye whale Fisher?) of Iron, made of a Bar of Iron bent into an oblong quadrangular form rivetted with three cross Bars of ye same set close together: out of which runs a strong tapering, angular & channel'd spike somewht like a Spear-point'; [28a/2056]: 'A Brume made of the adiantum aurum majus from Lancashire.'

111. [28a/623] 'The blew pinked *doublet* of a Scotch *Highlander* w^t. pockets in his short skirts, w^t. slitts in the back & sleeves'; [28a/624] '*Britches & stockins* made of yellow & red pladd of the same *Highlanders*' [28a/625] '*Highlanders* garters'; [28a/626] '*Highlander bonet*'; [28a/627] 'An *highlander* durk & *knife*'; [28a/628] 'A *Highlanders pistol*, all of iron'; [28a/629] 'An *Highlanders powder horn*'.

112. The manuscript is dated *c.*1706: BL, Sloane MS 3563, fols. 59–67.

113. The numbers are: 28a/2, 6, 10–11, 29–32, 36, 42, 50–1, 53, 65–6, 82, 112, 122–4, 131, 135, 142, 152–8, 165–7, 171, 205–212, 217, 227–8, 230, 236, 240, 265, 290, 314, 326–8, 378–380, 408, 459–61, 490, 492, 511, 527, 538, 550, 567, 569, 585–7, 614–5, 642–3, 645–6, 686–7, 689–92, 701, 709, 720–2, 726, 729–33, 739, 750, 754, 762, 783, 799, 871–2, 882, 975, 1002, 1009, 1032, 1083, 1085, 1089, 1092–3, 1093*–99, 1101, 1110–3, 1118, 1169, 1235–6, 1265, 1396, 1399, 1474–6, 1488–9, 1505, 1594, 1607, 1644–5, 1649, 1668–9, 1722, 1725, 1876, 1889–91, 1898, 1932, 1946, 1996–7, 2015, 2090.

114. These include [28a/1031] 'Bamboo *tarr* an ointment used for the cure of the gout & the rheumatism in Guinea. This I believe is a substance from the Duke of Chandois calld. Unguentum Encoo or the white balsam is the excrescence of a tree growing in the country Entan lying six days journey inland from Ashanta being to the eastward, it is also to be procured at Agrafar & Creepu Country to the Eastward of the river Volter & likwise at Whidah, the blacks made use of this ointmt. in anoint themselves in place of tallow being much preferable thereto & is extremely good for all manner of aches, paines & sores'; [28a/1070] 'A Japonese *box* for physick for powders & pills, with gold & silver labells & two [gold crossed out] silver bodkins'.

115. The main exception to this is footwear, perhaps the item of clothing most likely to be of zoological or botanical interest: Sloane collected large numbers of shoes from everywhere. It may also be that he felt constrained by limitations of space to collect, of costume, only shoes; or it may be that field collectors of modest means could afford to send only small artefacts, such as shoes, on ships to England.

116. Amongst the specimens of tobacco were the following: [28a/408] '*Tobacco* inclosed in a *plantain* leaf to be smoak'd as out of a pipe ...'; [28a/434] 'The best Spanish *tobacco* made up for use'; [28a/1383] '*Tobacco* rolld up in *plantain* leaves to be smok'd from Malacca by Mr. *Bell*'; [28a/1725] '*Tobacco* roll'd up to smoakd w^t. out the help of a pipe. Dr *Massy*'; [28a/1766] 'A ball of their *tobacco* from the *same*'.

117. See: Christian F. Feest, 'European collecting of American Indian artefacts and art', *Journal of the History of Collections* 5 no. 1 (1993), pp. 1–11.

118. For Bullock's enthography see Adrienne L. Kaeppler, 'Cook Voyage provenance of "Artificial Curiosities" of Bullock's Museum', *Man* new ser. 9 (1974), pp. 68–92, 1974. For Lever's ethnography from Cook's Voyages see Adrienne L. Kaeppler, '*Artificial Curiosities*' (Honolulu, 1978).

16 Prints and Drawings

John Rowlands

We are bound to wonder whether Sloane was a collector of drawings or prints properly speaking at all. Rather he appears at first sight to have acquired drawings as records ancillary to his main, and admittedly wide interests, which were chiefly natural history, medicine, travel and topography and history. From his wide-ranging curiosity, his clear love in his collecting of novelty for its own sake, and his habit, when he could do so, of acquiring important collections of material put together by others, it is not an entirely straightforward matter to divine his personal taste in artistic terms as one should be able to do with a collector of drawings and prints in later generations. For his propensity to accumulate in this way means that many drawings must have been acquired for other than artistic reasons, prompted instead by his scientific interests, or inherited incidentally in collections put together by others.

One should note that Sloane, even in the second half of the eighteenth century, was not regarded as worthy of remark as a collector of drawings: he was not mentioned in the list of the English collectors in the introduction to John Barnard's sale catalogue (1787) or in Henry Reveley's *Notices illustrative of the Drawings and Sketches* (1820, but written some years earlier).[1] Also, although we might hesitate in counting him a connoisseur of either prints or drawings in the fullest sense of the word, my task here will be to attempt, through a survey of the drawings in the Sloane collection, to uncover what discernable characteristics his acquisitions may have had, and what his partialities were.

While it is doubtful whether he would have considered himself an amateur lover of art, all the same there are some remarkably fine drawings, including some world-famous masterpieces in his collection, some of which will be mentioned among the drawings discussed below. But first we should look at its overall character. Although he was not a professed antiquarian, as far as his attitude to drawings was concerned, Sloane had a cast of mind and eye which predisposed him towards the archaic and to the works of the centuries before his birth, and also to the drawings of artists who were in fashion when he was a young man. He may have acquired this taste for the former through his familiarity with the medieval medical and astrological manuscripts that he collected (see Chapter 17). It is often the case that collectors experience a sort of blockage in their appreciation of art produced by the younger generations of contemporary artists active in their middle and later years. This seems to have been so with Sloane, for, with the notable exception of John Michael Rysbrack (1694–1770), whose statue of Sir Hans was ordered by the sitter (which is in any case, different as a living artist is bound

to be involved),[2] he did not collect the drawings of these younger artists in the last decades of his long life, apart of course from those of natural-history subjects. The statue by Rysbrack (Plate 3) and the portrait bust (Plate 2) on which it is based are outstanding of their kind, but the full-length portrait of Sloane in the British Museum attributed to John Vanderbank (1694–1739) (Plate 1) is a pompous, vacuous affair, and certainly conservative in taste. Drawings in Sloane's collection by artists active in his own lifetime are mostly confined to those who flourished in his youth, certainly before 1700.

Sloane displays a special affinity with art from north of the Alps, in particular towards the drawings by Netherlandish masters, many the work of anonymous hands, stretching back to the fifteenth century. There are interesting examples among the earlier Dutch and Flemish drawings: for instance, two sheets, drawn on both sides (cut in two at some stage and now reunited again) of drapery studies by a Flemish late fifteenth-century hand,[3] and the *St. Michael*, a Dutch drawing from the beginning of the sixteenth century.[4] On the first are studies of figures, possibly mourners which have lost a good deal of their original character through having been altered by the lively brush of Peter Paul Rubens (1577–1640) (Fig. 86).[5] There is only one example of early German draughtsmanship, but

Fig. 86 Anon., Flemish late fifteenth-century, retouched by P.P. Rubens: *Two studies of draperies*. BM, PD, 5237–92, 93ʳ. Reproduced by courtesy of the Trustees of the British Museum.

245

Fig. 87 Master of the Votive Painting of St. Lambrecht: *Entombment*. BM, PD, 5236–111ʳ. Reproduced by courtesy of the Trustees of the British Museum.

this is an exceptionally fine sheet with drawings attributed to the leading master of the 'soft style' in Austria, the so-called Master of the Votive Painting of St. Lambrecht (active in Vienna, *c*.1420–40), on the *recto*, *The Entombment* (Fig. 87), and on the *verso*, *The Lamentation over the dead Christ*.[6] It is possible that these studies were conceived as designs for companions to the panel painting in Berlin-Dahlem, the *Dead Christ at the foot of the Cross, with the Virgin and St. John*.[7] Although attempts have been made to associate this sheet with minor hands of that period, it seems most likely because of its quality that it was produced by this dominant figure who takes his name from the large votive painting from the Stiftskirche of the former Benedictine abbey at St. Lambrecht (Steiermark), and now in the Stiftsmuseum there.

Ignoring for a moment his obvious need as a naturalist to collect natural-history drawings, which he acquired substantially by both contemporary and earlier hands, Sloane's taste emerges as largely what one might expect for an educated gentleman of his day, for he was partial to the Dutch art of the seventeenth century, and northern artists of other nationalities working in the Dutch manner.[8] He liked especially those artists whose painting is highly sophisticated, and often has a strong decorative element in it. For instance, while not possessing anything by Nicolaes Berchem (1620–83), and only one, *A winding Road* by Jan Both (*c*. 1618?–

52),[9] leaders in the field of Italianate Dutch landscape painting and drawing, he had several by their followers: five drawings by Frederick de Moucheron (1633–86), four landscape drawings attributed to Karel Dujardin (1621/2?–78), and six views of classical Rome by Jan Asselyn (1610–52). Considering that the presiding genius under whose shadow all these artists were working was Claude Lorrain (1600–82), it may seem surprising that Sloane apparently had no interest in collecting Claude's drawings; however, if one recalls that of artist-connoisseurs of the seventeenth century, Sir Peter Lely (1618–80) evidently possessed only one and P.H. Lankrink (1628–92) four,[10] then Sloane's neglect is less remarkable. But by comparison with the leading collector of drawings among Sloane's contemporaries, Jonathan Richardson sen. (1665–1745), who had almost sixty drawings,[11] and an enthusiastic nobleman, the 2nd Duke of Devonshire (1665–1729), who had acquired by 1728 the 'Liber Veritatis',[12] Claude's famous drawn record of his paintings, it is possible that Sloane might disappoint us. Only with the arrival of the bequest of the Revd C.M. Cracherode at the end of the eighteenth century did the first examples of Claude's draughtsmanship enter the British Museum, which was ultimately to possess by far the finest and undoubtedly the largest representation of his drawings extant. Among the French artists of the period in whom Sloane had some slight interest was a master of decorative art working in England, Louis Chéron (1660–1725).[13] But apart from an isolated and somewhat fragmentary final study by Nicolas Poussin (1593–1665) for the main figures in his painting of c.1633, *Bacchanalian Revel before a Herm of Pan*, now in the National Gallery, London (NG 62),[14] leaving aside the work of the natural-history draughtsmen, the only French drawings of more than slight significance are a group of three small landscapes, done with great assurance in brown wash with black chalk, by the earlier artist, Jacques Callot (1592–1635).[15] These landscapes, one of which is of the bridge at Malzéville in Lorraine, were executed at the end of Callot's career, probably c.1629–31, when Gaston d'Orléans was at the court of Lorraine, whom, it is said, Callot instructed in draughtsmanship. But these drawings, related to some of the pen drawings by Callot in the album at Chatsworth, which belonged to Israël Silvestre, and an evidently posthumous series of etched landscapes, were very probably the result not of Sloane's own initiative but that of William Courten (1642–1702), whose collection Sloane had inherited on Courten's death (see Chapter 1). The reason for suggesting this is because it is most likely that the volume formerly numbered Sloane 5236 may be identifiable with 'Min[iature] 11 A book of drawings of Tintoret, Vasari, Pietro da Cortona, Callot & several great masters gathered chiefly beyond [the] sea by Mr Courten', as it is described in Sloane's handwritten catalogue.[16] As the volume itself no longer survives, following the dispersal of the drawings when it came to the Department of Prints and Drawings, Callot is now the only artist among those listed above whose drawings can now be identified with some degree of assurance as coming from Sloane 5236. If we assume that this is so, then all the drawings from Sloane 5236 are the outcome of Courten's and not Sloane's collecting.

But when it comes to looking at the Italian drawings, whether from Sloane or Courten, with the exception of a mere sprinkling of distinguished names the assemblage is disappointing. One can merely point to a single Andrea del Sarto (BM 5226–86), a Parmigianino (BM 5226–120), a Pordenone (BM 5214–288), and a slight *Virgin and Child* attributed to Giovanni Bellini (BM 5227–101) as of some interest. One is bound to say also that in general the seventeenth-century Dutch drawings from the Sloane collection are usually outstripped in quality by later acquisitions of most of these masters' work. Also with the few drawings in the collection accepted in Sloane's day as from the hand of Rembrandt, none has survived the scrutiny of modern scholarship. The *Gabriel appearing to Zacharias in the Temple*[17] which was rejected by Seidlitz as a 'Grobe Fälschung', has now been attributed to Nicolaes Maes (1634–1693) by Sumowski, and the *Pilate washing his hands*[18] is now given to another follower of Rembrandt, Aert de Gelder (1645–1727). It should come as no surprise that perhaps the single most artistically impressive group of Dutch drawings are the wonderful series of single flower studies most probably by Jan van Huijsum (1682–1749),

the leading exponent of the formal flower-piece which became very fashionable in the first half of the eighteenth century: there are some fifty-three sheets of these extracted from the volume Sloane 5283 in the Print Room.[19] *The Cabbage Rose* (Rosa centifolia) (Plate 29), which is likely to have been signed *J van Huijsum* by Jan rather than the less famous brother, Jacobus van Huijsum (c.1687–1740). This rose, thoroughly late baroque in the abundance of its bloom, has been drawn with a masterly control of the brush and a brilliant accuracy of tint to achieve a portrayal from nature, the qualities of which Sloane the botanist would be keenly aware.[20] Stimulated no doubt by the Dutch still-life paintings of the day, it was this taste for swags of such roses, and other showy flowers, mingled with fruit and game, which the skilled carver, Grinling Gibbons (1648–1721) exploited so effectively.

With the Flemish school of the same century one finds that the Sloane collection comprises a good representation of most of the leading artists of the second rank, for that of Rubens and Van Dyck is quite insignificant. As a representative of the former, apart from the sheet referred to above, the only piece associated with Rubens's name worth mentioning is a fragmentary drawing by Barent van Orley (c.1488–1541), retouched and enlarged by Rubens. This is *A Hawking Party*, part of an intermediate study for a tapestry for September, from a series illustrating the months.[21] Likewise among those connected with Van Dyck there are only two noteworthy typical portrait sketches on blue paper, both of gentlemen.[22] But with the lesser seventeenth-century masters, including such as Lucas Vorsterman I (1595–1675), Cornelis Schut (1597–1655), Lucas van Uden (1595–1672), Gillis Neyts (1623–1687), Jan Fyt (1611–1661), and Abraham van Diepenbeck (1596–1675), Sloane has provided an excellent collection, which was to form the basis for its later widening and enrichment. Although very probably from the Courten collection, a fine example of this quality is supplied by a pen and brush drawing by van Diepenbeck, a preparatory drawing for one of the illustrations for the book on horsemanship, *La Méthode et Invention nouvelle de dresser les Chevaux* (Antwerp, 1658), by the Duke of Newcastle, whose teacher had been M. de St. Antoine, riding master to Henry, Prince of Wales. The Duke went into exile after the battle of Marston Moor in 1644, and ran a riding school in Antwerp. The drawing shows the Duke himself executing an equestrian movement (Fig. 88), *Groupades par Le Droict*, before the Keep or 'Little Castle' as it is called, at Bolsover, Derbyshire. Sir Charles Cavendish (d.1617), the Duke's father, began to build this romantic 'castle' in 1612 and the work was not completed until 1621, probably begun according to the designs of his architect, Robert Smythson (d.1614), but completed with modifications by his son, John (d.1634).[23] This 'Little Castle', which has survived in remarkably good state, is full of fanciful details, such as the chimney-pieces, each different from the other. As the artist never came to England himself,

Fig. 88 Abraham van Diepenbeck: *The Duke of Newcastle on horseback*. BM, PD, 5236–112. Reproduced by courtesy of the Trustees of the British Museum.

this background was based on drawings by others, like those preserved at Renishaw Hall.[24]

There is also an abundance of Netherlandish drawings of the second half of the sixteenth century, both by known hands and anonymous; notable amongst these are a good representative group by the long-living Abraham Bloemaert (1564–1651), and by Jan Brueghel I (1568–1625). Drawings from the earlier years of the century comprise some interesting works, such as the *Virgin and Child with St. John* by Jan Gossaert, called Mabuse (active 1503–32),[25] a drawing by Pieter Coecke van Aelst (1502–1550), *An Incident in the Legend of St. Christopher*,[26] and two further drawings by Bernard van Orley, in addition to that retouched Rubens, *Claudius and Virginia*,[27] and *Ladies and Gentlemen in a garden*.[28] But probably the most significant of these is that topographical rarity, the *View of Bethlehem* (Fig. 89) by Jan van Scorel (1495–1562).[29] This latter drawing was an important discovery by A.E. Popham, found in a volume among drawings of Persian subjects done at the end of the seventeenth century by G. Hofsted van Essen (active *c*.1700). Popham established the attribution, partly on the grounds of its stylistic kinship with the only known signed drawing by Scorel, *A fantastic Mountain Landscape with a Bridge*[30] which, as it happens, is on the *recto* of a sheet also in the British Museum, and partly through the fact that we learn from Karel van Mander in his *Schilderboek*

(Haarlem, 1604) that Scorel went on a pilgrimage to the Holy Land in 1520/21, and that he drew in a sketchbook records of his journey, 'views of Candia, Cyprus, landscapes, cities, castles, and mountains, the whole very pleasant to behold, and also at Jerusalem, he made the acquaintance of the Prior of the Convent of Sion, who was greatly esteemed by both the Jews and Turks. He visited the country around Jerusalem, and the banks of Jordan, drawing the landscapes in pen and ink . . .' Popham, with admirable but probably excessive caution, while acknowledging that it is clearly by a Netherlandish artist, admits that it could be a copy, a possibility that in the interval has come to seem less likely. He notes, however, that there is a reference to a drawing done at the end of the sixteenth century on page 132 of the *Vrbis Hierosolimae quemadmodum ea Christi tempore floruit . . . descriptio* by Christianus Adrichomias (Cologne, 1592): 'a drawing of the city of Jerusalem, which Messire Joannes van Scorel, canon at Utrecht, where he was a most talented painter, did in 1521 from nature, seated on the Mount of Olives, the original of which was shown me by the pious and erudite Master Joanus Bollius of Louvain . . .' While this one is still missing, the present drawing inscribed by the artist *bethleem* is almost certainly one of the sketches referred to by van Mander, in the centre of which is evidently the Church of the Nativity, and on the left, according to a further inscription

Fig. 89 Jan van Scorel: *View of Bethlehem*. BM, PD, 5234–89. Reproduced by courtesy of the Trustees of the British Museum.

there, *ecclesia nicolai*, the Church of St. Nicholas.

Another important acquisition, associated with Sloane's lively interest in travel and exploration, was the group of drawings that he discovered *c*.1706–7 still in the possession of the descendants of John White (active 1585–93), the cartographer and draughtsman, who accompanied Sir Walter Raleigh on his expedition to the New World, which left Plymouth in April, 1585, and whose outcome was the founding of the first English colony in North America on Roanoke Island. These drawings were chiefly connected with White's stays in the Roanoke colony, and were thought by Sloane to be the originals of the engravings by Theodore de Bry (1528–1598), based on drawings supplied by White for his polyglot edition of Thomas Harriot's *A briefe and true report of the new found land of Virginia . . . Discovered by the English Colony. . .* (Frankfurt-am-Main, 1590), a book with which Sloane would have been familiar. In a letter to the Abbé Bignon written by Sloane between 1 July and 30 October 1709, a copy of which is preserved amongst Sir Hans's papers,[31] we learn that until he saw these drawings he had thought that de Bry must have embellished his fine engravings with his own ideas, but now that he has seen the 'originals' he can see that he was mistaken. As the family was not at first prepared to part with the drawings, Sloane had copies made of them; it is, however, now clear that the volume in question is that which was later in Sir Hans's possession.[32] The note of a loan to

a member of the family in a seventeenth-century hand, 'this Lent to my soon whit[e] 11 Aprell 1673', as well as evidence that it was used by children as a copybook, confirm that it is the same volume as that which Sloane had described to the Abbé. Despite Sloane's enthusiasm for them, they are copies, not originals by White, as he supposed. All the same, they are of considerable importance in that in some cases they are the only record of some of White's drawings. As Hulton has pointed out, Edward Topsell the naturalist used some of the drawings of Virginian birds in this volume as the model for illustrations in his manuscript, 'The Fowles of Heauen or History of Birdes', now in the Huntington Library, California. From Topsell, who was writing between 1604 and 1614, one can deduce that the Sloane copies were in the hands of the Revd Richard Hakluyt, the geographer (*c*.1553–1616) by the latter date.[33] On folio 12[v] of the Sloane volume of copies is a pen drawing with watercolour washes, *English Sailors in a Skirmish with an Eskimo* (Plate 30). This is evidently a copy of a lost drawing by White, but whether the original of this had a direct link with Sir Martin Frobisher's second voyage to the North West in 1577, is no more certain than it is with the two originals of the *Eskimo Man*, and the *Eskimo Woman and Baby*.[34] These drawings are the only clue to support the possibility that White could have gone on that expedition, and as we know that Frobisher brought back to England an Eskimo man, woman and baby, one might assume that they were done in England. Although this may be so, the copy recording an incident on the voyage suggests that he could also have gone to the North West,[35] and as Hulton has suggested the production of such drawings could be an explanation for his being chosen to go as the draughtsman to Virginia. The final section (folios 75ʳ–113ʳ) of Sloane's copies would have been especially attractive to Sir Hans, as it consists of copies of lost drawings by White of birds, fishes and reptiles of Virginia.

Sloane possessed yet another group of drawings connected with colonization. These are six of the drawings that Wenceslaus Hollar (1607–77) produced of the town and fortifications of Tangier when the artist travelled there with Lord Henry Howard's expedition in 1669, which Hollar as 'royal scenographer' had successfully petitioned to join. This meant that he spent the second half of that year in Tangier. It brought him the relatively small return of £100, and he may have in some measure restored his flagging fortunes by publishing a series of etchings after some of the views, *Divers Prospects in and about Tangier. . .* (London, 1673), three panoramic views, and a *Mapp of the Citty . . .*, some of which can be linked with surviving drawings. The view, *Tangier from the S.W.*,[36] executed on three joined sheets with pen and brown ink, grey wash and watercolours (Fig. 90), was published as one of the panoramic etchings, with modifications in the foreground. The sheets from the Sloane collection and another from the Esdaile collection are the more highly finished of those now in the British Museum, while the others formerly in the Skinner collection[37] are more in the nature of preliminary drawings. Altogether the Tangier drawings in the Museum are the most substantial surviving. Tangier, this small outpost of Empire, had come to the British Crown as part of the dowry of Queen Catherine of Braganza on her marriage to Charles

II in 1662, but it was found to be impossible to maintain and so it was abandoned in 1683.

Sloane was a keen collector not only of Hollar's drawings but also of his prints, which gives us now the opportunity to consider Sloane as a collector of the latter, a role which is unfortunately clouded in obscurity, for reasons which will soon be apparent. As in other cases, Sloane also evidently assembled his prints by Hollar wholesale. For George Vertue recorded in his notebooks 'Works of W. Hollar. collected in one Volum. said to be by himself [i.e Hollar] put together. sold by his widow to Sr. Hans Sloane . . .'[38] Hollar is one of the printmakers whose works, among those impressions from the Sloane collection (some 1,218 in number), can still be identified chiefly under Q4 to Q6 in the 1837 inventory;[39] however, there is some mystery about what it is that Vertue can have seen as he described the contents of the volume supposedly acquired from the artist's widow as having '. . . some few first prints. but a great many very bad ones', an assessment which hardly agrees with the prints now thought to be from the Sloane collection. One sees this clearly if one examines, for instance, his impressions from Hollar's famous series of etchings of muffs, a particularly fine example being the *Pile of Muffs* (Fig. 91).[40] It does not seem very likely that Vertue could have been mistaken about the quality of what he saw, as he was making a special study of Hollar's prints for his catalogue of his prints, the first edition of which appeared in 1745, and was the first work of its kind to be published in England. Perhaps he was told something in error about what he was shown on his visit to Sir Hans. Or could it be that Vertue was rather envious of Sloane's find, especially as he was so interested in Hollar himself and wondered how an accumulator such as Sloane could possess that which really someone like himself, a true collector and

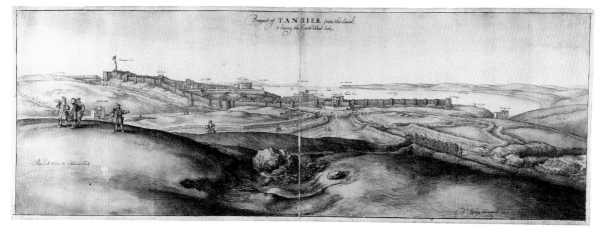

Fig. 90 Wenceslaus Hollar: *Tangier from the south-west.* BM, PD, 5214–19. Reproduced by courtesy of the Trustees of the British Museum.

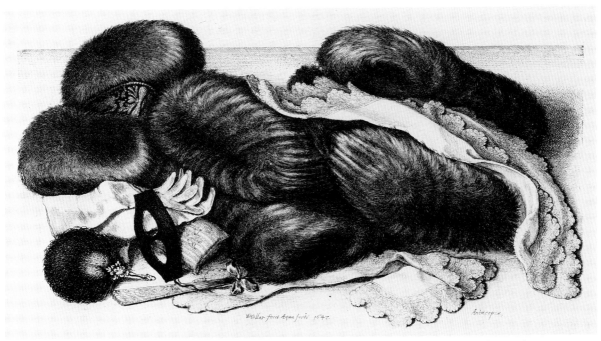

Fig. 91 Wenceslaus Hollar: *Pile of muffs* (etching). BM, PD, Q.5—607. Reproduced by courtesy of the Trustees of the British Museum.

discriminating connoisseur, should have? Hence his little private note to that effect, which nobody but the writer would see. While this is sheer speculation, literary figures and dilettantes like Horace Walpole after Sloane's death, and doubtless others before that, were not above being supercilious and mockingly witty about Sloane's collecting, notably of natural-historical specimens.[41]

Uncertainty likewise reigns over the rest of Sloane's collection of prints. Firstly, this is because all proper link with the way that the collection was preserved has been lost. If we look at Sloane's manuscript catalogue of his library, we find listed book after book of prints described in only the most general way: for instance,[42] 'A Collection of very large prints on imperial paper . . .' Sloane did employ from 1722 his young amanuensis from Zürich, Johann Caspar Scheuchzer (1702—29), to make indexes of the contents of the volumes of prints until he died in Sloane's house on 10 April 1729. It would have a particular fascination to be able to see one of the volumes listed as 'A collection of miscellaneous old prints by Albert Dürer and Lucas van Leyden & gathered by Jacobus Colius Ortelianus 1599 in folio without an index'.[43] But it is unlikely that our knowledge can now be increased since we can discover nothing about the contents of the book referred to in Sloane's catalogue. The reason for this is that the Museum's collection was completely reorganized by T. Philipe, the auctioneer, and arranged by him in an orderly manner by Schools.[44] This was put in hand, on the instructions of the Trustees, following the discovery of the theft of Rembrandt etchings by Robert Dighton (?1752—1814) from Cracherode's

bequest to the Museum. Another consequence of this was that the Department of Prints and Drawings was made entirely independent of the Library, of which until then it had been a subsidiary section. As a result the volumes in which the Sloane prints had been kept were done away with, and many prints found to be inferior duplicates were sold. In view of what now remains in the collection we can assume that the bulk of the contents of Colius's book must have been sold in the sale of British Museum duplicates, held by T. Philipe on 8 May and three following days in 1811.[45] In this sale there were 235 prints by or after Dürer (2nd day, lots 26—43**), and 254 by or after Lucas van Leyden (1st day, lots 23—27), without in the majority of cases any description of individual prints. Although there is no indication of their source, it is likely that the majority came from the Sloane collection. For if we take the collection of prints by Dürer now in the Print Room, we find that there are very few impressions, according to the pencil notes in the 1837 inventory, from the Sloane collection among the engravings, the vast majority being from the Cracherode bequest. The exception is the fine impression of *Hercules* (Fig. 92),[46] which strongly suggests that the engravings in the Colius volume were either inferior impressions or copies. The same appears to have been the case with the woodcuts. Among the impressions of the Great Passion, two of the late examples without text are from the Sloane collection,[47] and a fine one of the first state of *St. Jerome in the Cave* of 1512,[48] as well as a poor late impression of *Albrecht Dürer*.[49] If we turn to the engravings of Lucas van Leyden (active 1508—33), the disposal has been

251

Fig. 92 Albrecht Dürer: *Hercules* (engraving). BM, PD, E.4–136. Reproduced by courtesy of the Trustees of the British Museum.

more thorough, as there are evidently no impressions from the Sloane collection still in the Museum's collection.

Several groups of drawings, which are among the most important from the artistic point of view were not gathered singly by Sloane but were acquired as entities already assembled, and mounted in volumes. Even though they reflect his perception in only a general way, nevertheless as they were to be so significant for the formation of the collection, Sloane's initiative in securing them is most remarkable in those cases where they are chiefly of artistic rather than, say, of natural-historical interest. One of the most impressive is the folio album, now known as Sloane 5218. It is described in the manuscript catalogue of Sloane's library[50] as 'Min[iature] 3. Original drawings of Albert Du:rers own hand, pasted on Imperial paper in a very large fo. bound in black Russia leather fo max'; stamped on the cover in gold letters with Dürer's monogram and the inscription 'TEEKENINGE 1637', the contents of this folio formed the backbone of the Museum's pre-eminent collection of German drawings of the fifteenth and early sixteenth centuries. This is vividly demonstrated by the fact that out of a total of 138 drawings now in the collection, which I accept as originals by Albrecht Dürer, ninety-five come from Sir Hans's collection and all but two from Sloane 5218.[51] Of the remaining drawings from this volume, apart from a few copies after Dürer, a good number are either by followers of Dürer or by leading contemporaries of his. A few are not by German hands at all.

Sloane's drawings by Dürer are from every period of the Master's career, and include superb examples of every kind of drawing which he produced. Portraits abound chiefly in black chalk or charcoal of which perhaps the most memorable – certainly the most striking – is that of Conrad Merkel of 1508 (Fig. 93).[52] It is very probable that the ugly pig-like features that Dürer has given Merkel, arise from the pun (*Verkell* referred to in the inscription, i.e. *Ferkel*, a piglet) which Dürer plays on the sitter's surname. Dürer had earlier imparted a dramatic strength through a bold use of charcoal similar to that of the Merkel portrait in a pair of devotional drawings of 1503, *Head of a suffering man* and *Head of the dead Christ*.[53] But there is no doubt that the real gems among the Dürers are the landscape watercolours, revolutionary both in imaginative power of observation and in execution, isolated in their excellence from all that had gone before, and unrivalled for many years by what was to follow. Perhaps the first landscape watercolours after them with the same spark of genius were those of Van Dyck. Dürer's unfinished *Study of water, sky and pine trees* (Plate 31) is well nigh unique as an acute representation of nature, in which the time of day, at sunset, is depicted with telling sensitivity. The rendering seems so modern to our eyes that it is hard to accept that it was done somewhere in the countryside near Nuremberg soon after the artist had returned from Italy from his first visit, most probably either in 1496 or 1497.[54] This masterpiece of watercolour tech-

Fig. 93 Albrecht Dürer: *Portrait of Conrad Merkel*. BM, PD, 5218–27. Reproduced by courtesy of the Trustees of the British Museum.

nique, and its companion, *A 'Weierhaus'*[55] would be shining examples to emulate for those artists of the English water-colour school who were later to frequent the British Museum. Sloane himself would very probably have been most interested in the drawings of natural-historical subjects among his Dürers. It would no doubt have been a matter of much regret to Sloane, had he been aware of the deficiency, that no studies of plants in any of the volumes of drawings of plants are now accepted as by Dürer, including Sloane 5219 which is described in Sir Hans's manuscript catalogue[56] as 'Min[iature] 4 A Book of Fishes, Birds, Animals, Insects, Plants and fruits done Albert Durer & several hands, on large Imperial paper bound in black leather in 1637 Bought in Holland with Min 2 & 3 wants an index or table at the end fo.max'. But there is a choice group drawings of animals by Dürer among the drawings. The most notable of these is the famous *Rhinoceros* (Fig. 94),[57] which has always been widely known from the wood-cut that Dürer produced from it and which went through various editions into the following century. The drawing, although seemingly lively enough, was not done from nature but after another drawing, probably by a Moravian printer, Valentim Fernandes, sent to him from Portugal, of the animal, a gift to King Manuel I, which arrived in Lisbon

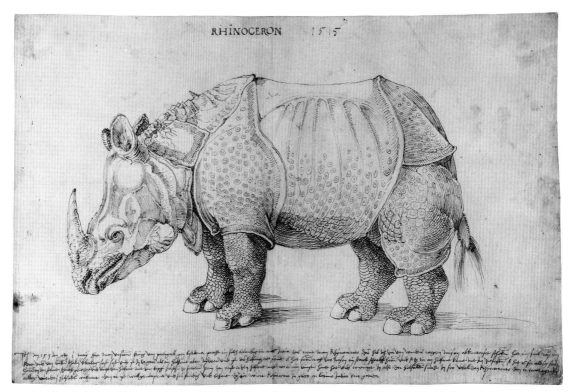

Fig. 94 Albrecht Dürer: *Rhinoceros*. BM, PD, 5218–167. Reproduced by courtesy of the Trustees of the British Museum.

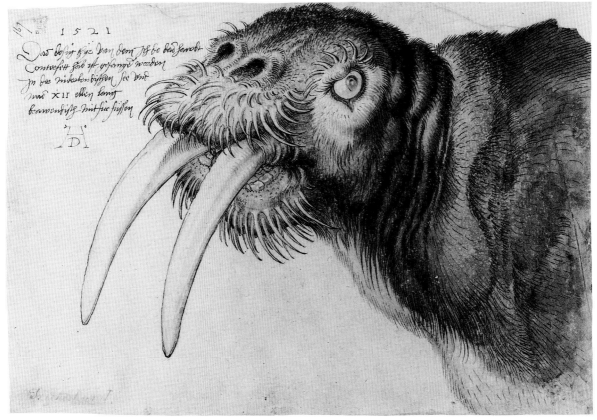

Fig. 95 Albrecht Dürer: *Walrus*. BM, PD, 5261–167. Reproduced by courtesy of the Trustees of the British Museum.

on 20 May 1515. A drawing of another animal, the walrus (Fig. 95),[58] along with that of the elk came to light in a volume devoted to drawings of quadrupeds. Dürer drew the former because it was an object of great curiosity to the artist: he found this 'stupid animal' as he described it, in Zeeland where he had gone in December 1520 in pursuit of a great stranded whale, whose carcass had, however, floated off with the tide. Rather surprisingly the drawing became the model for the dragon accompanying St. Margaret in one of his sketches for a projected *Sacra Conversazione* which was, however, never painted.[59] The latter, that of an elk, evidently done *c.*1501–3, which was to form the basis for the animal's representation in the engraving of 1504, *Adam and Eve*,[60] is a highly finished drawing, one of the most carefully observed of all Dürer's natural-history studies.[61] On the *verso* there is a sketch of a European Bison, small herds of which now survive only in Poland.

The four Dürer albums, Sloane 5228–31, bound like Sloane 5218 in black leather, have been understandably retained in the Library, as they contain a preponderance of material both written and drawn for Dürer's literary projects – in fact, about half of all that survives. It consists chiefly of drafts for the text and preparatory drawings for his treatise, *Vier Bücher von menschlicher Proportion . . .* (Nuremberg, 1528). But interspersed among them are various other types of drawings. One of the more fascinating of these is the *Plan and elevation of an Italian house* (Fig. 96), which is probably a fragment from a notebook. It has generally been assumed to have been of the house where the artist lived during his second stay in Venice, and is covered with notes identifying the rooms and their contents.[62] It may be, however, that it was either lodgings or the tavern of Peter Pender mentioned by Dürer in his correspondence with his close friend, Willibald Pirckheimer.[63]

Among the drawings in Sloane 5218 are important works formerly thought to be by Dürer, but as a result of modern scholarship now reattributed to his immediate followers and contemporaries. Hans Baldung Grien from Schwäbisch-Gmünd (1484/85–1545), who most probably worked for Dürer as a journeyman in Nuremberg from 1503 to *c.*1507, is well represented by a superb example of his highly individualized and sophisticated brushwork, the *Head of an old Man with a heavy beard* (Plate 32),[64] which is dated *1518* but with a false Dürer monogram. After being placed with those drawings doubtfully attributed to Dürer, it was given to Baldung only in the 1920s. It is certainly thoroughly convincing as an original of the year in question, when Baldung had just returned to Strasbourg, where he settled after completing a major commission, the painting of the high altar-piece in the cathedral at Freiburg-im-Breisgau. It has been found that Sloane 5218 contained six drawings which, it is now accepted, are by the more mundane though often charming hand of Hans Schäufelein (*c.*1480–1538/40), a leading apprentice of Dürer, who in his maturity settled first in Augsburg and then in the less demanding environ-

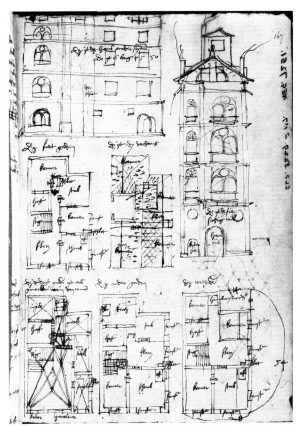

Fig. 96 Albrecht Dürer: *Plan and elevation of an Italian house.* BL, Sloane MS 5229, fol. 167ʳ. Reproduced by courtesy of the Trustees of the British Library.

ment of a small provincial town, Nördlingen, to the north of Augsburg. Among these are two designs for an important commission, which is still in the church for which it was painted. They are the finished compositional study for the central panel, the *Coronation of the Virgin* (Fig. 97) and the preparatory drawing for the predella of the high altarpiece,[65] signed by Schäufelein and dated *1513* on the central panel, in the former abbey church at Auhausen an der Wörnitz, near Nördlingen. Following his receipt of the main drawing the abbot, Georg Truchsess von Wetzhausen, ordered various changes to the arrangement of the composition of the central panel, which we find carried into the completed painting.

From this same source Sloane had also acquired drawings done in the first years of European colonization of America. These are two drawings of primitive people by Hans Burgkmair (1473–1531), which together with a drawing by Dürer in the margin of folio 41ʳ of the *Prayerbook of the Emperor Maximilian* were among the earliest attempted drawn representations of native South American Indians. As it happens, they are all thought to be of members of the Tupinamba tribe, but that by Dürer seems the more accurate. Those by Burgkmair were of a *Standing black youth dressed in a*

Fig. 97 Hans Schäufelein: *Coronation of the Virgin*. BM, PD, 5218–189. Reproduced by courtesy of the Trustees of the British Museum.

Fig. 98 Hans Burgkmair: *a, Black youth*, BM, PD, 5218–128; *b, Black youth*, BM, PD, 5218–129. Reproduced by courtesy of the Trustees of the British Museum.

feather skirt, cape, and head-dress and holding a club and shield and a *Standing black youth dressed in a feather skirt, cape and head-dress and holding an axe with a shrunken human head on the end* (Fig. 98a–b).[66] Augsburg, the artist's native city, at the beginning of the sixteenth century was at the centre of efforts to establish trading and colonizing links along the north coast of South America, especially in what is now Venezuela. These drawings, although no doubt arising from this activity, were not the result of direct observation of peoples in their native habitat but were made, no doubt with the figures apparelled with the help of someone who had been to the region, in the light of objects and clothing that had been brought back to Germany. One reason for thinking this to be so is that the head-dresses are shown in the drawings worn back-to-front. As to other details in them, the shield in Fig. 98a is evidently of Mexican origin, and the club may also be Mexican. If these identifications are correct, it could mean that the drawings were done after 1519, the year when Cortés became the first European to discover that country. The feather-work is considered comparable with objects known to be mainly South American, although some may be Mexican. As it was not until 1522 that it was firmly established that the West Indies were not a part of the continent of Asia, it is perhaps not surprising

Fig. 99 Arent van Bolten van Zwolle: *Two monsters*. BM, PD, 5217–166. Reproduced by courtesy of the Trustees of the British Museum.

257

that Burgkmair was confused as to what might be the proper characteristics of the various peoples depicted in his prints.[67] The same is so with these drawings; for he represents the South Americans as though they were negroid.

Another black leather volume, likewise dated 1637, which is stamped in gold on the front cover, 'BOLTEN VAN SWOL TEEKENINGE',[68] may well have interested Sloane merely because of the curiousness of its contents. It contains 425 drawings, almost the entire drawn œuvre of Arent van Bolten van Zwolle, a goldsmith, probably active in the last decades of the sixteenth century. His drawings reveal him as stylistically allied to the Haarlem mannerists, especially Karel van Mander. In addition to many designs for metalwork they include many of monsters and dwarfs, which undoubtedly would have appeared very bizarre to the eighteenth-century eye, and indeed they are still so today: the strangeness and horror of Bolten's prolific invention might lead one to suggest, as Popham did, that they could provoke a psychiatric analyst to deduce stark conclusions about the artist's mental state. Consider for example, the *Two Monsters* (Fig. 99)[69] in which the two creatures which face each other are so oddly formed: that on the left has a head partly made up of a scroll, with the body of a bird, the breasts of a woman and the legs of a deer; and that on the right has a cock's tail and the legs of an ox.

Many of the natural-history drawings in the Sloane collection, which are now divided between the British Museum and the British Library, are not so far attributable to recognized hands, which is not so unusual for drawings of this type. But for those who specialize in the study of these drawings the Sloane collection could prove a fruitful quarry in which to unearth unsuspected treasures. As an example to us, Popham made in 1928[70] a brilliant discovery in Sloane 5264, fol. 23, when he recognized the *Dead Partridge* (Plate 33) as by the hand of Jacopo de' Barbari (c.1440/50–c.1515). Despite its extraordinary significance, it was thereafter neglected by other scholars compiling ostensibly comprehensive studies of the artist. It is a unique survival in de' Barbari's œuvre being the only known watercolour study of its kind, and as an eloquent demonstration of its attribution to the artist has a remarkable kinship, especially in the execution of the plumage, with the partridge in the still-life painting by this artist, *Dead Partridge, with mailed gloves and crossbow bolt*, signed and dated *1504*, in the Alte Pinakothek, Munich.[71] This painting and the watercolour drawing are together among the first still-life works, closely studied after nature by Renaissance artists, and were no doubt the model for Dürer's and Lucas Cranach the Elder's essays in the genre of still-lives of dead birds and game. The book from which this exceptional drawing comes is one of a group of four volumes, Sloane 5263–5266, otherwise containing drawings of birds of all kinds, executed in varying degrees of artistic excellence and accuracy, ranging from the accomplished gouaches by George Edwards (1694–1773) to the amateur crudities of Sir Thomas Browne (1605–82), the

physician justly famous for his literary gem, *Religio Medici* (1643). One of the more interesting groups included in them are the drawings of birds, which can be attributed to an otherwise unknown artist from the last quarter of the sixteenth century, Veit Spierincx. This identification is based on stylistic grounds on a comparison with a drawing, inscribed with his name, *Vine Branch with two Bunches of Grapes*, among drawings of fruit and vegetables by this same hand in Sloane 5219, whose cover is lettered, 'VISCHEN VOGELEN DIEREN VRUCHTEN 1637' (Fishes Birds Animals Fruits), which like Sloane 5218 is bound in black leather.[72] Although nothing certain has so far emerged about this artist's background, it is possible that Veit was a relative as well as a contemporary of François Spierincx (1551–1630), whose second son was the notable art-collector, and agent to Queen Christina of Sweden, Pieter Spierincx Silfverkrona (d.1652). According to the late Jan van Gelder it is likely that the latter possessed the collection in the series of volumes, which he ordered to be bound in black leather and stamped with the date 1637.[73] One can say, however, to judge from this group of drawings that they are likely to have been executed by someone employed to produce designs for tapestries, and this would certainly be consistent with their being by a member of the Spierincx family, who ran such a business in Delft.

But as for the drawings directly related to Sloane's own concerns as a dedicated naturalist, the most important were those done by Maria Sibylla Merian (1647–1717), which were the outcome of her last ambitious scheme, her journey to Surinam in 1699, accompanied by her two daughters, Dorothea Henrica and Johanna Helena. This lady, one of Sir Hans's many learned correspondents, was an outstanding artist and naturalist. She stayed in South America until 1701 to record the unknown insects of the colony. The results of this observation she translated into skilfully designed compositions, made up of a combination of plant and insect life, exquisitely done in watercolours and bodycolours on vellum. In these, as a very gifted artist, she did not hesitate to heighten the effect of the work by ignoring the strict constraints of reality to achieve what she considered a more successful arrangement. These were subsequently reproduced to illustrate her final publication, *Metamorphosis Insectorum Surinam* (Amsterdam, 1705). Plate 18 in that book, *Spiders, ants, and two large Spiders in a Guajava Tree* (here Plate 34),[74] is a striking example, in which Sibylla Merian excels herself in the way she has provided an engraving to illustrate the detailed information given in her explanatory text about the habits of the insects. One may think that she has perhaps striven too much for drama, so that by modern standards the result appears unscientific.[75] A specimen of the large spider is shown in a Guajava tree about to kill a minute humming bird lying pathetically on its back as the spider puts a hairy leg on the throat of its victim, while another leg befouls a bird's nest. In fact, this spider, which can be identified as *Avicularia*

avicularia, according to present-day knowledge, feeds mainly on large insects, not small birds, and lives on the ground, not in the trees. Nevertheless such fine works were highly appropriate for Sir Hans's collection, for he was always keen to widen his knowledge to embrace the fauna and flora of unexplored regions. He would have been especially attracted to information from Surinam because of its geographical, and hence natural-historical, relation to Jamaica, and it would have been particularly useful to Sloane at this juncture, and indeed for many years thereafter, as he was still in the process of publishing his own findings on the natural history of Jamaica. Indeed Sloane can have wasted little time in acquiring these drawings as they were already noted by Zacharias Conrad von Uffenbach, and described by him as 'excellent', in his account of his visit to Sloane's museum in Bloomsbury in 1710 (see Chapter 1, Appendix 1).

Another token of Sloane's abiding interest in South America is provided by the thirty-two drawings by Frans Post (*c*.1612–80), executed from the sketches he made in Brazil as official artist during the entire governorship of Johan Maurits of Nassau-Siegen (1637–44). Most are topographical, but some are of military and naval engagements, and were evidently produced with an eye to their publication. Indeed they were etched the same size as the drawings (according to Hind) by Jan van Brosterhuisen (*c*.1596–1650), and with one exception appeared as illustrations of Kaspar van Baerle's *Rerum per octennium in Brasilia et alibi nuper gestarum sub Preafectura Illmi Comitis I. Mauritii Nassoviae . . . Historia* (Amsterdam, 1647). As some are dated 1645, it is most probable they were all done in Holland following his return.[76]

From the foregoing it should be plain that Sloane was indeed an accumulator on the grand scale. Nevertheless if we examine his collection in a positive way and look for the riches that he undoubtedly acquired, and avoid criticism of him for not following quite the same path as the 'serious' collectors of drawings of his day, certainly from the point of view of the later development of the British Museum's collections, we should be grateful for his individuality. Indeed we cannot fail to be impressed by the range, if not always the artistic quality of the drawings he acquired. Everyone, no doubt, will have their special interest in so varied a collection, and so I have retained that particular predilection until the last, which for me is the gem of the collection. These are the contents of the 'book of Drawings of Jewelling work drawn by Holben', evidently seen by George Vertue and recorded on the same occasion[77] – probably in the period 1713–21 – on which he inspected the Hollar prints discussed earlier. It is uncertain whether the designs for jewellers' and goldsmiths' work by Hans Holbein the Younger (1497/98–1543) in this book are those listed in 'a paper book conteyninge diverse paternes for Jewelles' noted in the inventory of Henry VIII's possessions made after the latter's death and kept in the 'Secret

Juelhous' in the Tower of London; it is more than likely that it was the book in the royal collection shown to Joachim von Sandrart (1608–88) by Inigo Jones (1573–1652) in 1627, the contents of which were described with a reasonable degree of accuracy in his *Teutsche Academie* of 1675,[78] and it may have been the volume that entered Sloane's collection and was eventually catalogued as Sloane 5308.[79] The book in question in which the drawings were kept, was evidently discarded when they were mounted for display in the King's Library in the British Museum in the 1860s. The Sloane book contained about half of all Holbein's surviving designs of an ornamental purpose from the artist's second stay in England (1532–43), the other half being from a book in Basel. By my reckoning there are some 191 drawings by Holbein formerly in the Sloane book, and now all mounted, of which many are admittedly very small in size. Only a handful are by other hands, the most interesting being two designs for a heart-shaped pendent jewel evidently by a mid-sixteenth-century French designer.[80] It is possible to draw a general distinction between the contents of the two books. The Basel designs include preliminary sketches, not to be found among the Sloane drawings, done in preparation for more finished drawings; nor are there any designs for whole pieces of goldsmiths' work in 5308. The Sloane book contained a much greater diversity and quantity of designs of more general use, such as the various types of arabesque designs which can be employed on different objects as needed, as well as those of details of jewellery, goldsmiths' work, and dress accessories. One class of work occurred only in the Sloane book, that is designs for types of lettering and cyphers, and designs for their use in jewellery. In addition there are also some jewellery designs incorporating the initials of the King and either Queen Anne Boleyn or Queen Jane Seymour. Allied to these are the drawings for the metal covers, heavily encrusted with arabesque design, for girdle prayerbooks, which were much in fashion in the sixteenth century. Within

Fig. 100 *a–b* Hans Holbein the Younger: *Two designs for a metalwork book-cover.* BM, PD, 5308–8,10. Reproduced by courtesy of the Trustees of the British Museum.

Fig. 101 *a–b* Hans Holbein the Younger: *Two designs for a medallion with a device.* BM, PD, 5308–22, 34.
Reproduced by courtesy of the Trustees of the British Museum.

the first design for one of these (Fig. 100*a*) are placed the initials very probably of the giver and recipient of the book, in the upper half, *T W I*, and below, *I W T*, and in the second, evidently done as an alternative (Fig. 100*b*), in the upper corners, *T W* and below, *W T*. It is most likely that the initials *T W* and *I W* referred to Sir Thomas Wyatt, son of the well-known poet, who had married Jane Hawste in 1537, and could well have been done about that time.[81]

But perhaps the finest of the designs in Sloane's book are those for medallions with a device. That for one with a hand issuing from a cloud resting on a closed book, with the motto in Italian 'SERVAR VOGLIO / QVEL CHE HO / GVIRATO' (I desire to observe that which I have sworn) occurs in two versions (Fig. 101*a–b*).[82] It is an unusual design as here the meaning is not clouded in obscurity of any kind, unlike so many Renaissance devices; for it is more than likely that the hand is placed on the Bible to swear the oath which the possessor of the device is resolved to maintain. Furthermore the rocky hillock must surely denote steadfastness. All these ornamental designs are executed with a mastery scarcely rivalled elsewhere in western art.

So in conclusion, surveying his collecting of drawings, and of prints in so far as we can judge it, we can say that Sir Hans Sloane was a diligent, often well-informed, sometimes very fortunate, certainly influential, sharp and opportunistic accumulator, who, as far as North European art is concerned, had a good instinct for the interesting, and sometimes, for the very finest drawings.

Acknowledgements

I would like to place on record my gratitude for the helpful advice and assistance given me by my colleagues, Antony Griffiths, Martin Royalton-Kisch, Giulia Bartrum, and Hilary Williams.

Notes and References

1. This observation was first made in a short but informative article by A.E. Popham, 'Sir Hans Sloane's collections in the Print Room', *British Museum Quarterly* 18 no. 1 (1953), pp. 10–14; see also Fritz Lugt, *Les Marques de collection de dessins & d'estampes . . .* (Amsterdam, 1921), p. 243.

2. Rupert Gunnis, *Dictionary of British Sculptors 1660–1851* (London, n.d.), pp. 333ff.

3. BM, PD, 5237–92,93; see A.E. Popham, *Catalogue of Drawings by Dutch and Flemish Artists . . . in the British Museum* v *Dutch and Flemish Drawings in the xv and xvi Centuries* (London, 1932), p. 63, no. 7 *verso* reproduced in pl. XXI.

4. BM, PD, 5227–18; Popham, op. cit. (note 3), p. 83, no. 75.

5. See John Rowlands, *Rubens: Drawings and Sketches*, British Museum (London, 1977), p. 54, no. 46 *recto* and *verso* reproduced.

6. BM, PD, 5236–111; for a discussion of the strong possibility that volume 5236 had come to Sloane as part of the Courten bequest in 1702, see below; see also John Rowlands, *The Age of Dürer and Holbein: German Drawings 1400–1550*, British Museum (London, 1988), pp. 19–20, no. 3 *recto* and *verso*, reproduced.

7. Inv. no. 1662; Alfred Stange, *Deutsche Malerei der Gotik* vol. IX (Berlin and Munich, 1961), p. 18, reproduced.

8. We can see that certain traits of Sloane's taste are already anticipated by Samuel Pepys, as ably described in Walter Liedtke's article, 'Pepys and the pictorial arts . . .', *Apollo* 133 (1991), pp. 227–37.

9. BM, PD, 5236–48, and for the Courten bequest see Chapter 1; see also A.M. Hind, *Catalogue of Dutch and Flemish Drawings . . . in the British Museum*, vol. III (London, 1926), p. 48, no. 1.

10. See Marcel Röthlisberger, *Claude Lorrain: the Drawings* (University of California Press, 1968), text vol., p. 454.

11. Röthlisberger, op. cit. (note 10), p. 456.

12. See Michael Kitson, *Claude Lorrain: Liber Veritatis* (London, 1978), p. 29.

13. BM, PD, 5223 A.20–21, A.20–22, 5226 A.7–64; see E. Croft-Murray and P. Hulton, *Catalogue of British Drawings*, vol. 1: *xvi & xvii centuries*, British Museum (London, 1960), text vol., pp. 270–1, nos. 1–2, 2 (a).

14. BM, PD, 5237–147; see Hugh Brigstocke, *A Loan Exhibition of Drawings by Nicolas Poussin*, Ashmolean Museum (Oxford, 1990), no. 37.

15. See Daniel Ternois, *Jacques Callot: Catalogue complet de son œuvre dessiné* (Paris, 1961), p. 168, nos. 1340 (BM, PD, 5236–73), 1343 (BM, PD, 5236–71), 1348 (BM, PD, 5236–72); see also Diane Russell, *Jacques Callot: Prints and related Drawings*, National Gallery of Art (Washington, DC, 1975), pp. 278, 303–4, nos. 254, 255, reproduced.

16. See below, p. 294, no. 30, BL, Sloane MS 3972 C, vol. VI, fol. 241 *verso*.

17. BM, PD, 5226–25; see Werner Sumowski, *Drawings of the Rembrandt School* (New York, 1984), vol. VIII, p. 4196, no. 1875a +.

18. BM, PD, 5237–62; Sumowski, op. cit., (note 17), vol. v, p. 2400, no. 1077 + +.

19. See Hind, op. cit., (note 9), vol. III, p. 163, nos. 12–63.

20. BM, PD, 5283, N.5–147.

21. BM, PD, 5237–77; see Rowlands, op. cit. (note 5), p. 56, no. 49, reproduced.

22. BM, PD, 5227–112 and 5227–113.

23. See Mark Girouard, *Robert Smythson and the Elizabethan Country House* (New Haven and London, 1983), pp. 206–10.

24. BM, PD, 5236–112, very probably from the Courten bequest, 1702; Lindsay Stainton and Christopher White, *Drawing in England from Hilliard to Hogarth*, British Museum (London, 1987), p. 82, no. 42, reproduced.

25. BM, PD, 5218–220; see Popham, op. cit. (note 3), p. 18, no. 1, reproduced in pl. IV.

26. BM, PD, 5214–240; see Popham, op. cit. (note 3), pp. 23–24, no. 8.

27. BM, PD, 5214–294; see Popham, op. cit. (note 3), p. 35, no. 2, reproduced in pl. XII.

28. BM, PD, 5237–144; see Popham, op. cit. (note 3), p. 35, no. 3.

29. BL, Sloane MS 5234–89, fol. 89: transferred to the Print Room from the Department of Manuscripts in 1928, and given the reg. no. 1928–3–10–100; see A.E. Popham, *Old Master Drawings* 3 (March, 1929), pp. 65–6, pl. 56, and Popham, op. cit. (note 3), pp. 39–40, no. 2.

30. BM, PD, reg. no. 1909–1–9–7; see Popham, op. cit. (note 3), p. 39, no. 1, reproduced in pl. XV.

31. BL, Sloane MS 4069, fols. 112ᵛ, 113ʳ.

32. BM, PD, 5270, transferred to the Print Room (press-mark 199 a.3) from the Department of Manuscripts, 20 June 1893.

33. See Paul Hulton, *America 1585 The Complete Drawings of John White* (North Carolina and London, 1984), especially pp. 21–6.

34. See Hulton, op. cit. (note 33), p. 184, pls. 63, 64.

35. See Hulton, op. cit. (note 33), p. 8.

36. BM, PD, 5214–19; see Croft-Murray and Hulton, op. cit. (note 13), text vol., pp. 359–60, no. 28; plate vol., reproduced in pl. 158 (b).

37. They were transferred from the Department of Manuscripts in 1932, having been presented to the Museum by Lieut. Monier Skinner, RE, of the War Office in 1887.

38. George Vertue *Note-Books*, vol. II (Walpole Society 20), (1931–2), p. 12.

39. See A. Griffiths and R. Williams, *User's Guide*, Department of Prints and Drawings, British Museum (London, 1987), p. 125; for further impressions under P2, P3, P4 and P6 see A. Griffiths and G. Kesnerová, *Wenceslaus Hollar: Prints and Drawings from the Collections of the National Gallery, Prague, and the British Museum, London*, British Museum (London, 1983).

40. BM, PD, Q.5–607; Gustav Parthey, *Wenceslaus Hollar; beschreibendes Verzeichniss seiner Kupferstiche* (Berlin, 1853), no. 1946, and see also Griffiths and Kesnerová, op. cit. (note 39), p. 84, no. 86b, reproduced. It is worth noting that Sloane also possessed a brush drawing of a muff by Hollar (BM, PD, 5214–7), the only one known to survive (see Croft-Murray and Hulton, op. cit. (note 13), text vol., p. 367, no. 47 *recto*, plate vol., reproduced in pl. 165).

41. Witness a letter (quoted *in extenso* on p. 48) that Walpole sent Sir Horace Mann, in which he says 'I employ my time chiefly, at present in the guardianship of embryos and cockle shells. Sir Hans Sloane valued his Museum at eighty thousand pounds, and so would anybody who loves hippopotamuses, sharks with one ear, and spiders as big as geese . . .', and referring to the Trustees, 'We are a charming wise set – all Philosophers, Botanists, Antiquarians, and Mathematicans – and adjourned our first meeting because Lord Macclesfield, our Chairman, was engaged in a party for finding out the Longitude.'

The jest about the missing chairman was a reference to a competition 'for finding out the Longitude', which had been instituted by Act of Parliament in 1713 for anyone who would make a chronometer to determine longitude within varying degrees of accuracy. The horologist, John Harrison from Faulby near Pontefract

(1693–1776), had initial success in 1735, but it was not until 1761 that he produced a wellnigh perfect time-piece, with which he was fully satisfied. Even so, the Board of Longitude continued to prevaricate, and he did not receive the final payments of his reward before 1773, which was chiefly brought about through the intervention of King George III (see John Betts, *John Harrison* (London, 1993)).

42. See below, p. 294, no. 30, BL, Sloane MS 3972 C, vol. IV, fols. 84ʳ and 84ᵛ.

43. This early collector, whose full name included the title, Ortelianus, given him by his uncle, the famous cartographer, Abraham Ortelius (1527–98), was the son of the latter's sister, Elizabeth, who had married as his second wife, the London merchant, Jacob Cole in 1562. Like his uncle, Jacob Cole the Younger collected coins and medals, but his interest in prints is otherwise unknown. We know something, however, of Ortelianus's collection of Roman coins from his copy of Adolphus Occo's *Imperatorum Romanorum Numismata . . .* (Antwerp, 1579), now in the University Library, Cambridge, in which he has noted those coins, of which both Occo and himself possessed specimens. An interesting collection of letters to Ortelianus was published by John Henry Hessel in *Ecclesiae Londino-Batavae Archivum*, vol. I (London, 1887); see especially nos. 324–31, 335, 348.

44. The plan on which the reorganization was based is recorded in BL, Additional MS 36269, fols. 184–92, where it is stated that the work took at some time within the years 1808–10 a total of sixty-five days.

45. In the Library of the Department of Prints and Drawings, British Museum, there is a marked copy with prices and the names of purchasers.

46. BM, PD, E.4–136; see C. Dodgson, *The Masters of Engraving and Etching: Albrecht Dürer* (London and Boston, 1926), pp. 37–39, no. 29.

47. See C. Dodgson, *Catalogue of Early German and Flemish Woodcuts . . . in the British Museum*, vol. I (London, 1903), pp. 275–6, nos. 15a, 21a.

48. Dodgson, op. cit. (note 47), p. 304, no. 122.

49. Dodgson, op. cit. (note 47), p. 361, no. 32c.

50. See below, p. 294, no. 30, BL, Sloane MS 3972 C, vol. VI, fol. 241ᵛ.

51. My detailed discussion of the drawings by Dürer or from his circle from the Sloane collection is to be found in John Rowlands, with the assistance of Giulia Bartrum, *Drawings by German Artists and Artists from German-speaking regions of Europe in the Department of Prints and Drawings in the British Museum: the Fifteenth Century & the Sixteenth Century by Artists born before 1530*, British Museum (London, 1993).

52. BM, PD, 5218–27; see Rowlands, op. cit. (note 6), p. 87, no. 58, reproduced.

53. BM, PD, 5218–30, 29; Rowlands, op. cit. (note 6), pp. 75, 78, nos. 49, 50, reproduced.

54. BM, PD, 5218–167; see Rowlands, op. cit. (note 6), p. 69, no. 43, reproduced in colour.

55. BM, PD, 5218–165; see Rowlands, op. cit. (note 6), p. 68, no. 42, reproduced in colour.

56. See below, p. 294, no. 30, BL, Sloane MS 3972 C, vol. VI, fol. 241ᵛ; for a modern scholarly description of the series of books, which includes among others in the British Museum Sloane 5218, mentioned above, bound in black leather with titles in Dutch stamped in gold on their covers, see Hind, op. cit. (note 9), vol. IV, pp. xiii–xv, and for the contents of Sloane 5219, see Popham, op. cit. (note 3), pp. 208–20.

57. BM, PD, 5218–161; see Rowlands, op. cit. (note 6), pp. 92, 94, no. 65, reproduced.

58. BM, PD, 5261–167; see Rowlands, op. cit. (note 6), p. 102, no. 74, reproduced.

59. F. Winkler, *Dürers Zeichnungen*, vol. IV *1520–1528* (Berlin, 1939), pl. 855.

60. Dodgson, op. cit. (note 46), pp. 51ff., no. 39, reproduced.

61. BM, PD, 5261–101 *recto*; see Rowlands, op. cit. (note 6), p. 80, no. 52, reproduced in colour.

62. BL, Sloane MS 5229, fol. 167ʳ; Sir Martin Conway, *Literary Remains of Albrecht Dürer* (Cambridge, 1889), p. 219.

63. See his letter of 13 October 1506, in Erich Rupprich, *Dürers schriftlicher Nachlass*, vol. I (Berlin, 1956), p. 58.

64. BM, PD, 5218–26; see Rowlands, op. cit. (note 6), pp. 142, 145, no. 114, reproduced in colour. There are a further four drawings from Sloane 5218 that I would accept as by Baldung (as well as two from his workshop), and another from Sloane 5214, the volume in which, among other items, the drawings by Hollar, referred to above, were kept.

65. BM, PD, 5218–189, 140; see Rowlands, op. cit. (note 6), pp. 202, 206, no. 173 (a) and (b), reproduced.

66. BM, PD, 5218–128, 129; for the most recent discussion of these drawings, see Rowlands, op. cit. (note 6), pp. 187–8, nos. 158 (a) and (b), reproduced in colour.

67. See the woodcuts which Burgkmair contributed to illustrate Balthasar Springer's account of the first German Indian expedition, organized by a consortium of Augsburg merchants under the leadership of the Welser company, which set sail from Lisbon in 1505, in *Hans Burgkmair: das graphische Werk*, Graphische Sammlung (Stuttgart, 1973), nos. 23–26, reproduced.

68. BM, PD, 5217; see Popham, op. cit. (note 3), pp. 96–136.

69. BM, PD, 5217–166; see Popham, op. cit. (note 3), p. 113, no. 166.

70. A.E. Popham, *Vasari Society*, 2nd ser. 9 (1928), p. 2, reproduced.

71. Inv. no. 5086.

72. It has been referred to earlier under note 56.

73. For further discussion of this question, see 'A note on the provenance of the Dürer Albums (Sloane 5218 and 5228–31)', in Rowlands, op. cit. (note 51), pp. xi–xiv annexed to the preface.

74. BM, PD, 5275 (press-mark 198* b.5), reg. no. N.1–18.

75. Jap Bolten makes interesting comments about this in *Oude Tekeningen van het Prentenkabinet der Rijksuniversiteit te Leiden* (The Hague, 1985), pp. 171–5, no. 64, where he has discussed plate 18 because of its relation to a drawing apparently by Merian at Leiden, for in that the same large spider, although inaccurately represented, also appears.

76. BM, PD, 5221, transferred to the Print Room (press-mark 197* a.2) from the Department of Manuscripts in 1928; see Hind, op. cit. (note 8), vol. IV, pp. 25–26, nos. 1–32.

77. George Vertue, *Note-Books*, vol. I (Walpole Society 18) (1929/30), p. 56; George Vertue, *Note-Books*, vol. II (Walpole Society 20) (1931/2), p. 12.

78. See the edition by A.R. Peltzer (Munich 1925), p. 102.

79. See below, p. 294, no. 30, BL, Sloane MS 3972 C, vol. VI, fol. 245ʳ, where it is listed as 'Min[iature] +279 Original drawings of Hans Holbein for Jew[e]ls &c bound in red marocco 4ᶜ'.

80. BM, PD, 5308–32, 30.

81. BM, PD, 5308–8, 10; see Rowlands, op. cit. (note 6), p. 241, no. 207 a & b, reproduced.

82. BM, PD, 5308–22, 34; see Rowlands, op. cit. (note 6), p. 242, no. 208 b & c, reproduced.

17 Books and Manuscripts

M. A. E. Nickson

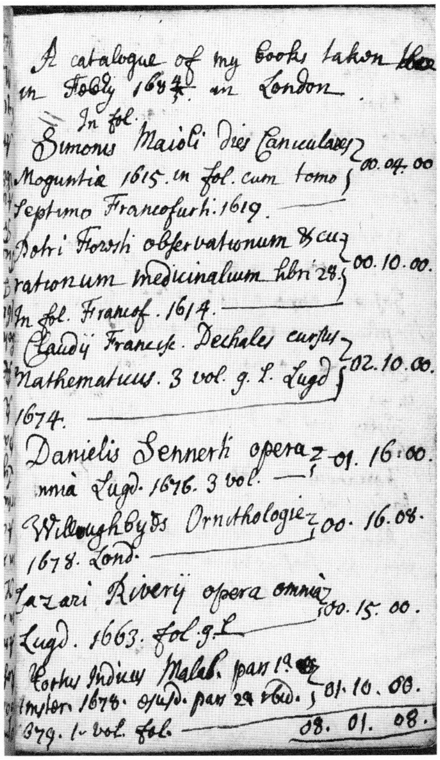

* When Sloane arrived in London from Ireland in 1679 it is unlikely that he brought any books with him, nor had he inherited any from his father, yet within a decade he had laid the foundations of one of the greatest and most comprehensive libraries of his time. This began, unremarkably enough, with books which any student of the natural sciences might have acquired, bought mostly with a few pennies during his years of study in London, Paris and the south of France. From an early date, however, Sloane showed unusual method and application in his treatment of his small library. By February 1685, he had collected enough books to make it necessary to begin a catalogue. For this he used a small notebook[1] (see Fig. 102) in which he entered a description, with the price, of each of the 29 folios, 63 quartos, 183 octavos and 32 duodecimos which he had so far acquired; the grand total expended was £30. 14s. 4d.[2] His method of description was precise, giving not only the author and title of each book, with the date and place of publication and the size and number of volumes, but also noting whether the leaves or back were gilded, or whether there were any other marks of interest; he did not, however, make any comments here about where he had bought the books. The folios, which were naturally the most expensive, included medical textbooks such as the *Opera omnia* (3 vols. Paris, 1676) of Daniel Sennertus, as well as the *Cursus mathematicus* (3 vols. Lyon, 1674) of C.F. Milliet Dechales, the first two parts of the *Hortus Indicus Malabaricus* (Amsterdam, 1678–9), the 1678 English edition of Willughby's *Ornithologia*, Pietro Castelli's *Exactissima descriptio rariorum plantarum in Horto Farnesiano* (Rome, 1625), Thomas Moufet's *Insectorum ... theatrum* (London, 1634), John Wilkins's *Essay towards a Real Character and Philosophical Language* (London, 1668) and George Wheler's recently published *Journey to Greece* (London, 1682). Other purchases were the second edition of John Ray's indispensable *Catalogus plantarum Anglie* (London, 1677),[3] J.P. Cornut's *Canadensium plantarum ... historia* (Paris, 1635), Pierre Magnol's *Botanicum Monspeliensis* (Lyon, 1676), other printed catalogues of botanical gardens in Paris,[4] Oxford,[5] Breda,[6] and Leiden,[7] John Josselin's *New England's rarities discovered* (London, 1672), Thomas Nicols's *Gemmarius fidelius or faithful lapidary* (London, 1659), Rice Vaughan's *A discourse of coines and coinage* (London, 1672), and Pierre Richelet's *Dictionnaire François* (Geneva, 1680). He had also acquired a small number of the theological works so popular in the seventeenth century, together with a French New Testament and Psalms, with a silver clasp, printed at Charenton in 1668 and part of a Hebrew Bible.

Some of the books had been obtained in France: amongst these were Anicet Caufapé's *Explication de la Gangrène*

Fig. 102 Sir Hans Sloane's first catalogue of his books, begun in February 1685. BL, Sloane MS 3995, fol. 114ᵛ. Reproduced by courtesy of the Trustees of the British Library.

(Toulouse, 1681),[8] the *De re medica* (Lyon, 1608) of Aulus Celsus[9] and the *Enchiridion chirurgicum* (Lyon, 1588) of Antonius Chalmetheus.[10] Sloane's interest in early medical texts was already evident, for listed amongst the folios was a copy of the recipes attributed to John Feckenham, abbot of Westminster before the Reformation, made about the beginning of the seventeenth century.[11]

I have dealt at some length with these purchases as it seems reasonable to suppose that at this stage in his life Sloane was buying books to read rather than as the nucleus of a collection, and that his choice therefore reveals both the natural bias of his mind and the influences which were moulding his intellectual outlook. A study of them soon shows that the main interests of Sloane's life, medicine, botany and horticulture, entomology, zoology, mineralogy, travel and discovery, linguistics and numismatics were represented in his library from the beginning. Another feature also characteristic of his later book-collecting was the relatively small number of books in English or published in England, which made up only about a quarter of the whole.

Having listed his purchases of books up to February 1685, Sloane continued his catalogue with similar entries for subsequent acquisitions, adding up his total expenditure from time to time. The cost of his library was obviously a matter for concern. Possibly because he was aware that

(margin notes, left column)
29/fol. 114ᵛ
29/fol. 114ᵛ
29/fol. 114ᵛ
29/fol. 114ᵛ
29/fol. 113ᵛ
29/fol. 113ᵛ
29/fol. 113ᵛ
29/fol. 111ᵛ
29/fol. 102ᵛ
29/fol. 110ᵛ
29/fol. 103ᵛ
29/fol. 108ᵛ
29/fol. 101ᵛ
29/fol. 88ᵛ
29/fol. 86ᵛ
29/fol. 93ᵛ
29/fol. 107ᵛ
29/fol. 91ᵛ
29/fol. 110ᵛ
29/fol. 90ᵛ
29/fol. 86ᵛ
29/fol. 91ᵛ

(margin notes, right column)
29/fol. 87ᵛ
29/fol. 88ᵛ
29/fol. 111ᵛ

* Marginal numerals in this chapter refer to Sloane catalogues: see the notes on pp. 274–7 and the list on p. 294

his financial circumstances might force him to re-sell some items, he entered the price of each book in code on the flyleaf, together with the date of purchase, and, for a short time only, the place of purchase also; this is how we know that some of his early purchases were made in France. Whether he did in fact ever need to dispose of any books is not clear. Certainly a large number of the books listed in his first catalogue can no longer be found in the British Library, but that is more likely to be for other reasons to be discussed later.

At first Sloane used a simple letter code for the price and did not bother to disguise the date, but from 1686 onwards he used an 'alchemical' code of his own devising for both price and date.[12] The meaning of these coded entries has only recently become known; for a long time they were believed to be a form of press-mark. Sloane continued to enter these coded dates and prices in his books and manuscripts long after he had established his position as a leading London physician, and did not abandon the practice until about 1698 when he relinquished the day-to-day work of the library to assistants.

By the time the last page of his catalogue had been reached, probably some time in 1687, Sloane had spent in all £194 and had acquired about 2,700 books and manuscripts. One of the first purchases after the initial listing 29/fol. 84ᵛ had been the *Opera universa* (London, 1685) of his master Thomas Sydenham, but Sydenham's well known advice to eschew theory for practice did not deter him from continuing a voracious search for all kinds of medical books, however old. Botany was also well to the forefront in his choice of books, together with accounts of the world outside 29/fol. 62ʳ Europe. Amongst the latter were Roger Williams's *Key into the Language of America* (London, 1643) and several books on various aspects of life in Jamaica: Thomas Trapham's 29/fol. 50ᵛ *Discourse of the state of health in the island of Jamaica* (London, 29/fol. 60ᵛ 1679), Richard Blome's *Description of the island of Jamaica* 29/fol. 75ᵛ (London, 1678), Edward Hickeringill's *Jamaica viewed* 29/fol. 81ʳ (London, 1661), and *The Laws of Jamaica* (London, 1684). His choice of books, however, showed more diverse interests too, for during this time he also purchased *The Natural* 29/fol. 31ʳ *History of coffee, tea, chocolate, tobacco . . .* (London, 1682), 29/fol. 41ʳ John Dury's *Reformed school and library keeper* (London, 29/fol. 12ʳ 1650), some maps of England, Calvin's *Institutes* translated 29/fol. 14ʳ into Spanish[13] and even a few literary works, including a 29/fol. 49ᵛ into Spanish and even a few literary works, including a 29/fol. 32ᵛ Greek Homer (1525), an imperfect copy of More's *Utopia*, 29/fol. 42ʳ Tasso's *Gierusalemma liberata* (n.d.), Ariosto's *Orlando* 29/fol. 43ʳ *furioso* (Venice, 1604) and Cervantes's *Don Quixote* which 29/fol. 25ʳ he bought in two instalments, the first part published in 29/fol. 55ᵛ Rouen in 1646 and the second part in Madrid in 1636.[14]

An interesting purchase in view of the later history of the 29/fol. 98ʳ library was two volumes of book and sale catalogues. Sloane was obviously already aware of the importance of this kind of material in the task of making his collection as comprehensive as possible in his chosen fields.

The visit to Jamaica brought about a hiatus in his book-

collecting but after his return to London in May, 1689, his financial security was assured and the library was able to grow at an ever increasing rate. Although Sloane was endowed from birth with the temperament of a collector, his chief aim in amassing so many books was scientific, and he was concerned that they should be easily available for study. His collection had already become more than just the working library of a professional man when he set out to devise a suitable system of arrangement and press-marking. With typical clarity of thought he chose a simple but effective method which allowed for expansion and which he was able to retain, with some modifications, for the rest of his life. Each book was designated by a letter of the alphabet and a number; capital letters A,B,C and P were reserved for folios, lower case letters d,e,f,i,q,r for quartos and g,h,k,l,m,n,o,s,t,u,x,y for octavos and smaller books.[15] No distinction was made, at this time, between printed books and manuscripts, nor did he attempt to arrange the books by subject, with the exception of the medical books in Latin. One of Sloane's earliest purchases had been the 1651 edition of a bibliography of medical 29/fol. 103ᵛ works in Latin compiled by J.A. van der Linden,[16] a physician of Leiden, and in this he had begun to record items of which he possessed a copy. In 1686 a greatly augmented version of this bibliography, by G.A. Mercklin, was published in Nuremberg under the title *Lindenius renovatus*. After his return from Jamaica Sloane obtained a copy of this[17] and used it to enter the press-marks of his own Latin medical books. He also provided it with interleaving on which he entered items which had been omitted or which had been published since 1686 as he acquired them. In doing this he was not only taking a short cut in the cataloguing of his own books but was also making a conscious effort to make as complete a collection as possible of this kind of material.

Sloane's copy of *Lindenius renovatus* thus became a separate catalogue of his medical books in Latin (see p. 294, no. 31); all his other printed books and manuscripts were entered in a main catalogue (p. 294, no.30), hand-written on folio sheets, which gave the author, title and imprint of each item, together with the press-mark. The first sheets contained entries for over 3,000 items acquired up to about 1693. The press-marks of these are only roughly in order (see Fig. 103) suggesting that the books had first been press-marked and then taken from the shelves, not always systematically, for entry in the catalogue. About the beginning of 1694 Sloane completed the reorganization of his printed books and began to list his manuscripts separately. These now amounted to nearly 200; the importance of the collection was already sufficiently well known for a list of them to have been requested for Edward Bernard's *Catalogus Manuscriptorum Anglie*.[18] When both books and manuscripts had been entered in the new catalogue Sloane began to list his acquisitions as they came in and from this point the catalogue became more or less an accession register.

In order to find specific items it was necessary to consult an author index, which was started separately at about the same time; this did not include references to works in *Lindenius renovatus*, since this was itself arranged in order of the writers' forenames. The press-marks, however, were allocated in one sequence, irrespective of the catalogue in which the item was to be entered. This has the happy result today that although *Lindenius renovatus* is not in accession order it is still possible to calculate the approximate date when Sloane acquired a Latin medical book by finding where its press-mark fits into the main catalogue.[19]

By the time of this reorganization Sloane's library was already large for late seventeenth-century England. Pepys's library was only slightly larger. Evelyn had about 5,000 books and Thomas Plume even more. The most significant comparison, however, is with the library of Sloane's friend John Locke. The similarities between Locke and Sloane as book-collectors are indeed remarkable. Locke had made his first catalogue at Oxford in 1681 in the same form as Sloane's first catalogue made in London in 1685, and with a collection of a similar size and content; he, too, secretly annotated each book with its price, though not in code (he wrote the figures in the bottom margin of a pre-determined page). When he began to make his main catalogue he chose an interleaved copy of an existing printed catalogue (in his case Hyde's catalogue of printed books in the Bodleian Library) which he used as Sloane used *Lindenius renovatus*. Although he had acquired this copy of Hyde while still in Holland in the mid 1680s, Locke did not carry out the work of press-marking and listing his books until 1692 and 1693, that is about the time that Sloane was engaged on the same task. Neither Locke nor Sloane attempted a subject arrangement of their books nor is there any evidence that either possessed a shelf list.[20] The editors of Locke's library catalogue have pointed out that 'Locke's methods of marking and cataloguing give him a claim of being a pioneer in ... the science of librarianship'. It would be interesting to know whether it was Locke or Sloane who was the pioneer, whether they had discussed the problems together, or whether they had both copied the same model.

Up to 1698 Sloane continued to select books for the library and to press-mark and catalogue them without assistance, a remarkable feat considering his professional duties and many other interests. From that time, however, he decided to entrust most of the work to assistants. Some of these are known to us only through their handwriting and were little more than amanuenses. The first was employed not only to catalogue the books which had actually been acquired but also to make lists of *desiderata* which were incorporated in the main catalogue so that press-marks could be added as the books were found and purchased.[21] This method was soon abandoned, presumably because it was too unwieldy and time-consuming.

In 1701 Sloane was fortunate enough to engage the services of Humfrey Wanley, better known in library

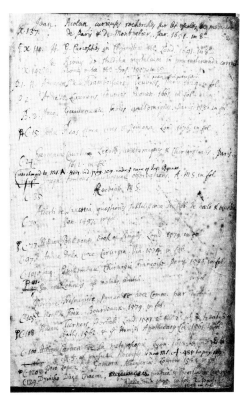

Fig. 103 Sir Hans Sloane's main library catalogue; first page, begun *c*.1693. BL, Sloane MS 3972C, vol. I, fol. 2ʳ. Reproduced by courtesy of the Trustees of the British Library.

history for his later employment as the librarian of Robert and Edward Harley, Earls of Oxford. Still in his twenties, Wanley already had the reputation of possessing 'the best skill in ancient hands and MSS. of any man not only of this, but ... of any former age'.[22] During his employment by Sloane, Wanley was allowed to take over all the cataloguing tasks of the library and he was probably influential in the selection of the books and manuscripts as well. For example one of the items obtained during his librarianship was a sixteenth-century blockbook[23] (see Plate 35) and another 30/MS CLXXXIII was Richard Smith's 'Treatise concerning the Invention and 30/MS XCVIII Progress of Printing'.[24] Wanley's descriptions are easily identifiable, being written in a characteristic neat hand. He seems to have been given a free hand by Sloane and he even introduced a change in the form in which the manuscripts were numbered, designating them with roman numerals.

Before beginning his work on cataloguing Sloane's latest acquisitions Wanley fulfilled a commission entrusted to him by his patron Dr Arthur Charlett, Master of University College, Oxford. With Sloane's agreement he compared 'many Thousands of his Books with Dr. Hyde's Catalogue and ... found out a great number ... which were Duplicates ... and yet wanting in the Bodleyan'.[25] Sloane agreed to donate these books to the University and Wanley was employed to arrange the transfer.[26] This generous gift to the Bodleian Library, which was followed later by others, must provide at least one of the reasons why so many of Sloane's early book purchases cannot be found in the present collections of the British Library.[27]

Wanley appears to have left Sloane's service by 1703 but his departure did not put an end to their friendship which lasted until Wanley's death in 1724. As a classicist and Anglo-Saxon scholar Wanley may not have felt entirely at home amongst Sloane's books, although he obviously
30/MS LXX enjoyed making a lengthy description of a fourteenth-century compilation of texts on veterinary medicine,[28] one of the few Greek manuscripts to be obtained for the library.

Another twenty years were to elapse before Sloane found a fit successor to Wanley. He therefore found it necessary to take back into his own hands the cataloguing of all items other than printed books. As the size of the library increased Sloane decided to introduce further classes, based not on subject matter but on format and type of material. He had already included separate sections for *Horti sicci*, Newspapers and Atlases in his main catalogue; about 1705 he began a series of Prints and 1706 saw the beginning of two more series, Charters and Rolls. In 1708 the important class of Miniatures was begun (see Fig. 104). This included both portfolios of drawings and illuminated books and manuscripts, and several items which had previously been classed as manuscripts were transferred to the new series. About 1718, realizing the extent to which the oriental section of his library had increased (he had acquired a
30/MS 272 Chinese book[29] as early as 1696) Sloane introduced first a new series of Oriental Manuscripts and a little later one of Oriental Prints; to both of these was added material which had been acquired in earlier years.

In 1725, when he had reached an age appropriate to retirement from his labours, Sloane was fortunate to find another scholar to whom he could entrust most of the running of the library. This was Johann Caspar Scheuchzer, a youthful prodigy from Zürich, who proved to have the skill and linguistic ability to deal with most of the items being added to the library. A special task was also given to him, for Sloane had recently bought the most important single collection he ever acquired, the papers, books and drawings which had belonged to the German traveller, Engelbert Kaempfer.[30] Kaempfer had travelled extensively in the Middle and Far East and had already published his *Amoenitatum exoticarum . . . fasciculi 5* (Lemgo, 1712) based on some of the materials he had collected there. However
30/MS A.616 his 'History of Japan'[31] was still only in manuscript when he died in 1716; Scheuchzer was now employed to prepare an English edition of this (see Chapter 18). His translation
30/Pr. DCCXL appeared in 1727 and he was able to add it to the catalogue himself.[32] For a period of about four years Scheuchzer worked very assiduously for the library and effected a reorganization of the manuscripts, which now totalled nearly 3,000, giving them a new numbering based on size.[33]

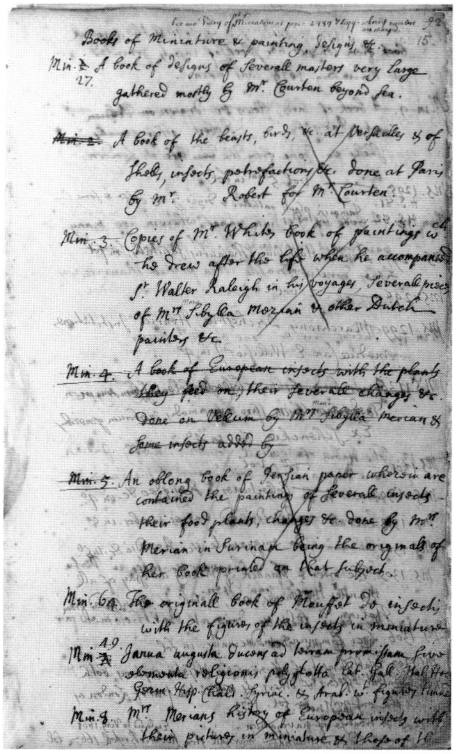
Books of Miniature & painting, designs &c.
Min. 1. A book of designs of severall masters very large gathered mostly by Mr Courten beyond sea.
Min. 2. A book of the beasts, birds, &c. at Versailles & of shells, insects, petrefactions &c. done at Paris by Mr Robert for Mr Courten
Min. 3. Copies of Mr White's book of paintings which he drew after the life when he accompanied Sr Walter Raleigh in his voyages, severall pieces of Mrs Sibylla Merian & other Dutch painters &c.
Min. 4. A book of European insects with the plants they feed on, their severall changes &c. done on velum by Mrs Sibylla Merian & some insects added by
Min. 5. An oblong book of Persian paper wherein are contained the painting of severall insects their food plants, changes &c. done by Mrs Merian in Surinam being the originalls of her book printed on that subject.
Min. 6. The originall book of Mouffet de insectis with the figures of the insects in miniature.

Fig. 104 Sir Hans Sloane's first list of Miniatures, *c.*1708. BL, Sloane MS 3972C, vol. IV, fol. 15r. Reproduced by courtesy of the Trustees of the British Library.

Sadly his early death occurred on 10 April 1729, while he was still a member of Sloane's household.

From this time onwards Sloane did not appoint another regular librarian but relied on the services of two of his associates, both active in the Royal Society, Cromwell Mortimer and Thomas Stack, who shared the work of entering new items in the catalogues. Mortimer was particularly responsible for books in German. In the mid 1730s Stack began a revision of the library, which took about five years to complete, searching for items in the catalogue which could no longer be found, identifying some which former amanuenses had failed to describe properly,[34] and entering some which had fallen through the net in earlier years. To him may be ascribed the embellishment of many books and manuscripts with the imposing description 'Bibliothecae Sloaneianae'. Even during this period, however, there were still occasions when Sloane himself made the entries, in a shaky but still characteristic hand; his last entry was made about 1741. In the last decade of Sloane's life the growth of the library slowed considerably and the catalogue was left to amanuenses of indifferent ability. It is unlikely, however, that Sloane ever relinquished his leading role in the selection of items for the library. Thus it remained to the end the creation of one man, whose chief aim was to bring together, as comprehensively as possible, all known works dealing with the natural world, from the earliest times and from the furthest places.

In order to accomplish this aim Sloane relied heavily on bibliographies and catalogues of other collections to provide him with information on what he should collect; and in order to find items for purchase he made great use of sale catalogues. From the beginning he had recognized the importance of these aids and by the time of his death the library contained at least 700 sale catalogues as well as many printed and manuscript catalogues of other libraries. Many of the sale catalogues still bear the marks made by Sloane to indicate which items he had decided to buy; his assistants were then required to check the collection in order to avoid the purchase of duplicates, and comments such as 'you have several editions of this' or 'you have rev. ed.' were added.

These marked catalogues form an important source for determining the provenance of Sloane's books and manuscripts, although they have not yet been used systematically for that purpose. It was, indeed, the acute observation of an American scholar, J.S. Finch, who was engaged in the study of the library of Sir Thomas Browne, author of *Religio medici*, which was sold in January 1711, that led to the rediscovery of Sloane's press-marks at a time (1942) when knowledge of them had disappeared completely from the collective consciousness of the British Museum Library.[35]

30/R. 2345

Having noticed that some of the items in the Browne sale catalogue[36] had been marked with a view to purchase Finch realized that 'the titles suggested that the owner had been a collector of coins as well as books, and probably a physician. Sir Hans Sloane seemed to fit the description; moreover, since he had acquired most of the Browne manuscripts, he would be expected to have owned a copy of the sale catalogue and to have purchased some of Browne's printed books'. From this it was a short step to recognizing the similarity between the press-mark R. 2345 given at an early date to the Browne catalogue and the press-marks of books in Sloane's catalogues, although Finch was prevented from completing the task of identifying the actual items bought in 1711 as the relevant volume of the catalogue, volume IV, could not be traced. It was typical of Sloane that amongst the books that he bought at this sale was

30/R. 2340

a copy of the *Religio medici* translated into Dutch.[37]

Although much work remains to be done in this field, it is possible to list some other important sales at which Sloane is known to have bought books or manuscripts. His first such purchase was probably made at the sale in 1682 of the library of Richard Smith, renowned amongst bookcollectors for having contained no less than eleven works from Caxton's press. The item bought by the young Sloane, however, was for practical rather than antiquarian purposes,

29/fol. 113ᵛ

being the *Universa medicina* (Frankfurt, 1592) of J. Fernelius, once physician to King Henri II of France, for which he paid two shillings.[38] At the sale of the physician Francis Bernard's library in October 1698, Sloane was an important

bidder, buying many items;[39] these included a *Pharmacopoeia Londinensis* (London, 1627) annotated by Theodore Turquet de Mayerne[40] and Thomas Moufet's *Insectorum ... theatrum* (London, 1634) annotated by a Dr More.[41] Sloane is also known to have bought several books at the sale in 1731 of the library of Daniel Defoe,[42] including a tract on the wickedness of Sunday non-observance printed in Amsterdam in 1636.[43] At the last posthumous sale, in 1734, of the library of the book-collector Thomas Rawlinson, who had died in 1725, Sloane purchased at least twelve manuscripts,[44] and in 1740 he bought extensively at the sale of Sir Joseph Jekyll, inheritor of the library of Lord Chancellor Somers.[45]

30/MS 305

30/MS 295

30/C. 3309

Another important source for information on Sloane's methods for obtaining his books is his correspondence. He was well aware that the letters written to him by his friends and associates deserved to be preserved in their own right and had incorporated them in the library about 1730.[46] This vast correspondence is still, alas, unpublished. It presents a picture of Sloane as a man genial in all respects; not a philosopher like Locke, nor a scientific pioneer like Ray, but a man of administrative ability allied with breadth of vision and sympathy for his fellow men. Sloane was adept at establishing a widespread network of like-minded scholars, ready to help him to increase his collections. At the end of the 1690s, for example, he was receiving letters concerning suitable purchases of books and manuscripts from friends in Edinburgh, Paris and Antwerp, while in Italy the botanist and diplomat William Sherard was searching for books on his behalf.[47] Sloane's position in the Royal Society, first as Secretary and later as President, was an undoubted help in enabling him to establish fruitful contacts with foreign scholars. For example, his friendship with the historian Gerhard Friedrich Müller led to Sloane being invited to join the Russian Academy of Sciences and to the sending of Sloane's botanical assistant Johann Amman to Russia in 1733 as Professor of Botany.[48] During the eight years that Amman spent there before his tragic early death in 1741 Sloane regularly sent him copies of the *Philosophical Transactions* and other books, receiving back books published in St. Petersburg, including a copy of Euler's *Mechanica* (1736).[49]

30/MSS A. 680–98

30/44:5,6

Although these foreign contacts were useful in obtaining books not available in England, most of Sloane's books and manuscripts must have been obtained in London. Unfortunately his booksellers' bills have not survived amongst his papers but a manuscript in the Harleian collection, the account book kept from 1703 to 1708 by John Bagford, shoemaker turned bookseller,[50] contains a record of some of Sloane's purchases at that time. Sloane had probably become acquainted with Bagford in the 1690s, and in 1703 they made an expedition together to the premises of another shoemaker in Thames Street in search of Italian manuscripts.[51] During the next five years Sloane appears in the account book as a regular customer, together with

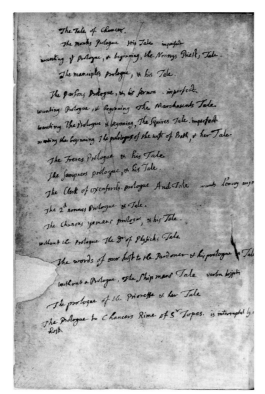

Fig. 105 Sir Hans Sloane's contents list for his copy of the *Canterbury Tales*, printed by Caxton c.1484. BL, IB 55095. Reproduced by courtesy of the Trustees of the British Library.

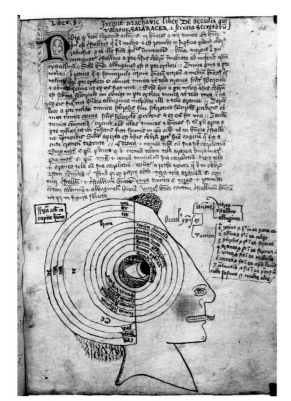

Fig. 106 The structure of the eye, from the treatise by Macharias, late fourteenth- or early fifteenth-century. BL, Sloane MS 981, fol. 68ʳ. Reproduced by courtesy of the Trustees of the British Library.

such illustrious clients as Robert Harley and Bishop Moore. The most important item which Bagford supplied to Sloane during this period was an imperfect copy of Caxton's second edition of the *Canterbury Tales*.[52] This must have been especially prized by Sloane as he took the trouble to write out a contents list on the flyleaf of the volume, which had been misbound by a previous owner (see Fig. 105). [30/H. 36]

The amount which Sloane expended on his library between his return from Jamaica in 1689 and his death in 1753 can only be guessed at, but it must have been considerable. A few items had come to him by bequest from William Courten alias Charleton,[53] and some by gift, such as a magnificent set of prints from the French Royal Library, presented by King Louis xv in 1734,[54] but most of them had been bought by Sloane himself. Since he always preferred to use the money available for the library on books and manuscripts rather than on the fine bindings which so delighted the noble collectors of his time, his books are rarely identifiable from their bindings alone; the nearest to a 'Sloane' binding is the workmanlike cover, with a label on the spine giving the press-mark, which may still be seen occasionally, particularly amongst the sale catalogues.[55] There is no reason to suppose, however, that he did not appreciate beautiful bindings when he acquired them. Indeed, by leaving his books in the bindings in which they were bought he may have preserved some of interest which another collector would have replaced. The most important of these is undoubtedly the medieval English embroidered binding on what is now known as the Felbrigge psalter, 'the only surviving example of Opus Anglicanum used in this way and apparently intended for this purpose'.[56] Later examples include the sumptuous bindings on the volumes of charts by William Hack, which Sloane probably received through his connection with the family of the Duke of Albemarle,[57] and the binding on Thomas Moufet's autograph draft of the *Theatrum . . . insectorum*, which had been used in 1634 when the work was prepared for the press by Turquet de Mayerne.[58] [30/Pr.ccxxi–ccxliii] [30/Min. 106, later 167] [30/Mss 47–52] [30/MS LXVI]

Such were the ways in which Sloane acquired and administered his library, but what of the books and manuscripts themselves? No statistical work has yet been done on the contents of the library and even the precise number of items contained in it is still a matter of conjecture. Leaving aside the problems caused by the way in which the collection was managed after it became part of the British Museum, to which I shall return later, Sloane's habit of continually revising some of his press-marks makes it impossible at this stage of research to say more than that the estimate of about 50,000 volumes given in the codicil to his will is probably correct, and that about 45,000 of these would have been printed books. Since Sloane never classified his books by subject matter either on the shelves or in the catalogue (with the exception of the medical books in Latin listed in *Lindenius renovatus*) it is also difficult to assign numbers of books to different subjects. Works on medicine certainly constituted the largest single group, although the size of this should not be over-estimated. A glance at the list of books owned by Sloane by February 1685, shows that even when he was a medical student no more than about a third of his books were works dealing specifically with medicine. I am inclined to think that this estimate could be projected on to the rest of the library without too much distortion of the truth.[59]

Even a third of Sloane's library is still, however, a vast collection of medical writings. His holdings in this field were based on the Latin medical books recorded in *Lindenius renovatus*, which he was able to amplify to a very great extent. By the time of his death he had succeeded very largely in his ambition to collect all the works listed there, including their various editions, and had also added a considerable number of items to Mercklin's list;[60] so much so that at one time he had contemplated producing a revised edition of it.[61] Moreover the additions he made included not only books published since the appearance of Mercklin's work in 1686 but also many earlier books and editions not known to Mercklin, such as, for example, a rare edition of an English translation of a treatise on pestilence attributed to Bishop Kanutus, printed by William of Machlinia about 1483;[62] a work which also has the distinction, unknown to Sloane, of being the first book printed in England to have a title page. Sloane's collection on medicine also contained many vernacular books, which were listed in the main catalogue. The jewel in the crown of his medical library, however, was not the books but the manuscripts; as Peter Murray Jones has recently pointed out, Sloane's 'must be the greatest collection of medical manuscripts ever made by a single individual'.[63] The greatness consisted not only in size but also in the remarkable quality of some of the items. Amongst the medieval texts were some strikingly beautiful illuminated works. Outstanding amongst these is an early fourteenth-century copy of the 'Chirurgia' of Roger Frugardi of Parma, which has been called the finest example of medical miniature-painting of the French school;[64] full-page miniatures illustrate the life of Christ above while below surgeons are shown at work treating dislocated limbs and even operating on a fracture of the skull. In some manuscripts the illustrations are diagrammatical, but no less terrifying on that account, as can be seen in the diagram which accompanies the text of the treatise on the eye ascribed to Macharias[65] (see Fig. 106). Of great interest for its depiction of the ordinary life of the time in which it was written is the 'Livre dou santé' of Aldobrandino of Siena, commissioned by Beatrix of Savoy, countess of Provence, in 1256 and the first medical work to have been written in French.[66] Sloane's copy of this text, which is acknowledged to be the finest, was illuminated in France in the late thirteenth century; it deals not only with the health and constitution of the body but also with matters of diet (see Plate 36).

These illustrated medical manuscripts are justly famous

but the true importance of Sloane's collection of medieval writings lies in their value for the transmission of texts. Most of the celebrated works of the Middle Ages can be found there: those ascribed to writers such as Albertus Magnus, Bernardus of Gordonio and Gulielmus of Saliceto, together with many anonymous treatises based on the teaching of Aristotle, Galen and Hippocrates. As might be expected the collection is particularly rich in texts written in England.[67] Sloane was interested in this kind of historical material from the earliest days of the library, but for his own study and practice he needed more recent works. The passing of case notes and prescriptions from one physician to another was a common practice in seventeenth-century England, and by obtaining the papers and annotated books of medical practitioners of his own time and a little earlier Sloane simply followed a well established custom, though, being Sloane, to a greater extent than anyone else. The earliest acquisition of this kind was a work on chemistry bought for 2s. 6d. in 1682 from its author Nicholas Staphorst, the Apothecaries' 'chemical operator' with whom he shared lodgings.[68] Amongst the physicians whose books and papers he acquired later were Joseph Fenton,[69] Joseph Colston,[70] Christopher Love Morley,[71] John Downes of St. Bartholomew's Hospital[72] and Theodore Turquet de Mayerne.[73] The most famous item of this kind was the autograph manuscript of the lectures given by William Harvey in 1616 in which he announced his discovery concerning the circulation of the blood.[74] It is interesting that Sloane, although an avid collector of books annotated by other physicians, does not seem to have annotated books himself.[75]

After medicine, works on plants and animals are the next largest category of material in Sloane's library. In the first section of the main catalogue these were often designated with a special clover-like symbol (see Fig. 103) presumably so that they could be found easily. During the time when this was compiled Sloane was actively associated with the informal group of naturalists, residing in or near London, who met at the Temple Coffee House to exchange notes, and in later years he collected and preserved many of the papers of these like-minded friends.[76] The most important of these collections was that made by James Petiver; as well as works on natural history by himself and others, this included the voluminous correspondence which Petiver had maintained with other naturalists up to his death in 1718.[77] Other former associates of Sloane whose papers were eventually acquired for the library were Adam Buddle,[78] Samuel Doody,[79] Martin Lister[80] and Leonard Plukenet, superintendent of the Hampton Court gardens;[81] he also obtained records relating to the Duke of Beaufort's garden at Badminton.[82] In at least one instance Sloane seems to have commissioned work from a naturalist; about 1708 Joseph Dandridge, one of the founders of English entomology, provided Sloane with illustrated accounts of the spiders[83] and caterpillars[84] which he had collected and observed around London (see Fig. 107).

31/N. 1648

30/MS. 1830, later Min. 156, later Min. 234

30/MS CXCI

30/MS 2288, later Min. 169

30/MS 144

30/MS 248

30/Min. 110, later 286
30/Min. 111, later 287

269

Fig. 107 A butterfly for Sloane: the caterpillar of the Meadow Brown (*Maniola jurtina*), collected and drawn by Joseph Dandridge, c.1707. BL, Additional MS 6054, fol. 27ʳ. Reproduced by courtesy of the Trustees of the British Library.

As might be expected Sloane did not limit his interest in the natural world to what he and his friends were able to discover in their own neighbourhood, or to what he had discovered during his stay in Jamaica. His collection of botanical manuscripts encompassed the whole known world, from the Japanese books for preserving simples, brought back by Kaempfer,[85] to the notes made by John Banister in Virginia[86] and an Italian dietary with the charming title 'Brieve racconto di tutte le radici, di tutte l'herbe et di tutti i frutti, che crude o cotti in Italia si mangiano'.[87] He also acquired many medieval herbals, his collection being particularly rich in copies of the English text known as 'Agnus castus' of which he eventually possessed no fewer than ten copies.[88] These early botanical compilations cannot easily be distinguished from medical works. Even in Sloane's own day the use of herbs was a primary part of medical practice and botany was only gradually becoming a scientific discipline in its own right; the way in which the two were intertwined in the Middle Ages is demonstrated, for example, in a late twelfth-century copy of the 'De virtutibus herbarum' of Pseudo-Apuleius which ends with a group of miniatures showing surgical operations in graphic detail.[89]

This interest in natural history was only one facet of Sloane's exceptional curiosity concerning the world around

30/MS C. 360
30/Min. 94, later 211
30/MS 819

30/Min. 158

him. Although his own journeys did not extend beyond his student years in France and the voyage to Jamaica he was always deeply interested in travel and discovery, particularly in the lands beyond Europe. One is reminded of the young Richard Hakluyt reading over 'whatsoever printed or written discoveries and voyages . . . extant either in the Greek, Latin, Italian, Spanish, Portugal, French or English languages'.[90] Indeed at one time Sloane seems to have envisaged making a comprehensive collection of accounts of travel, especially in the Americas, similar to his collection of medical books in Latin. Although this project was abandoned, he continued to collect manuscript and printed accounts of journeys to all quarters of the then expanding world, as well as atlases and maps. His own copy of Hakluyt[91] was obviously treasured and was described in great detail in his catalogue, where thirty-three pages were devoted to its contents.

The manuscript travel accounts collected by Sloane included contemporary records from both hemispheres, ranging from Pierre Radisson surveying the Canadian north for the Hudson's Bay Company in 1684,[92] to William Dampier sailing in the South Seas to the fringe of Australia from 1682 to 1691.[93] Amongst the earlier accounts are those by David Ingram who journeyed from Mexico towards Nova Scotia in 1582;[94] John Chilton who sailed to New Spain in 1568 to 1586;[95] John Jourdain who travelled in the East Indies and Arabia from 1608 to 1617;[96] Thomas Clement who sailed from England to Surat via the Cape of Good Hope and back from 1632 to 1635;[97] William Jackson who sailed to the West Indies in 1642;[98] and Richard Bell, gun-founder to the Great Moguls, who travelled in India and the Middle East from 1654 to 1669.[99] Sloane also collected many items of cartographical interest; the most famous of these is the superb 'Livro do estado India Oriental' made by Pedro Barretto de Resende in 1646, in which were depicted the fortifications built by the Portuguese along the coasts of India and southern Africa.[100] He also acquired some charts which had been used in the workshop of Johannes Blaeu[101] and three volumes of maps from the printed Atlas of Johann Jansson which were 'intended to be the foundation of [Moses] Pitt's English Atlas' and which had previously been owned by Robert Hooke.[102] The high regard in which Sloane held his collection of maps and atlases is shown by the fact that he selected two items from it as worthy of presentation to Queen Caroline; these were B. Molino's plans of Venetian forts[103] and Sir Bernard de Gomme's plans of towns and forts in the Low Countries, 1625–45.[104] Although the drawings of native costume which would have complemented this collection of travel and discovery were transferred to the Department of Prints and Drawings of the British Museum in the nineteenth century (and are discussed in Chapter 16) those drawings which were regarded as topographical were retained in the Department of Manuscripts and are amongst the holdings of the British

30/D. 153

30/B. 1357

30/A. 666

30/MS 1328
30/MS 45
30/MS 756

30/MS A. 750
30/MS 787

30/MS CXXXVI

30/Min. 63, later 87

30/Pr. LXXXVIII
30/xxxv–xxxviii

30/Min. 232, 233, later 80,81
30/Min. 241

Fig. 108 G. Hofsted van Essen, drawing of *The Khaju bridge in Isfahan,* late seventeenth- or early eighteenth-century. BL, Additional MS 5234, fol. 10ʳ. Reproduced by courtesy of the Trustees of the British Library.

Library at the present day. These too cover many different areas of the world; included in them are sketches made by Edward Browne on his travels and drawings made by G. Hofsted van Essen in the Middle East (see Fig. 108).[105]

Sloane was greatly interested not only in the physical conditions reported by travellers but also in the various languages which they encountered, and his library contained much of interest to the study of language itself. How far Sloane himself was a linguist is not clear. His studies in France had left him with a good knowledge of spoken and written French, which he continued to use in his correspondence throughout his life. Von Uffenbach was impressed with his readiness to converse in French, remarking that this was unusual in an Englishman, even one who was well capable of it.[106] But Sloane, of course, was not an Englishman! From the early 1680s onwards he bought dictionaries and grammars of all kinds, as well as translations and standard texts, presumably, at first, with the intention of furthering his own education. His medical studies would have required a good reading knowledge of Latin, and he seems to have known some Greek; it is also probable that he could read German, Dutch and Italian. His large collection of works in Spanish and Portuguese suggests that he was able to read these languages also. However he soon began to collect widely in languages which he could not have intended to study himself, buying such diverse items as the first printed dictionary of the language of the Cree Indians[107] (see Fig. 109), manuscripts in the languages of India,[108] a Tamil grammar in Spanish,[109] and an account in French of the Tartars of China and their language.[110] In

the study of language, as with the other fields in which he collected, Sloane recognized the importance of bringing together as much evidence as possible, and in this sense he may well be regarded as a pioneer in the development of what we now know as linguistics.

As well as books and manuscripts dealing with aspects of the external world Sloane's library also contained more than a sprinkling of theological and philosophical works of his own and earlier times.[111] During the later years of the library he made a small collection of Books of Hours, including one that had belonged to Queen Mary I.[112] Of course no important library of Sloane's time would have lacked some material of this kind. The extent of his collection of astrological, alchemical and magical works was more remarkable. As in the case of the medieval herbals, Sloane's intention in collecting these items was to provide a historical basis for study in his chosen fields, and since no definite division was drawn in the Middle Ages between astrology and medicine, it is not surprising that many of the early manuscripts which Sloane collected have an astrological content. One of the finest of these is a treatise on the signs of the zodiac illuminated in Flanders in the mid fourteenth century (see Plate 37).[113] Alchemy was the forerunner of chemistry and even in Sloane's own time eminent scientists such as Boyle and Newton still acknowledged its influence. Like his medical manuscripts, Sloane's collection of alchemical treatises is a prime source for modern research and contains a wealth of material dating from the late Middle Ages onwards, including writings by George Ripley,[114] Thomas Norton[115] and Ramon Lull,[116] together with some of the stranger outpourings of John Dee.[117] Although Sloane had collected in this field from the earliest days of the library, a high proportion of these items were not obtained until after 1730, suggesting that he made an effort in his later years to make his alchemical holdings as comprehensive as possible.

The foregoing examples demonstrate how Sloane's antiquarian interests were mainly focused on the scientific field. However, it is important to remember that his library also included many items of more general historical and literary interest. Amongst these may be found a fine manuscript copy of the 'Chroniques de France', illustrated in grisaille,[118] a mid-fifteenth-century text of the 'Gesta romanorum',[119] a copy of the 'De duodecim cesaribus' of Suetonius, written and illuminated in northern France or the Netherlands in 1472,[120] and the 'De casibus virorum' of John Lydgate.[121] His collection of Charters included many of local historical interest.[122] Sloane also subscribed to the scholarly historical publications of his time, such as Thomas Hearne's editions of English chronicles[123] and Muratori's great series of Italian chronicles which began to be published in 1723.[124]

This brief survey of the contents of Sloane's library is merely an attempt to give some idea of the fields in which he collected. The examples I have given have been drawn mostly from his manuscripts, partly because of their great intrinsic interest but also because they can be identified more easily than his printed books and maps. The riches of the Sloane collection of manuscripts have certainly been well known to scholars for a long period, even though no adequate catalogue of them has ever been published.[125] However, the fact that his library also contained a sizeable number of incunables has so far received little attention. Sloane began to buy early printed books in the 1680s but this was probably on account of their subject matter rather than because he was interested in the history of printing. As early as 1684 he had bought for one shilling the herbal known as *Aggregator*, printed by Peter Schoeffer in Mainz in 1484,[126] but his copy belonged to a variant state in which the first leaf was blank and therefore without the date. Before 1687 he had acquired at least three more books printed before 1500, the *De epidemia* of Jacobus Soldus printed at Antwerp in 1490,[127] the *Hortus sanitatis* printed at Mainz in 1491[128] and the works of Rhasis printed in Venice in 1497;[129] and the first page of his main catalogue contains an entry for a commentary on Aristotle by Albertus de Saxonia, also printed in Venice in 1497[130] (see Fig. 103).

By the early 1700s Sloane had developed an interest in the history and technique of printing for its own sake. This was probably aroused by his association with Humfrey Wanley and John Bagford. In 1704 Bagford took Sloane to see 'printing and card-making' in Bunhill Fields so that he should have a practical demonstration of the art in a primitive form, and three years later Wanley persuaded Sloane to accept Bagford's 'Essay on the Invention of Printing' for publication in the *Philosophical Transactions*.[131] By

Margin references (left column):
30/MSS A. 2,3,4
30/MS 138
30/MS 2347
30/MS 1561
30/A. 103–128
29/fol. 106v
29/fol. 13v
29/fol. 57r
29/fol. 106r
30/C. 70

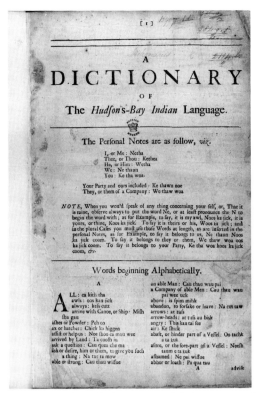

Fig. 109 Title page from the first Cree-English dictionary, early eighteenth-century. BL, C. 122. h. 12. Reproduced by courtesy of the Trustees of the British Library.

this time Sloane had become a serious collector in the field. Having bought the second edition of Caxton's *Canterbury Tales* from Bagford in 1704,[132] he went on to make a collection of early English printing, buying three more Caxtons, the *Confessio Amantis*,[133] the *Pilgrimage of the Soul*,[134] and the *Knight of the Tower*,[135] as well as five books printed by Richard Pynson, including the *Book to learn French*,[136] three by Wynkyn de Worde[137] and the *Kanutus* by William of Machlinia.[138] Sloane's period of greatest activity in buying incunables lasted from about 1706 to 1710, when the pages of his catalogue are peppered with the works of the early Continental printers. He continued occasionally to make such purchases in later years; about 1718, for example, he bought two of the first books to be printed in Delft, a Dutch translation by Jan van Brederode of the 'Somme le roy' (1478)[139] and a Book of Hours of 1480.[140] As well as books Bagford had also supplied Sloane with some volumes of printed fragments and paper specimens. Amongst these was a leaf illuminated in England taken from what is now generally accepted as the first book to have been printed in Europe, the 42-line Bible printed in Mainz by Gutenberg in the mid 1450s.[141] The importance of this fragment could not have been realized in Sloane's own time; nor could the fact that a manuscript of the 'Expositio sancti Ieronimi'

Margin references (right column):
30/H. 185
30/H. 760
30/H. 832
30/N. 1343
30/C. 291
30/C. 292
30/MS 1461

which he bought about 1708 was the exemplar of the first book to have been printed in Oxford.[142] Nevertheless the ability to make such unexpectedly fortunate purchases is surely the mark of the great collector.

I hope that I have been able to give some idea of the importance of Sloane's collection of books and manuscripts, both in his time and in ours. It is a remarkable fact that although Sloane's library is one of the best documented of its period it is also one of the least studied. Indeed, in preparing this chapter I have sometimes felt that I have been attempting a commentary on a book that has not yet been written. Sloane's own catalogues, neglected for so long, are still the chief source of information on the extent of his holdings for though Sloane's library was the main foundation collection of the British Museum Library no attempt has been made, until very recent times, to distinguish the printed books and maps which once belonged to Sloane from later acquisitions. Fortunately many of them still bear the press-marks allocated to them by Sloane and his librarians,[143] but much information has been lost as a result of the breaking up of items which were bound together in Sloane's day and by the division of the library between the various Departments of the British Museum, the Natural History Museum and the British Library, while many items have disappeared completely as the result of the ruthless sale of duplicates, in which even incunables were not spared.[144] It was Sloane's own wish that his collections should be kept together; the establishment of specialized institutions in modern times has made this no longer practicable and there is now no possibility that they will ever again be brought under one roof. In the case of the books and manuscripts, however, it is impossible not to regret that the orderly way in which they were kept by Sloane was not maintained after their entry into the British Museum. Fortunately some attempts are being made to expiate the past; the Kaempfer collection is being reunited gradually, though only on paper; British Library staff are engaged on the task of giving known Sloane books a distinctive binding; and this volume reveals, as never before, the importance of Sloane as a collector. The study of his library is still in its infancy and, in spite of some losses which can never be made good, future research is certain to show more and more the extent of the intellectual achievement accomplished by Sloane in its creation.

Acknowledgements

I should like to express my grateful thanks to Dr L. Hellinga and Mr J. Goldfinch for advice on incunabula, to Professor T.A. Birrell and Mrs A. Walker for information on sale catalogues, to Mr P. Barber for assistance with the maps, and to Mr J.L. Wood for the use of his notes on books with Sloane press-marks.

Notes and References

References to [30] are to BL, Sloane MSS 3972B and 3972C, vols. 1–8 only (Sloane MS 3972D is the index to these and Sloane MS 3972A was not compiled until after Sloane's death). The leaves containing descriptions of manuscripts were removed from the present Sloane MS 3972C, vols. 1–8, in 1758 and now form the greater part of Sloane MS 3972B; the original pagination 1–3944 is still visible, making it possible to reconstruct the catalogue in its original form. [30/MS 1] refers to Sloane's own manuscript number; references to the present BL Sloane manuscript numbers are given in the notes. I have usually given the earliest number or press-mark allocated by Sloane or his librarians, but in the case of the Miniatures I have given subsequent numbers also to aid identification. 'MS' has been added to Wanley's numbering of the manuscripts in roman numerals in order to distinguish them from the maps which were also given roman numbers. BL press-marks for printed books are given only when there is internal evidence for Sloane's ownership of the copy referred to (except in the case of incunables, where the rarity of the items has made the ascertaining of provenance much easier).

The descriptions of the incunables are based on the ISTC (*Incunable Short-Title Catalogue*) data base in the British Library. Bibliographical references are to the *Catalogue of Books Printed in the xvth Century now in the British Museum* (London, 1908–), (hereafter BMC); M.F.A.G. Campbell, *Annales de la typographie néerlandaise au quinzième siècle* (The Hague, 1874–90) (CA); M.E. Kronenberg, *Campbell's Annales de la typographie néerlandaise au quinzième siècle: contributions to a new edition* (The Hague, 1956) (Campbell–Kronenberg); Seymour de Ricci, *A Census of Caxtons* (Oxford, 1909) (De Ricci); E.G. Duff, *Fifteenth Century English Books* (Oxford, 1917) (Duff); *Gesamtkatalog der Wiegendrucke* (Leipzig and Stuttgart, 1925–) (GW); L. Hain, *Repertorium bibliographicum* (Stuttgart, 1826–38) (Hain); W.A. Copinger, *Supplement to Hain's Repertorium bibliographicum* (London, 1895–1902) (Hain–Copinger); and A.W. Pollard and G.R. Redgrave, *A Short-Title Catalogue of Books printed in England, Scotland and Ireland . . . 1475–1640*, 2nd edn. (London, 1976–91) (STC).

1. BL, Sloane MS 3995 (p. 294, no. 29). For an account of how this was identified as Sloane's first catalogue see M.A.E. Nickson, 'Sloane's codes: the solution to a mystery', *Factotum* 7 (1979), pp. 13–18; and M.A.E. Nickson, 'Hans Sloane, book collector and cataloguer, 1682–1698', *British Library Journal* 14 (1988), p. 53.

2. 29/fols. 114ᵛ–85ᵛ.

3. Ray's influence is already apparent; Sloane also had his [29/fol. 104ᵛ] *Observations . . . made in a journey* (London, 1673), [29/fol. 104ᵛ] *Collection of English Proverbs* (Cambridge, 1670), and [29/fol. 103ᵛ] *Catalogus plantarum circa Cantabrigiam nascentium* (Cambridge, 1660).

4. [29/fol. 108ᵛ] Dionys Joncquet, *Hortus regius Parisiensis* (Paris, 1666).

5. [29/fol. 101ᵛ] *Catalogus horti botanici Oxoniensis . . . cura . . . Philippi Stephani . . . et Gulielmi Brounei* (Oxford, 1658).

6. [29/fol. 88ᵛ] Johannes Brosterhusius, *Catalogus plantarum horti medici . . . Bredae* (Breda, 1647).

7. [29/fol. 86ᵛ] *Catalogus plantarum horti academici Lugduni Batavorum* (Leiden, 1658).

8. BL, 783. c. 19. This and the two following books are inscribed 'Montpelier 1683' in Sloane's hand. See J.L. Wood, 'Sir Hans Sloane's books', *Factotum* 2 (1978), p. 17.

9. BL, 549. a. 10.

10. BL, 549. a. 23.

11. BL, Sloane MS 167 or 3919 (the existence of two numbers is due to a mistake in the renumbering undertaken after the manuscripts entered the British Museum).

12. A key to the codes is given in Nickson, op. cit. [Sloane's codes] (note 1), pp. 16–17 and Nickson, op. cit. [Hans Sloane, book collector] (note 1), p. 60.

13. John Calvin, *Institucion de la Religion Christiana* (En casa de Ricardo del Campo [i.e. Richard Field: London], 1597). STC 4426.

14. Perhaps Sloane had received the same advice from Sydenham that the latter is said to have given to another pupil when he was asked to recommend a book from which to study medicine: 'read Don Quixote; it is a very good book – I read it still' (see G.R. de Beer, *Sir Hans Sloane and the British Museum* (London, 1953), p. 25).

15. The letters presumably referred to presses and the numbers to the arrangement of the books on the shelves; by 1693 each press seems to have held about 150 volumes. Unfortunately no plan of the library exists.

16. J.A. van der Linden, *De scriptis medicis libri duo . . . editio altera et emendatior* (Amsterdam, 1651), now BL, 550. a. 35.

17. BL, 878. n. 8. Bound in eight volumes, but there is no Sloane press-mark on any of the fly-leaves.

18. Oxford, 1697. Sloane's MSS 1–188 (and an un-numbered manuscript) were included in part 2, pp. 251–5. The descriptions, with a few alterations in arrangement, are as in BL, Sloane MS 3972C, pp. 86 et seq., showing that Sloane himself supplied the text. Bernard's division of them into 264 articles (8736–8999) was for the pur-

pose of his catalogue only; Sloane's own manuscript numbers were not given.

19. The argumentation for this reconstruction of Sloane's early library methods is given in Nickson, op. cit. [Hans Sloane, book collector] (note 1), pp. 58–63.

20. This comparison is based on the account of Locke's cataloguing of his library given in the introduction to *The Library of John Locke*, ed. John Harrison and Peter Laslett (Oxford Bibliographical Society 13) (Oxford, 1965).

21. See BL, Sloane MS 3972C, pp. CCXIII–CCCLIX and the list headed 'Autores que han escrito en Lenguas de las Indias' inserted at pp. 393–409.

22. George Hickes to Robert Harley, 23 April 1701, quoted in C.E. Wright and R.C. Wright (eds.), *The Diary of Humfrey Wanley, 1715–1726* (London, 1966), p. xiii.

23. BL, C. 36. aa. 4 (formerly BL, Sloane MS 966); a calendar with saints' days, festivals, etc., with (on the verso) the symbols of the months and the name of the printer, G. Brouscon du Conquet [Le Conquet, 1550?]. Vellum, folded as a booklet.

24. BL, Sloane MS 772.

25. Wanley to the Curators of the Bodleian Library, 20 October 1721, printed in P.L. Heyworth (ed.), *Letters of Humfrey Wanley . . . 1672–1726* (Oxford, 1989), p. 433.

26. Wanley still felt aggrieved, more than twenty years later, because the University had not paid him for his trouble. He assessed his services as having been worth £7. 10s. and suggested that this should be used to purchase 'one or more good & useful Book or Books' for the Bodleian. Sloane's gift was acknowledged by Charlett on 8 October 1700 (Heyworth, op. cit. (note 25), p. 433, note 1).

27. W.D. Macray, *Annals of the Bodleian Library* (Oxford, 1890), p. 169, states that between 1700 and 1738 Sloane gave considerably more than 1,400 volumes to the Bodleian 'but the majority of them do not appear to have been considered of much value, and only 415 are specified by name in the Benefaction Register'. Sloane also gave two volumes of manuscript notes by John Bale to the Bodleian in 1710; the first volume, concerning the Carmelite order, is now Bod. Lib. MS 73 and the second has been lost (see F. Madan, *Summary Catalogue of Western Manuscripts in the Bodleian Library* (Oxford, 1905), pp. 314–15).

28. BL, Sloane MS 745.

29. This book was missing or mislaid in Sloane's library at least as early as the mid 1720s, but

its appearance in his catalogue between two items acquired in 1696 suggests that it must have been acquired at the same time (see Nickson. op. cit. [Hans Sloane, book collector] (note 1), p. 79).

30. Now broken up and distributed amongst the departments of the British Library and the British Museum. An attempt to reconstitute it on paper has been made by Gerhard Bonn, 'Der wissenschaftliche Nachlass des Lippischen Forschungsreisenden Engelbert Kaempfer im Britischen Museum', *Lippische Mitteilungen* 48 (1979), pp. 69–116.

31. BL, Sloane MS 3060.

32. Present whereabouts unknown; it was probably sold as a duplicate by the British Museum after the acquisition of other copies from the collections of King George III, C.M. Cracherode and Sir Joseph Banks.

33. He prefixed them MS A (folio), MS B (quarto) and MS C (octavo and smaller); this renumbering was employed not only for new acquisitions but also retrospectively.

34. For example Stack was able to identify [30/ MS 1692] an item described earlier as 'A very Ancient ms (Poetry) upon vellum' as the 'De regimine principis' of Thomas Hoccleve (now BL, Sloane MS 1825).

35. J.S. Finch, 'Sir Hans Sloane's printed books', *The Library* 4th ser. 22 (1942), pp. 67–72.

36. BL, S.C. 354. A facsimile edited by J.S. Finch was published at Leiden in 1987 by the Sir Thomas Browne Institute.

37. Laege-duynen, 1665. BL, 4377. a. 10.

38. 'Fernelii universa medicina cum vita auth. MSS Francof. 1592' (Libri medici in folio, lot 26 at Smith's sale). The life of Fernelius is now BL, Sloane MS 1054, but the printed work can no longer be traced.

39. Sloane also bought at least seventy manuscripts which had belonged to Bernard; these were not included in the sale catalogue of 4 October although they were sold at about the same time.

40. BL, 77. k. 7 formerly Sloane MS 245. Sloane included this and the following item amongst his manuscripts, since both were annotated.

41. BL, 444. f. 1 formerly Sloane MS 214.

42. Sale catalogue: *Librorum ex bibliothecis Philippi Farewell D.D. et Danielis De Foe Gen. Catalogue . . . to be sold . . . the 15th of November, 1731.* BL, C. 57. c. 47, with Sloane's annotations, is the only copy extant (see A. O'Donovan, 'The sale catalogue of Defoe's library', *Book Collector,* 9 (1960), pp. 454–5).

43. *A Divine Tragedie . . . or a collection of sundry memorable examples of Gods judgements upon Sabbath-breakers* [with an introduction by W. Prynne]. STC 4140.7. BL, 873. e. 11.

44. Sale catalogue of 4 March 1733/34, lots 7, 22, 23, 101, 140, 189, 221, 223, 225, 228, 231 and 256, now BL, Sloane MSS 3462, 3443, 3444, 3463, 770, 3464, 3449–3452, 179B and 3466 respectively.

45. Sale catalogue, 21 January 1740. Most of the manuscripts bought by Sloane were alchemical manuscripts which had once belonged to Elias Ashmole.

46. BL, Sloane MSS 4036–4069.

47. BL, Sloane MS 4037 *passim.*

48. Christine Thomas, 'Sir Hans Sloane and the Russian Academy of Sciences', *British Library Journal* 14 (1988), pp. 21–37.

49. Leonhard Euler, *Mechanica sive motus scientia analytice exposita* (Petropoli: Ex Typographia Academiae Scientiarum, 1736), 2 vols. (present BL, 715. i. 9).

50. BL, Harley MS 5998.

51. For an account of Sloane's relationship with Bagford see M.A.E. Nickson, 'Bagford and Sloane', *British Library Journal* 9 (1983), pp. 51–5.

52. BL, IB 55095. Geoffrey Chaucer, *The Canterbury Tales* (Westminster, *c.*1484). Duff 88; De Ricci 23:2. When acquired by Sloane the volume was arranged in the order A1 (the 'Tale of Chaucer') – K8 followed by m2–ii6. The contents were later restored to the correct order, probably before the volume was re-bound some time in the eighteenth century.

53. E.J.L. Scott, *Index to the Sloane Manuscripts in the British Museum* (London, 1904), p. 126.

54. BL, 561* h. 1–29. On the making of these prints see Marianne Grivel, *Le commerce de l'estampe à Paris au xviie siècle* (Paris, 1986), pp. 181–90. Sloane's set was obviously regarded as one of the treasures of the library as it was referred to in Per Kalm's account of his visit in 1748 and also in the account of the visit by the Prince and Princess of Wales in the same year (see Chapter 1, Appendix 3 and 4).

55. I am grateful to Mr. Maurice Packer of the British Library for drawing my attention to these 'Sloane' bindings. The 'beautiful' and 'superb' bindings seen by visitors in 1748 must have been mainly in the eyes of the beholders.

56. The psalter was probably written and illuminated in northern France about 1250 and brought into England soon afterwards as the embroidered panels of the binding, which show the Annunciation and the Crucifixion, can be dated to about 1300 to 1330. In the early fifteenth century it belonged to Anne Felbrigge of the order of Poor Clares at Bruisyard in Suffolk. See Penelope Wallis, 'The embroidered binding of the Felbrigge Psalter', *British Library Journal* 13 (1987), pp. 71–8.

57. BL, Sloane MSS 44–49 (see Nickson, op. cit. [Hans Sloane, book collector] (note 1), p. 89, note 32).

58. BL, Sloane MS 741 or 4014.

59. A similar survey of the manuscripts collected by Sloane up to 1696 (i.e. MSS 1–274) shows a higher proportion (about one half) which may be regarded as medical. This is due largely to the fact that the number of medieval works is also higher than amongst the printed books so that no clear distinction can be made between medicine and botany.

60. By 1725 he had added 3,937 titles to Mercklin's list and many were added later. See Wood, op. cit. (note 8), p. 16.

61. Maarten Ultee, 'Sir Hans Sloane, scientist', *British Library Journal* 14 (1988), p. 15.

62. BL, IA 55478. *Regimen contra pestilentiam* [in an English translation], [London, *c.*1483]. The treatise is attributed to Benedicti Kanuti (Bengt Knutsson), Bishop of Västerås near Stockholm about 1462, but it may have been derived from a work by Johannes Jacobi. Duff 74; STC 4591. Sloane read the first letter of the author's name as R instead of K and his entry for this book is therefore misplaced in *Lindenius renovatus.*

63. P.M. Jones, *Medieval Medical Miniatures* (London, 1984), p. 10.

64. BL, Sloane MS 1977. See R. Herrlinger, *Geschichte der medizinischen Abbildung* (Munich, 1967), p. 44. This manuscript had at one time been owned by the Huguenot physician Theodore Turquet de Mayerne and was presumably brought to England by him.

65. Or, more probably, Zacharias. BL, Sloane MS 981. See Jones, op. cit. (note 63), pp. 48–51.

66. BL, Sloane MS 3983.

67. Linda Ehrsam Voigts, 'The "Sloane group": related scientific and medical manuscripts from the fifteenth century in the Sloane collection', *British Library Journal* 16 (1990), pp. 26–57, has recently discussed relationships between some of Sloane's manuscripts of English provenance.

68. BL, Sloane MS 124, fols. 1–42.

69. Scott, op. cit. (note 53), p. 188.

70. Ibid., p. 118.

71. Ibid., p. 379.

72. Ibid., p. 149.

73. Ibid., pp. 349, 350. According to the *Dictionary of National Biography,* Mayerne's library was bequeathed in 1655 to the Royal College of Physicians where it is thought to have been destroyed in the Great Fire of 1666; however, a number of books and manuscripts which had once belonged to him were acquired by Sloane from the 1690s onwards.

74. BL, Sloane MS 230A; bought by Sloane for 2s. 6d. in 1696. Its importance was signalled by Stack's note added to the catalogue about 1740 'this is the authors foundation & first lecture of ye circulation in his own Handwriting'.

75. He did, however, annotate his own copy [30/R. 2188 later MS C. 695] of the *Catalogus plantarum quæ in insula Jamaica sponte proveniunt* (London, 1696), BL, 968. f. 15.

76. See D.E. Allen, *The Naturalist in Britain* (London, 1976), pp. 10–11. See also Chapter 1.

77. Scott, op. cit. (note 53), pp. 417, 418.

78. Ibid., p. 85.

79. Ibid., p. 147.

80. Ibid., p. 312.

81. Ibid., p. 426.

82. Ibid., p. 35. Mary Somerset, wife of the 1st Duke of Beaufort, was a keen botanist and acquainted with the Sloane circle.

83. BL, Sloane MS 3999. See Natalie Rothstein, 'Joseph Dandridge – naturalist and silk designer', *East London Papers* 9 (1966), pp. 101–18.

84. BL, Additional MS 6054.

85. BL, Sloane MS 2937.

86. BL, Sloane MS 4002.

87. BL, Sloane MS 912.

88. BL, Sloane MSS 7, 120, 135, 297, 962, 1315, 2460, 2948, 3160, 3489.

89. BL, Sloane MS 1975.

90. From Hakluyt's 'Epistle Dedicatory' in the first edition of his *Voyages* (1589).

91. Richard Hakluyt, *Principall navigations, voiages and discoveries of the English nation*, 2nd edn. (London, 1598–1600), in three vols. STC 12626. Sloane's copy was bound as one volume.

92. BL, Sloane MS 3527.

93. BL, Sloane MS 3236.

94. BL, Sloane MS 1447.

95. BL, Sloane MS 42.

96. BL, Sloane MS 858.

97. BL, Sloane MS 3492.

98. BL, Sloane MS 793 or 894.

99. BL, Sloane MS 811.

100. BL, Sloane MS 197.

101. BL, Additional MS 5027A. See Cornelis Koeman, 'Een 17ᵉ eeuwse kartograaf aan het woord', *Kartographisch tijdschrift* 1 no. 4 (1975), pp. 11–19; charts which had presumably been acquired from the same source were also owned by Samuel Pepys (see S. Tyacke, 'Maps', in *Catalogue of the Pepys Library at Magdalene College, Cambridge* (Cambridge, 1989), p. xii). Sloane had obtained [30/XXI–XXXIII] Blaeu's *Atlas Major* as

early as 1698, although it was not added to his catalogue until about the mid 1730s (present BL, Maps C. 4.c.1).

102. BL, Maps C. 6.c.1. For an account of the association between Hooke and Pitt for the purpose of producing the *English Atlas*, and its descent into acrimony, see Leona Rostenberg, 'Moses Pitt, Robert Hooke and the *English Atlas*', *The Map Collector* 12 (1980), pp. 2–8.

103. BL, Maps K. Top. LXXVIII, 31a, b (6 Tab. 4,5). This and the following item were part of the Topographical Collection of George III which was given to the British Museum in 1823.

104. BL, Maps K. Top. CII (4 Tab. 48).

105. These two collections of drawings are now bound together in BL, Additional MS 5234. Although Hofstedt van Essen is said to have provided illustrations for Kaempfer (see Bonn, op. cit. (note 30), p. 99) these drawings were acquired by Sloane long before he bought the Kaempfer collection in the 1720s. Sloane also owned [30/Roll 20] a drawing of Constantinople by the same artist which being '15 foot long 1½ broad' was (according to a note made by Stack in the 1730s) exhibited 'on yᵉ wall in yᵉ passage to the Gallery' (this drawing is now BL, Additional MS 5024).

106. See Chapter 1, Appendix 1.

107. BL, C.122. h. 12. This tract, which is now the unique copy, was obtained by Sloane about 1718. The tract volume in which it was bound in Sloane's time was broken up after 1753 and the Cree dictionary was later bound with another Sloane item [30/G. 361], Thomas Bowrey's *Dictionary English and Malayo . . .* (London, 1701); present BL, 1560/1702. As a result of this chance association the Cree dictionary (which was undated) has been assigned to a date about 1701 (see F.F. Waldron, *Bibliography of Canadiana published in Great Britain, 1519–1763* (Toronto, 1990) p. 183) although its position in Sloane's catalogue shows that a later date is also possible. I am grateful to Mr H.C. Wolfart for drawing this item to my attention.

108. A. Gaur, in *Treasures of the British Museum*, ed. F. Francis (London, 1971), p. 250, mentions six Sanskrit and twenty Tamil manuscripts from the Sloane collection.

109. BL, Sloane MS 3003.

110. BL, Sloane MS 2872.

111. For example he had several copies of works by Saint Bernard of Clairvaux (see Scott, op. cit. (note 53), p. 52), an autograph copy of Edward Herbert's 'De veritate' (BL, Sloane MS 3957) and several collections of sermons (see Scott, op. cit. (note 53), pp. 488–9).

112. BL, Sloane MS 2565.

113. BL, Sloane MS 3983. See F. Saxl and H. Meier, *Verzeichnis astrologischer und mythologischer illustrierter Handschriften des lateinischen Mittelalters* vol. III: *Handschriften in Englischen Bibliotheken* (London, 1953), pt. 1, pp. 247–68.

114. Scott, op. cit. (note 53), pp. 453, 454.

115. Ibid., p. 396.

116. Ibid., pp. 325, 326.

117. Ibid., p. 138.

118. BL, Sloane MS 2433A–C.

119. BL, Sloane MS 4029. This was one of the first manuscripts acquired by Sloane; he bought it in 1693 for 2s. 6d.

120. BL, Sloane MS 2509. See A. Watson, *Catalogue of Dated and Datable Manuscripts c.700–1600 in the Department of Manuscripts, the British Library* (London, 1979), vol. I, pp. 160–1.

121. BL, Sloane MS 4031.

122. BL, Sloane Charters xxxi.1–xxxiv.1 (including some rolls). There is no published catalogue of these charters and rolls but they are indexed topographically in the *Index to the Charters and Rolls in the Department of Manuscripts, British Museum* (London, 1900–12).

123. T.A. Birrell, 'Anthony Wood, John Bagford and Thomas Hearne as bibliographers', *Pioneers in Bibliography* ed. R. Myers and M. Harris (Winchester, 1988), p. 36, points out that Sloane's subscription copies of these texts were still, at the time of writing, on the open shelves of the British Library Reading Room in Bloomsbury.

124. L.A. Muratori, *Rerum Italicarum scriptores*, vols. 1–29 (Milan, 1723–51).

125. BL, Sloane MSS 1–4100 are included in S. Ayscough's unsatisfactory *Catalogue of the manuscripts in the British Museum* (London, 1782) which is arranged in subject order. There is an excellent index by E.J.L. Scott (see above, note 53) but this does not include the Sloane charters nor the drawings and maps which were omitted from the first Museum numeration of the Sloane manuscripts. Most of the latter were afterwards included in the collections as Additional MSS 5018–5027 and 5214–5308 and were indexed, though poorly, in the *Index to the Additional Manuscripts . . . 1783–1835* (London, 1849).

126. BL, IA 289. *Herbarius latinus* (with German synonyms) (Mainz, Peter Schoeffer, [14]84). Hain 8443?; BMC, I, 39. Sloane described his copy as 'Aggregator practicus de Simplicibus'. See W.L. Schreiber, *Die Kräuterbücher des xv und xvi Jahrhunderts* (Munich, 1924), pp. iv–ix.

127. BL, IA 49826. Jacobus Soldus, *Opus de peste* ([Antwerp, Gerard Leeu], 1490). Campbell–Kronenberg I, 1566b; BMC IX, p. 195. Sloane's copy was part of a tract volume, now broken up.

128. *Hortus Sanitatis* (Mainz, Jacob Meydenbach, 23 June 1491). Hain–Copinger 8944*. Sloane paid 2s. 6d. for his copy, the present whereabouts of which are unknown (a copy obtained by him at a much later date is now BL, IB 344).

129. BL, IB 22966. Mohammed Rhasis, *Liber ad Almansorem sive tractatus medicinae I–x* ([Venice], Bonetus Locatellus, Bergomensis, for Octavianus Scotus, 7 October 1497). Hain–Copinger 13893*; BMC V, p. 448.

130. BL, IB 24591. Albertus de Saxonia, *Quaestiones in Aristotelis libros de caelo et mundo*, ed. Hieronymus Surianus (Venice, Otinus de Luna, Papiensis, 9 June 1497). GW 797; BMC V, p. 569.

131. See Nickson, op. cit. (note 51), p. 5.

132. See above, note 52.

133. BL, G. 11627. John Gower, *Confessio Amantis* (Westminster, 2 September 1483) [the printed date in the colophon '1493' must be erroneous]. Duff 166; De Ricci 48:9. After the acquisition of C.M. Cracherode's copy in 1799 this copy was sold as a duplicate (sale catalogue, February 1805, no. 429). It was later bought by Thomas Grenville whose collections were bequeathed to the British Museum in 1847.

134. BL, IB 55069. Guillaume de Digueville, *The pylgremage of the sowle*, translated and emended by John Lydgate (Westminster, 6 June 1483). Duff 267; De Ricci 73:1. According to a note by William Herbert in BL Additional MS 18202K, this book belonged in 1704 to Ralph Thoresby. It was acquired by Sloane about 1712.

135. BL, IB 55085. Geoffroy de La Tour-Landry, *The knight of the tower*, translated by William Caxton (Westminster, 31 January 1484). Duff 241; De Ricci 63:2. Sloane also had [30/MS CIV] a manuscript containing copies made in 1484 of Caxton's 1474 edition of the *Game of the Chesse* and his 1479 edition of the *Cordiale*, but without any attribution to Caxton (present BL, Sloane MS 779). S. de Ricci, *A Census of Caxtons* (Oxford, 1909), p. 185, listed five Caxtons as having belonged to Sloane but he was wrong in including amongst them Cicero's *Of old age* (31:5), *Parys and Vyenne* (83:1), and the *Royal Book* (89:11); he did not identify the *Canterbury Tales* (23:2) or the *Confessio Amantis* (48:9) as Sloane copies.

136. BL, IA 55535. *A little treatise for to learn English and French.* [London, c.1495]. Duff 406; STC 24867. The others are (a) [30/N. 526] BL, 55543. *Libellulus secundarum intentionum.* [London, c.1498]. Duff 252; STC 15572; (b) [30/l.775; l.910]. BL, IA 55518; IA 55531. *Manipulus curatorum.* [London, c.1498]. Duff 167; STC 12471; (c) [30/B.282]. IB 55492. Henry Parker, *Dives and Pauper* (London, 5 July 1493). Duff 339; STC 19212.

137. (a) [30/N.526] BL, IA 55214; IA 55226. Johannes de Garlandia, *Equivoca* (Westminster, 19 April 1499). Duff 157; STC 11602; bound with *Synonyma* (Westminster, 12 March 1500). Duff 162; STC 11610; (b) [30/A.660] BL, IB 55197. Henry Parker, *Dives and Pauper* (Westminster, 3 December 1496). Duff 340; STC 19213.

138. See above, note 62.

139. BL, IA 47104. Laurentius Frater, *Somme des vices et vertus* (Dutch) *Summe le roy of des conincs summe* (translated in part by Jan van Brederode) (Delft, Jacob Jacobszoon van der Meer and Mauricius Yemantszoen, April 1478). CA 832; BMC IX, p. 17.

140. BL, IA 47112. *Getijdenboek* (Delft [Jacob Jacobszoon van der Meer], 8 April 1480). CA 1627; BMC IX, p. 16. In Sloane's catalogue this item is described, rather quaintly, as 'Pope John's Liturgie'.

141. BL, IC 56a, leaf [DD] 7ᵛ. GW 4201. The style of the illumination shows that the Bible of which it once formed part must have been imported into England very soon after it was printed. See Eberhard König, 'A leaf from a Gutenberg Bible illuminated in England', *British Library Journal* 9 (1983), pp. 32–50.

142. BL, Sloane MS 1579. See A.C. de la Mare and L. Hellinga, 'The first book printed in Oxford: the *Expositio Symboli* of Rufinus', *Transactions of the Cambridge Bibliographical Society* 7 (1978), pp. 184–244.

143. A small number of books and manuscripts bear Sloane's signature; an example may be found in B. Molino's plans of Venetian forts (see above, note 103). Sloane did not use a bookplate, although the armorial bookplate of his grand-nephew, 'Hans Sloane Esq!' (later Stanley) is sometimes assigned to him erroneously.

144. See above, note 133, for the sale of Caxton's *Confessio Amantis* after the acquisition of the Cracherode copy. Many Sloane copies were duplicated when Sir Joseph Banks's collection of books relating to natural history was transferred to the British Museum in 1827. As Banks's library has been preserved virtually intact (see H.B. Carter, *Sir Joseph Banks (1743–1820), a guide to biographical and bibliographical sources* (Winchester, 1987), pp. 226–8) it seems reasonable to suppose that its acquisition by the Museum was the occasion for the disposal of numerous Sloane items which can no longer be traced in the British Library.

18 Japanese Books and Manuscripts
Sloane's Japanese Library and the making of the *History of Japan*

Yu-Ying Brown

As is well known, Sir Hans Sloane was very much the founding father of the British Museum. What is less well known is that his imagination, catholic tastes and generosity also played a crucial role in making the then closed island empire of Japan better understood in the West. He did this by single-mindedly pursuing, over two years in 1723–5, the acquisition of the personal papers and collections of Engelbert Kaempfer (1651–1716), the German physician and traveller who had spent two years (1690–92) in Nagasaki as medical officer to the Dutch East India Company (VOC). The great collector then went further and had Kaempfer's unpublished German manuscript, entitled *Heutiges Japan* or 'Japan Today',[1] translated into English by his Swiss-born amanuensis Johann Caspar Scheuchzer (1702–29). This was published in London in 1727 as the *History of Japan* (Fig. 110). The *History*, with its vivid descriptions of the general conditions of the country and everyday life, and with its scientific detail and objective approach, represented a fundamental departure from the ethnocentric and often evangelizing writings by the Jesuit fathers who had been so active in Japan before their summary expulsion in 1639 by the Tokugawa shogunate.

This first English edition, in two handsome volumes (encompassing five books or parts in forty-nine chapters), was an instant best-seller. It was simultaneously translated into French and Dutch in 1729 and was to become the basis for a German edition also, although this did not appear until fifty years later in 1777–9.[2] Kaempfer's image of Japan was to shape the European view across two centuries, notably through its influence on such intellectuals as Montesquieu, Voltaire, Swift, Kant and Goethe, as well as on such latter-day VOC employees and Japanologistis as Thunberg, Titsingh and Philipp Franz von Siebold.

Kaempfer and the British Library
The British Library, having inherited the foundation collections of the British Museum on its own establishment in 1973, is the exclusive repository of all the written materials relating to the making of the *History of Japan*. They comprise Kaempfer's Japanese books, documents, maps, and genre paintings, together with his own manuscripts and drawings, plus those of his translator Scheuchzer. The latter affords an interesting demonstration of how a masterpiece may be transformed from manuscript to printed version in another language.

Yet Kaempfer's Japanese library was a small part of a larger collection which included artefacts and natural specimens that he managed to smuggle out of Japan on his departure from Nagasaki in October 1692. Unfortunately, most of the objects and specimens have been lost or have perished over the years; and those that remain today in the departments of Ethnography (alias Museum of Mankind) and of Japanese Antiquities in the British Museum as well as in the Natural History Museum, no longer reflect the original scope.[3] Their fate stands in marked contrast to the materials preserved almost intact in the British Library.

Indeed, it was the library as such that provided the chief resource base for the *History of Japan*. Furthermore, it was, to all intents and purposes, the first systematically assembled Japanese literature ever seen in Europe. Moreover, it is within this assemblage of written material that hitherto unknown archival documents have now been discovered which shed new light on Kaempfer's time there. The discoveries were made during the preparation for an exhibition in 1990 organized by the Deutsches Institut für Japanstudien in Tokyo to celebrate the 300th anniversary of Kaempfer's arrival.[4] That exhibition provided a unique forum in which Kaempfer's life and work were comprehensively appraised for the first time. It also confirmed the position of the British Library as the veritable 'Mecca' for Kaempfer studies. It was perhaps appropriate that the core of the Kaempfer collection should have been displayed in its adopted home in London to mark the Japan Festival 1991,[5] and to afford many visitors a rare glimpse into old Japan as this pioneering interpreter had perceived it.

Kaempfer before the *History of Japan*
Kaempfer was among the most learned of the VOC employees and was one of the most extensive travellers of his day. Son of a local clergyman, he set out from his native Lemgo in Westphalia in 1680. By the age of twenty-nine he had studied a variety of subjects including philosophy, history, ancient and modern languages, music, politics, the natural sciences, and finally medicine, at various schools and universities within the German-speaking countries and elsewhere.

By the time he reached Nagasaki via Siam in September 1690 to take up his post at the Dutch factory on Deshima, he had already several years of oriental travel behind him. He had left Stockholm in 1683 as Secretary to the Swedish mission to the Persian Court. The journey via Russia was perilous but included such unexpected highlights as an interview with the eleven-year-old boy later to be known as Peter the Great. Not wishing to return to a war-torn Germany when the mission was over, he entered the service

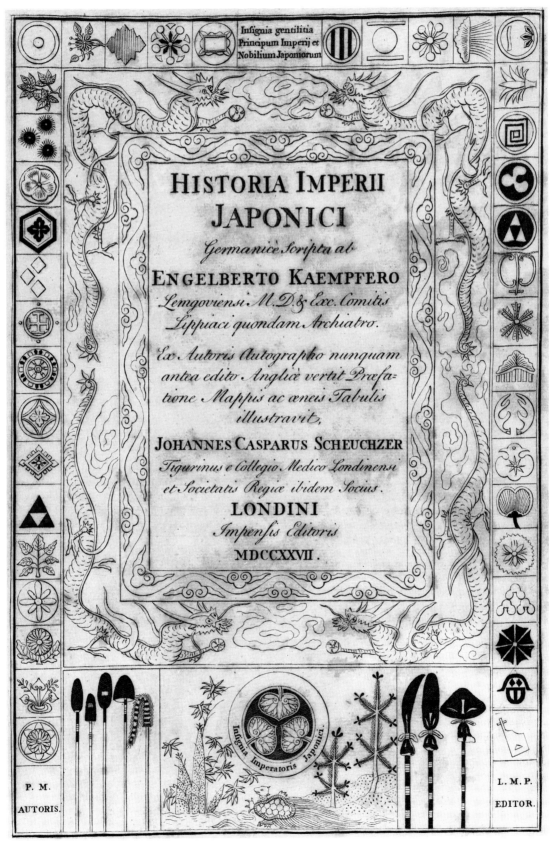

Fig. 110 Frontispiece from the *History of Japan* (London, 1727), designed by J.C. Scheuchzer, Sloane's librarian and translator of Kaempfer's *Heutiges Japan*. BL, 150.K.9. Reproduced by courtesy of the Trustees of the British Library.

of the VOC, spending two years (1686–8) in Bandar Abbās waiting for a voyage eastwards. Eventually he set sail, via Malabar, Ceylon, and Sumatra to Batavia (now Jakarta), the headquarters for the VOC's East Asia operations. From there he joined the company's annual voyage to Japan.

During these years, he collected material and studied everything that caught his interest. His medical, historical and social observations of Persia and other countries (including some sample chapters on such Japanese subjects as paper-making, acupuncture and tea culture) were incorporated in the 900-page miscellany written in Latin and entitled *Amoenitatum Exoticarum*, or 'Exotic Titbits' (Lemgo, 1712). This, the only major book published under his name during his lifetime, was meant, as its title implies, as no more than a light-hearted sample of several substantial works, including *Heutiges Japan*, which he announced in the Introduction as being ready for the press. Alas, after his return to Europe, the endless round of attendance as physician to the prince of Lippe and a subsequent diastrous marriage left him little leisure or money to pursue his research. And when he finally completed *Heutiges Japan*, he was unable to find a publisher. It would seem that Kaempfer's accounts of Japan from a comparative perspective put him rather ahead of his time. The investment needed to touch up and engrave on copper his numerous sketches had further deterred all prospective publishers. Thankfully, however, *Amoenitatum* caught the attention of Sloane who, having been impressed by its scholarship, set about purchasing Kaempfer's unpublished manuscripts and collections (see Chapter 1). These purchases were made from Kaempfer's nephew and heir in Lemgo for some £140.[6]

Kaempfer and 'Sakoku' Japan

Of all the places that Kaempfer visited, it was Japan, a country still largely unknown in the West, that attracted his greatest curiosity. It was in the Genroku era (1688–1704), half a century after the regime had withdrawn almost all contact with the outside world in response to an uprising by native Christian converts in 1637–8. Under the so called 'National Seclusion Policy' which was to last until the end of the Edo period in 1868, the only foreigners allowed to continue doing business in Japan were a handful of the VOC representatives together with a few Chinese merchants. Both communities lived almost like prisoners on their respective settlements; the Dutch were confined on Deshima, a fan-shaped islet 236 paces long by 82 wide, built on a piece of reclaimed land in Nagasaki Harbour. Practically the only time that they were able to get out of there and see something of Honshu and its people was on the annual tribute mission led by the factory chief to the shogun's court at Edo (present-day Tokyo)[7] (Plate 38).

Kaempfer used the two return trips (each of three months in duration) in which he participated to record in minute detail the scenes and people he encountered on the road, the castle at Edo, and the audiences with shogun Tokugawa

Tsunayoshi.[8] His meticulous accounts, which form the second half (Book v) of his *History of Japan*, remain the most widely quoted Western sources about these Dutch journeys through the Inland Sea and along the famed eastern coastal highway, Tōkaidō. For the social historian of today, they provide an unrivalled store of material for research into Genroku Japan.

The Genroku era is known as the 'Spring-time' of the Edo period (1600–1868), a time during which the country enjoyed unprecedented peace and prosperity brought about by rigid central control from the shogunate. It entered upon a phase of rapid development in the course of which most of the traditional arts and culture as we know them today evolved and diversified. When Kaempfer arrived in Japan he was to discover a society that astonished him: 'The citizens exceed all others in manners, the arts, virtue, and all kinds of polite behaviour, and they prosper as regards internal trade, fertility of soil, good health, inner strength, the necessities of life, and the peace of their land'. No doubt it was the contrast between a peaceful and civilized Japan and a war-ravaged, fragmented, depressed and witch-hunting Germany that led him further to conclude that 'Their country was never in a happier condition than it now is, governed by an arbitrary [secular] Monarch, shut up and kept from all commerce and communication with foreign nations'.

This favourable evaluation of the Shogunate's seclusion policy was first published in *Amoenitatum* but later translated by Scheuchzer into English and appended to the *History of Japan*. Copies of its Dutch edition eventually found their way to Japan, where Kaempfer's surprisingly positive endorsement of the national seclusion policy soon attracted attention. Shizuki Tadao, a scholar of Dutch learning translated it into Japanese as the *Sakoku-ron* (1801) or 'The theory of *sakoku*'. *Sakoku* was the literal translation of Kaempfer's description of 'the country that shut itself up'. His *Sakoku-ron* was to spark off an intense debate among intellectuals and officials about the desirability of this policy's continuation, a debate that was to climax in the 1850s when the armed fleet of America's Commodore Perry burst open Japan's closed door after more than two hundred years.

Today the majority of Japanese, who may or may not have heard of Kaempfer himself, would be familiar with the word *sakoku* which this first interpreter of Japan had coined. Indeed, it has entered the national vocabulary to signify that most singular phase in Japan's historical development. Thus the *Sakoku jidai* (the Sakoku period) became a synonym for the Edo period.

The Mystery of Kaempfer's Japanese Assistant

The Genroku era was a time when Japan's *sakoku* policy was being enforced more than ever. It had become virtually

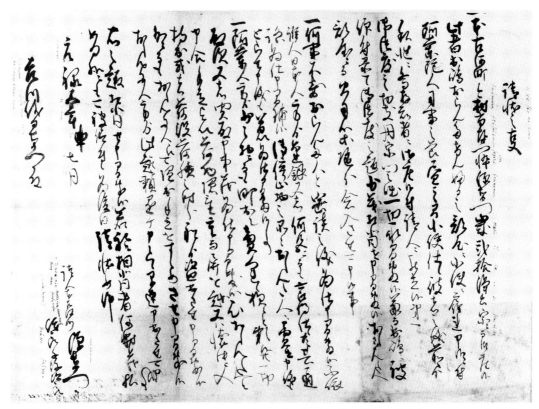

Fig. 111 *Ukejō no koto*. A newly found employment document revealing the identity of Kaempfer's Japanese servant, 1692. BL, OIOC, Or.14480/2. Reproduced by courtesy of the Trustees of the British Library.

impossible for the Dutch expatriates to find out anything about the country. That small circle of Japanese who were assigned to attend to their affairs in Deshima, chiefly the licensed interpreters, were all bound by a solemn oath not to discourse with them, and were, according to Kaempfer, 'tied down to watch and betray one another'. No Japanese who had any regard or friendship for the Dutch was looked upon as an honest man. How then did Kaempfer manage to gather the remarkable body of information and material contained in his *History of Japan*?

As if anticipating this question, Kaempfer explains in some detail in his Preface. He records how he won the confidence and friendship of his interpreters and security officers by teaching them western medicine and science (notably astronomy and mathematics) and by treating them when sick; and also, one should add, by plying them 'with cordial and plentiful supply of European liquors'.

But the information gleaned by such means would not have been sufficient for his intended history of the country. On his arrival in Deshima, however, Kaempfer had the good fortune to be assigned a studious young man of twenty-four to be his servant and also to learn Western medicine under his guidance. He clearly recognized the potential of this student by employing him as an auxiliary when called in to treat 'a distemper' of the chief officer of Deshima, the

result being that the young man was permitted to remain with him throughout his two-year stay, even accompanying him on both trips to Edo.

Realizing that without a competent knowledge of the Dutch language this youth could never achieve his aims, Kaempfer immediately started to teach him Dutch. He did so with such success that 'in a year's time he could write and read it better than any of our interpreters'. In addition, he paid this so-called servant the highest yearly salary he could afford. Kaempfer goes on to acknowledge most explicitly how vital a service the young man had rendered; lest his life should be endangered, his name was kept strictly secret.

In return, I employed him to procure me as ample accounts as possible of the then state and condition of the country, its Government, the Imperial Court, the Religions established in the Empire, the History of former ages, and remarkable daily Occurrences. There was not a Book I desired to see, on these and other subjects, which he did not bring to me, and explain to me out of it, whatever I wanted to know.

Ever since the *History* began to be studied in depth by Japanese historians in the 1920s, attempts have been made unsuccessfully to establish the identity of this discreet young man by whom Kaempfer had been so richly supplied with information concerning the affairs of Japan. In 1966,

Professor Numarta Jirō made a prophetic remark suggesting that if Kaempfer's papers and collections in the British Museum were searched thoroughly, the key to the mystery might be found.[9]

Such proved to be the case in the course of preparations for the tercentenary exhibition. The vital clue lay in a document entitled *Ukejō no koto*, an employment reference guaranteeing the good and law-abiding conduct of a Japanese servant assigned to Kaempfer's room[10] (Fig. 111). It was discovered among some stray Japanese documents hitherto uncatalogued but showing every sign of having belonged to Kaempfer. The servant in question was named therein as Imamura Gen'emon, son of a middle-ranked interpreter Imamura Ichizaemon of Motofurukawa Street; and the document had been submitted to Yoshikawa Gibuemon, the same *otona* or chief officer of Deshima whose illness had been treated in part by this young man, as described above.[11]

The significance of the revelation thus of the long-sought identity of Kaempfer's assistant has been underlined by the fact that he is not an historical nonentity.[12] In fact, Imamura Gen'emon was to become a notable figure in Japan-Dutch relations, being known formally as Imamura Ichibei or Eisei (1671–1736). After Kaempfer left Japan for Europe in 1692, Imamura passed the Dutch language examination with flying colours and then rose rapidly within the ranks of official interpreters. By 1707, he was promoted to the top of the profession as *ōtsūji*, the chief interpreter. His biography will now need to be rewritten in the light of this discovery made in the British Library.[13]

Incidentally, Kaempfer's critics, mainly Dutch, have queried whether he could possibly have gathered all the information contained in the *History* from a servant (whom moreover he had to teach Dutch) in the short space of two years.[14] One accusation that has been made, ever since the mid-eighteenth century, is that Kaempfer had plagiarized the notes given to him by his superior Johannes Camphuijs (1635–1695), three times the head of the Deshima factory and chief of the voc headquarters in Batavia where the two men had met prior to Kaempfer's voyage to Japan. However, the overwhelming evidence, as preserved in the British Library, should overturn any such suggestion once and for all.

Contents and Characteristics of the Kaempfer Collection

Judging from the collection of books, maps, paintings and other items now in the British Library, the student served his teacher with the greatest devotion, preparing to accept the grave consequences of breaking the laws specified in *Ukejō no koto*. How he managed to smuggle material to Kaempfer while in Deshima and presumably during the two return trips to Edo as well, yet without ever being caught, is another intriguing question. At all events, the numerous annotations that Kaempfer wrote in his collection of books and maps are further testimony to the young man's painstaking explanations and translations.

With characteristic thoroughness, Kaempfer has recorded how he himself managed to smuggle out the Japanese source material thus obtained, overcoming immense difficulties while doing so. On the last page of his diary he describes his departure from Japan: 'On the 30th [of October 1692] I went on board the other ships, to fetch away my [Japanese] printed books and manuscripts, which had been privately carried thither among other goods'. The fact that he makes no mention here of the artefacts and specimens of flora and fauna which we know from Sloane's inventory lists to be quite large may be an indication of how much more important Kaempfer regarded his Japanese library.

It has been estimated that over 200 insects, birds, fish and shell specimens plus some seventy 'curiosities' as Sloane called them along with over 400 herbarium specimens came from Kaempfer.[15] Today, only a fraction of these have survived. Still the dozen or so artefacts (such as a pair of women's slippers,[16] a roll of Japanese hand-made paper[17] and so on) hold a great deal of fascination for the Japanese themselves; there is nothing of that kind in Japan with such impeccable provenance and in such pristine condition, these two attributes being the hallmark of Kaempfer's materials, be they books or objects.

What can be said about Kaempfer's Japanese library, in addition, is that although it is small in size it has come down to us almost intact. This is despite the fact that, when Sloane acquired the whole of Kaempfer's collection, it may not have seemed to him the most important part of it. It was his librarian Scheuchzer, to whom he entrusted the daunting task of translating Kaempfer's *Heutiges Japan*, who first recognized its significance as Kaempfer's key data base on Japan.

Son of Sloane's close friend Johann Jakob Scheuchzer of Zürich, a leading figure in the early Swiss Enlightenment, the young Scheuchzer brought to bear his scientific training as a medical doctor and thus made the *History of Japan* one of the best-documented books ever published. The list of Japanese books included in the Introduction to the *History*, was punctiliously compiled from the transliterated titles he found in Kaempfer's manuscripts and annotations on the books themselves. It must be regarded as the first Japanese 'catalogue' of any materials to have appeared in print in the West. Although, as might be expected, it is incomplete and grossly inaccurate, it was eventually to provide an invaluable guideline from which to reconstruct and bring together Kaempfer's Japanese library which, until the late 1950s when the British Museum appointed its first specialist curator in Japanese, had been scattered in various locations.

Incidentally, the presence of these Japanese books in the British Museum during the eighteenth century must have been something of an embarrassment to the cataloguers of the time, for none could read or make any sense of them.

Such was the crisis that, on two particular days, 17 December 1770 and 4 January 1771, a visiting Chinese portrait modeller from Canton, by the name of Chetqua (died 1796), was invited to 'examine' them. His exotic appearance seems to have made him a celebrity among the artistic and aristocratic circles in London.[18] However, the unfamiliar *kana* writing and the sprawling cursive script in which so many Japanese books of the Edo period were written or printed proved altogether too much for Mr Chetqua, so he proceeded to fabricate where he could not make an intelligent guess. Yet credulous Museum staff copied it all down on the inside covers of the books with complete trust. Chetqua's descriptions of Kaempfer's books may seem highly imaginative and amusing today, but they reveal all too well how limited knowledge about Japan was then in the world at large. Besides which, they often provide the only distinguishing mark with which to separate Kaempfer's books from the rest of the Japanese collection.[19]

What can now safely be said is that all the books and manuscripts which could have belonged to Kaempfer have been found and brought together as a distinct unit in the Japanese collection of the department of Oriental and India Office Collections (OIOC).[20] It comprises thirty-two individual works in fifty-four volumes, plus ten maps and seven recently discovered archival documents.[21]

There is, in addition, a group of 'non-book' materials preserved in a large album in the department of Western Manuscripts. This has also recently come to light and the paintings therein can be regarded as part of Kaempfer's 'Japanese library', in that they have a direct bearing on the making of the *History of Japan*. But let us first look at the contents and characteristics of the library proper.

The discovery of the last group of the library collection, namely the seven archival documents, is perhaps the most significant. Apart from the key document which reveals the identity of Kaempfer's assistant as described above, it also includes at least two other important pieces. One is a Deshima pass which could have belonged to Imamura and is, perhaps, the oldest example of its kind to have survived.[22] The other, entitled *Gojōmoku* ('Strict shogunal commands'), is a long-lost historical text regulating the conduct of the Dutch traders in five articles.[23] Article two reads 'Report at once any Portuguese missionary activities'. These two documents, together with *Ukejō no koto*, were in fact translated by Kaempfer with incredible accuracy in *Heutiges Japan*. They were to be rendered into English with modifications by Scheuchzer for Book IV, Chapter X of the *History* which deals with 'Proclamations, Passports, Orders, etc'. Not knowing of the existence of the original Japanese archives with which Kaempfer's own translations can be compared, certain Kaempfer scholars have understandably raised questions as to the authenticity of this so called 'missing chapter'.[24] It may be of interest, too, that Chetqua examining *Gojōmoku* in 1771 called it 'a letter from the Emperor of China to the Emperor of Russia'.

Before Kaempfer's time, there were indeed visiting European missionaries and merchants who had collected Japanese printed books as samples or 'curios', but none, it would seem, had collected them systematically and for the purpose of writing a book. In this very distinctive sense, Kaempfer's Japanese library, though exceedingly small by modern standards, can be said to be one of the oldest for area studies, and certainly the oldest for the study of Japan itself. It can be classified under nine subject headings: travel guides known as *dōchū-ki* (or itinerary records); geographical and route maps; primers of Japanese *iroha* syllabary and Chinese characters; calendars and almanacs; illustrated encyclopaedias; laws and directories of the samurai; historical chronologies; novels, poetry and war tales; and *noh* drama and *jōruri* puppet plays.

It should be noted that all of them were quite ordinary books intended as basic texts for popular education and recreation, and written entirely in Japanese as opposed to the more erudite *kanbun* or Sino-Japanese script. They were quite representative of the kind of literature available in Japan during the Genroku era. In fact, their publication dates can be narrowed down to within the last twenty years prior to Kaempfer's departure in 1692. Amongst the newest was a calendar dated Genroku 5th year or 1692.

Conversely, Buddhist incunabulas or early editions of Chinese classics and Japanese works of literary merit, so treasured by modern antiquarian bibliographers, are conspicuously absent. Because of the language barrier, such works would not have been easy for him to digest. Nor would they provide the sort of factual and up-to-date information about Japan in which Kaempfer was primarily interested.

The few *noh* and *jōruri* puppet plays in the collection (which have much excited historians of Japanese drama)[25] seem to have made little impact on him. This would suggest that they were acquired as gifts rather than through conscious selection. The emphasis on facts rather than fiction can further be seen in the way Kaempfer uses the few literary works that are to be found among his collection. Take, for instance, *Shimabaraki* ('The Battle of Shimabara'), a quasi-fictional account of the Shimabara uprising (1637–8) against the Shogunate by 37,000 Christian converts in western Kyūshū. This was a subject of great interest to the Dutch expatriates, for it was this disturbance that finally persuaded the Shogunate to stamp out Christian influence by ushering in the seclusion policy. Quite understandably, Kaempfer studied this work intensively, not as a novel but as pure history. As much can be seen from his eight-page translation of the text in his notebook.[26] Yet, the copy is beautifully clean without any annotations in his own hand, such as often found in his other books. This may indicate that his student Imamura was regularly at hand, perhaps during the night, to translate the text for him.

Another marked characteristic of Kaempfer's Japanese books is their small, pocket-size format. Works such as *Dai*

Nihon ōdaiki,[27] 'The great imperial chronology of Japan'; *Nanatsu iroha*,[28] the primer on *iroha* syllabary; and *Ke'nai chōhōki*,[29] 'A household treasury' (which contains useful hints for every household, from divination to cookery) are all in portable format. Incidentally, the last named was referred to by Chetqua thus: 'this book is difficult for Chetqua to comprehend, but says it relates to something we have not in Europe'.

One of the phenomena that Kaempfer was to encounter during his two tribute missions was 'the great number of people who daily travel on the roads'. Indeed the highways were always crowded 'like the streets of Europe's most populous cities'. He further observed that the travellers 'always carry about them printed road-books in which were set down at what price, the best victuals are to be got'. The road-books in question are called *dōchū-ki* (itinerary records) and are well represented in the Kaempfer collection.[30] About them he further notes: 'they were sold by numbers of poor children begging along the road. The Dutch are not permitted, at least publicly, to buy any of these road books'. These little books, which had been published in huge numbers since the mid-seventeenth century to meet the demand of the ever-growing number of travellers on business (or more commonly on pleasure under the pretext of pilgrimage) are, due to their flimsiness and ephemeral utility, extremely rare today. Often, the Kaempfer copies are unique and therefore indispensable to studies of this cult of travel of the Japanese at their most formative era.

Forbidden Maps

Despite the fact that maps of any description were at the very top of the official prohibition list, Kaempfer managed to acquire and smuggle out as many as ten: four whole maps of Japan, one each for the main cities of Osaka, Kyoto and Nagasaki (Fig. 112); and two very rare maps for the seat of the shogunate, the city of Edo itself. It is interesting to note how Kaempfer lamented the difficulties he encountered, particularly in obtaining information on Edo: 'Edo has so many streets, ditches and canals that I could not easily make a plan of it. Nor could I gather anything to my satisfaction out of the plans of the Japanese themselves . . .' Yet it was his description of the intricate and baffling layout of Edo Castle that astonished one Nagasaki interpreter who read the Dutch edition of the *History of Japan*. In his book *Tōmon Jissaku* (1804), Aoki Okikatsu (1702–1812) remarked how 'terrible' he found it that a European had acquired such precise information on the inner structure of Edo Castle. There is no doubt that Imamura was instrumental in Kaempfer's amazingly fruitful collection of maps. The fact that he would thereby have put his own life in extreme danger is some measure of the respect and devotion he felt for his foreign teacher.

Other important maps in the history of cartography are a pictorial map in two rolls showing the entire land and

sea routes from Edo to Nagasaki; and the *Nagasaki ezu*,[31] an early map of Nagasaki; as well as the *Shinsen dai Nihon zukan*,[32] one of the earliest maps of Japan to show Ezogashima (today's Hokkaido). The latter was the map on which Kaempfer modelled his own manuscript map of Japan[33] (Plate 39). Alas, Kaempfer's Matsumai (today's capital city of Hokkaido, Sapporo), correctly drawn as being within Ezogashima, was not taken up by Scheuchzer when he redrew the map of Japan for copper engraving as Tab. VIII in the *History of Japan*; instead the translator based his own version on two other native maps in the Kaempfer collection, which show Matsumai as a separate island. Even so, Scheuchzer's elaborate and beautifully embellished map of Japan with exotic *kanji* place-names added, was to exercise an enormous influence on later generations of European cartography, including Matthäus Seutter.[34]

Kaempfer's Album of Mixed Non-Book Material

Within the covers of a large and weighty album,[35] bound in western style and preserved in the Western Manuscripts collections of the British Library already referred to, are to be found a curiously mixed assortment of items of Japanese and Chinese origin. The first and most important group is a series of fifty Japanese paintings, each measuring about 22 by 32 centimetres. Belonging to a genre of painting known as *meisho-e* (pictures of famous places), they depict celebrated views of Japan, chiefly in Kyoto, enlivened by vignettes of people engaged in a variety of activities, mostly pleasure outings or pilgrimages to shrines, temples and other historic sites. They were executed in brilliant colours on a gold leaf background by an anonymous artist working in the stylized Tosa-Sumiyoshi tradition (Plate 40).

A second group comprises seven Japanese figure drawings in colour, together with three padded appliqué pictures, now identified as *oshie*, or pressed pictures. A third seems to have originated in China rather than Japan: it consists of twenty-six pictures of silk flowers and embroidered human figures. Like the artefacts preserved in the British Museum, the *oshi* and the Chinese *objets d'art*, fascinating in their own right, deserve separate study within the field of Far Eastern folk-art. *Oshie*, for example was a popular handicraft among women during the Edo period. The craft itself has survived to this day in the form of a decorative piece affixed to a *hagoita* or shuttlecock for use in a New Year game for girls. But seventeenth-century examples such as in the Kaempfer collection, must be extremely rare, if not unique. At all events, the earliest in the newly established Hagoita Museum in Tokyo dates from the nineteenth century.

The fifty *meisho-e* paintings, on the other hand, are of great importance for historians of Japanese art and culture as well as for specialists in Kaempfer studies. They are now recognized as the forerunners of the *ukiyo-e* or floating-world art which, with its vivid portrayals of contemporary

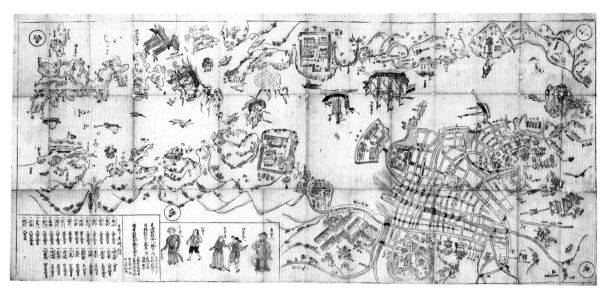

Fig. 112 Map of Nagasaki, with the fan-shaped Deshima island in the centre of the harbour with a Dutch ship nearby, *c*.1680. BL, OIOC, Or.75.g.25. Reproduced by courtesy of the Trustees of the British Library.

scenes, has become so well-known and admired in the West. No less significantly, they were the major pictorial source for Kaempfer and then for his translator Scheuchzer as they illustrate the manuscript and printed versions respectively of the *History of Japan*. They have, therefore, a major role to play in ascertaining the extent of the discrepancy between Kaempfer's original and Scheuchzer's adaptation.[36] Why then have they been overlooked for so long until their rediscovery of late?

Part of the explanation may simply be that they have been overshadowed by the world-renowned Chinese colour-prints known in the world of graphic art simply as the 'Kaempfer prints'. Twenty-nine sheets of these had resided in the same album until 1906 when they were extracted and then moved to what is now the Department of Oriental Antiquities in the British Museum (see Chapter 14 and Pl. 21).[37] Woodblock colour prints such as these were imported to Japan by Chinese traders in Nagasaki. They were to stimulate the development of colour printing using multiple blocks by the Japanese, a technique that was to be refined in the eighteenth and nineteenth centuries beyond the dreams of those Chinese pioneers. Evidently, Kaempfer had acquired these woodcuts, together with the Chinese silk and embroidered pictures in Nagasaki. Most probably he did so, yet again, through the good offices of his student-interpreter, Imamura. Kaempfer's botanist eye would naturally have been caught by the beautiful renderings of blossom in these woodcuts.

Kaempfer's virtuosity and precision not only as a researcher but also as a draughtsman are apparent in the celebrated drawings in his own hand of the 'Journey to the Court of Edo'[38] and of the 'Audience with the Shogun';[39] and, indeed, in many other sketches in *Heutiges Japan* and in his voluminous field notes. Among the best are those he copied from the set of Japanese paintings of famous sights to illustrate his accounts of the tribute mission. Unfortunately, his competent and accurate representations of the Hōkōji and Sanjūsangendō temples, which he visited in Kyoto, were to be revamped by Scheuchzer so as to fit a Western stereotype of the East.[40] Then again Scheuchzer added two new views copied directly from the album to illustrate Book III which deals with religious beliefs, this despite the fact that Kaempfer himself had not provided any illustrations for this section of the *History*. The pictures in question are Matsushima, the beauty spot in north-east Honshu celebrated for its pine-clad islands;[41] and Yoshida Shrine in Kyoto with its distinctive octagonal hall (Fig. 113).[42]

Without Kaempfer's drawings to set things in their proper context, Scheuchzer made in each case a wrong choice of place for the themes he was trying to illustrate. The temples at Matsushima are Buddhist not Shinto; and Yoshida Shrine he incorrectly captioned 'Tensio Daisin at Isie' (i.e. the Shrine of the Sun Goddess, otherwise known as the Grand Shrine of Ise). It is understandable that Scheuchzer should wish to include a picture of the Ise Grand Shrine. For Ise together with Kiyomizu temple in Kyoto were given full coverage by Kaempfer in Book V of the *History of Japan* which deals exclusively with the Dutch journeys to Edo. As already mentioned, he was fascinated

Fig. 113 Scheuchzer's erroneous temple of Ise shrine, copied from the Japanese painting of Yoshida shrine in Kyoto. From the *History of Japan*, tab. xviii. BL, 150.K.9. Reproduced by courtesy of the Trustees of the British Library.

by the great multitude of pilgrims on the road at all times, and commented: 'The Japanese are very much addicted to pilgrimages. They make several and to different places. The first and chief goes to Isje [*sic*] . . .' The Ise *mairi* (pilgrimage) was again described, and in great detail, in another chapter on Japanese religions.

The most startling display of Scheuchzer's idiosyncratic ingenuity as an artist is, however, a view of Kiyomizu temple drawn entirely from his own imagination. It looks more like a group of British factory buildings from the last century than the elegant temple complex it is, famous for its unusual 'stage' architecture supported by wooden stilts.[43]

Scheuchzer's Legacy
In his introduction to the *History of Japan*, Scheuchzer makes it clear that he was a substitute translator as 'a Gentleman of better abilities . . . has been called abroad, and employ'd in affairs of a different nature'. One cannot help wondering what kind of book the *History of Japan* would have been if the translation had been undertaken by this anonymous gentleman who, incidentally, has now been identified as Phillip Henry Zollman (a scholar and diplomat, and one of Sloane's most punctilious informants on desirable acquisitions).[44] As it was, Scheuchzer created in spite of everything

a great classic and immortalized Kaempfer as the first interpreter of Japan.

Alas, recent researches have called into question the accuracy, not only of the translation, but also of the layout and contents of the *History*, something for which Scheuchzer was solely responsible. The criticism has been particularly stringent from academic purists looking for a literal translation, even though Scheuchzer explicitly stated in his own Introduction that 'my aim is to express the sense of author'.[45] Had Scheuchzer simply attempted literal translation word-for-word, the *History of Japan* would probably not have been half as readable or influential. After all, Kaempfer's High German manuscript, *Heutiges Japan*, had been written in a prosaic and scientific style, that even Scheuchzer, himself a German speaker, found quite intricate and obscure.

As for the layout and contents, it is true that Scheuchzer incorporated a substantial amount of material found not in Kaempfer's main manuscript but in his field-notes and other sources. His inclusion of such Japanese topics as acupuncture, tea culture, paper-making, and the celebrated *Sakoku-ron* from Kaempfer's Latin miscellany *Amoenitatum exoticarum*, not to mention a chapter on Siam from elsewhere, surely enhances the value of the *History of Japan*. Above all, had Scheuchzer not translated Kaempfer's evaluation of the

Shogunate's policy of national seclusion and appended it to the *History of Japan*, Kaempfer might have remained in oblivion in Japanese history to this day.

Yet this is not to deny that Scheuchzer frequently misunderstood Kaempfer's interpretation of things Japanese. This was only to be expected from someone who had never been to Japan. In fact, he was only twenty-one when Sloane asked him to take on the project. He read forthwith all there was to read about Japan, which was not much even in Sloane's well-stocked library; and in less than three years the *History of Japan* was published with Scheuchzer's own dedication to King George I. Evidently Sloane had given him full rein and, under all the circumstances, he had responded magnificently.

The speed with which he mastered the nuances of Japanese culture is astonishing. Accordingly, one has to be amused, rather than affronted when Kaempfer's Fukurokuju, the god of longevity correctly-drawn with his traditionally elongated head, is transformed when Scheuchzer innocently wraps a turban round it.[46] As has already been noted, his western preconceptions led him into other such errors, while copying the paintings of the famous sights from the album of *meisho-e*.

Yet on the whole, Scheuchzer used the pictorial nature of many of Kaempfer's Japanese books to good effect. For instance, the essentially pictorial quality of Japanese *kana* syllabary and of the Sino-Japanese *kanji* characters in *Nanatsu iroha*;[47] *Kakubi senjibon*[48] and *Dai Nihon Ōdaiki*[49] were utilized to draw up three memorable tables of Japanese alphabets, calendars in cyclical combination, and an imperial chronology, respectively.[50] Their exotic appeal is shown by how widely they were copied in later European books dealing with Japan.

Then again, the famous pictorial encyclopaedia *Kinmō zui*,[51] was a mine of information (especially on botany and natural history) on which both Kaempfer and Scheuchzer drew avidly. Scheuchzer, in particular, copied all the illustrations in it for Chapters 10 and 11 of Book I of the *History*. These introductory chapters cover Japanese natural products: flora and fauna, and more particularly birds, fish, shells and insects. His original drawings are still preserved in the Sloane collection (Fig. 114)[52] and provide a valuable record of the artistic process of the making of the *History*. His skills as an illustrator were to culminate in the distinctive title page for the *History of Japan* (see Fig. 110). He had aptly decorated the border with coiled dragons modelled on that of the *Kinmō zui*, with vignettes in the form of *daimyō* crests and insignia from the samurai directory, *Taihei bukan taizen*.[53] Surely, this must constitute one of the earliest pieces of 'Japonisme'. The 1727 first edition of the *History of Japan* remains to this day not only a standard European reference work on Japan but also a copiously illustrated literary classic.

From what has been said so far, Scheuchzer was no mere translator. He was also a brilliant editor and book designer. Without him, the *History of Japan* as we know it today would never have existed. So Scheuchzer might fairly be called Kaempfer's student-interpreter in the West. It is sad that, unlike Imamura Gen'eman who was to rise to a great height professionally, Johann Caspar Scheuchzer died two years after the publication of the *History of Japan* in 1729. He was aged twenty-seven.

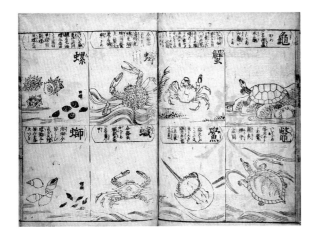
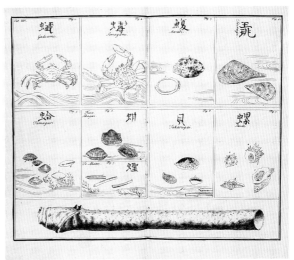

Fig. 114 *a*: Marine products from Japan, from *Kinmō zui*, the pictorial encyclopaedia, *c.*1673; BL, Or.75ff.1. *b*: Illustrations of shellfish as copied from the above, and the claw of a giant crayfish modelled on the actual specimen collected by Kaempfer; the claw has since perished. From the *History of Japan*, tab. xiv. BL, 150.K.9. Reproduced by courtesy of the Trustees of the British Library.

Fig. 115 Engelbert Kaempfer's *ex libris* seal. Reproduced by courtesy of the Trustees of the British Library.

Epilogue

By way of conclusion, I would like to share with our readers a secret message from Kaempfer, a message which I think he has been trying to pass on for the last 300 years. This is in a form of a small oblong seal in black ink (Fig. 115), recently found impressed in the right-hand corner of the inner cover of one of his Japanese books *Kakubiki senjimon* or 'The thousand characters classic'. The three *kanji* characters can be transliterated as *Ken-pu-ru* 堅不留;[54] evidently, this is Kaempfer's ex-libris seal. So again he makes history: this time as the first European known to have used a seal made in Japan.

The further significance of the seal itself is that, the three characters chosen for him are entirely different from those which conventionally have been adopted by scholars of Dutch learning in Japan for 200 years or so. They have commonly been written as 検夫爾 which simply represent the pronunciation of his name. Now with the emergence of the new characters, which obviously were authorized by Kaempfer himself, perhaps we should revise the previous rendering and henceforward employ this newly discovered original as his Japanese name.

But what do these three characters actually mean? There are two possible alternatives. One is 'For the courageous there is nothing impossible'. This seems to be very close to his Latin motto, which he used all through his life: that reads VIRTUTI NIHIL INVIUM, as inscribed on the monument erected in his memory in his home town at Lemgo in Germany. The other interpretation may be more whimsical, but is wonderfully paradoxical. It can be translated as 'Absolutely not to remain'. Could this be a hidden pledge or promise that the secret about Kaempfer's student-servant will never or must not be disclosed?

Whichever one chooses, these three *kanji* characters are more meaningful than those conventionally employed. One wonders who was responsible for selecting them. Imamura, perhaps?

Notes and References

Japanese names cited in this paper follow the traditional Japanese format, i.e. surname first.

1. BL, Sloane MS 3060.

2. C.W. Dohm (ed.), *Geschichte und Beschreibung von Japan* (Lemgo, 1777–9). This first German publication was, according to Dohm, based on two other manuscript copies discovered in Germany; the textual evidence, however, suggests that it was re-translated from the 1727 English edition. The whereabouts of the two manuscripts has never been ascertained.

3. Only four sheets of herbarium specimens have hitherto been identified as being compiled in Japan by Kaempfer himself (see NHM, H.S.211, fols. 27, 28, 82, 111; see also Chapter 8). For Sloane's original acquisitions of Kaempfer's artefacts and zoological specimens see the following lists: BL, Sloane MS 4019, fols. 54–5; MS 3329, fols. 3–4; 20 (with price paid for each item written in the margins); and Sloane's 'Catalogue of Miscellanies [28a/45c]. For an attempt to reconstitute Kaempfer's Japanese collection as a whole see Gerhard Bonn, 'Der wissenschaftliche Nachlass des Lippischen Forschungsreisenden Engelbert Kaempfer im Britischen Museum', in *Lippische Mitteilungen* 48 (1979), pp. 69–116.

4. Deutsches Institut für Japanstudien, *Doitsu-jin no mita Genroku jidai: Kenperu-ten* (The Genroku Period as seen by a German: the Kaempfer exhibition) (Tokyo, 1990). This catalogue accompanied the exhibition which toured Tokyo, Osaka, Yokohama and finally Nagasaki, between 18 December 1990 and 30 June 1991.

5. See Yu-Ying Brown, *Engelbert Kämpfer: first Interpreter of Japan*, a leaflet to accompany the exhibition held in the British Library, 11 October 1991–17 May 1992.

6. In his Introduction to the *History of Japan*, Scheuchzer states that Sloane first became interested in Kaempfer's collection of curiosities and manuscripts after reading the latter's *Amoenitatum Exoticarum* and other theses, and that he instructed his friend Dr Johan Georg Steigerthal, court physician to George I, to visit Lemgo while accompanying his royal master to Hanover. An extensive correspondence regarding the purchase from Kaempfer's nephew and heir Johann Hermann developed between Sloane, Steigerthal and Phillip Henry Zollman. It is to be found in BL, Sloane MSS 4047 and 4048.

7. For Kaempfer's own sketch of the retinue of the Dutch tribute mission on its way to Edo, see BL, Sloane MS 3060, fol. 501.

8. BL, Sloane MS 3060, fol. 514. This celebrated sketch by Kaempfer depicts the Dutch delegation in audience with shogun Tokugawa Tsunayoshi during their 1691 tribute-paying mission. Kaempfer himself is portrayed dancing

and singing at the order of shogun, this to satisfy the latter's curiosity about foreign 'barbarians'. Kaempfer regarded these antics as sheer humiliation.

9. Numata Jirō, 'Engelbert Kämpfer in Japan und sein Einfluß auf Japan', in *Mitteilungen der Deutschen Gesellschaft für Natur- und Völkerkunde Ostasiens*, Supplement Band XXVIII (Tokyo, 1966), pp. 27–42.

10. BL, OIOC, Or. 14480/2. For the first publication and discussion of this document, see Yu-Ying Brown, *'Daiei Toshokan shozō Kenpuru shōrai Nihon shiryō no igi'* [The significance of Kaempfer's Japanese source materials in the British Library], in the Kaempfer tercentenary catalogue, op. cit. (note 4), pp. 102–13; fig. 85.

11. The text was in fact translated by Kaempfer and included in his manuscript *Heutiges Japan* (BL, Sloane MS 3060, fol. 477). However, all the Japanese names have been deleted and substituted by the significantly anonymous 'N.N.'. This was retranslated by Scheuchzer as an example of an oath taken by servants of Deshima. It appeared as document no. VIII in Book IV, Chapter X of the *History of Japan*.

12. Imamura Gen'emon has been listed in almost all major bio-historical dictionaries, the latest being the projected 15-volume *Kokushi daijiten* [Encyclopaedia of national history] (Tokyo, 1979–93), vol. I, p. 799; and in Nichiran Gakkai (ed.), *Yōgaku-shi jiten* [Dictionary of western learning] (Tokyo, 1984), p. 67. For his individual biography, see Imamura Akitsune, *Rangaku no so Imamura Eisei* [Pioneer of Dutch learning: Imamura Eisei] (Tokyo, 1942).

13. The most celebrated episode concerning Imamura was that in 1709 in which he acted as interpreter for Arai Hakuseki (1697–1725), adviser to the shogunate during the latter's lengthy dialogues with Giovanni Battista Sidotti (1668–1714), the imprisoned Italian Jesuit. Sidotti had been caught smuggling himself into southern Japan the previous year in an attempt to revive the Christian mission. It was said that the fact that Arai could base his two influential works on foreign affairs on information supplied by Sidotti was largely due to Imamura's skill as an interpreter. Imamura was himself the author of several books and was credited also with introducing western horsemanship and horse-care to Japan.

14. The person who started these controversies was Onno Zwier van Haren (1713–79), a Dutch diplomat and writer. See, in particular, his *Het leven van Joannes Camphuis* (Zwolle, 1772). H. Doeff, a latter-day head of the VOC in Deshima, popularized Haren's suspicion in his *Herinneringen uit Japan* (Haarlem, 1833). This work was in its turn quoted by a Japanese scholar, Saitō Agu, in his 'Kenperu no "Nihonshi" ni tsuite' [On Kaempfer's 'History of Japan'], in *Shigaku zasshi* (Tokyo, 1929), pp. 40–1.

15. NHM, H.S.211, op. cit. (note 3). See also Kaempfer's volume of notes on Japanese plants, *Catalogus plantarum Japonicarum* (BL, Sloane MS 74).

16. BM, Ethno, As 1753 D10 1074.

17. BM, JA, Sloane 1139.

18. The Chinese modeller known to westerners as Chitqua or Shykinqua enjoyed considerable success in artistic circles, having met the King and Queen and having been invited to dinner at the Royal Academy. His two-year career in England, 1769–71, is described in W.T. Whitley, *Artists and their Friends in England* (London, 1928); and David Piper, 'A Chinese artist in England', *Country life*, 18 July 1952, pp. 198–9. His clay figures are illustrated in Carl L. Crossman, *The Decorative Arts of the China Trade* (New York, 1991). See also Patrick Conner, *The China Trade, 1600–1860* (Brighton, 1986).

19. Apart from examining Kaempfer's Japanese books and manuscripts, Chetqua was also asked to look at a number of Chinese printed books, mainly tracts on Christianity, of which he managed brief descriptions with slightly better accuracy. Incidentally, the majority of the items with Chinese connections amongst the Sloane manuscripts which he acquired from various sources are grammars or dictionaries or else religious miscellanea reflecting contemporary preoccupations. Notable among them are the Dutch-Latin-Chinese dictionary of 1628 by Heurnius (BL, OIOC, Sloane MS 2746) and the Four Gospels translated into Chinese at Canton in 1737–8 (BL, Sloane MS 3599). Sloane also purchased some of Thomas Hyde's orientalia which included a copy of the woodblock edition of Father Verbiest's 1671 *Typus eclipsus lunae . . .* with Chinese and Manchu text (BL, OIOC, Or. 70.bbb.3, formerly Sloane MS 3401). Another copy owned by Hyde of this very rare book seems to have entered the Royal Library as well (BL, OIOC, Sloane MS Or. 74.b.6, formerly Reg. 16.B.IX). See Frances Wood, 'Curiosities of the British Library Chinese collection', in *Chinese Studies* (British Library Occasional Papers 10) (London, 1988), pp. 97–105. For Kaempfer's Chinese colour prints and *objets d'art* in the Sloane collection, see Chapter 14 and note 37 (below).

20. This new departmental name was adopted in 1990 when Oriental Collections and India Office Library were merged into one. For the first endeavour to bring the scattered Japanese items together, see K.B. Gardner, 'Engelbert Kaempfer's Japanese library', *Asia Minor* 7 (1/2) (1959).

21. Most of the Japanese printed items can be identified in Sloane's catalogue (BL, Sloane MS 3972, vol. 6, pp. 2062–5).

22. (BL, OIOC, Or. 14480/1. Kaempfer's own translation of this pass can be found in his *Heutiges Japan* (BL, Sloane MS 3060, fol. 488). The other extant example of a Deshima pass is preserved in the Nagasaki Prefectural Library and dates only from 1769.

23. BL, Additional MS 4090, fol. 1 (Kaempfer's translation: BL, Sloane MS 3060, fol. 482).

24. Beatrice Bodart-Bailey, 'Preliminary report on the manuscripts of Engelbert Kaempfer in the British Library', in Yu-Ying Brown (ed.) *Japanese Studies* (British Library Occasional Papers 11) (London, 1990), pp. 34–6.

25. Torigoe Bunzō and Charles Dunn (eds.), *Kojōruri-shū: Daiei Hakubutsukan-bon* [Old jōruri drama texts at the British Museum], (Tokyo, 1966).

26. BL, Sloane MS 3061, fols. 69–83; MS 3062, fols. 285–311.

27. BL, OIOC, Or. 75.f.2.

28. BL, OIOC, Or. 75.h.4/1–2.

29. BL, OIOC, Or. 75.f.6.

30. There are seven such items at the following shelfmarks: BL, OIOC, Or. 75.f.3, 4, 7(1–3); Or. 75.f.29; Or. 75.g.7.

31. BL, OIOC, Or. 75.g.25; Kaempfer's manuscript copy of the map of Nagasaki at BL, Sloane MS 3060, fol. 466.

32. BL, OIOC, Or. 75.f.13(2).

33. Kaempfer's map of Japan is to be found in BL, Sloane MS 3060, fol. 450.

34. M. Seutter, *Regni Japoniae nova mappa geographica* (Nuremberg, 1737).

35. BL, Additional MS 5252.

36. See Yu-Ying Brown, 'Kaempfer's album of famous sights of seventeenth-century Japan', *British Library Journal* 15 (1989), pp. 90–103.

37. BM, OA, 1906–11–28, formerly Additional MS 5252, fols. 71–99. First listed in Laurence Binyon, *A Catalogue of Japanese and Chinese Woodcuts preserved in the Sub-Department of Oriental Prints and Drawings in the British Museum* (London, 1916). For an early discussion of the artistic significance of these prints, see Jan Tschichold, *Der frühe chinesische Farbendruck* (Basel, 1940). See also Basil Gray, 'Sloane and the Kaempfer collection', *British Museum Quarterly* 18 (1953), pp. 20–3.

38. See note 7, above.

39. See note 8, above.

40. The three versions of the Hōkōji temple are as follows: Japanese original painting: BL, Additional MS 5252, fol. 49; Kaempfer's drawing: BL, Sloane MS 3060, fol. 515; and Scheuchzer's adaptation: the *History of Japan*, tab. XXXV.

Those of the Sanjūsangendō temple are as follows. Japanese original painting: BL, Additional MS 5252, fol. 39; Kaempfer's drawing: BL, Sloane MS 3060, fol. 523; and Scheuchzer's adaptation: the *History of Japan*, tab. XXXVII.

41. Japanese painting of Matsushima: BL, Additional MS 5252, fol. 15. Scheuchzer's adaptation: BL, Additional MS 5232, fol. 223; and as it appeared in copper engraving in the *History*, tab. XVII.

42. Japanese painting of the Yoshida shrine: BL, Additional MS 5252, fol. 48; and Scheuchzer's adaptation captioned as Ise shrine in the *History*, tab. xviii.

43. *History*, tab. xxxiii.

44. See note 6, above. And in particular, the letter written from Paris by Zollman to Sloane, 31 May 1724 (BL, Sloane MS 4047). Also Derek Massarella, 'The purchase and publication of Engelbert Kaempfer's *History of Japan*', a paper presented at the Kaempfer symposium, 15–18 December 1990 at the Deutsches Institut für Japanstudien, Tokyo (see also note 4, above). The proceedings (Detlef Haberland of Humboldt-Gesellschaft, Bonn, ed.) were published by Franz Steiner Verlag, Stuttgart, in 1993.

45. Beatrice M. Bodart Bailey, 'Kaempfer restor'd', *Monumenta Nipponica* 43 no. 1 (1988), pp. 1–33.

46. For Kaempfer's sketches of three of the seven gods of good fortune see BL, Sloane MS 3061, fols. 131–2. Cf. those copied by Scheuchzer to appear as vignettes for the map of Japan in the *History*, tab. viii.

47. BL, OIOC, Or. 75.h.4 (1,2)

48. BL, OIOC, Or. 75.h.1

49. BL, OIOC, Or. 75.f.2

50. See the *History*, tabs. xv, xvi, xlx.

51. BL, OIOC, Or. 75.ff.1.

52. BL, Additional MS 5232. The majority of drawings in this album are Scheuchzer's works.

53. BL, OIOC, Or. 75.f.22.

54. It is of interest to note that Kaempfer's only ex-libris seal should be found impressed on a primer copy book. The three characters could well have been deliberately selected from among the three thousand listed in this book.

Sir Hans Sloane's Catalogues

The catalogue numbering system adopted in this volume is that established by Peter Murray Jones in his paper, 'A preliminary check-list of Sir Hans Sloane's catalogues', *British Library Journal* 14 no. 1 (1988), pp. 38–51. The following summarized list is reproduced with permission from the author and from the editor of the *British Library Journal*. Institutional and departmental titles have been amended in the light of changes that have taken place since the date of the original publication. A number of shelf-marks have also been altered since that time.

1. British Museum, Department of Egyptian Antiquities
'Ægyptian Antiquitys' (n.d.)

   Contents: (*a*) 'Figures of Metal'; (*b*) 'Scarabei'; (*c*) 'Periaptae'; (*d*) 'Ingravings'; (*e*) 'Models of Mummies'; (*f*) 'Single Fig^{rs} of Terra Cotta'; (*g*) 'Two or more fig$^{rs'}$; (*h*) 'Bustos and heads of Clay or Terracotta'; (*i*) 'Basso Relievos'; (*j*) 'Ægyptian fig^{rs} of Earth or Stone'; (*k*) 'Models of Mummies'; (*l*) 'Urns'.
   Notes: (i) in unknown eighteenth-century hand. (ii) entries cross-referenced to Sloane catalogue numbers, i.e. to 28 (below). Some provenances of items mentioned.

2. British Museum, Department of Medieval and Later Antiquities
[Gems, Cameos, Annuli] (n.d.)

   Contents: (*a*) Table of subjects for paintings; (*b*) gems, 1–232; (*c*) cameos, etc., 1–290; (*d*) note on an Anglo-Saxon inscription; short lists based on (*b*) and (*c*) above; (*e*) annuli; rings, 1–115; (*f*) five lists numbered 159q–u: of cameos, etc., 1–6; medallions, 1–7; cameos, etc., 1–7; intaglios, etc., 1–8; gems, etc., 1–12; (*g*) Latin verses, headed 'Conradus Ritterhusius', on back of a playing card.
   Notes: (i) all items in Sloane's hand except (*c*) 286–90, and (*e*) 115. (ii) identifications by A.W. Franks and others *passim*.

3. British Museum, Department of Medieval and Later Antiquities
'Indices variorum Musaei Sloaneani Catalogorum'. (*c*.1740)

   Contents: (*a*) Miscellanies, AA–Z; (*b*) Antiquities, A–Z; (*c*) Pictures &c., A–Z; (*d*) Agate-Handles &c., A–Z; (*e*) Agate-Cups &c., A–Z.
   Notes: (i) paper slip bound in before (*c*) with recipe 'Chandeles p[ou]r la Carnosite' (not in Sloane's hand). (ii) all indices in hand of Thomas Stack.

4. British Museum, Department of Medieval and Later Antiquities
[A.W. Franks's copy of Sloane's 'Miscellanies' catalogue]

   Contents: (*a*) Antiquities, 1–1129 (pp. 1–30); (*b*) non-Sloane additions to (*a*), 1–14, 1–5 (pp. 31, 32); (*c*) Miscellanies, 1–2111 (pp. 33–85); (*d*) Impressions of Seals, etc., 1–268 (pp. 86–95); (*e*) Index in Sigilla, Sigillorum, Impressiones, &c., A–Y (pp. 96–8); (*f*) Pictures and Drawings, 1–323 (pp. 99–106).
   Notes: copy of 28 (below) in A.W. Franks's hand; continued in typescript as 5 (below).

5. British Museum, Department of Medieval and Later Antiquities
[Typed Extracts from the MS Catalogue in the Department of Ethnography]

   Contents: (*a*) Pictures, 324–471; (*b*) Mathematical Instruments, 1–57 (and index); (*c*) Agate handles, etc., 1–239; (*d*) Agate cups, saucers, spoons, bottles, 1–303; (*e*) Annuli; rings, 1–115.
   Notes: typescript continuation of 4 (above); copy of 28 (below).

6. British Museum, Department of Oriental Antiquities
[Extracts from Sloane and other early registers relating to Oriental Antiquities] (one item in (*d*) dated 1737)

   Contents: (*a*) extracts from 28 (below) relating to oriental antiquities, index by country and subject, and index of sources (17 fols.); (*b*) 'Amuleta Mahumetica. Gemmae sive Lapides continentes Inscriptiones Arabicos, persicas, &c.', 1–24 (7 fols.); (*c*) notes on oriental coins, 18th century (3 fols.); (*d*) seal impressions and notes (6 fols.).
   Notes: (*b*) and parts of (*d*) in Sloane's hand, (*a*) typescript.

7. Natural History Museum, Botany Library
Shelf-mark: Banksian Collection MSS
[Sir Hans Sloane, 'Vegetable and Vegetable Substances: being the original register of the plant collections of Sir Hans Sloane excluding the Herbarium, arranged in the order of their acquisition'] (n.d.)

   Contents: 'Vegetables and Vegetable Substances', 1–3000.
   Notes: (i) Sloane's hand, with interpolations by others. (ii) note on flyleaf (Sloane's hand):
   'G + Gr Dr Grews Mus.S.Reg. + collection of seeds fruits & which I bought
   P + Pet. are Mr James Petivers collections of all sorts which I bought likewise
   P + Pl. Dr Plukenets collections which I likewise bought from Dr Moor Bp of Norwich who bought them of his Exrs.'

8. Natural History Museum, Botany Library
Shelf-mark: Banksian Collection MSS
[Vegetables and vegetable substances] (n.d.)

Contents: Vegetables and vegetable substances, 3001–6000.
Notes: (i) Sloane's hand, with very few interpolations; (ii) fol. 466, E.W. Groves (3/12/47): 'Nos. 4326 onwards are continued on p. 471'.

9. Natural History Museum, Botany Library
Shelf-mark: Banksian Collection MSS
[Vegetables and vegetable substances] (n.d., but Sloane note on fol. 1086 refers to storm of 8 January 1734)

Contents: Vegetables and vegetable substances, 6001–12523.
Notes: (i) Sloane's hand to fol. 1068; interpolated thereafter; (ii) infoliated note after fol. 804: 'Mr Barham's MSS Paraguay Tea'; (iii) fol. 1085ᵛ, note: 10558* to 10576* after 10857; 11088–97 missing.

10. Natural History Museum, Botany Library
Shelf-mark: Banksian Collection MSS
[Index to the 5 (sic) Volumes of Vegetables] (n.d.)

Contents: Index to Vegetables and Vegetable Substances, 1–12523.
Notes: (i) index pasted in on slips (not in Sloane's hand); (ii) note by W. Carruthers, August 1875: 'The index formerly in 5 portions has been arranged as a single index'.

11. Natural History Museum, Department of Botany
John Ray, Historia Plantarum (London, 1686–1706), 3 vols., on large paper annotated by Sloane and others with references to H[orti] S[icci] volumes and pages, passim.

Notes: a fuller catalogue of Sloane's herbarium is in 30 (below).

12. Natural History Museum, Botany Library
Shelf-mark: Special Book Collection
John Ray, Historia Plantarum (London, 1686–1706), 3 vols., on large paper; annotations copied by Sigismund Bacstrom from 11 (above) (may differ in detail from 11)

13. Natural History Museum, Entomology Library
Shelf-mark: S.B.q.S.8
'Insects' (n.d.)

Contents: (a) pasted slip: 'Sir Hans Sloane's Catalogue. Geological Department' (fol. 1); (b) 'Insects contained in Cabinet no. 234' (list follows) (fol. 2); (c) 'Tabula Synoptica Insectorum in Classes distributorum Cromwello Mortimero' (fols. 2ᵛ–4ᵛ); (d) 'An Explanation of Several Abbreviations & notes made use of in the Catalogue of Insects' (fols. 5–5ᵛ); (e) 'Insects', 1–2506 (fols. 8–413).
Notes: (i) Sloane's hand throughout, except fols. 2–5ᵛ in Dr Cromwell Mortimer's hand; (ii) pencil numbers added to each entry, keyed to boxes in which specimens kept.

14. Natural History Museum, Entomology Library
Shelf-mark: S.B.q.S.8
[Insects] (n.d.)

Contents: (a) [Insects], 2507–5447 (fols. 2–326); (b) 'Number of Insects not found in the review made by C. Mortimer' (fol. 378).
Notes: (i) Sloane's hand to 4205 (fol. 236); part Sloane, part C. Mortimer 4206–4832 (fol. 275); mostly C. Mortimer 4833–5447 (fol. 276); (ii) pencil numbers added, keyed to boxes.

15. Natural History Museum, Mineralogy Library
Shelf-mark: MSS, SLO
[Catalogue of Sir Hans Sloane's Collection of Minerals. Vol. I. Pretious stones (nos. 1–2256); Metalls (nos. 1–1406; continued in Vol. II) title page written 20 August 1903. L[azarus] F[letcher]] (n.d.)

Contents: (a) 'Pretious stones', 1–2256 (fols. 1–184); (b) 'Metalls', 1–1406 (fols. 189–342ᵛ).

Notes: (i) Sloane's hand, except fols. 181–4 (Metals 2230–56); (ii) fol. (i) L.J. Spencer, 2 April 1932; vols. 1–3 in hand of Sir Hans Sloane; vol. 4 (index) in hand of Thos. Stack; (iii) fols. (ii)–(iii), L.F., 1902–3: notes re Sloane and mineral collections; (iv) Precious stones, 1723–75 repeated; Metals, 670–99 repeated.

16. Natural History Museum, Mineralogy Library
Shelf-mark: MSS, SLO
[Catalogue of Sir Hans Sloane's Collection of Minerals. Vol. II. Metalls (nos. 1407–2727), title-page written 20 August 1903. L. F.] (n.d.)

Contents: Metals, 1407–2727 (fols. 2–76).
Notes: (i) Sloane's hand, fols. 2–64 (1–2640); (ii) after fol. 39, note by L.J.S., 1. 2. 1929: following entries agree with J. Winthrop, Amer. Journ. Sci., 1844, ser. 1, vol. 47, pp. 282–90 (list given).

17. Natural History Museum, Mineralogy Library
Shelf-mark: MSS, SLO
[Catalogue of Sir Hans Sloane's Collection of Minerals. Vol. III. Ambers, Bitumens, &c. (nos. 1–399); Asteriae, Trochitae, etc. (nos. 1–242); Earths, Salts, etc. (nos. 1–1037); Talcs, Micae, etc. (nos. 1–391); Christalls (nos. 1–1868); Fossils, Flints etc. (nos. 1–1280)] (n.d.)
Volume III is in two parts, IIIA and IIIB (this item and 18 (below)).

Contents: (a) 'Ambers bitumens, ambergrease etc.', 1–399 (fols. 1–35); (b) 'Asteriae, Trochite, Entrochi (scrive stones) etc.', 1–242 (fols. 42–70); (c) 'Salts, Earths, clays, &c.', 1–1037 (fols. 79–173); (d) 'Talks, micae &c.', 1–391 (fols. 184–212); (e) 'Christals', 1–487 (fols. 217–61).
Notes: (i) Sloane's hand, except changes on fols. 34, 69, 170, 211; (ii) (b) nos. 66–80 repeated; (c) nos. 160–207, 245–59, 526, 903–10, 918 repeated; (e) nos. 1135–1333 wanting.

18. Natural History Museum, Mineralogy Library
Shelf-mark: MSS, SLO
[Catalogue of Sir Hans Sloane's Collection of Minerals, Volume III] Vol. IIIB (n.d.)

Contents: (*a*) 'Chrystalls', 488–1868 (fols. 262–371); (*b*) 'Flints, Fossils, &', 1–1280 (fols. 382–495).

Notes: (i) Sloane's hand, fols. 262–367, 382–483; (ii) fol. 496 concordance of Sloane nos. with Winthrop nos. (see note to 16 (above)).

19. Natural History Museum, Mineralogy Library
Shelf-mark: MSS, SLO
'Indices variorum Musaei Sloaneani Catalogorum :scil. 1. Succinorum, Bituminum, &c.; 2. Asteriarum, Trochitarum, Entrochorum, &c.; 3. Terrarum, Salium, &c.; 4. Talcorum, Micarum, &c.; 5. Crystallorum &c.; 6. Fossilium. Index to the Ambers, Bitumes &. 1740'. (1740)

Contents: (*a*) 'Ambers, Bitumens &c.', A–Z (pp. 1–63); (*b*) 'Index to the Asteriae, Trochitae, Entrochi &c. 1740', A–Z (pp. 67–117); (*c*) 'Index to the Earths, Salts, &c. 1740', A–Z (pp. 119–235); (*d*) 'Index to the Talcs, Micae, &c. 1740', A–Z (pp. 239–303); (*e*) 'Index to the Crystals &. 1740', A–Z (pp. 307–491); (*f*) 'Index to the Fossils, Flints &c. 1740', A–Z (pp. 495–661).

Notes: (i) Thomas Stack's hand; (ii) pastedown on flyleaf has note by L.F., August 1903: indexes to vols. I and II are at present bound up with indexes to the volumes in the Geological Dept.; (iii) note by L.J.S., 2 April 1932, about hands of Sloane in vols. I to III, and Stack in vol. IV.

20. Natural History Museum, Mineralogy Library
Shelf-mark: MSS, SLO
'Catalogus Marmorum' (n.d.)

Contents: (*a*) notes (see below) and contents lists (fols. 1–5); (*b*) 'Catalogus Marmorum', 1–277 (fols. 6–22ᵛ); (*c*) note by Sloane, inc. 'Strata folinae' (fol. 23); (*d*) 'Minerae Auri', 1–20 and 'Observationes' (fols. 24–6); (*e*) 'Minerae Argenti', 1–272 and 'Observationes' (fols. 26ᵛ–51ᵛ); (*f*) 'Minerae Cupri', 1–133 (fols. 52ᵛ–62ᵛ); (*g*) 'Minerae Ferri', 1–114 and 'Observationes' (fols. 62ᵛ–74); (*h*) 'Minerae Stanni sive Plumbi candidi Agricolae', 1–91 and 'Observationes' (fols. 74ᵛ–83ᵛ); (*i*) 'Minerae Plumbi', 1–48 and 'Observationes' (fols. 84–89ᵛ); (*j*) 'Minerae Cinnabaris et Mercurii', 1–18 and 'Observationes' (fols. 90–1ᵛ); (*k*) 'Minerae Antimonii et Magnesiae', 1–29 and 'Observationes' (fols. 92–7ᵛ); (*l*) 'Minerae Vitrioli', 1–21 and 'Observationes' (fols. 98–100ᵛ); (*m*) 'Minerae aluminis', 22–4 and 'Salia', 25–8 and 'Observationes' (fols. 101–2); (*n*) 'Minerae Cobalti, Arsenici, Bismuthi, 1–48 and 'Observationes' (fols. 104–11ᵛ); (*o*) 'Pyritae Flavi et Subflavi', 1–40 and 'Observationes' (fols. 112–19ᵛ); (*p*) 'Minerae Sulphuris', 29–32 and 'Observationes' (fols. 120–1ᵛ); (*q*) 'Lapides', 33–46 (fols. 122–3ᵛ); (*r*) Lusus Minerales sive Concretiones crystallinae', 1–81 (fols. 124–33ᵛ); (*s*) Letter of William Brownrigg, Whitehaven 3 November 1742, to Sloane (fols. 134–6); (*t*) 'A Catalogue of Fossils, &c. other Bodies delivered to Sir James Lowther Bart.: For Sir Hans Sloane Bart.: by W[illiam] B[rownrigg]', 12 October 1742, nos. 1–19 (fols. 137–44).

Notes: (i) section (*b*) not in Sloane's hand, but annotated and supplemented by him. Fols. 21–49, 52ᵛ–64 in Sloane's hand; (ii) fol. 1, L.J. Spencer, 1928: 'This old catalogue, written in Latin, evidently belonged to Sir Hans Sloane (1660–1753) for

there is bound up with it a letter and list of specimens sent to him by William Brownrigg in 1742; also the style of binding is the same as that of the Sloane catalogues in the Geology Department (BM). None of the entries appear to agree with any in the Sloane MS Catalogue. This Catalogue by Sir Hans Sloane but not re-catalogued with his general collection. Nearly all of the specimens are from Germany and Austria.'

21. Natural History Museum, Palæontology Library
Shelf-mark: MSS, SLO
'Coralls, Sponges, & some other submarines' (n.d.)

Contents: (*a*) 'Coralls', 1–1421 (fols. 2–108; fols. 1ᵛ–16ᵛ); (*b*) 'Serpents &', 1–525 (fols. 109–56; fols. 108ᵛ–11ᵛ); (*c*) 'Echini', 1–660 (fols. 157–219); (*d*) 'Crustacea', 1–364 (fols. 226–57); (*e*) 'Starrfishes', 1–174 (fols. 265–76); (*f*) 'Humana', 1–760 (fols. 277–360).

Notes: (i) mostly in Sloane's hand (except last entries; see fols. 9ᵛ, 111ᵛ, 218, 257, 360); (ii) fol. 155ᵛ: 'see continuation of snakes no. 457 etc. about 20 leaves back – being misplaced by the bookbinder. W[illiam] C[arruthers]'; (iii) modern binding titled 'Catalogue of Fossils I'.

22. Natural History Museum, Palæontology Library
Shelf-mark: MSS, SLO
'Shells' (n.d.)

Contents: 'Shells', 1–2502 (fols. 3–388).
Notes: (i) Sloane's hand, with interpolations by others; (ii) fol. 3: 'Mem? after 2966 by mistake I went on to 2697; to 2730 many wᶜʰ are therefore double'; (iii) pencil renumbering of specimens throughout; (iv) G.L. Wilkins, Sept. 1952: specimens marked with red dot in right-hand margins are still in the Museum collection; (iv) modern binding titled 'Catalogue of Fossils II'.

23. Natural History Museum, Palæontology Library
Shelf-mark: MSS, SLO
[Shells] (n.d.)

Contents: 'Shells', 2503–4911 (fols. 1–423).
Notes: (i) Sloane's hand; (ii) 2697–730 numbers repeated, see note to 22 (above); (iii) modern binding titled 'Catalogue of Fossils III'.

24. Natural History Museum, Palæontology Library
Shelf-mark: MSS, SLO
[Shells] (*c* dated 1728)

Contents: (*a*) 'Shells', 4912–5846 (fols. 2–62); (*b*) classified list of shells, up to 4911 (fols. 210–61); (*c*) 'Musei Fossilium Conspectus' (totals) (fol. 262).
Notes: (i) mostly in Sloane's hand, except for fols. 52–62; (ii) fol. 56ᵛ has loose paper in Sloane's hand pasted down; (iii) modern binding titled 'Catalogue of Fossils IV'.

25. Natural History Museum, Palæontology Library
Shelf-mark: MSS, SLO
[Fishes, Birds, Quadrupeds] (n.d.)

Contents: (*a*) 'Fishes', 1–1563 (fols. 2–131; fols. 2ᵛ–8ᵛ); (*b*) 'Birds',

1–907 (fols. 132–208; fols. 132ᵛ–141ᵛ); (c) 'Eggs', 1–272 (fols. 209–24); (d) alphabetical index to eggs (fols. 227–34); (e) 'Quadrupeds', 1–1903 (fols. 236–383ᵛ; fols. 236ᵛ–261ᵛ).
Notes: (i) mostly in Sloane's hand, except fols. 6ᵛ–8ᵛ, 136ᵛ–41ᵛ, 224, 227–34, 256ᵛ–260ᵛ; (ii) fol. 1: 'sperma wh. whale cast on Essex shore called a Cashalot at a place called the Scewer near Bradwell. The whale whose skeleton in my garden'; (iii) fol. 1: 'N.B. nos. 224–6, 670, 815, 931 are among the insects in the Gallery on shelf r. 8.'; (iv) more notes at fols. 118, 133, 263 (last by Sloane); (v) fol. 245: printed list of merchandise, Amsterdam, 1737, with elephant skull starred; certificate of sale in Dutch for the skull from East India Co; (vi) modern binding titled 'Catalogue of Fossils v'.

26. Natural History Museum, Palæontology Library
Shelf-mark: MSS, SLO
'Indices variorum' (n.d.)

Contents: (a) Precious stones index (fols. 2–64); (b) Metals index (fols. 68–129); (c) Fish index (fols. 132–77); (d) Birds index (fols. 180–220); (e) Quadrupeds index (fols. 224–77); (f) Corals index (fols. 280–304); (g) Serpents index (fols. 310–18); (h) Echini index (fols. 322–35); (i) Crustacea index (fols. 338–46); (j) Starfishes (fols. 350–4); (k) Humana (fols. 357–79).
Notes: (i) Thomas Stack's hand; (ii) first two indexes are to catalogues in Mineralogy Library; (iii) modern binding titled 'Catalogue of Fossils VI'.

27. Natural History Museum, Zoology Library
Shelf-mark: MSS, SLO
'Echini Marini' (c.1720?)

Contents: (a) 'Echini Marini' (table of classification) (2 fols.); (b) 'Echini Marini, Classis I, Sectio I', a1–39 (38 fols.); (c) 'Echini Marini, Classis I, Sectio II', b1–27 (11 fols.); (d) 'Echini Marini, Classis I, Sectio III', c1 (3 fols.); (e) 'Echinorum Marinorum, Classis II, Sectio I', d1–27 (21 fols.); (f) 'Echinorum Marinorum, Classis II, Sectio II', e1–13 (9 fols.).
Notes: (i) Sloane's hand throughout; (ii) some entries given pencil numbers, all comprising 225 followed by a letter, probably indicating storage case and drawers; (iii) echinoderms also catalogued in 21 (above).

28. Museum of Mankind (British Museum, Dept. of Ethnography)
'Miscellanies' (some items with dates 1730–38)
fols. ii + 1–329; and fols. 5*, 5**, 142*, 180* (July 1968); fols. 206–31 foliated originally I–XXVI

Contents: (a) 'Miscellanies', 1–2111 (fols. 2–152ᵛ; entries 1799–2111 on versos); (b) 'Antiquities', 1–1129 (fols. 153–205; entries 700–1129 on versos); (c) 'Impressions of Seals, etc.', 1–268 (fols. 206–31); (d) 'Index in Sigilla, Sigillorum, Impressions &c.', (fols. 232–236ᵛ); (e) 'Pictures &c.', 1–471 (fols. 237–71); (f) 'Mathematicall Instruments &c.', 1–57 (fols. 272–7); (g) 'Index to the Mathematicall Instruments' (fols. 278–81); (h) 'Agate handles &c.', 1–239 (fols. 282–303); (i) 'Agate cups botles spoons &c.', 1–303 (fols. 304–29).
Notes: (i) mostly Sloane's hand, except fols. 17ᵛ, 174ᵛ, 215, 232–236ᵛ, 278–81 (last two items in hand of Thomas Stack);

(ii) fol. ii: 'N.B. from 96 to 105 a[re] veget. corall – 709 to 920 duplicates'; (iii) fol. 1: 'N.B. The Indexes to the Seals and Mathematicall Instruments are in this Volume at the end of the respective Catalogues: and the Indexes to the rest of this Volume are bound up in a separate Volume in the same Order as they occur in this'; (iv) fol. 178: donations by William Lethieullier, Pitt Lethieullier, Smart Lethieullier, Thomas Hollis, *et al.*; (v) fol. 206 Thomas Stack: 'All this Class is in Drawer t. of Cab. 216. and they are marked in the Margin wᵗʰ blacklead 1. 2. 3. etc. according to the Cards or Boxes that contain the several Articles. Aug. 31. 1738. Sept. 12.38 I made the Index to p. xxvi No. 264'; (vi) fols. 5*, 5**: notes in French; (vii) fol. 142*: 'Experiments made with the German Water sent me by his Grace the Duke of Newcastle'; (viii) fol. 180*: checklist of casts of medals.

29. British Library, Department of Manuscripts
Catalogue number: Sloane MS 3995
'A catalogue of my books taken in Febry. 1684/5 in London'

30. British Library, Department of Manuscripts
Catalogue number: Sloane MS 3972A, B, C, D
[Catalogues of printed books, manuscripts, charters, rolls, *horti sicci*, maps, miniatures, prints, periodicals]

31. British Library, Department of Printed Books
Shelf-mark: 878.n.8
[Sloane's Latin medical books] G.A. Mercklin, *Lindenius renovatus* (1686), interleaved.

Index

Note: the names of cities, districts and states beyond the British Isles have been grouped, where appropriate, under regional or national headings as follows: Africa, America (North, Mesoamerica, South), Atlantic islands, Austria, China, Denmark, East Indies, Egypt, Far East, Flanders, France, Germany, Greece, Greenland, Hungary, India, Italy, Japan, Mediterranean islands, Middle and Near East, Netherlands, Pacific islands, Portugal, Russia, South-East Asia, Spain, Sweden, Switzerland, Turkey, West Indies. With the exception of localities and institutions within London, British place names are unclassified.

Abercorn, Earl of 215
Abingdon, Earl of 83
Acupuncture 286; needles for 224
Adams, Mr 130, 242 (n. 82)
Adare, Dr Patrick 125, 130
Addison, Joseph 39 (n. 83), 167, 170-1
Adipocere 71, 75 (n. 8)
Adrichomias, Christianus 248
Aelst, Pieter Cocke van 248
Aethred 199
Aetites 88
Africa 25, 35, 57, 61, 89, 107, 232–4, 237–8, 239 (n. 2), 242 (nn. 78–9); Angola 242 (n. 78); Asante 244 (n. 114); Bakongo 234; Calabar 119; Congo (Kongo) 231, 234, 242 (nn. 78, 82); Entan 244 (n. 114); Ethiopia 89, 242 (n. 78); Gambia 242 (n. 78); Guinea 16, 83, 119, 242 (nn. 78–9, 81–2); Pls 24, 26; Madagascar 86, 117, 242 (nn. 78, 81); Mauritius 84, 116; Pl. 5; Nigeria 235, 242 (n. 81); Pl. 25; North Africa 234; St Thomas 242 (n. 78); Senegal 242 (nn. 77–8); South Africa 23, 86, 234, 270 (Cape of Good Hope) 34–5, 86, 116, 142–3, 270; Fig. 42; Pl. 5; Sudan Pl. 24; River Volta 244 (n. 114); West Africa 234, 243 (n. 93); Pl. 26; Western Sahara Pl. 24. For the North African littoral see Middle and Near East
Africa Company 86
'Agnus castus' 270
Ainsworth, Robert 170, 173 (n. 52)
Al Juzil, Abd-al-Ali 214, 226; Pl. 23
Alabasters 212, 219 (n. 63). See also Minerals
Albemarle, Duke of see Monck, Christopher
Albemarle, Duchess of 13, 53, 82, 95
Albertus de Saxonia 272, 277 (n. 130)
Albertus Magnus 269
Albin, Eleazar 119
Albinos 84, 86
Albucius (potter) 188
Albumasar Pl. 37
Alcanna (henna) 43 (n. 187)
Aldborough, Suffolk 62
Aldobrandino of Siena 269; Pl. 36
Aldrovandi, Ulisse 85, 93, 123–5, 130, 217
Alexander III, Pope 211
Alexander the Great 32, 35, 199
Alfred Jewel 199, 218 (n. 11)
Algonquins 234
Allerton Mauleverer, Yorkshire 56
Allewelt, Captain 224
Almeyda, Don Pedro d' 126
Alphabets and texts: Callmuck 43 (n. 187); Coptic 174; Egyptian 32; Tangutan (Tibetan) 43 (n. 187)
Amber 22, 28, 31, 124–8, 132, 230, 292–3; cabinets of 128, 240 (n. 46)
Ambergreese 28, 124, 292
America 25, 35, 58, 68 (n. 83), 84, 93, 107, 113, 116–17, 122 (n. 39), 228, 231, 233, 237, 241 (n. 62), 243 (n. 96), 270
America (North) 29, 46, 61, 66 (n. 13), 86, 91 (n. 36), 124, 127, 129–30, 144, 229, 232, 234, 238, 239 (n. 2), 249; Arctic 127, 229, 234, 237; Canada 229, 234, 237, 241 (n. 70), 242 (n. 84), 270, (Davis Straits) 242 (nn. 74, 86), (Moose Factory) 229, (Moose River) 242 (n. 87), (Hudson Bay) 34, 86, 233–4, 238, 239 (n. 20), 242 (nn. 86, 88), (Hudson Straits) 242 (n. 87), (James Bay) 242 (n. 87), (Newfoundland) 62, 108, (Nova Scotia) 270; California 241 (n. 70), (Huntington Library) 249; Carolina 24–5, 86, 108, 116–17, 138, 233–4, 241 (n. 70), 242 (n. 75), 243 (nn. 93–4, 102);

Figs 78–9, (Charlestown) 241 (n. 72), (Roanoke) 249; Connecticut 129; Georgia 42 (n. 158), 59–61, 66 (n. 13); Kentucky 238; Maryland 108, 116, 122 (n. 21), 126, 131–2, 141–2, 144; Fig. 41; (University of) 141–2, 149 (n. 15), (Annapolis) 141, (Christ Church, Calvert County) 116; Massachusetts (Boston) 129, (Newbury) 130; New England 125, 129, 194 (n. 23), 216, 232, 243 (n. 93); Fig. 31; Pennsylvania 141; Fig. 79; Providence 108; Virginia 23, 25, 71, 83, 233–4, 241 (n. 70), 243 (n. 93), 249–50; Washington, DC (Smithsonian Institution) 121
America (Mesoamerica) 25, 84, 234, 236, 243 (n. 96); Fig. 81; Columbia 243 (n. 96); Costa Rica 82; Darien 234; Guyana 234, 240 (n. 23), 243 (nn. 96, 98); Mexico 228, 231, 238, 243 (n. 96), 257, 270; Fig. 82; (Campeche) 209, 236, 243 (n. 101); Mosquitos 82; New Spain 270
America (South) 25, 84, 91 (n. 21), 124, 127, 232, 234, 236, 238, 243 (n. 98), 257–9; Amazon 117; Andes 236; Brazil 86, 243 (n. 96), 259, (Buenos Aires) 84–5; Chile 84, 105, (Straits of Magellan) 105; Fig. 25; Paraguay 292; Peru 35, 231, 236, 243 (n. 103); Fig. 83; (Governor of) 39 (n. 77), (Lima) 13; Surinam 28, 31, 107, 116–17, 258–9; Tierra del Fuego 105, 234, 243 (n. 96); Venezuela 257
Ames, Joseph 56, 62
Amesbury, Wiltshire 71, 185
Amman, Dr Johann 26, 43 (n. 187), 138, 148 (n. 7), 163, 241 (n. 70)
Amulets and talismans 42 (n. 160), 89, 109, 174, 177, 185, 191, 194 (n. 23), 220 (n. 76), 231, 237–8, 243 (nn. 98, 101), 291; Fig. 85; see also Cramp rings
Anatomical specimens 27, 29, 31, 34, 42 (n. 149), 49, 55, Ch. 3 passim, 85–6, 180, 185, 293–4; skeletons 31, 34, 48, 68 (nn. 71, 84), 70, 75
Ancaster, Duke of 66 (n. 13)
Andrews, Joseph (Townshend) 56
Anglesea, Isle of 215
Animals 16, 22, 25, 27, 29, 35, 42 (n. 141), 53, 70, 74, 77, 94, 115, 121 (n. 9), 258; live 13, 82–3, 130, 238; dried 30; in spirits 30, 34–5, 83; marine 16; stuffed 28, 30, 34, 68 (n. 71); abortions of 70, 85; antlers of 28–9, 30, 35, 83, 232; bones of 71, 86, 88, 196 (nn. 67, 81); claws of 83, 213; hair of 234; horns of 28–9, 31, 35, 68 (n. 71), 88–90, 213; Fig. 22; skins of 31, 68 (n. 71), 83, 85–6, 88, 238; teeth of 31, 86, 88, 91 (n. 31), 213, 234, 242 (n. 87). See also Birds, Fossils, Mammals, Reptiles
Annius Perpetuus 191
Anne, Empress of Russia 152, 163
Anne, Queen 15–16, 26, 38 (n. 59), 163, 213, 216, 229
Anson, George, Lord 64
Antiochus IV, King 152
Antiquaries of London, Society of 25, 46, 48, 53, 56, 58, 60-2, 152, 162–3, 166 (n. 65), 179 (n. 28), 180, 182–3, 185, 193 (n. 5), 194 (n. 31), 195 (nn. 42, 49), 200, 211, 217; Figs 76–7
Antiquities 24–9, 35, 42 (n. 160), 43 (n. 170), 50, 55–6, 62–3, 67 (n. 40), 68 (n. 71), 116, 175, 198–9, 222, 231, 233, 236, 240 (n. 45), 243 (nn. 104–5), 291, 294; Prehistoric 178 (n. 3), 180-6; Pls 16–17; Classical 55, Ch. 10 passim; Roman, Romano-British 24, 28–9,

Index

Chirac, Pierre 12
Chishull, Edmund 170, 173 (n. 52)
Chocolate 15, 39 (n. 69), 139, 141, 241 (n. 70); Figs 2, 40
Christian Maximilian 126
Christina, Queen of Sweden 258
Churchill, John 84
Churchman, Mr 215
Cicero 61, 217, 277 (n. 135)
Cirencester, Gloucestershire 191, 199, 218 (n. 16); Fig. 63
Cisterns 216
Clanbrassill, Earl of see Hamilton, James
Clandeboye, Viscount see Hamilton, James
Clarke, Samuel 58, 66 (n. 32), 67 (n. 43)
Claudius, Emperor 181; Fig. 48
Claus, Mr (i.e. Claus Smart) 215, 218 (n. 30)
Claxton, Norfolk 69, 75 (n. 5)
Clays 16, 53, 240 (n. 28), 292
Clayton, John 25
Clement xii, Pope 168, 212
Clement, Thomas 270
Clerck (Clark), William 108
Clerk, Mr 243 (n. 93)
Climate 16
Clockmakers Company 220 (n. 83)
Clockwork 240 (n. 31)
Clothing 27, 30-1, 33–5, 37 (n. 20), 216, 221 (n. 107), 230, 236–8, 240 (n. 47), 241 (n. 70), 242 (nn. 74, 86); aprons 233–4, 240 (n. 23), 241 (n. 72); belts 234, 240 (n. 25), 242 (nn. 79, 88); britches 216, 230, 243 (nn. 99, 108), 244 (n. 111); coats 91 (n. 25), 240 (n. 25), 242 (nn. 74, 86), 243 (nn. 99, 108); doublets 216; feather garments 234, 257; fur garments 238, 240 (n. 25), 243 (n. 108); garters 216, 234; gloves 110; Pl. 11; 'habits' 68 (n. 71), 230, 240 (nn. 25, 47, 49), 243 (n. 108); Highlander's 216, 237, 244 (n. 111); mourner's costume 232; shirts 31; skin garments 238, 241 (n. 70), 242 (nn. 74, 86); stockings 216, 243 (n. 108), 244 (n. 111). See also Headgear, Shoes
Cnut, King 162; Fig. 49
Coal pits 130; plants from 134 (n. 32)
Cock's (auctioneers) 168
Codrington, Sir William 57–8
Coffins 71, 75, 175, 177, 189, 197 (n. 98), 199, 219 (n. 37)
Coins 25–7, 29–30, 35, 42 (nn. 141, 160), 43 (n. 170), 44 (n. 209), 53, 56, 62, 66 (n. 16), 67 (n. 40), 93, Ch. 9 passim, 167, 169, 171, 172 (nn. 7–8), 195 (n. 49), 198–9, 219 (n. 35), 238; Hoards 151–2, 162–3, 187, 240 (n. 44), 242 (n. 75); Greek 152, 162, 165 (n. 23); Roman 25, 62, 151–2, 162, 165 (nn. 23, 26), 167, 183, 196 (n. 74); Figs 48–9; Byzantine 162; Ancient British 162, 166 (n. 65); Anglo-Saxon 162, 165 (n. 4), 199; Fig. 49; Norman 162; Fig. 49; Medieval and later 162–3; Fig. 49; Asian 230; Cilician 152; Danish 165 (n. 23); Dutch 165 (n. 23); Egyptian 162; English 165 (n. 23); Fig. 49; French 163, 165 (n. 23); German 163, 165 (n. 23); Hebrew 163; Hungarian 165 (n. 23); Indian 242 (n. 75); Irish 165 (n. 23); Italian 163, 165 (n. 23); Oriental 165 (n. 23); Phoenician 152; Polish 165 (n. 23); Pontic 152; Russian 165 (n. 23); Scottish 165 (nn. 23, 25); Spanish 152, 163, 165 (n. 23); Spanish-American 165 (n. 20); Swedish 165 (n. 23); Syrian 152; Fig. 48; Gunmoney 163, 166 (n. 72); Siege pieces 163. See also Medals
Colbatch, Sir John 130, 199
Colchester, Essex 59
Cole, Jacob 262 (n. 43)
Coleraine, Lord 162
Collier, Mr 240 (n. 30)
Collinson, Peter 25, 42 (n. 174), 48, 58, 182, 194 (n. 31)
Colonna, Fabio 93
Colston Joseph 269
Combe, Dr 106

Combe, Taylor 162
Combs 32, 196 (n. 71), 222, 232, 234, 242 (n. 87)
Commontar 86
Compton, Hon. and Revd Henry 141
Condamine, Charles Marie de la 84
Condé, Duc de 223
Constantine, Emperor 151
Containers 224
Contareno, Marcius (Doge of Venice) 219 (n. 50)
Conyers, John 24, 42 (n. 160), 89, 151, 165 (n. 31), 169, 181, 186–9, 191, 193 (n. 11), 194 (nn. 12, 14), 195 (n. 61), 196 (nn. 63, 68, 70, 72, 79), 197 (n. 90), 211; Figs 60-1
Conyers, Mrs 173 (n. 34)
Cook, Captain James 55, 232, 241 (n. 62)
Cooke, Benjamin 182, 194 (n. 31), 195 (n. 33)
Copping, Dean 185
Corals 22, 24–5, 28, 30-1, 33–5, 42 (n. 141), 69, 93, 95, 105, 109, 293–4; Fig. 24; Abies marina 196 (n. 196); Barba neptuni 33; Corallium album 108; Corallium asperum 95; Corallium porosum 95; Madrepora lactuca 109; madrepores 31; sea fan 108
Coram, Captain Thomas 38 (n. 55)
Cornut, J.P. 263
Corsham House, Wiltshire 60
Corsini, Laurenzo de 179 (n. 32)
Cortés, Hernando 257
Cortona, Pietro da 247
Cosman, Mr 86
Cossart, Henry 58
Costume see clothing
Cotterstock, Northamptonshire 187, 189
Cotton 238
Cotton, Sir John 55, 66 (n. 16)
Cotton, Sir Robert Bruce 66 (n. 16), 150, 162, 191
Cotton, Sir Thomas 66 (n. 16)
Cottonian library 46, 49–50, 53–5, 65, 66 (nn. 16–17), 67 (n. 43), 220 (n. 79)
Courten (Charleton), William 22–5, 27, 30, 41 (nn. 138, 141), 42 (n. 142), 46, 84–6, 91 (n. 17), 106–7, 116–17, 119–20, 122 (n. 18), 125–6, 151, 162–3, 165 (n. 25), 168–9, 172 (n. 8), 180, 198–9, 218 (n. 4), 247, 261 (nn. 6, 9, 24), 268
Courtenay, William (Archbishop of Canterbury) 211
Covell, Dr 212, 219 (n. 65), 243 (n. 99)
Cowdray Park, Sussex 216
Cowper, Dr William 69–71, 74, 75 (n. 4)
Cowper, Lord William 210
Cracherode, Revd C.M. 109, 172, 246, 251, 277 (nn. 133, 144)
Cramp, rings and amulets to ward off 75, 86, 213, 220 (n. 77)
Cranach, Lucas (the Elder) 258
Cree 229, 234, 271, 276 (n. 107); Fig. 109
Cricklade, Wiltshire 163
Cripp, Mr 86
Crispus (potter) 188
Cromwell, Oliver 117, 163, 200, 209, 218 (n. 30), 219 (n. 30); Fig. 65
Crook, J. Maurdaunt 45–6
Crow, Francis 232, 241 (n. 63)
Croydon, Surrey 116
Crucibles 197 (n. 90)
Crucifixes, rosaries etc. 230
Crustacea 29, 31, 105, 109, 293–4; Cancer totus spinosus 108; Concha anatifera 95; Barnacles 95; Cockles 108; Crab 29, 31, 80-1, 108, 240 (n. 27), (Soldier crab) 31; Crayfish 31, 81, 108, 240 (n. 27); Limpets 108; Lobster 29, 31; Mussels 108; Oysters 108, 196 (n. 85); Periwinkles 108; Prawns 108; Shrimp 81
Cryptogams 143–5; Padina pavonica 144–5; Fig. 94; Algae 144; Fig. 44; Bryophytes 144; Ferns 143, 147; Fungi 143–4; Lichen 143–4, 149 (n. 27); Fig. 43; Liverwort 144; Moss 143–4; Seaweed 143–4
Cumberland 60
Cumberland, William, Duke of 50, 64

Cunningham(e), Captain James 23, 108, 116, 130, 222, 225, 229, 233, 239 (n. 8), 241 (n. 70)
Cupid 191, 218 (n. 19)
Cups 31–2, 34, 132, 188, 196 (n. 70), 198, 215, 222–4, 236, 242 (n. 82), 243 (n. 98), 291, 294; Fig. 60; of rhino horn 88, 224
Cuvier, Georges, Baron 109
Cybele 169; Fig. 52
Cyclops 88
Cynocephalus 177
Cyprianos (Ciprien), Dr Abraham 31, 69, 72
Cysts 74

Da Costa, Emanuel Mendes 106, 109, 125
Dal Pozzo, Cassiano 167, 172 (n. 11)
Dale, Samuel 125, 138–9, 145
Dalmatia 211
Dampier, Captain William 23, 84, 91 (nn. 14–15), 108, 270
Dandridge, Joseph 30, 115–17, 119–21, 122 (nn. 27–8, 45), 269; Fig. 107; Pl. 14
Dandy, James E. 42 (n. 146), 138–9, 143, 148 (n. 5), 149 (n. 9)
Daniel, Samuel 116
Darlington, Lady 223
Darwin, Charles 90
Dassier, Jacques-Antoine Fig. 5
Davall (Duval), Peter 64
Daventry, Northamptonshire 125
Davis, John 43 (n. 181)
Dealers 222
Death-masks 200, 218 (n. 30), 219 (n. 30); Fig. 65
Dechales, C.F. Milliet 263
Dee, Dr John 213, 272
Defoe, Daniel 267
Deities 24, 28, 32, 42 (n. 160), 171, 177, 209, 223, 226, 232
Denmark 66 (n. 13), 85, 224; Copenhagen 123, 240 (n. 33), 242 (n. 89), (National Museum) 228, (Royal Collection) 223–4; Zeeland 255
Derby, Mayor of 72
Derham, Mr 117
Dering, Mr and Mrs 86, 234, 242 (n. 79)
Desmarets, Mr 214
Devil's Arrows, Boroughbridge 182
Devizes, Wiltshire 60
Devonshire, Duchess of 223
Devonshire, Duke of 163, 166 (n. 85), 246
De Witt, House of 35
Diana 196 (n. 68)
Dictionaries, encyclopaedias and grammars 271, 276 (n. 107), 283, 287, 289 (n. 19); Figs 109, 114a
Diepenbeck, Abraham van 247; Fig. 88
Dighton, Robert 251
Ding, Dr 75
Ding Laingxian Pl. 20
Ding family 225
Dingley, Northamptonshire 185
Diodorus Siculus 90
Diseases and ailments 16, 35, 231; anencephaly 74; cramp 75, 86, 213, 220 (n. 77); cataracts 83; distempers 88, 130; fevers 130, 230, 240 (n. 27); gout 230, 240 (n. 27); heartburn 230, 240 (n. 27); hydrocephaly 74; piles 213, 230, 240 (n. 27); rheumatism 85, 244 (n. 114); scrofula 213, 240 (n. 27); sea-sickness 13, 94; smallpox 130 (see also Innoculation); snake-bite 230, 240 (n. 27); syphillis 31; worms 74, 233
Dishes 223
Divini, Eustachio 214, 220 (n. 85)
Djed pillars 177
Djedkhonsiufankh 179 (n. 29)
Doeff, H. 289 (n. 14)
Dohm, C.W. 288 (n. 2)
Dolley, R.H.M. 164 (n. 4)
Dolney, Dr 86
Dominis, Antonio de (Bishop of Zeugg and Modorus) 211
Donegal, Lord 109

298

FRIDAY, 30TH. MAY 1947.